MW00632769

ANNOTATED GUIDE – RN

TO THE

TEXAS NURSING PRACTICE ACT

11TH EDITION 2013

INCLUDING

NURSING PRACTICE ACT

NURSING PEER REVIEW LAW

BON RULES & POSITION STATEMENTS

OTHER NURSING-RELATED LAWS & RULES

Annotations By
JAMES H. WILLMANN, J.D.
General Counsel, Texas Nurses Association

ISBN 978-1-930614-04-8

DISCLAIMER

This Annotated Guide to the Nursing Practice Act has been prepared to provide the reader general background and insight into the Nursing Practice Act (NPA), Texas Board of Nursing (BON) rules, and other laws, rules, and regulations governing the practice of nursing. To the best of the annotator's knowledge, the annotations are accurate interpretations of the NPA, BON rules and other laws and regulations. However, they are intended only to provide general information and do not purport to offer legal advice or to be a substitute for the advice of legal counsel as to how the NPA, BON rules or other laws and regulations apply to specific situations.

INTRODUCTION

This Annotated Guide includes not only the Nursing Practice Act, but also Texas Board of Nursing (BON) practice-related rules, position statements, guidelines and policies and selected other laws and regulations relating to nursing. The nurse's practice must comply not only with the NPA, but also with BON rules as well as other laws and regulations relating to her or his specific practice setting. Patient rights laws are an example of the latter. In fact, BON rules and such other laws normally provide more detailed guidance to the nurse than the NPA itself. This Guide addresses only state laws and regulations. Federal laws and regulations may also affect the practice of nursing and nurses also need to be familiar with these as they relate to their specific practice setting. Examples of the latter would be the federal EMTALA and HIPAA laws governing patient transfers and privacy, respectively.

The inclusion of annotations is the most unique, and probably most important, feature of this Annotated Guide. These annotations are designed to assist the nurse in understanding the implications and significance of a particular law or rule for the nurse's practice.

The goal of this Annotated Guide is to create a "nurse-friendly" NPA. It is hoped that nurses will find it a useful aid in their day-to-day nursing practice.

WAYS TO USE THIS GUIDE

Readers Seeking General Information about NPA or BON Rules. Readers unfamiliar with the NPA should find it helpful to review the detailed Table of Contents for this Guide. This will provide a quick overview of the provisions of the NPA and BON rules. To see how the NPA has changed over time, the reader can review the NPA history set out in the Appendices.

Readers Interested in Particular Subject. Readers interested in a particular subject (e.g., peer review) should first check to see if that topic is the focus of any of the subject-specific Parts of this Guide:

- Part IV Nursing Peer Review
- Part V Practice Related Materials
- Part VI Patient Advocacy Protections
- Part VII Mandatory Reporting

Second, they can check for that topic in the Subject Matter Index in Part XI of this Guide. Third, they should scan the detailed Table of Contents of this Guide for relevant materials.

Readers Interested in Particular NPA Provision or BON Rule. Readers who know the section number of the provision they are interested in should simply go to that section in the NPA. Readers who know the number of the BON rule they are interested in should locate that rule in the Cross Reference Index in Part XI of this Guide. This cross-index will identify where that rule can be found in this Guide.

USE OF GUIDE WITH OTHER RESOURCES

The Board of Nursing (BON) has numerous resources for nurses available on its website. The Texas Center for Nursing Workforce Studies is a source of data about nursing workforce issues. A goal of this Guide is to serve as coordination point for these, and other, resources by directing the reader where to find additional information on specific topics. Part V of this Guide sets out an extensive outline of the practice-related materials available to nurses both in this Guide and on the BON website. The Appendices also includes or identifies other resources nurses may find helpful.

UPDATING INFORMATION

As indicated at various points in this Annotated Guide, the laws and regulations governing nursing are subject to change. The Texas Legislature meets in odd-numbered years from January through May and may enact legislation amending the NPA and other state laws affecting nursing. State agencies such as the BON can amend their rules as necessary through the rule-making process. A good source of information about such changes are the BON newsletter (*Texas Board of Nursing Bulletin*) and the BON website at www.bon.texas.gov. Included in the Appendices is a listing of other websites that provide useful information for nurses wanting to keep current on the laws and regulations governing their practice.

LEGISLATION

Statutes (laws) included in this Annotated Guide are current through the Regular and Third -Called Special Session of the 83rd (2013) Texas Legislature. No amendments will be made to the NPA until the 84th Texas Legislature convenes in January 2015. Even if the Governor calls another special session before 2015, no amendments to the Nursing Practice Act are expected.

RULES AND REGULATIONS

Agency rules and regulations included in this Edition are current through the July 31, 2013 Texas Register. The State Appropriations Act requires each state agency to review its rules within four years of adoption/re-adoption to determine if the reason for adopting/re-adopting the rule continues to exist. Agencies also make changes as needed. The BON likely will need to make some additions and changes to its rules to implement legislation enacted by the 2013 Legislature.

SIGNIFICANT CHANGES SINCE PREVIOUS EDITION

The 2013 Legislature passed several bills directly related to nurses and nursing practice. SB 406 expanded the scope of prescriptive authority for APRNs and replaced the current site-based model with a prescriptive authority agreement model. HB 581 expands the patient advocacy protections for public hospital employed nurses by giving them the right to file a lawsuit for damages suffered from retaliation because of patient advocacy. HB 705 enhanced the penalty for assaulting ER nurses from a misdemeanor to a felony. SB 1058 made several amendments to the Nursing Practice Act (NPA). The most significant changes were 1) making permanent the Board of Nursing's (BON) current pilot authority to take deferred action against a nurse's license for certain violations, 2) making BON orders sending nurses to the Texas Peer Assistance Program confidential, and 3) mandating criminal background checks for nursing students.

The BON has also amended several of its rules but has not made any major revisions. The Board will need to amend some of it s rules to implement legislation passed by 2013 Legislature. The most significant will likely be its APRN Rule 221. The board is also expected to make changes to its rule relating to delegation in independent living environments (Rule 225) and to address its rules governing corrective and deferred action. The BON adopted a new position statement on nurses' use of social media.

ACKNOWLEDGMENT

The Annotator wishes to acknowledge the special contribution of wife M'Liss for her assistance in proofing copy as she has done for the previous ten editions of the Guide. Her contribution has made this Guide come much closer to its goal of being "nurse-friendly."

[Intentional Blank Page]

TABLE OF CONTENTS

OVERVIEW

This Annotated Guide consists of the eleven parts identified below. On the pages following this overview is a detailed Table of Contents for each part using descriptive article and section titles. Consequently, this detailed Table of Contents can serve as a quick reference guide to the Nursing Practice Act and the reader is encouraged to use it as such.

INTRODUCTION

PART I
NURSING PRACTICE ACT
CHAPTER 301, TEXAS OCCUPATION CODE

PART II
SELECTED RULES OF THE TEXAS BOARD OF NURSING

PART III
SELECTED BON POSITION STATEMENTS, GUIDELINES, AND OTHER PRACTICE-RELATED POLICIES

PART IV
NURSING PEER REVIEW
CHAPTER 303, TEXAS OCCUPATIONS CODE

PART V
NURSING PRACTICE, STANDARDS AND SCOPE OF PRACTICE

PART VI
PATIENT ADVOCACY PROTECTIONS

PART VII
MANDATORY, OPTIONAL AND ALTERNATE REPORTING

PART VIII
NURSE LICENSURE COMPACTS

PART IX
SELECTED OTHER LAWS AND RULES RELATING TO NURSING PRACTICE

PART X
APPENDICES

PART XI
INDEXES

[Intentional Blank Page]

PART I.

NURSING PRACTICE ACT
OCCUPATIONS CODE, CHAPTER 301

Page

ANNOTATOR'S NOTE 1*: To assist the reader in identifying provisions of the NPA of greatest significance to nursing practice, these provisions have been identified by a ✔ and shading.*

ANNOTATOR'S NOTE 2*: The Table of Contents to this Guide lists each section of the NPA and can provide a quick overview of the content of the NPA.*

✔Shading Denotes More Important Practice-Related NPA Sections

ACT

This column sets out the provisions of the Nursing Practice Act (NPA) as amended through the 2013 legislative session. Some of the more important NPA provisions for the practicing nurse are:

Sec. 301.002	*Definitions of "professional nursing" and "vocational nursing"*
Sec. 301.004	*Defines scope of application of NPA and who exempted*
Secs. 301.151-.152	*BON rule-making authority*
Sec. 301.251	*Establishes NPA as a practice-control act requiring anyone practicing nursing to be licensed and restricts use of "RN," "LVN," and "nurse" titles to licensees*
Secs. 301.351	*Requires identification as "RN" or "LVN" when practicing*
Secs. 301.352	*Protections for refusing to violate NPA or BON rules*
Secs. 301.3532	*Supervision of LVNs*
Secs. 301.401-.419	*Sets out reporting obligations, rights and protections*
Sec. 301.413	*Sets out retaliation protections for nurses when advocating for patients*
Sec. 301.4515	*Restricts use of titles such as "nurse aide" and "nurse assistant"*
Sec. 301.452	*Sets out grounds for which BON may deny or take action against a nurse's license.*

ANNOTATOR'S NOTE: *The Nursing Peer Review Law and Nurse Licensure Compact are not part of the NPA (Occupations Code Chapter 301) but rather are separate chapters of the Occupations Code (Chapters 303 and 304). The Nursing Peer Review Law is set out in Part IV of th is Guide and the Nurse Licensure Compact in Part VII..*

OCCUPATIONS CODE
CHAPTER 301. NURSES

SUBCHAPTER A.
GENERAL PROVISIONS

✔Sec. 301.001. SHORT TITLE.

This chapter may be cited as the Nursing Practice Act.

✔Sec. 301.002. DEFINITIONS.

In this chapter:

✔Shading Denotes More Important
Practice-Related NPA Sections

ANNOTATIONS

This column sets out explanatory comments prepared by the annotator to facilitate understanding of the Nursing Practice Act (NPA). These annotations are not part of the NPA itself. They are designed to provide general background or insight into the NPA section involved and are not intended to substitute for the advice of legal counsel on how the NPA applies to a specific situation.

The NPA must be read in conjunction with the rules of the Texas Board of Nursing. Rules will address an issue in more detail than is possible in the NPA itself. An attempt has been made to reference BON rules when appropriate.

ANNOTATOR'S NOTE: *The Nursing Peer Review Law and Nurse Licensure Compact are not part of the NPA (Occupations Code Chapter 301) but rather are separate chapters of the Occupations Code (Chapters 303 and 304). The Nursing Peer Review Law is set out in Part IV of this Guide and the Nurse Licensure Compact in Part VII..*

This provides a simple, official way to reference the law governing professional and vocational nursing. It doesn't include nursing peer review which is set out as a separate Chapter 303 of the Occupations Code. See Part IV (Nursing Peer Review) of this Guide.

Because they largely define the legal scope of practice of RNs and LVNs, the definitions of "professional nursing" (Definition 2) and "vocational nursing" (Definition 5) are key definitions.

✔Shading Denotes More Important Practice-Related NPA Sections

(1) "Board" means the Texas Board of Nursing.

(1-a) “Chief nursing officer" means the registered nurse who is administratively responsible for the nursing services at a facility.

✔(1-b) “Patient safety committee" has the meaning assigned by Section 303.001.

✔(2) "Professional nursing" means the performance of an act that requires substantial specialized judgment and skill, the proper performance of which is based on knowledge and application of the principles of biological, physical, and social science as acquired by a completed course in an approved school of professional nursing. The term does not include acts of medical diagnosis or the prescription of therapeutic or corrective measures. Professional nursing involves:

(A) the observation, assessment, intervention, evaluation, rehabilitation, care and counsel, or health teachings of a person who is ill, injured, infirm, or experiencing a change in normal health processes;

(B) the maintenance of health or prevention of illness;

(C) the administration of a medication or treatment as ordered by a physician, podiatrist, or dentist;

(D) the supervision or teaching of nursing;

(E) the administration, supervision, and evaluation of nursing practices, policies, and procedures;

(F) the requesting, receiving, signing for, and distribution of prescription drug samples to patients at practices at which an advanced practice registered nurse is authorized to sign prescription drug orders as provided by Subchapter B, Chapter 157;

(G) the performance of an act delegated by a physician under Section 157.0512, 157.054, 157.058, or 157.059; and

(H) the development of the nursing care plan.

✔(3) "Nurse" means a person required to be licensed under this chapter to engage in professional or vocational nursing.

✔(4) "Nursing" means professional or vocational nursing.

✔(5) "Vocational nursing" means a directed scope of nursing practice, including the performance of an act that requires specialized judgment and skill, the proper performance of which is based on knowledge and application of the principles of biological, physical, and social science as acquired by a completed course in an approved school of vocational nursing. The term does not include acts of medical diagnosis or the prescription of therapeutic or corrective measures. Vocational nursing involves:

(A) collecting data and performing focused nursing assessments of the health status of an individual;

Prior to 2007, the board's name was the Texas State Board of Nurse Examiners (BNE).

Section 303.001 is the definition section for the Nursing Peer Review Law which is set out in Part IV (Peer Review) of this Guide. "Patient safety committee" is defined very broadly to include any committee including the medical staff that reviews patient safety and quality of care.

This definition defines the legal scope of practice of RNs. The stem sentence and Subdivisions A-E were enacted in 1967 and track a model definition supported by professional nursing at that time. The definition is tied to specialized judgment and skill, and the body of knowledge acquired in professional nursing school. A requirement that the person receive compensation for performance of the act was deleted in 2005. Subsections (A) - (H) set out in more detail what functions fall within professional nursing. Medical diagnosis and prescription of therapeutic measures are explicitly excluded. Section 301.004(b) also explicitly states that the NPA does not authorize the practice of medicine. See BON Rule 217.11(3) and BON Position Statement 15.28 in Part III of this Guide for more discussion of RN scope of practice.

IN 1983, the Missouri Supreme Court, in interpreting a similar definition of professional nursing in the Missouri Nursing Practice Act, held that the Missouri definition was a dynamic definition that could change over time to reflect what the profession itself defined professional nursing to be. See Sermchief v. Gonzales, 660 S.W.2d 683 (Mo. 1983). It is unknown if Texas courts would interpret this definition in a similar manner. However, it is clear that what is considered to be within the practice of nursing does change over time and that many activities that nurses routinely do as part of nursing care may once not have been considered as nursing. NPA Sec. 301.151 gives the BON authority "to determine whether an act constitutes the practice of nursing."

In 2004, in response to a request by the Texas Optometry Board whether RNs could administer medications ordered by a therapeutic optometrist, the Texas Attorney General issued Opinion No. GA-0236 holding that Subsection (C) only authorized RNs to administer medications or treatments ordered by a physician, podiatrist or dentist. The opinion also upheld the BON's position that even though APRNs and PAs are not listed, RNs may administer medications and treatments ordered by them since they issue such orders under the delegated authority of a physician. Texas Attorney General opinions can be found on the Attorney General's website at www.oag.state.tx.us. See also BON Position Statements 15.18 and 15.1. Legislation to amend Subsection (C) to include other practitioners has been filed several times but has not passed. Because the definition of "vocational nursing" does not contain a provision similar to Subsection (C), LVNs are not so limited and may administer a medication prescribed by a therapeutic optometrist. See definition of "vocational nursing" (Definition 5) below.

Sections 301.251 limits use of the title "nurse" to RNs and LVNs. Section 301.4515 limits use of title "nurse aide," "nurse assistant," and similar titles.

This definition defines the legal scope of practice of RNs. The same as professional nursing, "vocational nursing" is defined in terms of the educational preparation of LVNs and specifically sets out certain functions falling within the definition. Although the definition does not explicitly state that LVNs may administer medications or treatments prescribed by physicians and other practitioners, BON Position Statement 15.25 states LVNs can. See NPA Sec. 301.353 which requires LVN practice to be supervised. See also BON Rule 217.11(2) (Standards of Nursing Practice) in Part II of this Guide and BON Position Statement 15.27 in Part III for discussion of LVN scope of practice including what "focused nursing assessment" and other terms mean.

(B) participating in the planning of the nursing care needs of an individual;

(C) participating in the development and modification of the nursing care plan;

(D) participating in health teaching and counseling to promote, attain, and maintain the optimum health level of an individual;

(E) assisting in the evaluation of an individual's response to a nursing intervention and the identification of an individual's needs; and

(F) engaging in other acts that require education and training, as prescribed by board rules and policies, commensurate with the nurse's experience, continuing education, and demonstrated competency.

Sec. 301.003. APPLICATION OF SUNSET ACT.

The Texas Board of Nursing is subject to Chapter 325, Government Code (Texas Sunset Act). Unless continued in existence as provided by that chapter, the board is abolished September 1, 2017.

✔Sec. 301.004. APPLICATION OF CHAPTER.

✔(a) This chapter does not apply to:

(1) gratuitous nursing care of the sick that is provided by a friend;

(2) nursing care provided during a disaster under the state emergency management plan adopted under Section 418.042, Government Code, if the person providing the care does not hold the person out as a nurse unless the person is licensed in another state;

(3) nursing care in which treatment is solely by prayer or spiritual means;

(4) an act performed by a person under the delegated authority of a person licensed by the Texas Medical Board;

(5) an act performed by a person licensed by another state agency if the act is authorized by the statute under which the person is licensed except that if the person also holds a license under this chapter and the act is within the practice of nursing, the board may take action against that license based on that act;

Sunset review is the process by which the Texas Legislature determines if state agencies should continue in existence or be allowed to "sunset." Sunset review of an agency normally occurs every 12 years and is conducted by the Sunset Advisory Commission. The BON was reviewed in 1981, 1993, and 2007 (2005 review was delayed due to formation of a single board of nursing in 2004). The next review will be in 2017 with other health professional licensing boards. More information about the sunset review process is available on the Sunset Commission's website at www.sunset.state.tx.us.

To practice nursing, a person must either be licensed as an RN or LVN or be exempted under this section. Courts have held that exemptions to licensing acts should be narrowly construed in favor of licensure. Persons practicing or engaging in activities that constitute the practice of nursing under the authority of an exemption normally cannot use the title "RN," "LVN," "nurse," or other title implying that they are licensed as a nurse. See NPA Secs. 301.251 and 301.4515.

Volunteers who are not family or friends are not exempted even if provide the care without compensation. Neither the definition of professional nursing nor the definition of vocational nursing require that care be compensated to constitute the practice of nursing.

This subsection is designed to cover persons participating in disaster relief including nurses licensed in another state who come to Texas to assist with disaster relief, e.g., Red Cross nurses. In 2013, the Legislature passed legislation (HB 746) enacting a Uniform Emergency Volunteer Health Practitioners Act as Chapter 115 of the Occupations Code. That act will apply to out-of-state nurses.

Subdivision (4) applies only if the physician delegates the act in accordance with the provisions of the Medical Practice Act (MPA) governing delegation by physicians. Those provisions make the physician accountable and legally responsible for the acts of the persons to whom the acts are delegated. The MPA also authorizes physicians to delegate only to individuals as opposed to organizations such as hospitals. See Texas Attorney General Opinion No. JM-173 (1984) which can be found at www.oag.state.tx.us under "Opinions" tab.

There is a great deal of overlap among the various health care professional licensing acts in how they define scope of practice. This exception avoids health care professionals licensed under other acts having to be licensed also as nurses simply because a task authorized by their license overlaps with the scope of practice of professional nursing. Most health care professional licensing acts have a similar provision. The qualifier at end of subdivision was added in 2013 to make clear that if a nurse who also holds another license performs an act which falls within both the scope of the nursing and the other license, the BON may take action against the nursing license based on that act.

(6) the practice of nursing that is incidental to a program of study by a student enrolled in a nursing education program approved under Section 301.157(d) leading to an initial license as a nurse; or

(7) the practice of nursing by a person licensed in another state who is in this state on a nonroutine basis for a period not to exceed 72 hours to:

(A) provide care to a patient being transported into, out of, or through this state;

(B) provide nursing consulting services; or

(C) attend or present a continuing nursing education program.

✔(b) This chapter does not authorize the practice of medicine as defined by Chapter 151.

Sec. 301.005. REFERENCE IN OTHER LAW. (a) A reference in any other law to the former Board of Nurse Examiners means the Texas Board of Nursing.

(b) A reference in any other law to an "advanced nurse practitioner" or "advanced practice nurse" means an advanced practice registered nurse.

SUBCHAPTER B.
TEXAS BOARD OF NURSING

✔**Sec. 301.051. BOARD MEMBERSHIP.** (a) The Texas Board of Nursing consists of 13 members appointed by the governor with the advice and consent of the senate as follows:

(1) six nurse members, including:

(A) one advanced practice nurse;

(B) two registered nurses who are not advanced practice nurses or members of a nurse faculty; and

This exemption covers nursing students only when providing care as part of their formal studies, e.g., in clinicals. When nursing students are employed by hospitals or others to provide patient care, this exemption doesn't apply. They are functioning as unlicensed personnel and can perform nursing tasks only with appropriate delegation.

This exemption applies to nurses licensed in another state and temporarily in Texas in connection with a patient transport, to consult, or to present CNE. The CNE exemption is necessary since the definition of nursing includes teaching. Also, CNE programs may have a clinical component that involves the participants in patient care.

The practice of medicine is explicitly prohibited. However, there is significant overlap between the practice of medicine and professional nursing. The Texas Attorney General Opinion JC-0117 (1999) [www.oag.state.tx.us under "Opinions"] recognizes that a task may be the practice of medicine when performed by a physician and the practice of nursing when performed by a nurse. Many specific tasks, e.g., taking blood pressure and administering medications, constitute both the practice of medicine and the practice of professional nursing. Nurses performing these tasks do so under the scope of their nursing license and are not engaged in the practice of medicine. If nurses engage in activities exclusively within the practice of medicine, e.g., diagnosing a disease, they must do so under physician delegation. Tasks that a physician may delegate differ for RNs and LVNs and even for RNs and APRNs because of differences in education and expertise.

When the BON's name was changed in 2007, the legislation made a conforming amendment to a number of other laws but this catchall provision was added in case some were missed. The same considerations applied when "Advanced Practice Registered Nurses" was adopted by Legislature in 2013 as the preferred terminology for nurses in advanced practice.

The BON is the administrative agency responsible for administering and enforcing the NPA and for regulating both vocational and professional nursing. Its primary purpose is to protect the public and to ensure patients receive safe, quality nursing care. The BON's purpose is not to promote nursing as a profession. Rather, promoting the profession is more appropriately the role of professional associations such as the Licensed Vocational Nurses Association of Texas and the Texas Nurses Association. However, promoting the public good and promoting the nursing profession are not mutually exclusive since promoting the profession includes promoting safe, quality nursing care.

The BON has 13 members consisting of approximately two-thirds nurses (9) and one-third public members (4). NPA Sec. 301.057 provides for the president of the Board to be appointed by the Governor. The nine nurse members are:

1 APRN (practicing or educator)
2 practicing RNs who are not APRNs or educators
3 practicing LVNs who are not educators

(C) three vocational nurses who are not members of a nurse faculty;

(2) three members who are nurse faculty members of schools of nursing:

(A) one of whom is a nurse faculty member of a school of nursing offering a baccalaureate degree program in preparing registered nurses;

(B) one of whom is a nurse faculty member of a school of nursing offering an associate degree program in preparing registered nurses; and

(C) one of whom is a nurse faculty member of a school of nursing at an institution of higher education preparing vocational nurses; and

(3) four members who represent the public.

(b) Appointments to the board shall be made without regard to the race, color, disability, sex, religion, age, or national origin of the appointee.

Sec. 301.052. MEMBER ELIGIBILITY. (a) A person is not eligible for appointment as a registered nurse or vocational nurse member of the board unless the person has practiced nursing in the role for which the member was appointed for at least three of the five years preceding the date of appointment.

(b) A person is not eligible for appointment as a public member of the board if the person or the person's spouse:

(1) is registered, certified, or licensed by an occupational regulatory agency in the field of health care;

(2) is employed by or participates in the management of a business entity or other organization that:

(A) provides health care services;

(B) sells, manufactures, or distributes health care supplies or equipment; or

(C) is regulated by or receives money from the board;

(3) owns or controls, directly or indirectly, more than a 10 percent interest in a business entity or other organization that:

(A) provides health care services;

(B) sells, manufactures, or distributes health care supplies or equipment; or

(C) is regulated by or receives money from the board; or

(4) uses or receives a substantial amount of tangible goods, services, or funds from the board, other than compensation or reimbursement authorized by law for board membership, attendance, or expenses.

Sec. 301.053. MEMBERSHIP AND EMPLOYEE RESTRICTIONS. (a) In this section, "Texas trade association" means a cooperative and voluntarily joined statewide association of business or professional competitors in this state designed to assist its members and its industry or profession in dealing with mutual business or professional problems and in promoting their common interest.

(b) A person may not be a member of the board and may not be a board employee employed in a "bona fide executive, administrative, or professional capacity," as that phrase is used for the purposes of establishing an exemption to the overtime provisions of the federal Fair Labor Standards Act of 1938 (29 U.S.C. Section 201 et seq.), if:

(1) the person is an officer, employee, or paid consultant of a Texas trade association

3 nurse educators with 2 representing professional nursing education (ADN and BSN) and 1 representing vocation nursing education

This composition reflects the recommendations of a task force which recommended in 2004 that Texas have a single board of nursing. The task force felt this composition best addressed the functions a single board would perform and also was equitable in light of the fact there are a little over twice as many RNs as LVNs in Texas.

Having educators on a health professional licensing board is the exception rather than the norm but most health professional licensing boards do not have the same degree of regulatory responsibility for professional education that the BON historically has had.

One-third public members is the general rule for professional licensing agencies but having exactly one-third is not always practical when all factors are considered. Some consumer groups advocate a majority of public members. Professional associations generally believe having less than two-thirds professional members deprives a board of the professional expertise needed to regulate the profession.

To help ensure they have the knowledge and expertise to fulfill adequately the role for which appointed, nurse members of the board must be actively practicing in the role in which appointed.

The purpose of the criteria for public members is to ensure that they represent the interests of the public and not the regulated profession. However, as indicated above, the two are not mutually exclusive since promoting the profession includes promoting safe, quality care.

The Board's role is to protect the public. This provision is designed to ensure board members and employees don't have a conflict of interest that would compromise their carrying out this role.

in the field of health care; or

(2) the person's spouse is an officer, manager, or paid consultant of a Texas trade association in the field of health care.

(c) A person may not be a member of the board or act as the general counsel to the board if the person is required to register as a lobbyist under Chapter 305, Government Code, because of the person's activities for compensation on behalf of a profession related to the board's operation.

Sec. 301.054. TERMS. Members of the board serve staggered six-year terms, with the terms of as near to one-third of the members as possible expiring on January 31 of each odd-numbered year.

Sec. 301.055. GROUNDS FOR REMOVAL. (a) It is a ground for removal from the board that a member:

(1) does not have at the time of taking office the qualifications required by Section 301.051(a);

(2) does not maintain during service on the board the qualifications required by Section 301.051(a);

(3) is ineligible for membership under Section 301.053;

(4) cannot, because of illness or disability, discharge the member's duties for a substantial part of the member's term; or

(5) is absent from more than half of the regularly scheduled board meetings that the member is eligible to attend during a calendar year unless the absence is excused by majority vote of the board.

(b) The validity of an action of the board is not affected by the fact that the action is taken when a ground for removal of a board member exists.

(c) If the executive director has knowledge that a potential ground for removal exists, the executive director shall notify the presiding officer of the board of the potential ground. The presiding officer shall then notify the governor and the attorney general that a potential ground for removal exists. If the potential ground for removal involves the presiding officer, the executive director shall notify the next highest ranking officer of the board, who shall then notify the governor and the attorney general that a potential ground for removal exists.

Sec. 301.056. PER DIEM; REIMBURSEMENT. (a) Each board member is entitled to receive a per diem as set by the General Appropriations Act for each day the member engages in the business of the board.

(b) A board member is entitled to reimbursement for travel expenses incurred while conducting board business, including expenses for transportation, meals, and lodging, as provided by the General Appropriations Act.

Sec. 301.057. OFFICERS. (a) The governor shall designate a member of the board as presiding officer to serve in that capacity at the pleasure of the governor.

(b) The board shall elect other officers from its members.

Sec. 301.058. MEETINGS. The presiding officer shall call a special board meeting on the written request of at least two board members.

Sec. 301.059. TRAINING. (a) A person who is appointed to and qualifies for office as a member of the board may not vote, deliberate, or be counted in attendance at a meeting of the

Staggered six-year terms promote continuity by having no more than 1/3 of the membership change at any one time.

A board member may be removed for the reasons listed.

NPA Sec. 301.051(a) referred to sets out the membership of the BON – practicing RNs (3), practicing LVNs (3), RN educators (2), LVN educators (1), APRN (1), and consumers (4). BON members appointed to these positions have to maintain the qualifications for the position.

NPA Sec. 301.053 referred to is a conflict of interest provision that prohibits officers and board members of health care trade/professional associations and health care lobbyists from being on the BON.

A board action is not rendered invalid because grounds for a member's removal existed at the time the action was taken.

The BON executive director has an affirmative obligation to notify the Board president if grounds may exist for a member's removal.

Board members serve primarily as volunteers and are paid only a per diem when actually engaged in board business. They are reimbursed for expenses. This is typical of state agency boards.

The BON president is appointed by the Governor. The other officers are elected by the board.

The BON currently meets four times a year in January, April, July, and October. Normally, it holds a strategic planning meeting in late summer.

Board members must complete a training program before taking their position on the board. The training is designed to assure board members are aware of programs of the BON, the board until the person completes a training program that complies with this section.

(b) The training program must provide the person with information regarding:

(1) the legislation that created the board and the board's programs, functions, rules, and budget;

(2) the results of the most recent formal audit of the board;

(3) the requirements of laws relating to open meetings, public information, administrative procedure, and conflicts of interest; and

(4) any applicable ethics policies adopted by the board or the Texas Ethics Commission.

(c) A person appointed to the board is entitled to reimbursement, as provided by the General Appropriations Act, for the travel expenses incurred in attending the training program regardless of whether the attendance at the program occurs before or after the person qualifies for office.

(d) *[Repealed]*

SUBCHAPTER C.
EXECUTIVE DIRECTOR AND PERSONNEL

✔Sec. 301.101. EXECUTIVE DIRECTOR. (a) The board shall employ an executive director. The executive director may not be a member of the board.

(b) Under the direction of the board, the executive director shall perform the duties required by this chapter or designated by the board.

Sec. 301.102. *[Repealed.]*

Sec. 301.103. PUBLIC RECORDS; REGISTRY. (a) The executive director shall keep:

(1) a record of each meeting of the board; and

(2) a registry of the name of each nurse registered under this chapter.

(b) Information maintained under this section is open to public inspection at all times.

Sec. 301.104. PERSONNEL; EMPLOYMENT PRACTICES. The board shall employ persons as necessary to carry on the work of the board.

Sec. 301.105. DIVISION OF RESPONSIBILITIES. (a) The board shall develop and implement policies that clearly define the respective responsibilities of the board and the staff of the board.

(b) The board shall determine the salaries and compensation to be paid to employees and persons retained by the board.

requirements of the open records and open meeting laws, potential conflicts of interests, etc.

The executive director is the chief executive officer of the BON. Because most of this Subchapter deals with internal operations and does not have significant practice implications, it is not annotated. The provisions in this Subchapter are similar to those in other health professionals licensing acts.

Sec. 301.106. QUALIFICATIONS AND STANDARDS OF CONDUCT INFORMATION. The board shall provide, as often as necessary, to its members and employees information regarding their:

(1) qualifications for office or employment under this chapter; and

(2) responsibilities under applicable laws relating to standards of conduct for state officers or employees.

Sec. 301.107. CAREER LADDER PROGRAM; PERFORMANCE EVALUATIONS. (a) The executive director or the executive director's designee shall develop an intra-agency career ladder program. The program must require intra-agency posting of all nonentry level positions concurrently with any public posting.

(b) The executive director or the executive director's designee shall develop a system of annual performance evaluations based on measurable job tasks. All merit pay for board employees must be based on the system established under this subsection.

Sec. 301.108. EQUAL EMPLOYMENT OPPORTUNITY POLICY; REPORT. (a) The executive director or the executive director's designee shall prepare and maintain a written policy statement to ensure implementation of an equal employment opportunity program under which all personnel transactions are made without regard to race, color, disability, sex, religion, age, or national origin. The policy statement must include:

(1) personnel policies, including policies relating to recruitment, evaluation, selection, application, training, and promotion of personnel that are in compliance with the requirements of Chapter 21, Labor Code;

(2) a comprehensive analysis of the board workforce that meets federal and state guidelines;

(3) procedures by which a determination can be made of significant underuse in the board workforce of all persons for whom federal or state guidelines encourage a more equitable balance; and

(4) reasonable methods to appropriately address those areas of underuse.

(b) A policy statement prepared under Subsection (a) must:

(1) cover an annual period;

(2) be updated annually;

(3) be reviewed by the Commission on Human Rights for compliance with Subsection (a)(1); and

(4) be filed with the governor.

(c) The governor shall deliver a biennial report to the legislature based on the information received under Subsection (b). The report may be made separately or as part of other biennial reports to the legislature.

SUBCHAPTER D.
GENERAL POWERS AND DUTIES OF BOARD

This Subchapter addresses the BON's role and responsibilities in regulating nursing - both practice and education.

✔Shading Denotes More Important Practice-Related NPA Sections

✔Sec. 301.151. GENERAL RULEMAKING AUTHORITY. The board may adopt and enforce rules consistent with this chapter and necessary to:

(1) perform its duties and conduct proceedings before the board;

(2) regulate the practice of professional nursing and vocational nursing;

(3) establish standards of professional conduct for license holders under this chapter; and

(4) determine whether an act constitutes the practice of professional nursing or vocational nursing.

✔Sec. 301.152. RULES REGARDING SPECIALIZED TRAINING; ADVANCED PRACTICE REGISTERED NURSES (APRNs). (a) In this section, "advanced practice registered nurse" means a registered nurse licensed by the board to practice as an advanced practice registered nurse on the basis of completion of an advanced educational program. The term includes a nurse practitioner, nurse midwife, nurse anesthetist, and clinical nurse specialist. The term is synonymous with "advanced nurse practitioner " and "advanced practice nurse."

(b) The board shall adopt rules to:

(1) license a registered nurse as an advanced practice registered nurse;

(2) establish:

From a practice perspective, rule-making is one of the BON's more important roles. This section sets out the BON's general rule-making authority. The NPA gives the BON the broadest authority permitted by law. The purpose of giving professional licensing boards rule-making authority is to permit them to provide more detailed regulation of the profession than is feasible in the statute itself. In fact, agency rule-making is frequently described as filling in the details of policies set by the Legislature. Through rules, the BON can apply the NPA to emerging practice settings. The Board's standards of practice and unprofessional conduct rules are adopted under the authority of this section. Other provisions of the NPA address specific rule-making powers such as adopting rules minimizing reporting of minor incidents, rules governing CNE, rules governing filing of complaints, etc. Subsection (4) also gives the BON authority to determine whether an act constitutes the practice of professional or vocational nursing. Such determination must be consistent with the statutory definitions of "professional nursing" and "vocational nursing" set out in NPA Sec. 301.002.

Advanced Practice Registered Nurses (APRNs) include Nurse Practitioners (NPs), Clinical Nurse Specialists (CNSs), Certified Nurse Midwives (CNMs) and Certified Nurse Anesthetists (CRNAs). This Sec. 301.152 was revised in 2013 to simplify and to replace the terminology of the BON "approving APRNs" with "licensing APRNs."

The reference to being synonymous with "advanced nurse practitioner" is included because that was terminology previously used and some statutes and state agency rules still contain that terminology. See NPA Sec. 301.005 that a reference in any law to "advanced nurse practitioner" or "advanced practice nurse" is a reference to "advanced practice registered nurse." The BON has adopted Rules 221 and 222 implementing this section.

(A) any specialized education or training, including pharmacology, that an advanced practice registered nurse must have to prescribe or order a drug or device as delegated by a physician under Section 157.0512 or 157.054;

(B) a system for approving an advanced practice registered nurse to prescribe or order a drug or device as delegated by a physician under Section 157.0512 or 157.054 on the receipt of evidence of completing the specialized education and training requirement under Paragraph (A); and

(C) a system for issuing a prescription authorization number to an advanced practice registered nurse approved under Paragraph (B); and

(3) concurrently renew any license or approval granted to an advanced practice registered nurse under this subsection and a license renewed by the advanced practice registered nurse under Section 301.301.

(c) At a minimum, the rules adopted under Subsection (b)(2) must:

(1) require completion of pharmacology and related pathophysiology education for initial approval;

(2) require continuing education in clinical pharmacology and related pathology in addition to any continuing education otherwise required under Section 301.303.

(d) The signature of an advanced practice registered nurse attesting to the provision of a legally authorized service by the advanced practice registered nurse satisfies any documentation requirement for that service established by a state agency.

Sec. 301.153. RULES REGARDING ADVERTISING AND COMPETITIVE BIDDING.

(a) The board may not adopt rules restricting advertising or competitive bidding by a person except to prohibit false, misleading, or deceptive practices by the person.

(b) The board may not include in its rules to prohibit false, misleading, or deceptive practices by a person regulated by the board a rule that:

(1) restricts the person's use of any medium for advertising;

(2) restricts the person's personal appearance or use of the person's voice in an advertisement;

(3) relates to the size or duration of an advertisement by the person; or

(4) restricts the use of a trade name in advertising by the person.

Sec. 301.154. RULES REGARDING DELEGATION OF CERTAIN MEDICAL ACTS.

(a) The board may recommend to the Texas Medical Board the adoption of rules relating to the delegation by physicians of medical acts to registered nurses and vocational nurses licensed by the board. In making a recommendation, the board may distinguish between nurses on the basis of special training and education.

(b) A recommendation under Subsection (a) shall be treated in the same manner as a petition for the adoption of a rule by an interested party under Chapter 2001, Government Code.

(c) The board in recommending a rule and the Texas Medical Board in acting on a recommended rule shall, to the extent allowable under state and federal statutes, rules, and regulations, act to enable the state to obtain its fair share of the federal funds available for the delivery of health care in this state.

✔Sec. 301.1545. RULES ON CONSEQUENCES OF CRIMINAL CONVICTION OR DEFERRED ADJUDICATION. (a) The board shall adopt rules and guidelines necessary to comply with Chapter 53, except to the extent the requirements of this subtitle are stricter than the requirements of that chapter.

(b) In its rules under this section, the board shall list the offenses for which a conviction

APRNs must retain their license as RNs. The APRN license is renewed concurrently with the RN license.

There are First Amendment freedom of speech issues involved with limiting professionals' right to advertise and this language is designed to assure that the BON not adopt rules that would violate First Amendment rights. See Occupations Code Sec. 101.201 which identifies what constitutes false, misleading and deceptive advertising.

This section was passed in 1981when nurse practitioners were first emerging in Texas. It was designed to allow the BON to request the Texas Medical Board to authorize physicians to delegate to APRNs using protocols or standing orders. The Medical Practice Act was amended that same year explicitly to authorize physicians to delegate under standing orders. The latter greatly reduced the need for this section, and the BON has never made any request to the Texas Medical Board under the authority of this section. Both pieces of legislation had been prompted by Texas Attorney General Opinion H-1295 (1978) that had held that, under the law at that time, physicians could not use protocols to order the administration of medications. LVNs were added to Subsec. (a) in 2003 but their inclusion is unlikely to be of any significance due to the entire section being largely outdated. This section is of historical interest because of the reference to distinguishing among nurses on the basis of education and training represented the first statutory recognition of RNs in advanced practice.

The Chapter 53 referred to governs how professional licensing boards take disciplinary action based on criminal convictions. Since the BON conducts FBI criminal background checks of all new licensees and in 2013 was mandated to do so for students accepted for admission, nurses with a criminal history will almost certainly be identified by the board. BON Rule 213.28 sets out how the board will handle criminal convictions. The board has also adopted guidelines and policies would constitute grounds for the board to take action under Section 53.021 or for which placement on deferred adjudication community supervision would constitute grounds for the board to take action under this chapter.

Sec. 301.155. FEES. (a) The board by rule shall establish fees in amounts reasonable and necessary to cover the costs of administering this chapter. The board may not set a fee that existed on September 1, 1993, in an amount less than the amount of that fee on that date.

(b) The board may adopt a fee in an amount necessary for a periodic newsletter to produce and disseminate to license holders the information required under Section 301.158.

(c) The board shall assess a surcharge of not less than $3 or more than $5 for a registered nurse and a surcharge of not less than $2 or more than $3 for a vocational nurse to the fee established by the board under Subsection (a) for a license holder to renew a license under this chapter. The board may use nine cents of the registered nurse surcharge and six cents of the vocational nurse surcharge to cover the administrative costs of collecting and depositing the surcharge. The board quarterly shall transmit the remainder of each surcharge to the Department of State Health Services to be used only to implement the nursing resource section under Section 105.002, Health and Safety Code. The board is not required to collect the surcharge if the board determines the funds collected are not appropriated for the purpose of funding the nursing resource section.

Sec. 301.156. GIFTS AND GRANTS. The board may receive gifts, grants, or other funds or assets.

Sec. 301.157. PROGRAMS OF STUDY AND APPROVAL

(a) The board shall prescribe three programs of study to prepare a person to receive an initial license as a registered nurse under this chapter as follows:

(1) a baccalaureate degree program that is conducted by an educational unit in nursing that is a part of a senior college or university and that leads to a baccalaureate degree in nursing;

(2) an associate degree program that is conducted by an educational unit in nursing within the structure of a college or a university and that leads to an associate degree in nursing; and

(3) a diploma program that is conducted by a single-purpose school, usually under the control of a hospital, and that leads to a diploma in nursing.

(a-1) A diploma program of study in this state that leads to an initial license as a registered nurse under this chapter and that is completed on or after December 31, 2014, must entitle a student to receive a degree on the student's successful completion of a degree program of a public *relating to criminal convictions.*

Specific fees are set out in Rule §223. The fees collected by the BON (and most other professional licensing boards) exceed the costs of operating the agency. Excess funds go into the State's General Revenue Fund and contribute to balancing the state budget. To protect this source of revenue, the Legislature, when it removed specific fee amounts from the NPA in 1993, prohibited the BON from lowering fees from 1993 levels. Although all BON expenditures are covered by fees collected from nurses, the board can only expend funds as appropriated by the Texas Legislature in the General Appropriations Bill. This process may not permit the BON the flexibility needed to adjust expenditures.

The Board publishes a quarterly newsletter ("Texas Board of Nursing Bulletin") that provides valuable information for nurses about changes in the NPA, BON rules and other matters affecting nursing practice. Nurses should read those newsletters carefully. Current and past newsletters are posted on the BON's website at www.bon.texas.gov.

A license renewal surcharge funds the Texas Center for Nursing Workforce Studies (TCNWS) which is administratively tied to the Statewide Health Coordinating Council (SHCC) and the Department of State Health Services. TCNWS was established in 2003 and replaced a nursing workforce data center administratively tied to the BON that had been created in 2001 but not funded.

Unlike most other health care licensing boards, the BON historically has played a significant role in approving and regulating nursing education programs. The BON 2007 Sunset legislation reduced this role and it has shared responsibility with the Texas Higher Education Coordinating Board. Subsecs. (b-1) and (d-1) require the board to defer to national accreditation of both the institution and nursing program and not to duplicate or overlap with the accreditation process.

The BON is required to recognize the three types of professional nursing educational programs:

- *nonacademic diploma programs*
- *ADN programs in community colleges*
- *BSN programs in colleges and universities*

Currently, there is only one diploma program. The BON also recognizes a special masters program track for individuals who have a baccalaureate degree that is not in nursing.

Subsection (a-1) reflects the fact that professional nursing is an academically-prepared profession. Historically, graduates of hospital-based diploma programs are not awarded an academic degree. Beginning in 2015 graduation from a diploma school must entitle the student or private institution of higher education accredited by an agency recognized by the Texas Higher Education Coordinating Board.

(b) The board shall:

(1) prescribe two programs of study to prepare a person to receive an initial vocational nurse license under this chapter as follows:

(A) a program conducted by an educational unit in nursing within the structure of a school, including a college, university, or proprietary school; and

(B) a program conducted by a hospital;

(2) prescribe and publish the minimum requirements and standards for a course of study in each program that prepares registered nurses or vocational nurses;

(3) prescribe other rules as necessary to conduct approved schools of nursing and educational programs for the preparation of registered nurses or vocational nurses;

(4) approve schools of nursing and educational programs that meet the board's requirements;

(5) select one or more national nursing accrediting agencies, recognized by the United States Department of Education and determined by the board to have acceptable standards, to accredit schools of nursing and educational programs; and

(6) deny or withdraw approval from a school of nursing or educational program that:

(A) fails to meet the prescribed course of study or other standard under which it sought approval by the board;

(B) fails to meet or maintain accreditation with the national nursing accrediting agency selected by the board under Subdivision (5) under which it was approved or sought approval by the board; or

(C) fails to maintain the approval of the state board of nursing of another state and the board under which it was approved.

registered nurses may not be less than two academic years or more than four calendar years.

(b-1) The board may not require accreditation of the governing institution of a school of nursing. The board shall accept the requirements established by the Texas Higher Education Coordinating Board for accrediting the governing institution of a school of nursing. The governing institution of a professional nursing school, not including a diploma program, must be accredited by an agency recognized by the Texas Higher Education Coordinating Board or hold a certificate of authority from the Texas Higher Education Coordinating Board under provisions leading to accreditation of the institution in due course.

(c) A program approved to prepare

(d) A person may not be certified as a graduate of any school of nursing or educational program unless the person has completed the requirements of the prescribed course of study, including clinical practice, of a school of nursing or educational program that:

(1) is approved by the board;

(2) is accredited by a national nursing accreditation agency determined by the board to have acceptable standards; or

(3) is approved by a state board of nursing of another state and the board, subject to Subsection (d-4).

(d-1) A school of nursing or educational program is considered approved by the board and, except as provided by Subsection (d-7), is exempt from board rules that require ongoing *to an academic degree. When this provision was passed in 2007 there were two diploma programs in Texas but one has converted to an ADN program.*

Subdivision (b)(1) addresses vocational education and requires that the board recognize programs conducted by 1) educational entities (both colleges and proprietary schools) and 2) hospitals.

Subdivision (5) was part of the changes in the BON's role in regulating education made in 2007 as part of the board's Sunset legislation. It directs the board to select a national accrediting agency(s) to accredit schools and programs. The two national accrediting bodies for nursing programs are the National League for Nursing Accrediting Commission (NLNAC) and the Commission on Collegiate Nursing Education (CCNE).

The board is required to accept accreditation of the governing institution by the Texas Higher Education Coordinating Board. The requirement that the governing institution be accredited by an agency recognized by the Coordinating Board means that it must be an academic institution. It can be a proprietary college because they are so accredited. But it cannot be a career school since they are not so accredited.

Individuals seeking licensure must be graduates of a board-approved or appropriately accredited educational programs.

The board does not re-approve schools on a periodic basis but rather relies on the schools' maintaining national accreditation and an acceptable pass rate on the licensing exam. However, approval if the school or program:

(1) is accredited and maintains accreditation through a national nursing accrediting agency selected by the board under Subsection (b)(5); and

(2) maintains an acceptable pass rate as determined by the board on the applicable licensing examination under this chapter.

(d-2) A school of nursing or educational program that fails to meet or maintain an acceptable pass rate on applicable licensing examinations under this chapter is subject to review by the board. The board may assist the school or program in its effort to achieve compliance with the board's standards.

(d-3) A school or program from which approval has been withdrawn under this section may reapply for approval.

(d-4) The board may recognize and accept as approved under this section a school of nursing or educational program operated in another state and approved by a state board of nursing or other regulatory body of that state. The board shall develop policies to ensure that the other state's standards are substantially equivalent to the board's standards.

(d-5) The board shall streamline the process for initially approving a school of nursing or educational program under this section by identifying and eliminating tasks performed by the board that duplicate or overlap tasks performed by the Texas Higher Education Coordinating Board or the Texas Workforce Commission.

(d-6) The board, in cooperation with the Texas Higher Education Coordinating Board and the Texas Workforce Commission, shall establish guidelines for the initial approval of schools of nursing or educational programs. The guidelines must:

(1) identify the approval processes to be conducted by the Texas Higher Education Coordinating Board or the Texas Workforce Commission;

(2) require the approval process identified under Subdivision (1) to precede the approval process conducted by the board; and

(3) be made available on the board's Internet website and in a written form.

(d-7) A school of nursing or educational program approved under Subsection (d-1) shall:

(1) provide the board with copies of any reports submitted to or received from the national nursing accrediting agency selected by the board;

(2) notify the board of any change in accreditation status; and

(3) provide other information required by the board as necessary to evaluate and establish nursing education and workforce policy in this state.

(d-8) For purposes of Subsection (d-4), a nursing program is considered to meet standards substantially equivalent to the board's standards if the program:

(1) is part of an institution of higher education located outside this state that is approved by the appropriate regulatory authorities of that state;

(2) holds regional accreditation by an accrediting body recognized by the United States secretary of education and the Council for Higher Education Accreditation;

(3) holds specialty accreditation by an accrediting body recognized by the United States secretary of education and the Council for Higher Education Accreditation, including the National League for Nursing Accrediting Commission;

(4) requires program applicants to be a licensed practical or vocational nurse, a

schools and programs must provide the BON certain information under Subsec. (d-7)

Schools must maintain a minimum licensing exam pass rate set by the board.

In recognizing an out-of-state program, the board should rely on approval of the program by the BON or other appropriate regulatory body in the other state.

The board is directed to work with the Coordinating Board and Workforce Commission to minimize duplication and overlap of regulation.

Schools must keep the board informed of any changes in their status.

Subsections (d-8) - (d-11) were enacted in 2009 to address the status of graduates of a New York based nursing program (Excelsior College) that does not have supervised clinicals but rather utilizes a single competency assessment conducted at the end of the program. Excelsior College graduates have been eligible for licensure in Texas for a number of years. However, as part of the BON's Sunset review in 2007, Subsec. (d-4) was added establishing a "substantially equivalent to Texas Programs" standard for out-of-state programs. A question arose whether the Excelsior College program with its single competency assessment was substantially equivalent to Texas programs with their supervised clinical experiences requirement.

Subsections (d-8) - (d-11) address this issue by providing Excelsior College a type of "safe harbor" under which its graduates will continue to be eligible for licensure in Texas until military service corpsman, or a paramedic, or to hold a college degree in a clinically oriented health care field with demonstrated experience providing direct patient care; and

(5) graduates students who:

(A) achieve faculty-determined program outcomes, including passing criterion-referenced examinations of nursing knowledge essential to beginning a registered nursing practice and transitioning to the role of registered nurse;

(B) pass a criterion-referenced summative performance examination developed by faculty subject matter experts that measures clinical competencies essential to beginning a registered nursing practice and that meets nationally recognized standards for educational testing, including the educational testing standards of the American Educational Research Association, the American Psychological Association, and the National Council on Measurement in Education; and

(C) pass the National Council Licensure Examination for Registered Nurses at a rate equivalent to the passage rate for students of approved in-state programs.

(d-9) A graduate of a clinical competency assessment program operated in another state and approved by a state board of nursing or other regulatory body of another state is eligible to apply for an initial license under this chapter if:

(1) the board allowed graduates of the program to apply for an initial license under this chapter continuously during the 10-year period preceding January 1, 2007;

(2) the program does not make any substantial changes in the length or content of its clinical competency assessment without the board's approval;

(3) the program remains in good standing with the state board of nursing or other regulatory body in the other state; and

(4) the program participates in the research study under Section 105.008, Health and Safety Code.

(d-10) In this section, the terms "clinical competency assessment program" and "supervised clinical learning experiences program" have the meanings assigned by Section 105.008, Health and Safety Code.

(d-11) Subsections (d-8), (d-9), (d-10), and (d-11) expire December 31, 2017. As part of the first review conducted under Section 301.003 after September 1, 2009, the Sunset Advisory Commission shall:

(1) recommend whether Subsections (d-8) and (d-9) should be extended; and

(2) recommend any changes to Subsections (d-8) and (d-9) relating to the eligibility for a license of graduates of a clinical competency assessment program operated in another state.

(e) The board shall give each person, including an organization, affected by an order or decision of the board under this section reasonable notice of not less than 20 days and an opportunity to appear and be heard regarding the order or decision. The board shall hear each protest or complaint from a person affected by a rule or decision regarding:

(1) the inadequacy or unreasonableness of any rule or order the board adopts; or

(2) the injustice of any order or decision of the board.

(f) Not later than the 30th day after the date an order is entered and approved by the board, a person is entitled to bring an action against the board in a district court of Travis County to have the rule or order vacated or modified, if that person:

(1) is affected by the order or decision;

(2) is dissatisfied with any rule or order of the board; and

(3) sets forth in a petition the principal grounds of objection to the rule or order.

(g) An appeal under this section shall be tried de novo as if it were an appeal from a

12/31/17. The Center for Nursing Workforce Studies (CNWS) was charged with conducting a study of the clinical component of nursing education including Excelsior's single competency assessment approach. However, due to funding and other issues, it appears the study will not be conducted.

The Texas Sunset Advisory Commission is directed to review this issue when the BON undergoes Sunset review in 2017 and make recommendations to the Texas Legislature about the eligibility of Excelsior College graduates continuing to be eligible for Texas licensure.

"Trial de novo" means the appeal will be conducted as a completely new trial, i.e., as if it had never been decided by the BON. All evidence will have to be reintroduced, etc.

justice court to a county court.

(h) The board, in collaboration with the nursing educators, the Texas Higher Education Coordinating Board, and the Texas Health Care Policy Council, shall implement, monitor, and evaluate a plan for the creation of innovative nursing education models that promote increased enrollment in this state's nursing programs.

Sec. 301.158. DISSEMINATION OF INFORMATION. The board shall disseminate, at least twice a year and at other times the board determines necessary, information that is of significant interest to nurses and employers of nurses in this state, including summaries of final disciplinary action taken against nurses by the board since its last dissemination of information.

Sec. 301.1581. INFORMATION PROVIDED TO LICENSE HOLDERS. At least once each biennium, the board shall provide to license holders information on:

(1) prescribing and dispensing pain medications, with particular emphasis on Schedule II and Schedule III controlled substances;

(2) abusive and addictive behavior of certain persons who use prescription pain medications;

(3) common diversion strategies employed by certain persons who use prescription pain medications, including fraudulent prescription patterns; and

(4) the appropriate use of pain medications and the differences between addiction, pseudo-addiction, tolerance, and physical dependence.

Sec. 301.1582. POISON CONTROL CENTER INFORMATION. The board shall provide to license holders information regarding the services provided by poison control centers.

Sec. 301.159. BOARD DUTIES REGARDING COMPLAINTS. (a) The board by rule shall:

(1) adopt a form to standardize information concerning complaints made to the board; and

(2) prescribe information to be provided to a person when the person files a complaint with the board.

(b) The board shall provide reasonable assistance to a person who wishes to file a complaint with the board.

Sec. 301.1595. ADVISORY COMMITTEES. (a) The board may appoint advisory committees to perform the advisory functions assigned by the board.

(b) An advisory committee shall provide independent expertise on board functions and policies, but may not be involved in setting board policy.

(c) The board shall adopt rules regarding the purpose, structure, and use of advisory committees, including rules on:

(1) the purpose, role, responsibility, and goal of an advisory committee;

(2) the size and quorum requirements for an advisory committee;

(3) the composition and representation of an advisory committee;

(4) the qualifications of advisory committee members, such as experience or area of residence;

(5) the appointment procedures for advisory committees;

(6) the terms of service for advisory committee members;

(7) the training requirements for advisory committee members, if necessary;

(8) the method the board will use to receive public input on issues addressed by an

Despite the fact that its 2007 Sunset legislation reduced the BON's role in regulating education, the board was directed to develop a plan to create innovative models for nursing education to increase enrollments. This provision probably grew out of a perception by some legislators that BON requirements, particularly those related to clinical faculty to student ratio, had interfered with schools increasing enrollments to address the nursing shortage.

The Board publishes a quarterly newsletter titled "Texas Board of Nursing Bulletin." This publication is a valuable source of information about changes in the NPA, BON rules and other matters affecting their practice. The BON's website at www.bon.texas.gov is also a good source of information for licensees and the public.

This section is similar to provisions in several other health professional licensing acts. The BON and other health care licensing boards have established a page on the Pharmacy Board's website at www.tsbp.state.tx.us/sb144.htm.

This section is similar to provisions in several other health professional licensing acts. The BON has information on poison control centers under the Practice Section of its website.

The BON is required to facilitate the filing of complaints and to assist persons in filing complaints. See also NPA Secs. 301.201 and 301.202 requiring the BON to provide information of public interest including procedures for filing complaints.

The purpose of Sec. 301.1595 is to ensure that the board's advisory committees provide objective, independent advice and that the board (not advisory committees) function as the policy setting body. See Rule 211.6 relating to BON advisory committees for a list of advisory committees.

advisory committee; and

(9) the development of board policies and procedures to ensure advisory committees meet the requirements for open meetings under Chapter 551, Government Code, including notification requirements.

(d) A board member may not serve as a member of an advisory committee, but may serve as a liaison between an advisory committee and the board. A board member liaison that attends advisory committee meetings may attend only as an observer and not as a participant. A board member liaison is not required to attend advisory committee meetings. The role of a board member liaison is limited to clarifying the board's charge and intent to the advisory committee.

(e) To the extent of any conflict with Chapter 2110, Government Code, this section and board rules adopted under this section control.

Sec. 301.160. PILOT PROGRAMS.

(a) In this section:

(1) "Proactive nursing peer review" means peer review that is not initiated to determine culpability with respect to a particular incident.

(2) "Targeted continuing nursing education" means continuing education focusing on a skill that would likely benefit a significant proportion of nurses in a particular practice area.

(b) The board may develop pilot programs to evaluate the effectiveness of mechanisms, including proactive nursing peer review and targeted continuing nursing education, for maintenance of the clinical competency of a nurse in the nurse's area of practice and the understanding by nurses of the laws, including regulations, governing the practice of nursing.

(c) A pilot program under Subsection (b) must be designed to test the effectiveness of a variety of mechanisms in a variety of practice settings.

(d) The board may approve a pilot program under Subsection (b) that is to be conducted by a person other than the board.

(e) The board may spend funds to develop or fund a pilot program and may contract with, make grants to, or make other arrangements with an agency, professional association, institution, individual, or other person to implement this section.

(f) - (g) *[Repealed]*

(i) Except as provided by this subsection, in developing or approving a pilot program under this section the board may exempt the program from rules adopted under this chapter. Subchapter I and Chapter 303 apply to pilot programs, except that Sections 303.002(e), 303.003, and 303.008(b) do not apply to a pilot program using proactive peer review. The board may establish alternative criteria for nursing peer review committees conducting proactive peer review.

(j) The board shall issue an annual report regarding any pilot programs developed or approved and a status report on those programs, including preliminary or final findings concerning their effectiveness. The board shall mail the report to statewide associations of nurses and nurse educators and employers of registered nurses that request a copy.

Sec. 301.1605. PILOT PROGRAMS FOR INNOVATIVE APPLICATIONS. (a) The board may approve and adopt rules regarding pilot programs for innovative applications in the practice and regulation of nursing.

(b) The board shall specify the procedures to be followed in applying for approval of a pilot program. The board may condition approval of a program on compliance with this section and rules adopted under this section.

(c) In approving a pilot program, the board may grant the program an exception to the mandatory reporting requirements of Sections 301.401-301.409 or to a rule adopted under this chapter or Chapter 303 that relates to the practice of nursing, including education and reporting

The role of BON members on advisory committees is limited.

This Sec. 301.160 was the first provision (1997) giving the BON authority to conduct pilots and directed the board to develop two specific pilots – one addressing continued competency and one addressing nurses' knowledge of the laws and regulations governing nursing. Secs. 301.1605 and 301.1606 were added in 2003 to give the BON additional authority to conduct pilot programs. Section 301.160 was subsequently amended to broaden its scope to give the BON general authority to conduct pilots to "evaluate the effectiveness of mechanisms . . . for maintenance of the clinical competency of a nurse in the nurse's area of practice and the understanding by nurses of the laws governing the practice of nursing."

Partially as a result of the two original pilots, legislation was passed 1) authorizing the BON to utilize mechanisms other than CNE for nurses to demonstrate continued competency (2003) and 2) requiring a jurisprudence exam for initial licensure (2007). See Secs. 301.303 and 301.252(a-1).

This Sec. 301.1605 gives the board general authority to conduct pilot projects but does not require it to actually conduct any pilot programs. Because of the large number of nurses licensed in Texas (over 300,000) and the potential cost of implementing any requirement for all nurses, potential changes may need to be pilot tested for effectiveness rather than just implementing without knowing if they will be effective or feasible.

The board is authorized to exempt pilot programs from the mandatory reporting requirements of the NPA and also from the requirements of the Board's rules if appropriate. For example, it may not be appropriate to require that nurses participating in a targeted CE pilot meet the normal requirements for nurses. The board may not grant an exception to:

(1) the education requirements of this chapter unless the program includes alternate but substantially equivalent requirements; or

(2) the mandatory reporting requirements unless the program:

(A) is designed to evaluate the efficiency of alternative reporting methods; and

(B) provides consumers adequate protection from nurses whose continued practice is a threat to public safety.

Sec. 301.1606. PILOT PROGRAMS ON NURSE REPORTING SYSTEMS.

(a) The board may solicit proposals for pilot programs designed to evaluate the efficacy and effect on protection of the public of reporting systems designed to encourage identification of system errors.

(b) The board may grant a pilot program approved under this section an exception to the mandatory reporting requirements of Sections 301.401-301.409 or to a rule adopted under this chapter or Chapter 303 that relates to the practice of nursing, including education and reporting requirements for nurses. If the board grants an exception, the board may require that the program:

(1) provide for the remediation of the deficiencies of a nurse who has knowledge or skill deficiencies that unless corrected may result in an unreasonable risk to public safety;

(2) provide for supervision of the nurse during remediation of deficiencies under Subdivision (1);

(3) require reporting to the board of a nurse:

(A) who fails to satisfactorily complete remediation, or who does not make satisfactory progress in remediation, under Subdivision (1);

(B) whose incompetence in the practice of nursing would pose a continued risk of harm to the public; or

(C) whose error contributed to a patient death or serious patient injury; or

(4) provide for a nursing peer review committee to review whether a nurse is appropriate for remediation under Subdivision (1).

(c) The board may require that the entity conducting a pilot program under this section reimburse the board for the cost of monitoring and evaluating the pilot program.

(d) The board may contract with a third party to perform the monitoring and evaluation.

(e) The board may limit the number of pilot programs that it approves under this section.

Sec. 301.1607. *[Repealed]*

Sec. 301.161. ENFORCEMENT. (a) The board shall aid in the enforcement of this chapter.

(b) The board may:

(1) issue a subpoena;

(2) compel the attendance of a witness;

(3) administer an oath to a person giving testimony at hearings; and

(4) cause the prosecution of each person violating this chapter.

(c) The attorney general shall provide legal assistance necessary to enforce this chapter. This subsection does not relieve a local prosecuting officer of any duty under the law.

(d) The board may establish a criminal investigations unit to investigate suspected criminal acts relating to the practice of nursing as authorized by this chapter.

(e) The board may assist federal, state, or local law enforcement agencies in the investigation and prosecution of crimes related to the practice of nursing.

CE requirement. Likewise, pilots testing reporting mechanisms to encourage greater identification of system errors may need to be exempted from some of the mandatory reporting requirements of the NPA. If the board grants certain types of exceptions, it has to assure there are alternate mechanisms in place to protect the public. See Rule 227 relating to educational pilots under this Section and Rule 226 relating to reporting pilots under Sec. 301.1606.

This Sec. 301.1606 specifically addresses pilots to evaluate reporting systems designed to encourage identification of system errors. Its purpose, at least in part, was to permit MD Anderson to complete a national research project it was conducting on reporting of system errors. The BON did approve that project as a pilot which has been completed. Because the MD Anderson pilot was testing the efficacy of no-fault reporting mechanisms in identifying system errors, it was an example of a pilot for which exceptions to mandatory reporting requirements were needed. See Rule 226 relating to pilots under this Section.

This section authorized the BON to conduct a pilot to evaluate its taking deferred disciplinary action. Legislation passed in 2013 (SB 1058) converted this pilot authority to permanent authority. See NPA Secs. 301.651-.657 for the permanent provisions.

This provision gives the BON the authority needed to gather information and evidence necessary to resolve complaints.

As the attorney for the state, the Attorney General's office provides legal representation for the BON. The BON also has attorneys on staff.

✔Shading Denotes More Important Practice-Related NPA Sections

✔Sec. 301.1615. OBTAINING CRIMINAL HISTORY RECORD INFORMATION; HEARING. (a) In addition to the information to which the board is entitled under Section 411.125, Government Code, the board may request and receive criminal history record information from the Federal Bureau of Investigation as provided by Section 411.087, Government Code.

(b) Criminal history record information received by the board may be used only by the board and is privileged. The information may not be disclosed to any person other than:

(1) as required under a court order; or

(2) to a nursing board that is a member of the nurse licensure compact under Chapter 304.

(c) If, on the basis of criminal history record information obtained by the board, the board proposes to deny an application for a license, refuse to renew a license, or suspend or revoke a license or temporary permit, the applicant or license holder is entitled to a hearing under Section 301.454.

Sec. 301.162. LEGAL COUNSEL. The board may retain legal counsel to represent the board if first:

(1) the board requests the attorney general to represent the board; and

(2) the attorney general certifies to the board that the attorney general cannot provide those services.

Sec. 301.163. RECORD OF PROCEEDINGS; REPORT. The board shall keep a record of its proceedings under this chapter and make an annual report to the governor.

Sec. 301.164. ASSISTANCE OF PROSECUTOR. A board member may present to a prosecuting officer a complaint relating to a violation of this chapter. The board, through its members, officers, counsel, or agents, shall assist in the trial of a case involving an alleged violation of this chapter, subject to the control of the prosecuting officers.

Sec. 301.165. *[Repealed]*

Sec. 301.166. USE OF TECHNOLOGY. The board shall implement a policy requiring the board to use appropriate technological solutions to improve the board's ability to perform its functions. The policy must ensure that the public is able to interact with the board on the Internet.

Sec. 301.167. NEGOTIATED RULEMAKING; ALTERNATIVE DISPUTE RESOLUTION. (a) The board shall develop and implement a policy to encourage the use of:

(1) negotiated rulemaking procedures under Chapter 2008, Government Code, for the adoption of board rules; and

(2) appropriate alternative dispute resolution procedures under Chapter 2009, Government Code, to assist in the resolution of internal and external disputes under the board's jurisdiction.

(b) The board's procedures relating to alternative dispute resolution must conform, to the extent possible, to any model guidelines issued by the State Office of Administrative Hearings for the use of alternative dispute resolution by state agencies.

(c) The board shall designate a trained person to:

(1) coordinate the implementation of the policy adopted under Subsection (a);

(2) serve as a resource for any training needed to implement the procedures for negotiated rulemaking or alternative dispute resolution; and

(3) collect data concerning the effectiveness of those procedures, as implemented by

This Sec. 301.1615 gives the BON broad authority to conduct criminal background checks in conjunction with granting and renewing a nurse's license including obtaining criminal histories from the FBI. The BON conducts criminal background checks for all new licensees, and 2013 legislation mandated background checks for students. See Sec. 301.2511.

Related NPA sections are Secs. 301.2511, and 301.3011. Information about criminal background checks is also available on the BON website. See also Sec. 301.207 which makes criminal history information provided as part of the licensure process confidential.

The BON has a General Counsel and other attorneys on staff.

Most of the enforcement of the NPA is through disciplinary action against nurses by the BON. However, enforcement against unlicensed persons for the unauthorized practice of professional nursing is also necessary.

Sec. 301.167 is an across-the-board recommendation of Sunset Commission for all agencies. Chapters 2008 and 2009 of the Government Code are provisions that address negotiated rule-making and alternate dispute resolutions by state agencies. See Rule 213.20.

the board.

Sec. 301.168. DUTIES REGARDING PRESCRIPTIVE AUTHORITY AGREEMENTS. The board shall in conjunction with the Texas Medical Board and the Texas Physician Assistant Board perform the functions and duties relating to prescriptive authority agreements assigned to the board in Sections 157.0512 and 157.0513.

SUBCHAPTER E. PUBLIC INTEREST INFORMATION AND COMPLAINT PROCEDURES

Sec. 301.201. PUBLIC INTEREST INFORMATION. (a) The board shall prepare information of public interest describing the functions of the board and the procedures by which complaints are filed with and resolved by the board.

(b) The board shall make the information available to the public and appropriate state agencies.

✔Sec. 301.202. COMPLAINTS. (a) The board by rule shall establish methods by which consumers and service recipients are notified of the name, mailing address, and telephone number of the board for the purpose of directing complaints to the board. The board may provide for that notice:

(1) on each registration form, application, or written contract for services of a person regulated by the board;

(2) on a sign prominently displayed in the place of business of each person regulated by the board; or

(3) in a bill for service provided by a person regulated by the board.

(b) [repealed]

(c) The board shall list with its regular telephone number any toll-free telephone number established under other state law that may be called to present a complaint about a health professional.

✔Sec. 301.203. RECORDS AND ANALYSIS OF COMPLAINTS. (a) The board shall maintain a system to promptly and efficiently act on complaints filed with the board. The board shall maintain information about:

(1) parties to the complaint ;

(2) the subject matter of the complaint;

Legislation passed in 2013 (SB 406) requires the BON to work with the medical and physician assistant boards in implementing expansion of prescriptive authority for APRNs. This section was added to the NPA to give the BON authority to do so.

This Subchapter addresses 1) public information to be provided by the BON including information and assistance in filing complaints against nurses, 2) policy issues relating to the complaint process, and 3) public input on issues.

The BON is required to facilitate the filing of complaints and assisting persons in filing complaints. The Health Professions Council maintains a 1-800 line for all health professional licensing boards. See also Sec. 301.159 and 301.202. The BON website has detailed information and forms for filing a complaint.

The BON provides the public with information about how to file complaints against nurses for unsafe or inappropriate care. Also, it may require nurses to provide notice to patients. See also NPA Secs. 301.159 and 301.201.

The Legislature has enacted legislation requiring such a toll-free number. The Health Professions Council maintains a 1-800 line for all health professional licensing boards.

The Board must keep records about every complaint.

(3) a summary of the results of the review or investigation of the complaint; and

(4) the complaint's disposition.

(b) The board shall make information available describing its procedures for complaint investigation and resolution.

(c) The board shall periodically notify the parties to the complaint of the status of the complaint until final disposition unless notice would jeopardize an undercover investigation.

(d) The board shall develop a method for analyzing the sources and types of complaints and violations and establish categories for the complaints and violations. The board shall use the analysis to focus its information and education efforts on specific problem areas identified through the analysis.

(e) The board shall analyze complaints filed with the board to identify any trends or issues related to certain violations, including:

(1) the reason for each complaint;

(2) how each complaint was resolved; and

(3) the subject matter of each complaint that was not within the jurisdiction of the board and how the board responded to the complaint.

✔Sec. 301.204. GENERAL RULES, POLICIES, AND PROCEDURES REGARDING COMPLAINT INVESTIGATION AND DISPOSITION. (a) The board shall adopt rules, policies, and procedures concerning the investigation of a complaint filed with the board. The rules, policies, or procedures adopted under this subsection must:

(1) distinguish between categories of complaints;

(2) ensure that complaints are not dismissed without appropriate consideration;

(3) require that the board be advised of a complaint that is dismissed and that a letter be sent to the person who filed the complaint explaining the action taken on the dismissed complaint;

(4) ensure that the person who filed the complaint has an opportunity to explain the allegations made in the complaint;

(5) prescribe guidelines concerning the categories of complaints that require the use of a private investigator and the procedures for the board to obtain the services of a private investigator; and

(6) by rule allow appropriate employees of the board to dismiss a complaint if an investigation demonstrates that:

(A) a violation did not occur; or

(B) the subject of the complaint is outside the board's jurisdiction.

(b) The board shall:

(1) dispose of all complaints in a timely manner; and

(2) establish a schedule for conducting each phase of a complaint that is under the control of the board not later than the 30th day after the date the board receives the complaint.

(c) The board shall notify the parties of the projected time requirements for pursuing the complaint.

(d) The board shall notify the parties to the complaint of any change in the schedule not later than the seventh day after the date the change is made.

(e) The executive director of the board shall notify the board of a complaint that is unresolved after the time prescribed by the board for resolving the complaint so that the board may take necessary action on the complaint.

(f) At each public meeting of the board, the executive director shall report to the board each complaint dismissed under Subsection (a)(6) since the board's last public meeting.

Sec. 301.205. PUBLIC PARTICIPATION. (a) The board shall develop and implement policies that provide the public with a reasonable opportunity to appear before the board and to

This information is available on the BON website.

The person filing a complaint must be kept informed about the status of the complaint.

Promoting patient safety by better identifying areas of practice in which nurses need additional continuing education or systems need improving is the goal of having a system for analyzing complaints/violations to identify trends/issues relating to violations.

This Sec. 301.204 sets out some general public policies relating to handling of complaints to assure the board is fulfilling its purpose of protecting the public and to assure appropriate involvement of the board (and not just staff) and that the complainant has an opportunity for input.

BON staff must advise the board and persons filing complaints if a complaint is dismissed.

Board staff are permitted to dismiss certain complaints. Subsec. (f) below requires this be reported to the board at each meeting. See BON Rule 213.13.

The BON Executive Director must notify the board if complaints are not resolved in a timely manner.

The BON holds an open forum in conjunction with each of its meetings.

speak on any issue under the board's jurisdiction.

(b) The board shall prepare and maintain a written plan that describes how a person who does not speak English can be provided reasonable access to the board's programs.

301.206. CONFIDENTIALITY OF INFORMATION COLLECTED FOR EMERGENCY RELIEF PROGRAMS. (a) In this section, "emergency relief program" means a program operated or sponsored by the federal government, the state, or a nonprofit organization to provide nurses to assist in providing health care to victims or potential victims of a disaster or state or local emergency.

(b) A nurse's personal contact information, including e-mail addresses, telephone numbers, and fax numbers, collected by the board for use by an emergency relief program is:

(1) confidential and not subject to disclosure under Chapter 552, Government Code; and

(2) not subject to disclosure, discovery, subpoena, or other means of legal compulsion for release to anyone other than for the purpose of contacting the nurse to assist in an emergency relief program.

Sec. 301.207. CONFIDENTIALITY OF INFORMATION PROVIDED FOR LICENSURE. The following information that a person submits to the board for a petition for a declaratory order of eligibility for a license or for an application for an initial license or a license renewal under this chapter is confidential to the same extent information collected on a nurse as part of an investigation of a complaint is confidential under Section 301.466:

(1) information, including diagnosis and treatment, regarding a person's physical or mental condition, intemperate use of drugs or alcohol, or chemical dependency;

(2) information regarding a person's criminal history; and

(3) any other information in the petition for declaratory order of eligibility.

SUBCHAPTER F.
LICENSE REQUIREMENTS

✔Sec. 301.251. LICENSE REQUIRED. (a) A person may not practice or offer to practice professional nursing or vocational nursing in this state unless the person is licensed as provided

This section is designed to protect the confidentiality of personal contact information that nurses provide the BON for purpose of participating in disaster relief programs. See also Section 301.207 making confidential personal information provided by nurses on their applications for initial licensure and license renewal. As a general rule, Texas's Public Information Act (Government Code, Ch. 552) makes any information created or maintained by a state agency public information unless it is specifically made confidential by statute or case law (court opinion).

This Sec. 301.207 is designed to ensure the confidentiality of personal information provided by nurses on their licensure applications. As a general rule, Texas's Public Information Act (Government Code, Ch. 552) makes any information maintained by a state agency public information unless specifically made confidential by statute or case law (court opinion). Personal information should not become public because it is provided to the BON as part of the licensure process. See also Sec. 301.206 making confidential personal contact information nurses provide the BON relating to participating in disaster relief programs.

Since a declaratory order is used only when there is a question (e.g., criminal conviction or mental health issue) about the nurse's eligibility to be licensed, the mere filing of the petition could be a disclosure of confidential information.

This Subchapter addresses issues relating to who must be licensed and to obtaining initial licensure, licensure by endorsement and inactive status.

This section establishes the Nursing Practice Act as a practice control act for both RNs and LVNs, i.e., it controls the practice of professional and vocational nursing and not just use of the by this chapter.

(b) Unless the person holds a license under this chapter, a person may not use, in connection with the person's name:

(1) the title "Registered Nurse," "Professional Nurse," "Licensed Vocational Nurse," "Vocational Nurse," "Licensed Practical Nurse," "Practical Nurse," or "Graduate Nurse";

(2) the abbreviation "R.N.," "L.V.N.," "V.N.," "L.P.N.," or "P.N."; or

(3) any other designation tending to imply that the person is a licensed registered nurse or vocational nurse.

(c) This section does not apply to a person entitled to practice nursing in this state under Chapter 304.

(d) Unless the person holds a license under this chapter, a person may not use, in connection with the person's name:

(1) the title "nurse"; or

(2) any other designation tending to imply that the person is licensed to provide nursing care.

✔Sec. 301.2511. CRIMINAL HISTORY RECORD INFORMATION FOR LICENSE APPLICANTS. (a) An applicant for a registered nurse license must submit to the board, in addition to satisfying the other requirements of this subchapter, a complete and legible set of fingerprints, on a form prescribed by the board, for the purpose of obtaining criminal history record information from the Department of Public Safety and the Federal Bureau of Investigation.

(b) The board may deny a license to an applicant who does not comply with the requirement of Subsection (a). Issuance of a license by the board is conditioned on the board obtaining the applicant's criminal history record information under this section.

(c) The board by rule shall develop a system for obtaining criminal history record information for a person accepted for enrollment in a nursing educational program that prepares the person for initial licensure as a registered or vocational nurse by requiring the person to submit to the board a set of fingerprints that meets the requirements of Subsection (a). The board may develop a similar system for an applicant for enrollment in a nursing educational program. The board may require payment of a fee by a person who is required to submit a set of fingerprints under this subsection.

✔Sec. 301.252. LICENSE APPLICATION. (a) Each applicant for a registered nurse license or a vocational nurse license must submit to the board a sworn application that demonstrates the applicant's qualifications under this chapter, accompanied by evidence that the applicant:

(1) has good professional character;

(2) has successfully completed a program of professional or vocational nursing education approved under Section 301.157(d); and

(3) has passed the jurisprudence examination approved by the board as provided by Subsection (a-1).

(a-1) The jurisprudence examination shall be conducted on the licensing requirements under this chapter and board rules and other laws, rules, or regulations applicable to the nursing profession in this state. The board shall adopt rules for the jurisprudence examination under Subsection (a)(3) regarding:

titles "RN" and "LVN." Only persons who are licensed as RNs or LVNs or exempted from licensure under Sec. 301.004 can engage in acts constituting the practice of professional or vocational nursing. See definition of "professional nursing" and "vocational nursing" in Sec. 301.002.

Only licensed RNs and LVNs can hold themselves out as licensed or use the title "nurse." Persons exempted under Sec. NPA 301.004 cannot represent they are licensed or use the title "nurse." See Subsec. (d) below for restrictions on use of the generic title "nurse." See NPA Sec. 301.351 which requires RNs and LVNs to wear nametags when practicing identifying themselves as an "RN" or "LVN."

BON Rule §217.10 sets out additional titles the BON has identified as misleading.

Chapter 304 is a reference to nurses practicing under a multistate licensure privilege under the Nurse Licensure Compact. RNs and LVNs holding a multistate licensure privilege do not have to hold a Texas license to practice or use the "RN" or "LVN" title.

This Subsec. (d) restricts use of the generic title "nurse" to LVNs and RNs. See also NPA Sec. 301.4515 restricting use of titles such as "nurse aide" and "nurse assistant."

The BON has broad authority to conduct criminal background checks in conjunction with granting and renewing a nurse's license. This includes obtaining criminal histories from the FBI, which reflect criminal history in all states and not just Texas. Other NPA provisions addressing the BON's authority to do criminal background checks are NPA Secs. 301.1615 and 301.3011. The BON conducts criminal background checks for new licensees and 2013 legislation (SB 1058) mandated it do so for students. Information about criminal background checks is available on the BON website. See BON Rule 213 28. See also Sec. 301.207 which makes criminal history information provided as part of the licensure process confidential.

This Subsec. (c) was amended in 2013 to mandate criminal background checks for students accepted for enrollment. (SB 1058).

BON Rule §213.27 sets out the Board's criteria for determining good professional character. The board may conduct physical and psychological evaluations under certain circumstances. See NPA Sec. 301.4521 and BON Rule 213.33.

The jurisprudence exam requirement is an across-the-board Sunset recommendation for all professional licensing boards. All new nurse licensure applicants have had to meet this requirement since 9/1/2008. Legislation in 2013 (SB 1058) added a continuing education requirement in jurisprudence and ethics. See NPA Sec. 301.305.

(1) the development of the examination;
(2) applicable fees;
(3) administration of the examination;
(4) reexamination procedures;
(5) grading procedures; and
(6) notice of results.

(b) The board may waive the requirement of Subsection (a)(2) for a vocational nurse applicant if the applicant provides satisfactory sworn evidence that the applicant has completed an acceptable level of education in:

(1) a professional nursing school approved under Section 301.157(d); or
(2) a school of professional nurse education located in another state or a foreign country.

(c) The board by rule shall determine acceptable levels of education under Subsection (b).

Sec. 301.253. EXAMINATION. (a) Except as provided by Section 301.452, an applicant is entitled to take the examination prescribed by the board if:

(1) the board determines that the applicant meets the qualifications required by Section 301.252; and

(2) the applicant pays the fees required by the board.

(b) Each examination administered under this section must be prepared by a national testing service or the board. The board shall ensure that the examination is administered in various cities throughout the state..

(c) The examination shall be designed to determine the fitness of the applicant to practice professional nursing or vocational nursing.

(c-1) The board shall:

(1) adopt policies and guidelines detailing the procedures for the testing process, including test admission, test administration, and national examination requirements; and

(2) post on the board's Internet website the policies that reference the testing procedures by the national organization selected by the board to administer an examination.

(d) The board shall determine the criteria that determine a passing score on the examination. The criteria may not exceed those required by the majority of the states.

(e) A written examination prepared, approved, or offered by the board, including a standardized national examination, must be validated by an independent testing professional.

(f) The board shall develop a written refund policy regarding examination fees that:

(1) defines the reasonable notification period and the emergencies that would qualify for a refund; and

(2) does not conflict with any examination fee or refund policy of the testing service involved in administering the examination.

(g) The board may recommend to a national testing service selected by the board to offer examinations under this section the board's written policy for refunding an examination fee for an applicant who:

(1) provides advance notice of the applicant's inability to take the examination; or

(2) is unable to take the examination because of an emergency.

Sec. 301.254. EXAMINATION RESULTS. (a) The board shall notify each examinee of the results of the examination not later than the 30th day after the date the examination is administered. If an examination is graded or reviewed by a national testing service, the board shall notify each examinee of the results of the examination not later than the 14th day after the date the board receives the results from the testing service.

(b) If the notice of the examination results graded or reviewed by a national testing service will be delayed for longer than 90 days after the examination date, the board shall notify each

BON Rule §217.2 addresses process of licensure by examination in more detail. See also the BON website for information about the examination.

BON Rule §217.2 addresses process of licensure by examination in more detail. See also the BON website.

examinee of the reason for the delay before the 90th day.

(c) If requested in writing by a person who fails an examination, the board shall provide to the person an analysis of the person's performance on the examination.

Sec. 301.255. REEXAMINATION. The board by rule shall establish conditions under which an applicant who fails an examination may retake the examination. For an applicant who fails the examination two or more times, the board may:

(1) require the applicant to fulfill additional educational requirements; or

(2) deny the applicant the opportunity to retake the examination.

Sec. 301.256. ISSUANCE OF LICENSE. If the results of an examination taken under Section 301.253 or 301.255 satisfy the criteria established by the board under that section, the board shall issue to the applicant a license to practice professional nursing or vocational nursing in this state. The license must be signed by the board's presiding officer and the executive director and attested by the board's seal.

✔Sec. 301.257. DECLARATORY ORDER OF LICENSE ELIGIBILITY. (a) A person may petition the board for a declaratory order as to the person's eligibility for a license under this chapter if the person has reason to believe that the person is ineligible for the license and:

(1) is enrolled or planning to enroll in an educational program that prepares a person for an initial license as a registered nurse or vocational nurse; or

(2) is an applicant for a license.

(b) The petition must state the basis for the person's potential ineligibility.

(c) The board has the same powers to investigate the petition and the person's eligibility that it has to investigate a person applying for a license.

(d) The petitioner or the board may amend the petition to include additional grounds for potential ineligibility at any time before a final determination is made.

(e) If the board determines that a ground for ineligibility does not exist, instead of issuing an order, the board shall notify the petitioner in writing of the board's determination on each ground of potential ineligibility. If the board proposes to find that the petitioner is ineligible for a license, the petitioner is entitled to a hearing before the State Office of Administrative Hearings.

(f) The board's order must set out each basis for potential ineligibility and the board's determination as to eligibility. In the absence of new evidence known to but not disclosed by the petitioner or not reasonably available to the board at the time the order is issued, the board's ruling on the petition determines the person's eligibility with respect to the grounds for potential ineligibility set out in the written notice or order.

(g) The board may require an individual accepted for enrollment or enrolled in an educational program preparing a student for initial licensure as a registered nurse or vocational nurse to submit information to the board to permit the board to determine whether the person is aware of the conditions that may disqualify the person from licensure as a registered nurse or vocational nurse on graduation and of the person's right to petition the board for a declaratory order under this section. Instead of requiring the person to submit the information, the board may require the educational program to collect and submit the information on each person accepted for enrollment or enrolled in the program.

(h) The information required under Subsection (g) must be submitted in a form approved by the board.

(i) If, as a result of information provided under Subsection (g), the board determines that

BON Rule §217.2 addresses process of licensure by examination in more detail.

BON Rule §217.2 addresses process of licensure by examination in more detail.

This section provides a process for individuals who have reason to believe they may be ineligible for licensure to request the BON to make a determination of that issue. The purpose is to avoid individuals' investing one to four years in their nursing education only to find they are ineligible for licensure. Likewise, it is an inefficient use of a school's resources to educate persons not eligible for licensure. A frequent reason for seeking a determination is a prior criminal conviction but there may be noncriminal reasons (chemical dependency). Out-of-state nurses wishing to move to or be licensed in Texas may also seek a declaratory order of eligibility. Legislation (SB 1058) passed in 2013 mandates the BON to do criminal background checks of students and permits te board to self-initiate a declaratory order proceeding based on that background check. See NPA Secs. 2511(c) and Subsec. (j). BON Rule §213.30 addresses declaratory orders in more detail.

This subsection (g) is designed to facilitate the early identification of students who may be disqualified from being licensed upon graduation and to ensure they are aware of their right to seek a declaratory order of eligibility under this section. The BON wants students not to wait until graduation to seek this determination because waiting may delay licensure. Legislation (SB 1058) passed in 2013 mandates the BON to do criminal background checks of students and permits the board to self-initiate a declaratory order proceeding based on that background check. See NPA Secs. 2511(c) and Subsec. (j). There may also be noncriminal reasons that a student might be ineligible for licensure (chemical dependency).

The BON has adopted Rules 215.8(b) (RN education) and 214.8(b) (LVN education) requiring schools to inform students of what might disqualify them from being licensed upon graduation and of their right to seek a determination of the issue. The rules do not require the student to disclose the basis of any potential disqualification to the school.

The school would be notified if the BON determines the student may not be eligible for a person may not be eligible for a license on graduation, the board shall notify the educational program of its determination.

(j) The board may file a petition under this section based on the results of a criminal history record information check conducted under Section 301.2511. The board by rule shall adopt requirements for the petition and determination under this subsection. The rules must:

(1) identify the criminal offenses that constitute grounds for the board to file the petition; and

(2) describe the documents required by the board to make a determination of license eligibility.

(k) The board shall make a determination of license eligibility under Subsection (j) not later than the 120th day after the date the person submits the required documents to the board under that subsection.

Sec. 301.258. TEMPORARY PERMIT.

(a) Pending the results of a licensing examination, the board may issue to an applicant who is a graduate of an approved educational program a permit to practice professional nursing under the direct supervision of a registered nurse or to practice vocational nursing under the direct supervision of a registered nurse or vocational nurse.

(b) The board may not issue a permit under this section to an applicant who has previously failed an examination administered by the board or another state.

(c) A permit issued under Subsection (a) expires on the date of receipt of:

(1) a permanent license; or

(2) a notice from the board that the permit holder has failed the examination.

(d) The board may issue a temporary permit to practice professional nursing or vocational nursing for the limited purpose of allowing a nurse to satisfy a requirement imposed by the board necessary for:

(1) renewal of an expired license;

(2) reactivation of an inactive license; or

(3) reissuance of a suspended, revoked, or surrendered license.

(e) A permit issued under Subsection (d) expires on the earlier of:

(1) the date of receipt of a permanent license; or

(2) six months after the date the permit is issued.

(f) A person who holds a temporary permit issued under this section is considered to be a licensed registered nurse or vocational nurse for all purposes except to the extent of any stipulation or limitation on practice imposed by the board as a condition of issuing the permit.

Sec. 301.259. RECIPROCAL LICENSE BY ENDORSEMENT FOR CERTAIN FOREIGN APPLICANTS. On payment of a fee established by the board, the board may issue a license to practice as a registered nurse or vocational nurse in this state by endorsement without examination to an applicant who holds a registration certificate as a registered nurse or vocational nurse, as applicable, issued by a territory or possession of the United States or a foreign country if the board determines that the issuing agency of the territory or possession of the United States *licensure upon graduation.*

Permits the BON to self-initiate the declaratory order of eligibility process based on a student's positive criminal background check under NPA Sec. 301.2511. Added by legislation (SB 1058) in 2013.

This Sec. 301.258 governs temporary permits other than a temporary license issued in connection with licensure by endorsement which is governed by NPA Sec. 301.260. BON Rule §217.3 governs temporary permits under this section. With the switch to administering the licensing exam by computer and the reduced time between graduation and licensure, the BON now issues only a verification letter for U.S. graduates rather than a formal temporary permit.

BON Rule 217.1 defines "direct supervision" as requiring that the supervising nurse be "immediately available to coordinate, direct and observe at firsthand." Rule §217.3(a)(3) governs supervision of the graduate nurse. The graduate nurse may not be in a charge position or work in an independent setting. The BON has adopted Guidelines for Employment of New Graduates which can be found on the board's website.

The temporary permit assumes the person will pass the licensing exam. Applicants failing the licensing exam are not eligible for a temporary permit. Under (c)(2), a permit expires upon receipt of results that failed.

This Subsec. (d) permits the BON to impose conditions on reactivation or reinstatement of a license that include activities (e.g., supervised practice) requiring a professional nursing license without having to issue the permanent license itself. If the nurse fails to meet the requirements, the temporary permit simply expires.

A temporary permit issued under Subsec. (d) expires at the end of six months or upon receipt of a permanent license, whichever is earlier.

A temporary permit has the same effect as a permanent license except to the extent of any conditions or restrictions imposed as a condition of issuing the permit.

Only foreign nurse graduates of territories and countries with licensure standards equivalent to Texas can be licensed by endorsement. Graduates from other countries not eligible for endorsement must take a BON-recognized examination and also attend a special accustomation course required by the BON before they can take the examination. More detailed information about licensure of foreign graduates can be found in BON Rule §217.4 and on the BON website.

or foreign country required in its examination the same general degree of fitness required by this state.

Sec. 301.260. TEMPORARY LICENSE BY ENDORSEMENT. (a) An applicant for a license under this chapter who is licensed as a registered nurse or vocational nurse by another state may qualify for a temporary license by endorsement to practice as a registered nurse or vocational nurse, as applicable, by submitting to the board:

(1) an endorsement fee as determined by the board and a completed sworn application in the form prescribed by the board;

(2) evidence that the person possessed, at the time of initial licensing as a nurse, the other qualifications necessary at that time to have been eligible for licensing in this state; and

(3) proof of initial licensing by examination and proof that the license and any other license issued to the applicant by another state have not been suspended, revoked, canceled, surrendered, or otherwise restricted..

(b) A holder of a temporary license under this section is entitled to receive a permanent license if the applicant:

(1) verifies the applicant's academic and professional credentials; and

(2) satisfies any other requirement established by statute.

(c) The board shall grant or deny an application for a permanent license not later than the 180th day after the date the board receives all required forms or information. The board may extend that deadline to allow for the receipt and tabulation of examination results.

Sec. 301.261. INACTIVE STATUS. (a) The board may place on inactive status the license of a person under this chapter who is not actively engaged in the practice of professional nursing or vocational nursing if the person submits a written request to the board in the form and manner determined by the board. The inactive status begins on the expiration date of the person's license.

(b) The board shall maintain a list of each person whose license is on inactive status.

(c) A person whose license is on inactive status may not perform any professional nursing or vocational nursing service or work.

(d) The board shall remove a person's license from inactive status if the person:

(1) requests that the board remove the person's license from inactive status;

(2) pays each appropriate fee; and

(3) meets the requirements determined by the board.

(e) The board by rule shall permit a person whose license is on inactive status and who was in good standing with the board on the date the license became inactive to use, as applicable, the title "Registered Nurse Retired," "R.N. Retired," "Licensed Vocational Nurse Retired," "Vocational Nurse Retired," "L.V.N. Retired," or "V.N. Retired" or another appropriate title approved by the board.

Sec. 301.262. SPECIAL LICENSE. (a) The board may issue a license under this section to a person licensed to practice nursing in Mexico if the person:

(1) graduated from an accredited nursing program in Mexico;

(2) provides a report acceptable to the board issued by a credentials evaluation service approved by the board;

(3) applies on a form prescribed by the board and pays the fee required by the board;

(4) has received a score of at least 475 on a Test of English as a Foreign Language examination;

(5) has received a score acceptable to the board on an English language version of the appropriate National Council Licensure Examination;

(6) is eligible for employment in the United States; and

This Sec. 301.260 establishes special criteria for issuance of a temporary license for RNs and LVNs seeking licensure by endorsement. For more detailed information, see BON Rule §217.5 and BON website. Temporary permits in other situations are governed by Sec. 301.258.

RNs and LVNs seeking licensure by endorsement who have any restrictions on their licenses cannot receive temporary licenses. They may still be eligible for a permanent license if the BON determines they meet the qualifications for permanent licensure.

RNs and LVNs not wishing to continue to practice professional nursing may go on inactive status. RNs and LVNs on inactive status do not have to comply with the continued competency required for license renewal. RNs and LVNs may return to active status but must meet any conditions imposed by the BON. BON Rule §217.9 addresses inactive status.

Retired RNs and LVNs, who want to do only charity work, may qualify to practice as a "Volunteer Retired Nurse." See BON Rule 217.9(d).

Nurses whose license is in good standing may electe "retired" status and use the title "RN Retired."

This Sec. 301.262 expires 9/1/2013. See Subsec (e). It was added in 2009 in response to a legislative effort by a hospital located in the Rio Grande Valley. It permitted the BON to issue a special license to Mexico educated nurses who pass the English-language version of the NCLEX exam and receive a score of 475 on the TOEFL exam (normally have to make a score of 560). Subsecs. (b) and (c) impose additional restrictions.

- *Subsec. (b) - Limits to nurses practicing in a Texas county that borders Mexico.*
- *Subsec. (c) - Limits to nurses employed by a hospital located in a Texas county that borders Mexico.*

This section was not widely utilized.

(7) will practice nursing in a county that borders Mexico.

(b) A license issued under this section is valid for one year and may not be renewed. A person who holds or has held a license issued under this section may apply for another type of license under this chapter.

(c) A person who holds a license issued under this section may practice nursing only as an employee of a hospital located in a county that borders Mexico.

(d) A person who holds a license issued under this section is not entitled to a multistate licensing privilege to practice under the Nurse Licensure Compact under Chapter 304.

(e) This section expires September 1, 2013.

SUBCHAPTER G.
LICENSE RENEWAL

✔**Sec. 301.301. LICENSE RENEWAL.** (a) The board by rule may adopt a system under which licenses expire on various dates during the year.

(b) A person may renew an unexpired license issued under this chapter on payment to the board of the required renewal fee before the expiration date of the license, payment to the board of any costs assessed under Section 301.461, and compliance with any other renewal requirements adopted by the board. A person whose license has expired may not engage in activities that require a license until the license has been renewed.

(c) A person whose license has been expired for 90 days or less may renew the license by paying to the board the required renewal fee and a late fee in the amount considered appropriate by the board to encourage timely renewal.

(c-1) A person whose license has been expired for more than 90 days but less than one year may renew the license by paying to the board all unpaid renewal fees and a late fee that is equal to twice the amount of a late fee under Subsection (c).

(d) The board by rule shall set a length of time beyond which an expired license may not be renewed. The board by rule may establish additional requirements that apply to the renewal of a license that has been expired for more than one year but less than the time limit set by the board beyond which a license may not be renewed. The person may obtain a new license by submitting to reexamination and complying with the requirements and procedures for obtaining an original license.

(e) At least 30 days before the expiration of the person's license, the board shall send written notice of the impending license expiration to the person at the person's last known address

This Subchapter addresses issues relating to license renewal including continued competency requirements such as continuing education.

The reference to Sec. 301.461 is to the assessment of costs of a disciplinary hearing against a nurse.

Nurses, who do not renew their license before the expiration date but within one year of expiration, may still renew upon payment of an additional fee. Subsec. (c-1) provides for a higher fee if nurses do not renew within 90 days of expiration.

The BON may set a time period (more than one year) beyond which a license may not be renewed. It has established additional conditions for renewing a license expired for more than one year. See Rule 217.6.

If a nurse does not notify the BON of a change in address as required by Rule 217.7, the nurse may not receive this notice. However, the nurse will still be considered to have received it since according to the records of the board.

(f) A registered nurse who practices professional nursing or a vocational nurse who practices vocational nursing after the expiration of the nurse's license is an illegal practitioner whose license may be revoked or suspended.

✔Sec. 301.3011. CRIMINAL HISTORY RECORD INFORMATION REQUIREMENT FOR RENEWAL. (a) The board may require that an applicant for renewal of an unexpired license submit to the board, in addition to satisfying any other requirements for license renewal, a complete and legible set of fingerprints, on a form prescribed by the board, for the purpose of obtaining criminal history record information from the Department of Public Safety and the Federal Bureau of Investigation.

(b) The board may refuse to renew the license of a person who does not comply with the requirement of Subsection (a). Renewal of a license by the board is conditioned on the board obtaining the person's criminal history record information under this section.

Sec. 301.302. RENEWAL OF EXPIRED LICENSE BY OUT-OF-STATE PRACTITIONER. (a) A person who was licensed to practice professional nursing or vocational nursing in this state, moved to another state, and is currently licensed and has been in practice in the other state for the two years preceding application may obtain a new license without examination.

(b) The person must pay to the board a fee that is equal to the amount of the initial fee for the license and the renewal fee.

✔Sec. 301.303. CONTINUING COMPETENCY. (a) The board may recognize, prepare, or implement continuing competency programs for license holders under this chapter and may require participation in continuing competency programs as a condition of renewal of a license. The programs may allow a license holder to demonstrate competency through various methods, including:

(1) completion of targeted continuing education programs; and

(2) consideration of a license holder's professional portfolio, including certifications held by the license holder.

(b) The board may not require participation in more than a total of 20 hours of continuing education in a two-year licensing period.

(c) If the board requires participation in continuing education programs as a condition of license renewal, the board by rule shall establish a system for the approval of programs and providers of continuing education.

(d) *[Repealed]*

(e) The board may adopt other rules as necessary to implement this section.

(f) The board may assess each program and provider under this section a fee in an amount that is reasonable and necessary to defray the costs incurred in approving programs and providers.

(g) The board by rule may establish guidelines for targeted continuing education required under this chapter. The rules adopted under this subsection must address:

(1) the nurses who are required to complete the targeted continuing education program;

(2) the type of courses that satisfy the targeted continuing education requirement;

(3) the time in which a nurse is required to complete the targeted continuing education;

(4) the frequency with which a nurse is required to meet the targeted continuing

it was sent to the last known address the nurse has on file with the BON.

Nurses practicing with expired licenses are subject to disciplinary action including having their licenses permanently revoked.

The BON has broad authority to conduct criminal background checks in conjunction with granting and renewing a nurse's license. This includes obtaining criminal histories from the FBI which reflect criminal history in all states and not just Texas. The board has completed a multi-year project of doing a background check for all licensed nurses as part of the license renewal process. The BON conducts criminal background checks for all new licensees and 2013 legislation (SB 10158) mandates checks for students. See NPA Sec. 301.2511. See also NPA Sec. 301.1615 and the BON website for information about criminal background checks. See also Sec. 301.207 which makes criminal history information provided as part of the licensure process confidential.

This Section permits the BON to utilize various mechanisms to promote continued competency as part of the license renewal process. Currently, the BON permits nurses to demonstrate continued competency through either CNE (20 hours) in the nurses' area of practice or national certification . See BON Rule 216.3.

The board may not require more than 20 hours of CNE in a two-year licensing period. However, CNE to renew APRN licensure may be in addition to these 20 hours.

This Subsec. (g) addresses problems that may be created when targeted continuing education is required for all nurses without taking into account differences in practice. Its purpose is to give the board flexibility in implementing targeted CE.

Currently Sec. 301.306 mandates forensic evidence collection CNE for ER nurses. Sec. 301.304 was added in 2011 and does not require but encourages CNE in tick-borne illnesses. Now expired sections, previously required all nurses to take CNE in Hep C and bioterrorism. Almost every session, legislation is introduced to require all nurses (and other health practitioners) to take such CE regardless of their practice area or expertise. Concern has been education requirement; and

(5) any other requirement considered necessary by the board.

Sec. 301.304. CONTINUING EDUCATION IN TICK-BORNE DISEASES. (a) As part of the continuing education requirements under Section 301.303, a license holder whose practice includes the treatment of tick-borne diseases shall be encouraged to participate, during each two-year licensing period, in continuing education relating to the treatment of tick-borne diseases.

(b) The board shall adopt rules to identify the license holders who are encouraged to complete continuing education under Subsection (a) and establish the content of that continuing education. In adopting rules, the board shall seek input from affected parties and review relevant courses, including courses that have been approved in other states. Rules adopted under this section must provide that continuing education courses representing an appropriate spectrum of relevant medical clinical treatment relating to tick-borne diseases qualify as approved continuing education courses for license renewal.

(c) If relevant, the board shall consider a license holder's participation in a continuing education course approved under Subsection (b) if:

(1) the license holder is being investigated by the board regarding the license holder's selection of clinical care for the treatment of tick-borne diseases; and

(2) the license holder completed the course not more than two years before the start of the investigation.

(d) The board may adopt other rules to implement this section, including rules under Section 301.303(c) for the approval of education programs and providers.

Sec. 301.305. CONTINUING EDUCATION IN NURSING JURISPRUDENCE AND NURSING ETHICS. (a) As part of a continuing competency program under Section 301.303, a license holder shall complete at least two hours of continuing education relating to nursing jurisprudence and nursing ethics before the end of every third two-year licensing period.

(b) The board shall adopt rules implementing the requirement under Subsection (a) in accordance with the guidelines for targeted continuing education under Section 301.303(g).

(c) The board may not require a license holder to complete more than four hours of continuing education under this section.

Sec. 301.306. FORENSIC EVIDENCE COLLECTION COMPONENT IN CONTINUING EDUCATION. (a) As part of continuing education requirements under Section 301.303, a license holder who is employed to work in an emergency room setting and who is required under board rules to comply with this section shall complete at least two hours of continuing education relating to forensic evidence collection not later than:

(1) September 1, 2008; or

(2) the second anniversary of the initial issuance of a license under this chapter to the license holder.

(b) The continuing education required under Subsection (a) must be part of a program approved under Section 301.303(c).

(c) The board shall adopt rules to identify the license holders who are required to complete continuing education under Subsection (a) and to establish the content of that continuing education. The board may adopt other rules to implement this section, including rules under Section 301.303(c) for the approval of education programs and providers.

Sec. 301.307. CONTINUING EDUCATION IN OLDER ADULT OR GERIATRIC CARE. (a) As part of a continuing competency program under Section 301.303, a license holder *expressed about the value and practicality of such subject-specific CE. Ths Subsec. (g) was added to provide the board some flexibility in addressing such CE. for all nurses.*

Added in 2011, this section encourages but does not require nurses to take CNE in tick-borne illnesses.

Added in 2013 to require all nurses have CNE in jurisprudence and ethics. The amount required will be between two to fours hours every three license renewal periods (6 years).

This CNE requirement applies only to nurses in emergency departments and is a one-time requirement. See Rule 216.3(6).

See annotations to NPA Sec. 301.303 (Continuing Competency) for a discussion of specific-subject CNE such as the CNE required by this section.

Legislation (SB1191) passed in 2013 prohibits persons in hospital emergency departments from performing a forensic examination for a sexual assault patient unless the person has basic forensic evidence collection training. Completing CNE approved or recognized by the BON satisfies this requirement.

Added in 2013 to require nurses whose practice includes older adults or geriatric populations to take targeted CNE or maintain certification in care of older adults or geriatric populations.

whose practice includes older adult or geriatric populations shall complete at least two hours of continuing education relating to older adult or geriatric populations or maintain certification in an area of practice relating to older adult or geriatric populations.

(b) The board shall adopt rules implementing the requirement under Subsection (a) in accordance with the guidelines for targeted continuing education under Section 301.303(g).

(c) The board may not require a license holder to complete more than six hours of continuing education under this section.

SUBCHAPTER H.
PRACTICE BY LICENSE HOLDER; PROTECTIONS FOR NURSES

✔Sec. 301.351. DESIGNATIONS. (a) A person who holds a license as a registered nurse under this chapter:

(1) is referred to as a registered nurse; and

(2) may use the abbreviation "R.N."

(b) A person who holds a license as a vocational nurse under this chapter:

(1) is referred to as a licensed vocational nurse or vocational nurse; and

(2) may use the abbreviation "L.V.N." or "V.N."

(c) While interacting with the public in a nursing role, each nurse shall wear a clearly legible insignia identifying the nurse as a registered or vocational nurse. The insignia may not contain information other than:

(1) the registered or vocational nurse designation;

(2) the nurse's name, certifications, academic degrees, or practice position;

(3) the name of the employing facility or agency, or other employer;

(4) a picture of the nurse; or

(5) any other information authorized by the board.

(d) The board may adopt rules establishing specifications for the insignia.

✔Sec. 301.352. PROTECTION FOR REFUSAL TO ENGAGE IN CERTAIN CONDUCT.

The CNE required by this section is a one time requirement of two to six hours. The BON could require additional CNE under the general authority it is granted by NPA Sec. 301,303 to regulate continued competency.

The NPA Sec. 301.303(g) referred to relates to the BON establishing guidelines for targeted or specific-subject CNE.

This Subchapter addresses important practice issues including nonretaliation protections for nurses when advocating for patients.

***ANNOTATOR'S NOTE**: See Part VI (Patient Advocacy Protections) of this Guide for all the protections provided nurses when advocating for patients.*

Licensure gives RNs and LVNs the right to use the titles "RN" and "LVN." NPA Sec. 301,3251 prohibits anyone else from using "RN," "LVN," or "nurse." Sec. 301.4515 prohibits use of "nurse aide," nurse assistant," and similar titles unless person is working under RN delegation.

RNs and LVNs must wear insignia identifying them as RNs or LVNs, respectively. APRNs practicing in an advanced practice role must identify themselves with their APRN title, e.g., PNP. See Rule §221.11. To promote readability of the nametag, the information that can be on it is restricted. The phrase "while interacting with the public in a nursing role" is intended to cover those situations when a nurse interacts with the public but is not providing direct patient care. An example might be a faculty member or a nurse administrator. While the nametag for both RNs and LVNs can have only the information listed, it is not required that this information be on the nametag. Only the RN or LVN designation is required under Subsection (a). BON rule 217.10(b) does require the nurse's first or last name but not both. In a psychiatric or correctional facility, for example, the nurse may not want her or his full name to appear on the nametag. See BON Rule 217.10(b).

This provision is designed to provide protection to the RN or LVN who refuses to engage in conduct the nurse believes would be a violation of the NPA or BON rules. Nurses can be placed in situations in which they feel they are faced with having to choose between a) refusing to carry out an employer's directive, or b) engaging in conduct the nurse believes violates the NPA or BON rules. Sec. 303.005 (Safe Harbor Nursing Peer Review Law) is a companion provision permitting RNs and LVNs to request nursing peer review if they believe they are requested to engage in

(a) A person may not suspend, terminate, or otherwise discipline, discriminate against, or retaliate against:

(1) a nurse who refuses to engage in an act or omission as provided by Subsection (a-1); or

(2) a person who advises a nurse of the nurse's rights under this section.

(a-1) A nurse may refuse to engage in an act or omission relating to patient care that would constitute grounds for reporting the nurse to the board under Subchapter I, that constitutes a minor incident, or that violates this chapter or a board rule if the nurse notifies the person at the time of the refusal that the reason for refusing is that the act or omission:

(1) constitutes grounds for reporting the nurse to the board; or

(2) is a violation of this chapter or a rule of the board.

(b) An act by a person under Subsection (a) does not constitute a violation of this section if a nursing peer review committee under Chapter 303 determines:

(1) that the act or omission the nurse refused to engage in was not:

(A) conduct reportable to the board under Section 301.403;

(B) a minor incident; or

(C) a violation of this chapter or a board rule; or

(2) that:

(A) the act or omission in which the nurse refused to engage was conduct reportable to the board, a minor incident, or a violation of this chapter or a board rule; and

(B) the person:

(i) rescinds any disciplinary or discriminatory action taken against the nurse;

(ii) compensates the nurse for lost wages;

(iii) restores to the nurse any lost benefits.

(c) A nurse's rights under this section may not be nullified by a contract.

(d) An appropriate licensing agency may take action against a person who violates this section.

(e) *[Repealed]*

(f) A violation of this section is subject to Section 301.413.

✔**Sec. 301.353. SUPERVISION OF THE VOCATIONAL NURSE.** The practice of vocational nursing must be performed under the supervision of a registered nurse, physician, physician assistant, podiatrist, or dentist.

conduct that violates their duty to a patient. Normally, it is to the nurse's benefit to utilize the protections of safe harbor than those of this Sec. 301.352. See Part VI (Patient Advocacy Protections) of this Guide for all the protections available to nurses when advocating for patients including Sec. 303.005.

Discriminating or retaliating against a nurse for refusing to engage in conduct that would violate a BON rule or subject the nurse to being reported to the BON is prohibited.

The RN or LVN at the time of refusing to engage in the conduct must state that the reason for the refusal is that the nurse believes it violates the NPA or BON rules. The most important BON rules are those defining standards of practice (Rule 217.11) and unprofessional conduct (Rule 217.12). The references to "minor incidents" and "violations of this chapter [NPA] or BON rules" are included to ensure protection for the nurse even if the conduct involved is a minor incident not reportable to the BON under Rule 217.16. A nurse should not be placed in a position of being required to engage in even a minor violation of the NPA or a BON rule.

Subsection (b) sets out two situations in which the employer is deemed not to have violated this section.

1. *If the incident is reviewed by a nursing peer review committee and the committee finds that, in its opinion, the nurse's engaging in the conduct she/he refused to do would not in fact have been a violation of the NPA or BON rules, i.e., the nurse was not being asked to engage in reportable conduct or a violation (even a minor violation) of the NPA or BON rules.*
2. *If the peer review committee finds that to have engaged in the conduct would have been a violation of the NPA but the employer makes the nurse whole -- that is, rescinds any disciplinary action taken, pays all back wages and restores any lost benefits.*

Nurses may not be required to contract away their rights, for example, agree in an employment contract to give up their right under this Sec. 301.352.

Violation of this section is a basis for a licensing agency to take action against that organization or person. For example, if a nurse administrator violates this section, she/he would be subject to disciplinary action by the BON. If a hospital violates this section, it would be subject to action by the Department of State Health Services. See also Sec. 301.413(b-1).

Sec. 301.413 sets out the remedies available to a nurse who is discriminated or retaliated against in violation of this Sec. 301.352. Those remedies include a lawsuit for damages (minimum of $5,000) and attorney's fees.

This section needs to be read in conjunction with the definition of "vocational nursing" set out in Sec. 301.002(5). The content of this section and the definition of "vocational nursing" is consistent with the language of BON Rule 217.11(2) (Standards of Nursing Practice) that was developed by consensus of all stakeholder groups. See also BON Position Statement 15.27 The LVN Scope of Practice in Part III of this Guide for a discussion of type of supervision required.

✔Sec. 301.354. NURSE FIRST ASSISTANTS; ASSISTING AT SURGERY BY OTHER NURSES

(a) In this section, "nurse first assistant" means a registered nurse who:

(1) has completed a nurse first assistant educational program approved or recognized by an organization recognized by the board; and

(2) is either:

(A) certified in perioperative nursing by an organization recognized by the board; or

(B) recognized by the board as an advanced practice nurse and qualified by education, training, or experience to perform the tasks involved in perioperative nursing.

(b) Unless the person is a nurse first assistant, the person may not use:

(1) the title "nurse first assistant" or "registered nurse first assistant";

(2) the abbreviation "R.N.F.A."; or

(3) any other title or abbreviation that implies to the public that the person is qualified as a nurse first assistant under this section.

(c) A health maintenance organization or an insurer, including an insurer offering a preferred provider benefit plan, may not, by contract or any other method, require a physician to use the services of a nurse first assistant.

(d) A nurse who is not a nurse first assistant may assist a physician, podiatrist, or dentist in the performance of surgery if the nurse:

(1) assists under the direct personal supervision and in the physical presence of the physician, podiatrist, or dentist;

(2) is in the same sterile field as the physician, podiatrist, or dentist;

(3) is employed by:

(A) the physician, podiatrist, or dentist;

(B) a group to which the physician, podiatrist, or dentist belongs; or

(C) a hospital licensed or owned by the state; and

(4) is qualified by education, training, or experience to perform the tasks assigned to the nurse.

(e) A patient or third-party insurer may not be billed separately for the services performed by a nurse described by Subsection (d).

Sec. 301.355. *[Repealed]*

Sec. 301.356. REFUSAL OF MANDATORY OVERTIME. The refusal by a nurse to work mandatory overtime as authorized by Chapter 258, Health and Safety Code, does not constitute patient abandonment or neglect.

SUBCHAPTER I.
REPORTING VIOLATIONS AND PATIENT CARE CONCERNS

Sec. 301.401. DEFINITIONS
Sec. 301.4011. GOOD FAITH REPORT BY NURSE
Sec. 301.402. MANDATORY REPORT BY NURSE
Sec. 301.4025. OPTIONAL REPORT BY NURSE
Sec. 301.403. DUTY OF PEER REVIEW COMMITTEE TO REPORT

This section governs nurses practicing as RN first assistants. The BON has adopted Rule 217.18 implementing this Sec. 301.354.

Subsections (a) and (b) limit who can be "nurse first assistants" to 1) nurses who are either CNOR certified or APRNs, and 2) have completed a first assisting educational program. Subsection (d) permits other nurses to perform certain functions relating to assisting the performance of surgery but not to function as "first assistants."

Subsection (d) authorizes nurses other than "nurse first assistants" to assist in the performance of surgery if certain conditions are met. The requirement that the nurse be in the same sterile field means the physician, dentist or podiatrist cannot leave the sterile field and let the nurse open or close – even if the physician, dentist or podiatrist remains in the room. Whenever the term "nurse" is used in the NPA, it refers to both RNs and LVNs.

Chapter 258 prohibits hospitals from requiring nurses work mandatory overtime under certain situations. This Sec. 301.356 clarifies that it is not patient abandonment when a nurse refuses to work mandatory overtime prohibited under Chapter 258. Chapter 258 is set out in Part IX (Other Laws) of this Guide.

Mandatory reporting of nurses by nurses was first enacted in 1987 as part of legislation commonly referred to as the Professional Nursing Quality Assurance Act and has been significantly amended since then. The legislation (2003) creating a single licensing act for RNs and LVNs extended reporting requirements to LVNs. Legislation (SB 993) passed in 2007 shifted the perspective reflected in the regulation and reporting of nursing . The pre-2007 perspective was that errors are primarily caused by "bad" individuals, and when an error occurs the job of the regulatory system is to identify and punish the individual who made the error. The post-2007 perspective is to view errors as primarily the result of system inadequacies that either made the

✔Shading Denotes More Important Practice-Related NPA Sections

✔Sec. 301.401. DEFINITIONS. In this subchapter:

✔(1) "Conduct subject to reporting" means conduct by a nurse that:

(A) violates this chapter or a board rule and contributed to the death or serious injury of a patient;

(B) causes a person to suspect that the nurse's practice is impaired by chemical dependency or drug or alcohol abuse;

(C) constitutes abuse, exploitation, fraud, or a violation of professional boundaries; or

(D) indicates that the nurse lacks knowledge, skill, judgment, or conscientiousness to such an extent that the nurse's continued practice of nursing could reasonably be expected to pose a risk of harm to a patient or another person, regardless of whether the conduct consists of a single incident or a pattern of behavior.

error likely to occur or failed to provide the safeguards needed to prevent the error from occurring. Implementing this new perspective involved modifying the NPA mandatory reporting provisions to emphasize that the nurses who should be reported to the BON are those whose continued practice poses a risk of harm to patients and not competent, safe nurses who made a single mistake. For a graphic depiction of this reporting process see the flowcharts in the Appendices of this Guide.

This new perspective resulted from the work of a Texas Nurses Association task force which considered the implications of two reports of the Institute of Medicine -- To Err Is Human (2000) and Keeping Patients Safe: Transforming the Work Environment of Nurses (2003) -- that recommended promoting safer patient care by creating "cultures of safety." An important aspect of promoting creation of cultures of safety is an environment in which nurses can advocate for their patients without fear of retaliation. In addition to focusing reporting on system issues, the 2007 legislation also clarified and strengthened the protections for nurses when advocating for patients and facilitated greater sharing of information between nursing peer review and other committees that review patient care incidents and system issues. .

The sections of this subchapter can be grouped as follows:

- *Sec. 301.401 defines "conduct subject to reporting."*
- *Secs. 301.402-.4025 identify the reporting responsibilities of nurses including voluntary reporting of other providers and facilities.*
- *Secs. 301.403-.409 identify the responsibilities of other persons/entities to report nurses to the BON.*
- *Secs. 301.410-.4106 address reporting of nurses whose practice is impaired by chemical dependency, mental illness, or diminished mental capacity and how the board handles the reports.*
- *Secs. 301.411-.413 address issues of liability and protections from retaliation related to reporting.*
- *Secs. 301.414-.418 address how the BON is to handle reports received, notifying the reported nurse, investigation of report, etc.*
- *Sec. 301.419 addresses reporting of minor incidents and other general issues relating to reporting.*

Additional information about nurses' reporting obligations, rights and protections are set out in Part VII (Mandatory and Optional Reporting) of this Guide.

This definition of "conduct subject to reporting" is used in subsequent sections setting out specific reporting requirements for nurses, employers, and others. The definition identifies three specific types of conduct subject to reporting and a fourth broader type simply identified as conduct indicating an inability to practice safely. The three specific types of conduct are:

1. *death or serious injury related conduct*
2. *suspected chemical dependency*
3. *bad character conduct such as fraud, abuse, etc.*

The fourth broadly identified conduct is:

4. *conduct, whether a one time incident or pattern of behavior, that indicates nurse's continued practice would pose risk to patients*

The intent of this definition is to make the focus of reporting be on the nurse that lacks the competence or conscientiousness to practice safely rather than the competent nurse who made a single error or who was placed in a situation in which the lack of adequate systems made the error more likely to happen.

In some cases, near misses and close calls may be "conduct subject to reporting." The role

✔(2) "Minor incident" means conduct by a nurse that does not indicate that the nurse's continued practice poses a risk of harm to a patient or another person. This term is synonymous with "minor error" or "minor violation of this chapter or board rule."

(3) "Nursing educational program" means an educational program that is considered approved by the board that may lead to an initial license as a registered nurse or vocational nurse.

(4) "Nursing student" means an individual who is enrolled in a nursing educational program.

✔**Sec. 301.4011. GOOD FAITH REPORT BY NURSE.** In this subchapter, a report is considered to be made in good faith if:

(1) the person reporting believed that the report was required or authorized; and

(2) there was a reasonable factual or legal basis for that belief.

✔**Sec. 301.402. MANDATORY REPORT BY NURSE.**

(a) *[Repealed]*

✔(b) A nurse shall report to the board in the manner prescribed under Subsection (d) if the nurse has reasonable cause to suspect that:

(1) another nurse has engaged in conduct subject to reporting; or

(2) the ability of a nursing student to perform the services of the nursing profession would be, or would reasonably be expected to be, impaired by chemical dependency.

(c) *[Repealed]*

✔(d) A report by a nurse under Subsection (b) must:

(1) be written and signed; and

(2) include the identity of the nurse or student and any additional information required

of the licensing/regulatory system whenever possible is to identify the incompetent or unsafe practitioner before harm is done. Exposing a patient to risk of harm and not just actual harm can be the basis for the BON to discipline an RN or LVN. See Rule 217.12(4). An example of reportable conduct that does not involve actual harm would be a nurse who through recklessness is about to administer a medication by the wrong route (with almost certain harm to patient) but another nurse catches the mistake before the medication is administered. Being on duty under the influence is another example.

A minor incident is one that does not indicate a nurse's continuing to practice poses a risk of harm to patients. Sometimes, in a non-typical situation, a minor nursing error can unexpectedly result in significant patient harm, e.g., a non-typical reaction to a medication. Even though the error is minor, it seems counter-intuitive to describe the situation as a "minor" incident. However, the fact that patient harm, even significant harm, resulted from a nurse's error does not automatically mean it is not a minor incident or violation. This definition permits describing such cases as a "minor violation or "minor error" instead of "minor incident."

This definition of "good faith" was added in 2011 and is the standard consistently used throughout the NPA and Nursing Peer Review Law to identify protected patient advocacy activities. It combines a subjective standard of the person's belief with an objective standard that the belief be reasonable. The definition is based on the definition the Texas Supreme Court established for whistleblower cases in Wichita Co. v. Hart, 917 S.W.2d 779 (Tex. 1996). It does not get into the nurse's motives in making the report.

This section addresses the reporting responsibilities' of individual RNs and LVNs.

Nurses must report other nurses reasonably suspected of having engaged in conduct subject to reporting as defined by Sec. 301.401 above. Subsec. (e) below permits alternate reporting to:

- *a nursing peer review committee*
- *a nursing educational program in which the student is enrolled*

Reporting a nurse to a supervisor or employer does not satisfy a nurse's reporting obligation under this subsection. See Sec. 301.410 for specific provisions relating to nurses suspected of chemical dependency or mental illness.

A nursing student is required to be reported only if there is reason to suspect the student has a problem with chemical dependency which would negatively affect the student's practice after she/he is licensed. The nurse reporting has to predict behaviors after the student is licensed. The requirement to report students with a suspected chemical dependency problem applies not only to faculty members, but also to other nurses, e.g., nurses who interface with the student in clinicals may discover a student has a dependency problem. Under Subsec. (d), an individual nurse can satisfy his/her reporting duty by reporting to the educational program, which may have a duty under Sec. 301.404 to report to the BON.

A report must be in writing and signed. That is the nurse may not report anonymously. However, the nurse's identity is confidential to everyone except the BON. See Sec. 301.417.

by the board.

✔(e) Instead of reporting to the board under Subsection (b), a nurse may make a report required under:

(1) Subsection (b)(1) to a nursing peer review committee under Chapter 303; or

(2) Subsection (b)(2) to the nursing educational program in which the student is enrolled.

✔(f) A person may not suspend or terminate the employment of, or otherwise discipline, discriminate against, or retaliate against, a person who:

(1) reports in good faith under this section; or

(2) advises a nurse of the nurse's rights and obligations under this section.

(g) A violation of Subsection (f) is subject to Section 301.413.

✔Sec. 301.4025. OPTIONAL REPORT BY NURSE.

(a) In a written, signed report to the appropriate licensing board or accrediting body, a nurse may report a licensed health care practitioner, agency, or facility that the nurse has reasonable cause to believe has exposed a patient to substantial risk of harm as a result of failing to provide patient care that conforms to:

(1) minimum standards of acceptable and prevailing professional practice, for a report made regarding a practitioner; or

(2) statutory, regulatory, or accreditation standards, for a report made regarding an agency or facility.

(b) A nurse may report to the nurse's employer or another entity at which the nurse is authorized to practice any situation that the nurse has reasonable cause to believe exposes a patient to substantial risk of harm as a result of a failure to provide patient care that conforms to minimum standards of acceptable and prevailing professional practice or to statutory, regulatory, or accreditation standards. For purposes of this subsection, an employer or entity includes an employee or agent of the employer or entity.

(c) A person may not suspend or terminate the employment of, or otherwise discipline, discriminate against, or retaliate against, a person who:

(1) reports in good faith under this section; or

(2) advises a nurse of the nurse's right to report under this section.

(d) A violation of Subsection (c) is subject to Section 301.413.

The individual nurse can satisfy his/her reporting duty with respect to:

- *a nurse by reporting to a nursing peer review committee,*
- *a nursing student by reporting to the educational program. The educational program may have a duty to report to the BON under Sec. 301.404. The program will likely be in a better position to make the determination about the student's chemical dependency than is an individual faculty member.*

Subsec. (f) explicitly prohibits discrimination or retaliation against a nurse for reporting a nurse under this Sec. 301.402.

A person who advises a nurse on her or his right to report is also protected from retaliation.

Sec. 301.413 gives the nurse illegally retaliated against two remedies – filing a lawsuit for damages and filing a complaint with the appropriate licensing agency. If the nurse prevails in the lawsuit the minimum recovery is $5,000 in damages plus attorney fees. If the licensing agency finds retaliation, it can impose a fine of up to $25,000.

This Sec. 301.4025 sets out rights and protections nurses have when:

- *reporting practitioners other than nurses and facilities; or*
- *raising patient care concerns within the facility.*

Reporting other practitioners and facilities is authorized but not required. However, if a nurse's patient is put at risk of harm by the conduct, the option to report will likely become a duty to report. See Part X (Appendix) of this Guide for a discussion of when a nurse's option to report facility or practitioner becomes a duty to report.

The standard for reporting is "exposed a patient to substantial risk of harm as a result of failing to provide patient care that conforms to:"

1. *(for practitioners) "minimum standards of acceptable and prevailing professional practice"*
2. *(for facilities) "statutory, regulatory, or accreditation standards"*

This Subsection (b) provides nurses protections when reporting within a facility. The best way to address a quality of care concern is frequently to report that concern to the facility. However, the nurse could end up being labeled a "troublemaker" and retaliated against in some way. Subsection (c) below provides nurses protections from retaliation or discrimination for reporting under this Subsec. (b). If an unsafe situation reported involves a nurse's conduct, reporting the situation under this section would not satisfy a nurse's duty to report another nurse under NPA Sec. 301.402 unless the report was to the nursing peer review committee.

Subsection (c) explicitly prohibits discrimination or retaliation against a nurse for reporting as authorized by this Sec. 301.4025.

A person who advises a nurse on her or his right to report is also protected from retaliation.

Sec. 301.413 gives the nurse illegally retaliated against two remedies – filing a lawsuit for damages and filing a complaint with the appropriate licensing agency. If the nurse prevails in the lawsuit the minimum recovery is $5,000 in damages plus attorney fees. If the licensing agency finds retaliation, it can impose a fine of up to $25,000.

✔Shading Denotes More Important Practice-Related NPA Sections

✔Sec. 301.403. DUTY OF PEER REVIEW COMMITTEE TO REPORT. (a) Except as provided by Subsection (b), a nursing peer review committee operating under Chapter 303 that determines that a nurse has engaged in conduct subject to reporting shall file with the board a written, signed report that includes:

(1) the identity of the nurse;

(2) a description of any corrective action taken against the nurse;

(3) a recommendation whether the board should take formal disciplinary action against the nurse and the basis for the recommendation;

(4) a description of the conduct subject to reporting;

(5) the extent to which any deficiency in care provided by the reported nurse was the result of a factor beyond the nurse's control; and

(6) any additional information the board requires.

(b) A report under Subsection (a) is not required if:

(1) the nursing peer review committee determines that the reported conduct was a minor incident that is not required to be reported under board rule; or

(2) the nurse has been reported to the board for the conduct under Section 301.405.

Sec. 301.404. DUTY OF NURSING EDUCATIONAL PROGRAM TO REPORT. A nursing educational program that has reasonable cause to suspect that the ability of a nursing student to perform the services of the nursing profession would be, or would reasonably be expected to be, impaired by chemical dependency shall file with the board a written, signed report that includes the identity of the student and any additional information the board requires.

✔ Sec. 301.405. DUTY OF PERSON EMPLOYING NURSE TO REPORT. (a) This section applies only to a person who employs, hires, or contracts for the services of a nurse, including:

(1) a health care facility, including a hospital, health science center, nursing home, or home health agency;

(2) a state agency;

(3) a political subdivision;

(4) a school of nursing; and

(5) a temporary nursing service.

(b) A person that terminates, suspends for more than seven days, or takes other substantive disciplinary action, as defined by the board, against a nurse, or a substantially equivalent action against a nurse who is a staffing agency nurse, because the nurse engaged in conduct subject to reporting shall report in writing to the board:

(1) the identity of the nurse;

(2) the conduct subject to reporting that resulted in the termination, suspension, or other substantive disciplinary action or substantially equivalent action; and

(3) any additional information the board requires.

Nursing peer review committees must report a nurse determined by the committee to have engaged in conduct subject to reporting as defined by Sec. 301.401 except when:

- *the conduct constitutes a minor incident not required to be reported by BON rules [See Rule 217.16 (Reporting of Minor Incidents)]; or*
- *the nurse has already been reported to the BON by the facility or employer under Sec. 301.405.*

When reporting a nurse to the BON, the committee's report must include the information required by Subsections (a)(1)-(6). The determination of external factors described in Subsec. (a)(5) is required to be made by the nursing peer review committee under Section 303.011 of the Nursing Peer Review Law. Requiring the committee report to include the information listed in (2)-(6) is designed to assist the BON in deciding how to handle the report and what action to take against the RN or LVN as a result of the report.

The operations of nursing peer review committees are governed by Chapter 303 of the Occupations Code relating to nursing peer review. See Part IV (Nursing Peer Review) of this Guide. An individual nurse's reporting an incident to peer review satisfies that nurse's duty to report to the BON under Sec. 301.402. See Sec. 301.402(e). Individual nursing peer review committee members are restricted in what they may report to the BON independently of the committee. See Sec. 303.006(f) of the Nursing Peer Review Law.

Educational programs must report only if there is reason to suspect the student has a problem with chemical dependency which would negatively affect the student's practice after she/he is licensed. The program reporting has to predict behaviors after the student is licensed. Individual nurses have a similar duty to report under Sec. 301.402(b)(2) but that duty can be satisfied by reporting the student to the education program. See Sec. 301.402(e). An educational program reporting nurse faculty members would be governed by Sec. 301.405 (employer reporting).

Employer is defined very broadly to include any person or entity who employs, hires or contracts for a nurse's services. The relationship does not have to be that of employer-employee.

The taking of substantive disciplinary action against a nurse because of practice-related conduct (technically, "conduct subject to reporting") is what triggers the duty of employers to report. There is no duty on an employer to report a nurse unless it takes such disciplinary action against the nurse because of practice-related conduct. It seems reasonable to assume an employer would not take substantive disciplinary action against a nurse for practice-related conduct unless that conduct in fact constituted "conduct subject to reporting" as defined by Sec. 301.401. This duty to report applies to all employers regardless of the number of nurse they employ or utilize

The taking of disciplinary action against a nurse for administrative/personnel reasons, e.g., being consistently late in turning in time sheets, is not reportable. In some cases, administrative or personnel-related and practice-related conduct can overlap. For example, being late to work could endanger a patient if there is no coverage. However, normally it should be fairly clear as to which conduct forms the basis for the disciplinary action.

A temporary agency nurse must be reported to the BON if the employer takes action against the temporary agency nurse substantially equivalent to action that would require reporting an

(c) If a person who makes a report required under Subsection (b) is required under Section 303.0015 to establish a nursing peer review committee, the person shall submit a copy of the report to the nursing peer review committee. The nursing peer review committee shall review the conduct to determine if any deficiency in care by the reported nurse was the result of a factor beyond the nurse's control. A nursing peer review committee that determines that there is reason to believe that the nurse's deficiency in care was the result of a factor beyond the nurse's control shall report the conduct to the patient safety committee at the facility where the reported conduct occurred, or if the facility does not have a patient safety committee, to the chief nursing officer.

(d) *[Repealed]*

(e) The requirement under Subsection (c) that a nursing peer review committee review the nurse and the incident does not subject a person's administrative decision to discipline a nurse to the peer review process.

(f) - (g) *[Repealed]*

Sec. 301.406. DUTY OF CERTAIN PROFESSIONAL ASSOCIATIONS AND ORGANIZATIONS TO REPORT. A professional association of nurses or an organization that conducts a certification or accreditation program for nurses and that expels, decertifies, or takes any other substantive disciplinary action, as defined by the board, against a nurse as a result of the nurse's failure to conform to the minimum standards of acceptable nursing practice shall report in writing to the board the identity of the nurse and any additional information the board requires.

✔**Sec. 301.407. DUTY OF STATE AGENCY TO REPORT.** (a) This section applies only to a state agency that:

(1) licenses, registers, or certifies:

(A) a hospital;

(B) a nursing home;

(C) a health science center;

(D) a home health agency; or

(E) another health care facility or agency; or

(2) surveys a facility or agency listed in Subdivision (1) regarding the quality of nursing care provided by the facility or agency.

(b) Unless expressly prohibited by state or federal law, a state agency that has reason to believe that a nurse has engaged in conduct subject to reporting shall report the nurse in writing to the board or to a nursing peer review committee under Chapter 303.

Sec. 301.408. DUTY OF LIABILITY INSURER TO REPORT. (a) Each insurer that provides to a nurse liability insurance that covers claims arising from providing or failing to provide nursing care shall submit to the board the report or data required by this section at the time prescribed.

(b) The report or data must be provided for:

(1) a complaint filed in court against a nurse that seeks damages related to the nurse's

employed nurse. An example may be a facility telling the temporary agency that it may not assign a nurse to the facility.

Sec. 303.0015 requires persons, who employ or utilize 10 or more nurses (LVNs and/or RNs), to establish a nursing peer review committee. An exception is provided when four or fewer of the 10 nurses are RNs in which case peer review for RNs is not required. The review required by a nursing peer review committee under this section is not a review of the nurse, but rather of the incident for purpose of determining the potential role of external factors. Since the nurse has been reported to the BON by the employer, the nurse's conduct will be evaluated by the board. If external factors played a role, then other nurses may be placed in a similar situation in which the lack of adequate systems makes the error more likely to occur. The committee need not make a definitive determination of the role of external factors but rather the standard is if there "is reason to believe" the factors contributed to the deficiency in care. The nursing peer review committee then refers the issue to another committee (or CNO) with more expertise in conducting error investigation review and analysis. That committee (or CNO) is also more likely to be able to initiate the process for addressing external factors.

Review by the nursing peer review committee is advisory only and does not limit what administrative/personnel action the employer may take against the nurse. The employer is not prohibited from taking administrative/personnel action prior to peer review.

Various state agencies license or survey health care facilities, e.g., the Department of State Health Services (DSHS) surveys hospitals and the Department of Aging and Disability Services (DADS) surveys nursing homes. In the course of licensing or surveying a facility, the agency may review nursing care. This section imposes a duty on the agency to report a nurse, if it has reson to believe a nurse has engaged in conduct subject to reporting.

If these agencies identify nurses who have engaged in reportable conduct, they must report those nurses to the BON or to a nursing peer review committee. The committee may not have to report the nurse to the BON. See Sec. 301.403(b) above.

Reporting by insurers can create difficulties because of the delay that can occur in filing of a suit and because all nurses associated with a patient may be initially named as defendants and later dropped. To address this problem, Sec. 301.416(c) gives the BON discretion in handling reports by insurers.

Professional liability insurance carriers must report an insured RN or LVN named as a defendant in a lawsuit or on whose behalf a claim is settled even if no suit is filed.

conduct in providing or failing to provide nursing care; and

(2) a settlement of a claim or lawsuit made on behalf of a nurse.

(c) Not later than the 30th day after the date the insurer receives a complaint subject to Subsection (b), the insurer shall provide to the board:

(1) the name of the nurse against whom the claim is filed;

(2) the policy number;

(3) the policy limits;

(4) a copy of the petition;

(5) a copy of the answer; and

(6) other relevant information known by the insurer, as required by the board.

(d) Not later than the 30th day after the date of a judgment, dismissal, or settlement of a suit involving an insured nurse or settlement of a claim on behalf of the nurse without the filing of a lawsuit, the insurer shall provide to the board information regarding the date of the judgment, dismissal, or settlement and, if appropriate:

(1) whether an appeal has been taken from the judgment and by which party;

(2) the amount of the settlement or judgment against the nurse; and

(3) other relevant information known by the insurer, as required by the board.

(e) A nurse shall report the information required to be reported under this section if the nurse is named as a defendant in a claim arising from providing or failing to provide nursing care and the nurse:

(1) does not carry or is not covered by liability insurance; or

(2) is insured by a nonadmitted carrier.

Sec. 301.409. DUTY OF PROSECUTING ATTORNEY TO REPORT. (a) The attorney representing the state shall cause the clerk of the court of record in which the conviction, adjudication, or finding is entered to prepare and forward to the board a certified true and correct abstract of the court record of the case not later than the 30th day after the date:

(1) a person known to be a nurse who is licensed, otherwise lawfully practicing in this state, or applying to be licensed to practice is convicted of:

(A) a felony;

(B) a misdemeanor involving moral turpitude;

(C) a violation of a state or federal narcotics or controlled substance law; or

(D) an offense involving fraud or abuse under the Medicare or Medicaid program; or

(2) a court finds that a nurse is mentally ill or mentally incompetent.

(b) A prosecuting attorney shall comply with Subsection (a) even if the conviction, adjudication, or finding is entered, withheld, or appealed under the laws of this state.

(c) The abstract required under Subsection (a) must include:

(1) the name and address of the nurse or applicant;

(2) a description of the nature of the offense committed, if any;

(3) the sentence, if any; and

(4) the judgment of the court.

(d) The board shall prepare the form of the abstract and distribute a copy to each district attorney and county attorney in this state with appropriate instructions for preparation and filing.

✔Sec. 301.410. REPORT REGARDING IMPAIRMENT BY CHEMICAL DEPENDENCY, MENTAL ILLNESS, OR DIMINISHED MENTAL CAPACITY. (a) A person who is required to report a nurse under this subchapter because the nurse is impaired or suspected of being impaired by chemical dependency or mental illness may report to a peer assistance program approved by the board under Chapter 467, Health and Safety Code, instead of

Subsections (c) and (d) set out what information must be reported to the BON by the insurance company or nurse not carrying professional liability insurance. Initial information must be reported within 30 days of when the insurers notice that a complaint was filed against the nurse in a court.

Additional information must be provided to the BON within 30 days of resolution of the lawsuit or settlement.

RNs and LVNs who do not carry professional liability insurance must notify the BON themselves if they are named as a defendant in a professional liability lawsuit or settle a professional liability claim without suit being filed.

Sec. 301.452(b)(3) makes the conviction of a felony or a misdemeanor involving moral turpitude a basis for disciplinary action against a nurse. This section requires the criminal justice system to report such convictions. The greater use of criminal background checks by the board has made this section less important.

Misdemeanors involving moral turpitude are ones such as theft that indicate lack of moral character.

A finding of mental illness or incompetency must also be reported. See Sec. 301.410 for reporting nurses with chemical dependency or mental illness.

If it is believed the reported nurse's conduct results from chemical dependency or mental illness and no practice violation is involved, the nurse may be reported to a board-approved peer assistance program instead of to the BON. The Texas Peer Assistance Program for Nurses (TPAPN) is the only program approved by the BON.

reporting to the board or requesting review by a nursing peer review committee.

(b) A person who is required to report a nurse under this subchapter because the nurse is impaired or suspected of being impaired by chemical dependency or diminished mental capacity must report to the board if the person believes that an impaired nurse committed a practice violation.

✔**Sec. 301.4105. BOARD RESPONSIBILITY FOLLOWING REPORT.** The board shall determine whether a nurse violated this chapter or a rule adopted under this chapter for any case reported to the board in which the nurse's ability to perform the practice of nursing was impaired or suspected of being impaired by chemical dependency or diminished mental capacity and in which the nurse is suspected of committing a practice violation. The board, in deciding whether to take disciplinary action against the nurse for a violation of this chapter or board rules, shall balance the need to protect the public and the need to ensure the impaired nurse seeks treatment.

✔**Sec. 301.4106. PEER ASSISTANCE PROGRAMS.** The board by rule shall develop guidelines to:

(1) outline the roles and responsibilities of the board and a peer assistance program established or approved by the board under Chapter 467, Health and Safety Code;

(2) outline the process for a peer assistance program to refer to the board complaints alleging a violation of the practice of nursing;

(3) establish requirements for successfully completing a peer assistance program and for notification of the board of the successful completion by a nurse the board has ordered to attend or referred to the program; and

(4) establish a procedure for evaluating the success of a peer assistance program established or approved by the board under Chapter 467, Health and Safety Code.

✔**Sec. 301.411. EFFECT OF FAILURE TO REPORT.** (a) A person is not liable in a civil action for failure to file a report required by this subchapter.

(b) The appropriate state licensing agency may take action against a person regulated by the agency for a failure to report as required by this subchapter.

If a practice violation is involved, then Subsec. (b) requires reporting directly to the BON. The Board and TPAPN have implemented a screening process to determine if such cases are appropriate for the Board to refer to TPAPN. The BON 2007 Sunset legislation added Subsec. (b) as well as Secs. 301.4105 and 301.4106 relating to peer assistance and reporting of nurses whose practice is suspected of being impaired by chemical dependency or diminished mental capacity. The term "diminished mental capacity" is not defined and its meaning is somewhat unclear.

Sunset Commission staff described the purpose of Subsec. 301.410(b) as follows:

> *The bill requires third parties, who already have an obligation to report impaired nurses to a peer assistance program, to report to the Board when a practice violation occurs as a result of a nurse's chemical dependency or diminished mental capacity. In these cases, the Board is responsible for determining if a nurse violated the Act, and is therefore subject to appropriate discipline by the Board. The Board must also develop guidelines, in rule, to improve information sharing and communication between the Board and its peer assistance provider.*
>
> *. . . The Board would establish a process to consistently evaluate impairment cases to determine whether a nurse ordered or referred to the Texas Peer Assistance Program for Nurses (TPAPN) committed other violations of the Act or Board rules, including standards-of-practice or unprofessional conduct violations. If an investigation reveals that such a violation did occur, the Board would determine whether it should assess disciplinary sanctions in addition to ordering the nurse to TPAPN.*

This section needs to be read in conjunction with Sec. 301.410(b) above. This section describes how the BON should handle reports involving suspected impairment and a practice violation.

The BON does not have to take disciplinary action against a nurse just because a practice violation is involved. It may still be appropriate to refer the nurse to TPAPN without any additional disciplinary action subject to the nurse successfully completing TPAPN.

The BON has adopted Rule 217.13.

No civil liability is incurred because of failure to report. However, failure to report can be the basis for disciplinary action against the person's or facility's license. Immunity from civil liability is necessary because of the ambiguity that can surround determining if a report is required and if a failure to report caused the alleged harm. Without this protection, every injured patient alleging practitioner negligence could probably allege that the practitioner would not have been practicing but for another practitioner's failure to report previous conduct.

✔ **Sec. 301.412. REPORTING IMMUNITY.** A person who in good faith makes a report required or authorized under this subchapter, or a person who advises a nurse of the nurse's right or obligation to report under this subchapter:

(1) is immune from civil and criminal liability that, in the absence of the immunity, might result from making the report or giving the advice; and

(2) may not be subjected to other retaliatory action as a result of making the report or giving the advice.

✔ **Sec. 301.413. RETALIATORY ACTION.**

(a) A person may file a counter claim in a pending action or prove a cause of action in a subsequent suit to recover defense costs, including reasonable attorney's fees and actual and punitive damages, if:

(1) the person is named as a defendant in a civil action or subjected to other retaliatory action as a result of:

(A) filing a report required or authorized, or reasonably believed to be required or authorized, under this subchapter as a result of refusing to engage in conduct as authorized by Section 301.352;

(B) requesting in good faith a nursing peer review committee determination under Section 303.005; or

(C) providing advice to a person regarding:

(i) filing a report required or authorized, or reasonably believed to be required or authorized, under this subchapter as a result of refusing to engage in conduct as authorized by Section 301.352; or

(ii) requesting in good faith a nursing peer review committee determination under Section 303.005; and

(2) the suit or retaliatory action is determined to be frivolous, unreasonable, or taken in bad faith.

(b) A person may not suspend, terminate, or otherwise discipline, discriminate against, or retaliate against a person who:

(1) reports in good faith under this subchapter;

(2) requests, in good faith, a nursing peer review committee determination under Section 303.005;

(3) refuses to engage in conduct as authorized by Section 301.352; or

Persons reporting in good faith are protected from both civil and criminal liability and also from retaliation for making the report. Practitioners are often justifiably concerned that if they report another practitioner, they are going to be sued for professional slander or some other reason. This section is designed to prevent such concerns from having a chilling effect on good faith reporting. "Authorized" reports include reports of other practitioners and facilities under Sec. 301.4025.

Persons who advise a nurse about the nurse's right or duty to report and protections available when reporting are also protected.

This Sec. 301.413 sets out the remedies available to nurses who have been retaliated or discriminated against because they engaged in protected patient advocacy activities or because they advised another nurse of these patient advocacy protections. The activities protected are:

1. *Refusing to engage in conduct subject to reporting or that would violate NPA or BON rule (NPA Sec. 301.352)*
2. *Reporting a nurse (NPA Sec. 301.402), a practitioner (other than a nurse) or a facility (NPA Sec. 301.4025(a)) or raising of patient care concern within a facility (Sec. 301.4025(b))*
3. *Requesting safe harbor nursing peer review (NPR Law Sec. 303.005)*
4. *Advising a nurse on protections (1)-(3)*

See Subsection (b) below.

See Part VI (Patient Advocacy Protections) for protections for nurses as patient advocates.

This Subsec. (a) provides general legal recourse to any person sued or otherwise retaliated against for engaging in protected patient advocacy activities.

It appears that there should be an "or" between "subchapter" and "as a result" but this it the way the statute reads. See history of change to this Subsec. (a) in SBs 993 (2007), 476 (2009), 192 (2011) and also wording of Subsecs. (b), (c).

Persons who advise a nurse about the nurse's right or duty to report and protections available when reporting are also protected under this section.

It appears that there should be an "or" between "subchapter" and "as a result" but this it the way the statute reads. See history of changes to this Subsec. (a) in SBs 993 (2007), 476 (2009), 192 (2011) and also wording of Subsecs. (b), (c).

This Subsec. (b) provides specific protections for persons reporting, in good faith, from being terminated or retaliated against at their job. It covers not only mandatory reporting, but also any reporting authorized by this section, e.g., reporting other providers under Sec. 301.402. In a 1998 opinion, Clark v. Texas Home Health, Inc., the Texas Supreme Court upheld a liberal interpretation of this section as providing "a cause of action for retaliatory acts against persons reporting under this [Sec. 301.401-.419]." The opinion is set out in the Appendices to this Guide.

Persons who advise a nurse about the nurse's right or duty to report and protections available

(4) advises a nurse of the nurse's right to:

(A) report under this subchapter;

(B) request a nursing peer review committee determination under Section 303.005; or

(C) refuse to engage in conduct as authorized by Section 301.352.

(b-1) A person suspected of violating Subsection (b) may be reported to the appropriate licensing agency and, notwithstanding any other provision, that agency may impose an administrative penalty not to exceed $25,000 against the person if the agency finds a violation of Subsection (b). An administrative penalty imposed under this subsection is in addition to other penalties the agency is authorized to impose and is subject to the procedural requirements applicable to the appropriate licensing agency.

(c) A person who reports under this subchapter, refuses to engage in conduct as authorized by Section 301.352, or requests a nursing peer review committee determination under Section 303.005, or a person who advises a nurse of the nurse's right to report under this subchapter, refuse to engage in conduct as authorized by Section 301.352, or request a nursing peer review committee determination under Section 303.005, has a cause of action against a person who violates Subsection (b), and may recover:

(1) the greater of:

(A) actual damages, including damages for mental anguish even if no other injury is shown; or

(B) $5,000;

(2) exemplary damages;

(3) court costs; and

(4) reasonable attorney's fees.

(d) In addition to the amount recovered under Subsection (c), a person whose employment is suspended or terminated in violation of this section is entitled to:

(1) reinstatement in the employee's former position or severance pay in an amount equal to three months of the employee's most recent salary; and

(2) compensation for wages lost during the period of suspension or termination.

(e) A person who brings an action under this section has the burden of proof. It is a rebuttable presumption that the person was suspended, terminated, or otherwise disciplined, discriminated against, or retaliated against for reporting under this subchapter, for refusing to engage in conduct as authorized by Section 301.352, for requesting a peer review committee determination under Section 303.005, or for providing advice to a person regarding reporting under this subchapter, refusing to engage in conduct as authorized by Section 301.352, or requesting a peer review committee determination under Section 303.005 if:

(1) the person was suspended, terminated, or otherwise disciplined, discriminated against, or retaliated against within 60 days after the date the report, refusal, or request was made or the advice was given; and

(2) the board or a court determines that:

(A) the report that is the subject of the cause of action was:

(i) authorized or required under Section 301.402, 301.4025, 301.403, 301.405, 301.406, 301.407, 301.408, 301.409, or 301.410; and

(ii) made in good faith;

(B) the request for a peer review committee determination that is the subject of the cause of action was:

(i) authorized under Section 303.005; and

(ii) made in good faith;

when reporting are also protected under this section.

Licensed practitioners or facilities that retaliate may be reported to their licensing board which may impose a fine of up to $25,000. The agency could also take action against the practitioner's or facility's license.

Subsections (c)-(f) address issues related to the filing of a lawsuit and the relief that can be provided.

The person reporting may recover not only actual damages including mental anguish, but also exemplary damages and attorney's fees. The minimum recovery for actual damages is set at $5,000.

The nurse may be reinstated or awarded severance pay.

Proving that a person's motive was retaliation can be difficult. This section addresses this difficulty by creating a rebuttal presumption that any adverse action taken within 60 days of the protected conduct was taken in retaliation. A rebuttal presumption is one that creates an initial presumption that can be overcome by opposing evidence. The person alleged to have retaliated against the nurse would have to present such opposing evidence. Once it does, then the burden of proof returns to the nurse to prove the retaliation. What the rebuttal presumption does is prevent the defendant from simply denying the retaliation without putting on any evidence of the reason for the alleged retaliatory conduct. Once the defendant puts in evidence, that evidence can be evaluated, challenged and refuted.

(C) the refusal to engage in conduct was authorized by Section 301.352; or

(D) the advice that is the subject of the cause of action was given in good faith.

(f) An action under this section may be brought in a district court of the county in which:

(1) the plaintiff resides;

(2) the plaintiff was employed by the defendant; or

(3) the defendant conducts business.

(g) Subject to Subsection (h), a nurse employed by a hospital operated by or on behalf of a state or local governmental entity who alleges a violation of Subsection (b) may sue the state or local governmental entity for relief under this section, and the sovereign immunity of the state or local governmental entity from suit and from liability is waived for the limited purpose of allowing the nurse to maintain a lawsuit in state court to obtain that relief. Relief under this section is in addition to any other remedies a nurse may have under state or federal law as a public employee. In this subsection:

(1) "Local governmental entity," "public employee," and "state governmental entity" have the meanings assigned by Section 554.001, Government Code.

(2) "Hospital" has the meaning assigned by Section 241.003, Health and Safety Code, and includes a mental hospital licensed under Chapter 577, Health and Safety Code.

(h) Relief may be granted in a lawsuit brought under Subsection (g) for an alleged violation of Subsection (b)(1) based on a report made by a nurse under Section 301.4025(b) only if the nurse:

(1) made the report:

(A) in writing, which may be provided electronically; or

(B) verbally, if authorized by the nurse's employer or another entity at which the nurse is authorized to practice;

(2) made the report to:

(A) the nurse's supervisor;

(B) a committee authorized under state or federal law to receive reports under Section 301.4025(b); or

(C) an individual or committee authorized by the nurse's employer or another entity at which the nurse is authorized to practice; and

(3) made the report not later than:

(A) the fifth day after the date the nurse became aware of the situation if the situation involves a single incident; or

(B) the fifth day after the date the nurse became aware of the most recent occurrence of the situation if the situation involves multiple incidents or a pattern of behavior.

(i) For purposes of Subsection (h), "supervisor" means an individual who has authority over the responsibilities of the nurse making the report or an individual who is in the nurse's chain of command.

(j) The following provisions of Chapter 554, Government Code, apply to a lawsuit under Subsection (g):

(1) the type of relief and the amount of damages available to a public employee under Section 554.003;

(2) the time during which a public employee must seek relief under Section 554.005; and

(3) the requirement that a public employee use the grievance or appeal procedures of the state or local governmental entity before suing for relief under Section 554.006.

Subsections (g)-(l) were added in 2013 (HB 581) to provide public hospital employed nurses a right to file a lawsuit to recover damages resulting from retaliation for engaging in patient advocacy activities protected under Subsection (b). Without this type of explicit waiver of sovereign immunity, public hospital employed nurses would have to seek recovery under the Public Employee Whistleblower Law (Government Code, Chap. 554). That law covers only external reporting and not all of the activities listed under Subsection (b). This Subsection applies only to public hospital employed nurses and not to nurses employed by other public entities such as a jail or county health department. The Public Employee Whistleblower Law is set out in Part VI (Advocacy Protections) of this Guide.

Subsections (h) and (i) were added by the Legislature to address concern that a county or other entity operating a public hospital might be sued for retaliation without ever being aware that the nurse made a protected report of unsafe care. A report under Sec. 301.4025(b) is an optional report in a facility about unsafe care.

A supervisor is anyone in the nurse's chain of command. Supervisor was defined this way so nurse could raise concerns to administration if felt an immediate supervisor was not adequately addressing a concern.

The type of relief that a public hospital employed nurse can recover is subject to the limitations set out in the Public Employee Whistleblower Law. It sets a limit on the amount of damages based on the size of the governmental entity and also does not permit punitive damages. The Public Employee Whistleblower Law is set out in Part VI (Advocacy Protections) of this Guide.

(k) A lawsuit under Subsection (g) against a state governmental entity shall be brought in a district court in Travis County or a county in which all or part of the acts or omissions giving rise to the cause of action occurred.

(l) A lawsuit under Subsection (g) against a local governmental entity shall be brought in a district court in a county in which all or part of the entity is located.

Sec. 301.414. NOTICE AND REVIEW OF REPORT. (a) The board shall notify each nurse who is reported to the board under Section 301.402, 301.403, 301.405, 301.406, 301.407, 301.408, or 301.409 of the filing of the report unless the notification would jeopardize an active investigation.

(b) The nurse or the nurse's authorized representative is entitled on request to review any report submitted to the board under a section specified under Subsection (a) unless doing so would jeopardize an active investigation. The board may not reveal the identity of the person making or signing the report.

✔Sec. 301.415. REBUTTAL STATEMENT. (a) A nurse who is entitled to receive notice under Section 301.414 or the authorized representative of the nurse may file with the board a statement of reasonable length containing the nurse's rebuttal of any information in the report to the board.

(b) The statement made under Subsection (a) must accompany the part of the report being rebutted.

(c) In investigating the report, the board shall:

(1) review the statement made under Subsection (a); and

(2) evaluate each reason asserted by the nurse to justify the nurse's conduct.

✔Sec. 301.416. INVESTIGATION. (a) Except as provided by Subsections (b) and (c), a report under this subchapter shall be treated as a complaint under Section 301.457.

(b) If the board determines that the reported conduct does not indicate that the continued practice of nursing by the nurse poses a risk of harm to a client or other person, the board, with the written consent of the nurse and the person making the report, may elect not to proceed with an investigation or to file formal charges. The board shall:

(1) maintain a record of the report; and

(2) investigate the report if it receives two or more reports involving separate incidents regarding the nurse in any five-year period.

(c) The board is not required to investigate a report filed by an insurer under Section 301.408, but shall:

(1) maintain a record of the report; and

(2) investigate the report if it receives two or more reports involving separate incidents regarding the nurse in any five-year period.

✔Sec. 301.417. CONFIDENTIALITY REQUIREMENTS; DISCLOSURE OF INFORMATION. (a) A report required or authorized under this subchapter and the identity of the person making the report are confidential and may not be disclosed except as provided by this section and Section 301.414.

(b) The board may disclose the information to the same extent that the board may disclose information relating to a complaint under Section 301.466

(c) *[Repealed]*

(d) In addition to the other authorizations of this section, the information may be disclosed in:

(1) a civil action in which a reporting person is named as a defendant as a result of

Subsections (k) and (l) determine where a lawusit by a public hospital employed nurse must be filed.

This section and the next identify the rights of the reported nurse. It is designed to provide the nurse some protections from groundless reports. The reported nurse's rights include:

- *being notified that a report has been filed;*
- *reviewing the report but not the identity of the person making the report; and*
- *filing a rebuttal statement that must accompany the report itself.*

See also Sec. 301.419(c) below relating to the expunging of groundless reports.

A reported nurse has the right to file a rebuttal statement with the BON. See also Secs. 301.414 [notice of being reported] and 301.419(c) [expunging of groundless reports].

The rebuttal statement must be included with any disclosure of the report. See also Sec. 301.417.

Normally a report is treated by the BON the same as a complaint against the nurse.

This section gives the BON authority not to take action on reports of minor incidents. See definition of "minor incident" in Sec. 301.401. All parties have to agree to the BON's not acting on the report. In some cases (e.g., the nurse believes the report is groundless), the reported nurse may want the BON to investigate the incident so it can be cleared from the nurse's record. Sec. 301.419 requires the BON to adopt rules to minimize reporting of minor incidents. See BON Rule §217.16 relating to reporting of minor incidents.

The BON does not have to act on reports by insurance carriers. This is designed to address the problem of lawsuits being filed a considerable time after the incident or that of all nurses involved with a patient being initially named as defendants and then later being dropped from the lawsuit. Insurance companies are required to report under Sec. 301.408.

Reports are confidential and may be disclosed only as permitted by this section. Sec. 301.414 above gives the reported nurse a right to review the report but not to learn the identity of the person making the report. Disclosure of the reporting person's identity could have a chilling effect on good faith reporting, This provision does not authorize anonymous reporting. Reports to the Board must be in writing and signed. See Sec. 301.402 above relating to reporting by individual nurses and also 301.457(a) relating to complaints.

making the report; or

(2) the prosecution of a cause of action based on a claim that the reporting person was subject to retaliatory action as a result of making the report.

✔Sec. 301.418. DISCLOSURE OF CHARGES OR DISCIPLINARY ACTION. (a) This subchapter does not prevent disclosure under Section 301.466 of formal charges filed by the board or a final disciplinary action taken by the board as a result, in whole or in part, of submission of a report under this subchapter.

(b) A report or information submitted as required or authorized by this subchapter arising out of the provision or failure to provide nursing services may not be made available in a liability action for:

(1) discovery;

(2) court subpoena; or

(3) introduction into evidence.

(c) A person is not prevented from taking disciplinary action against a nurse by:

(1) the filing of a report under this subchapter with the board;

(2) an investigation by the board; or

(3) the disposition of a matter by the board.

✔Sec. 301.419. GENERAL PROVISIONS REGARDING DUTY TO REPORT; MINOR INCIDENTS.

(a) *[Repealed]*

(b) The board shall adopt rules governing reporting required under this subchapter to minimize:

(1) unnecessary duplicative reporting; and

(2) the reporting of a minor incident.

(c) If the board determines that a report submitted under this subchapter is without merit, the board shall expunge the report from the nurse's file.

(d) The board shall inform, in the manner the board determines appropriate, nurses, facilities, agencies, and other persons of their duty to report under this subchapter.

(e) The reporting required under this subchapter does not constitute state action on behalf of the person reporting.

(f) The duty to report or any other requirement of this subchapter may not be nullified by a contract.

SUBCHAPTER J.
PROHIBITED PRACTICES AND DISCIPLINARY ACTIONS

The confidentiality provisions of Sec. 301.417 above apply only to the initial report. If, after investigating, the BON files formal charges against the nurse, those formal charges are public record and not confidential.

Reports may not be used in professional liability suits. This provision is designed to keep the regulatory/disciplinary process separate from the tort/liability system.

The filing of a report does not prevent an employer from taking disciplinary action against the nurse. This is consistent with Sec. 301.405(e) which permits the employer to take administrative action independently of any required review by a nursing peer review committee.

This Subsection. (b) directs the BON to adopt rules to minimize the reporting of minor incidents. Sec. 301.416(b) gives the BON discretion not to take action if it receives a report involving a minor incident. The BON has adopted rules implementing this section that elaborate on when a minor incident need not be reported. See BON Rule §217.16.

Mandatory reporting has the potential for causing harm to RNs and LVNs wrongly reported. This section is designed to provide protection from groundless reports by having the report expunged from the nurse's file.

The reporting obligations imposed by this Subchapter (Secs 301.401-.419 relating to reporting) cannot be contracted away. For example, a nurse's agreement as a condition of employment to give up his/her right to the remedies under Sec. 301.413 would not be valid.

This Subchapter contains important provisions governing disciplinary actions against RNs or LVNs. The BON website at www.bon.texas.gov has extensive information about the disciplinary process. BON Rule 213 governs the disciplinary process. The BON has also adopted a disciplinary matrix and disciplinary sanction policies for selected disciplinary grounds. These can be found on the BON website www.bon.texas.gov under the "Disciplinary Action" tab. Some of the key provisions of this subchapter are:

Sec. 301.451 Prohibited Practices (unauthorized practice of nursing)
Sec, 301.4515 Use of Certain Nursing Titles ("nurse aide," nurse assistant," etc.)
Sec. 301.452 Grounds for Disciplinary Action (and denial of license)
Sec. 301.453 Disciplinary Authority of Board; Methods of Discipline

✔Shading Denotes More Important
Practice-Related NPA Sections

Sec. 301.454. NOTICE AND HEARING
Sec. 301.455. TEMPORARY LICENSE SUSPENSION OR RESTRICTION
Sec. 301.4551. TEMPORARY LICENSE SUSPENSION FOR DRUG OR ALCOHOL USE
Sec. 301.456. EVIDENCE
Sec. 301.457. COMPLAINT AND INVESTIGATION
Sec. 301.458. INITIATION OF FORMAL CHARGES; DISCOVERY
Sec. 301.459. FORMAL HEARING
Sec. 301.460. ACCESS TO INFORMATION
Sec. 301.461. ASSESSMENT OF COSTS
Sec. 301.462. VOLUNTARY SURRENDER OF LICENSE
Sec. 301.463. AGREED DISPOSITION
Sec. 301.464. INFORMAL PROCEEDINGS
Sec. 301.465. SUBPOENAS; REQUEST FOR INFORMATION
Sec. 301.466. CONFIDENTIALITY
Sec. 301.467. REINSTATEMENT
Sec. 301.468. PROBATION
Sec. 301.469. NOTICE OF FINAL ACTION
Sec. 301.470. REFUND
Sec. 301.471. EMERGENCY CEASE AND DESIST ORDER

✔Sec. 301.451. CERTAIN PROHIBITED PRACTICES. A person may not:

(1) sell, fraudulently obtain, or fraudulently furnish a nursing diploma, license, renewal license, or record;

(2) assist another person in selling, fraudulently obtaining, or fraudulently furnishing a nursing diploma, license, renewal license, or record;

(3) practice nursing under a diploma, license, or record that was:

(A) obtained unlawfully or fraudulently; or

(B) signed or issued unlawfully or under false representation; or

(4) practice nursing in a period in which the person's license is suspended or revoked.

✔Sec. 301.4515. USE OF CERTAIN NURSING TITLES. Unless the person is practicing under the delegated authority of a registered nurse or is otherwise authorized by state or federal law, a person may not use, in connection with the person's name:

(1) the title "nurse aide," "nurse assistant," or "nurse technician"; or

(2) any other similar title.

✔Sec. 301.452. GROUNDS FOR DISCIPLINARY ACTION.

(a) In this section, "intemperate use" includes practicing nursing or being on duty or on call while under the influence of alcohol or drugs.

(b) A person is subject to denial of a license or to disciplinary action under this subchapter for:

This Sec. 301.451 addresses the unauthorized practice of nursing by persons representing they have an RN or LVN license that was fraudulently obtained or which is no longer valid. The provisions of the NPA addressing prohibited practices by RNs and LVNs holding a valid license are set out in NPA Sec. 301.452. The requirements that any person practicing nursing must be licensed as an RN or LVN and that only licensees may use "RN" and LVN" titles is set out in Sec. 301.251.

Unlicensed persons cannot use titles such as "nurse aide," "nurse assistant," "nurse technician," or similar title implying that they are assisting a nurse unless they actually are practicing under the delegated authority of an RN. While LVNs cannot delegate to unlicensed persons, LVNs can assign nursing tasks to an unlicensed person to whom an RN has delegated the authority to do that task. Assignment by LVNs is addressed by Rule 217.11(2)(B). Rules 224 and 225 govern delegation by RNs. Section 301.251(d) protects the titles "RN," "LVN," and "nurse."

"Intemperate use" by nurses is prohibited by Subdivision (b)(9). Intemperate use includes being on-call while under the influence.

This section sets out 13 grounds on which the BON may take disciplinary action against a nurse's license, deny a license or refuse to renew a license. These grounds are broadly worded and don't provide much guidance about specific conduct. The BON has adopted rules elaborating on a number of these grounds for disciplinary action set out in this section, including rules defining unprofessional conduct (Rule 217.12), minimum standards of practice (Rule 217.11), rules governing delegation to unlicensed personnel (Rules 224, 225), and other practice-related rules. The board has also adopted position statements and posted practice-related FAQs on its

(1) a violation of this chapter, a rule or regulation not inconsistent with this chapter, or an order issued under this chapter;

(2) fraud or deceit in procuring or attempting to procure a license to practice professional nursing or vocational nursing;

(3) a conviction for, or placement on deferred adjudication community supervision or deferred disposition for, a felony or for a misdemeanor involving moral turpitude;

(4) conduct that results in the revocation of probation imposed because of conviction for a felony or for a misdemeanor involving moral turpitude;

(5) use of a nursing license, diploma, or permit, or the transcript of such a document, that has been fraudulently purchased, issued, counterfeited, or materially altered;

(6) impersonating or acting as a proxy for another person in the licensing examination required under Section 301.253 or 301.255;

(7) directly or indirectly aiding or abetting an unlicensed person in connection with the unauthorized practice of nursing;

(8) revocation, suspension, or denial of, or any other action relating to, the person's license or privilege to practice nursing in another jurisdiction or federal law;

(9) intemperate use of alcohol or drugs that the board determines endangers or could endanger a patient;

(10) unprofessional or dishonorable conduct that, in the board's opinion, is likely to deceive, defraud, or injure a patient or the public;

(11) adjudication of mental incompetency;

(12) lack of fitness to practice because of a mental or physical health condition that could result in injury to a patient or the public; or

(13) failure to care adequately for a patient or to conform to the minimum standards of acceptable nursing practice in a manner that, in the board's opinion, exposes a patient or other person unnecessarily to risk of harm.

website. These materials provide much more detailed guidance about what conduct is prohibited and nurses should be familiar with them. The most significant practice-related material are identified in Part V of this Guide.

Nurses must comply not only with the NPA, but also with rules of the BON. BON rules, in turn, require nurses know and conform to other laws and rules affecting their area of practice, e.g., abuse reporting laws, patient rights laws, etc. Some of these other laws are set out in Part IX (Other Laws) of this Guide.

BON Rule 213.28 elaborates on criminal convictions as grounds for disciplinary action or denial of a license. While any felony can provide the basis for disciplinary action, the only misdemeanors that can are those involving moral turpitude, i.e., those that demonstrate moral depravity such as theft. The BON is permitted to take action against a nurse's license for deferred adjudications as well as convictions. The criminal justice system is making greater use of deferred adjudications and for more serious offenses. If a nurse pleads guilty to conduct that brings into question the nurse's ability to practice without putting patients at risk, the BON needs to have the ability to take action against that nurse's license. See also Section 301.4535 which makes certain crimes an absolute bar to licensure. Denial or revocation of a professional license for a criminal offense is addressed by Occupations Code, Chapter 53.

Disciplinary action by a board of nursing in another state may be the basis for the BON to take action against a nurse's Texas license. See Sec. 301.456 for how such action is proved.

See definition of "intemperate use" in Subsec. (a). Being on duty or on call under the influence is intemperate use. Nurses should not consume any alcohol or drugs while on duty or on call or prior to going on duty or on call unless there is sufficient time for the drug or alcohol to clear the nurse's system. It is also improper for a nurse to be on duty or on call under the influence of a prescription drug if the nurse should know such medication will impair his or her ability to provide nursing care. The BON's position is that the mentioning of a side-effect in the literature provides a sufficient basis for saying a nurse should know of it. See BON Rule §213.29. See also the BON's disciplinary sanction policy on chemical dependency on the BON website.

Along with standards of practice [Subd. (13) below], this is one of the most important grounds for disciplinary action. BON Rule §217.12 (Unprofessional Conduct) sets out the types of conduct the BON considers unprofessional. This rule and Rule 217.11 (Standards of Practice) are also what define a nurse's duty to a patient for purpose of requesting safe harbor nursing peer review under Sec. 303.005. RNs and LVNs should be familiar with both these rules.

The BON in its rules provides guidelines for how it will apply these two grounds (mental incompetency and lack of fitness) for disciplinary purposes. The application for initial licensure and license renewal includes questions addressing these areas. See Rules 213.29 and 213.33(k),(l).

Along with unprofessional conduct [Subd.(10) above], this is one of the most important grounds for disciplinary action. The minimum standards of acceptable nursing practice for all nurses are set out in BON Rule §217.11 (Standards of Practice). This rule and Rule §217.12 (Unprofessional Conduct) also define a nurse's duty to a patient for purpose of requesting peer review under Sec. 303.005. RNs and LVNs should be familiar with both these rules.

The BON has not adopted any rule defining "failure to care adequately for a patient." However, most instances of such conduct would likely be conduct prohibited by Rules 217.11

(c) The board may refuse to admit a person to a licensing examination for a ground described under Subsection (b).

(d) The board by rule shall establish guidelines to ensure that any arrest information, in particular information on arrests in which criminal action was not proven or charges were not filed or adjudicated, that is received by the board under this section is used consistently, fairly, and only to the extent the underlying conduct relates to the practice of nursing.

Sec. 301.4521. PHYSICAL AND PSYCHOLOGICAL EVALUATION. (a) In this section:

(1) "Applicant" means:

(A) a petitioner for a declaratory order of eligibility for a license; or

(B) an applicant for an initial license or renewal of a license.

(2) "Evaluation" means a physical or psychological evaluation conducted to determine a person's fitness to practice nursing.

(b) The board may require a nurse or applicant to submit to an evaluation only if the board has probable cause to believe that the nurse or applicant is unable to practice nursing with reasonable skill and safety to patients because of:

(1) physical impairment;

(2) mental impairment; or

(3) chemical dependency or abuse of drugs or alcohol.

(c) A demand for an evaluation under Subsection (b) must be in writing and state:

(1) the reasons probable cause exists to require the evaluation; and

(2) that refusal by the nurse or applicant to submit to the evaluation will result in an administrative hearing to be held to make a final determination of whether probable cause for the evaluation exists.

(d) If the nurse or applicant refuses to submit to the evaluation, the board shall schedule a hearing on the issue of probable cause to be conducted by the State Office of Administrative Hearings. The nurse or applicant must be notified of the hearing by personal service or certified mail. The hearing is limited to the issue of whether the board had probable cause to require an evaluation. The nurse or applicant may present testimony and other evidence at the hearing to show why the nurse or applicant should not be required to submit to the evaluation. The board has the burden of proving that probable cause exists. At the conclusion of the hearing, the hearing

(Standards of Practice) and 217.12 (Unprofessional Conduct).

Exposing a patient to risk of harm and not just actual harm can be the basis for the BON to discipline an RN or LVN. If an RN's or LVN's conduct indicates an unsafe practitioner, that conduct violates this section and is also reportable conduct under 301.402. Near misses and close calls can be a violation. An example of reportable conduct that does not involve actual harm would be a nurse who recklessly is about to administer a medication by the wrong route (with almost certain harm to patient) but another nurse catches the mistake before the medication is administered. Being on duty under the influence is another example. See BON Rule 217.12(4).

The grounds for taking disciplinary action set out in Subsec. (b) can also be the grounds for refusing to permit a person to take the licensing exam.

BON Rule 213.28(h) implementing this section states:

> *The fact that a person has been arrested will not be used as grounds for disciplinary action. If however, evidence ascertained through the board's own investigation from information contained in the arrest record regarding the underlying conduct suggests actions violating the Nursing Practice Act or rules of the Board, the board may consider such evidence as a factor in its deliberations regarding any decision to grant a license, restrict a license, or impose licensure discipline.*

This section was added in 2009 to clarify when the BON may request a physical or psychological evaluation of a nurse or applicant for licensure as part of determining the nurse's fitness to practice nursing. The Board believes that, in some cases, a physical or psychological evaluation may be the only way it can determine a nurse's "fitness to practice." This section permits the board to require evaluations in some situations and request them in others. See BON Rule 213.33(k), (l) implementing this section. This rule allows for the use of a polygraph test under certain circumstances. The types of evaluations the board may require are medical, pain management, mental health/psychological, neuropsychological, anger management, sex offender and chemical dependency. The board may request a forensic psychological evaluation with or without a polygraph examination. The board has prepared Guidelines for Physical and Psychological Evaluations.

If the BON has probable cause to believe a nurse or applicant has certain types of impairment, the BON may require the nurse to submit to evaluation. See Rule 213.13(k). In other situations, the board may request an evaluation but the nurse has a right to refuse. See Subsec. (f) below.

The BON's request for an evaluation must be in writing and state the reasons the BON believes it has probable cause for requesting an evaluation. If the nurse refuses, the matter goes to an administrative hearing for a final determination on the issue of whether the BON had probable cause to believe the nurse or applicant was impaired.

Subsec. (d) sets out the process for an administrative hearing if the nurse refuses to submit to an evaluation, which the BON may require under Subsec. (b).

officer shall enter an order requiring the nurse or applicant to submit to the evaluation or an order rescinding the board's demand for an evaluation. The order may not be vacated or modified under Section 2001.058, Government Code.

(e) If a nurse or applicant refuses to submit to an evaluation after an order requiring the evaluation is entered under Subsection (d), the board may:

(1) refuse to issue or renew a license;

(2) suspend a license; or

(3) issue an order limiting the license.

(f) The board may request a nurse or applicant to consent to an evaluation by a practitioner approved by the board for a reason other than a reason listed in Subsection (b). A request for an evaluation under this subsection must be in writing and state:

(1) the reasons for the request;

(2) the type of evaluation requested;

(3) how the board may use the evaluation;

(4) that the nurse or applicant may refuse to submit to an evaluation; and

(5) the procedures for submitting an evaluation as evidence in any hearing regarding the issuance or renewal of the nurse's or applicant's license.

(g) If a nurse or applicant refuses to consent to an evaluation under Subsection (f), the nurse or applicant may not introduce an evaluation into evidence at a hearing to determine the nurse's or applicant's right to be issued or retain a nursing license unless the nurse or applicant:

(1) not later than the 30th day before the date of the hearing, notifies the board that an evaluation will be introduced into evidence at the hearing;

(2) provides the board the results of that evaluation;

(3) informs the board of any other evaluations by any other practitioners; and

(4) consents to an evaluation by a practitioner that meets board standards established under Subsection (h).

(h) The board shall establish by rule the qualifications for a licensed practitioner to conduct an evaluation under this section. The board shall maintain a list of qualified practitioners. The board may solicit qualified practitioners located throughout the state to be on the list.

(i) A nurse or applicant shall pay the costs of an evaluation conducted under this section.

(j) The results of an evaluation under this section are:

(1) confidential and not subject to disclosure under Chapter 552, Government Code; and

(2) not subject to disclosure by discovery, subpoena, or other means of legal compulsion for release to anyone, except that the results may be:

(A) introduced as evidence in a proceeding before the board or a hearing conducted by the State Office of Administrative Hearings under this chapter;

(B) included in the findings of fact and conclusions of law in a final board order; and

(C) disclosed to a peer assistance program approved by the board under Chapter 467, Health and Safety Code, and to which the board has referred the nurse.

(k) If the board determines there is insufficient evidence to bring action against a person based on the results of any evaluation under this section, the evaluation must be expunged from the board's records.

(l) The board shall adopt guidelines for requiring or requesting a nurse or applicant to submit to an evaluation under this section.

(m) The authority granted to the board under this section is in addition to the board's authority to make licensing decisions under this chapter.

If the administrative hearing results in a ruling that the BON has probable cause to request the evaluation and the nurse or applicant still refuses to be evaluated, the BON can take action on that refusal.

In situations other than those identified in Subsec. (b), such as when the BON wants to request a forensic evaluation, the BON may request the evaluation but the nurse or applicant may refuse to be evaluated. The request must be in writing and explain the reasons and type of evaluation being requested. See Rule 213.3(l). The board may request a forensic psychological evaluation with or without a polygraph examination.

The nurse or applicant may refuse to be evaluated but certain consequences are attached.

If the nurse or applicant refuses the BON request then there are limitations on the nurse's or applicant's right to have her/his own evaluation done and admitted into evidence at a hearing.

The BON must establish the qualifications of licensed practitioners who do the evaluations.

The nurse or applicant must pay the costs of an evaluation even if required by the BON.

The results of the evaluation are confidential and can be disclosed only as authorized by this Subsec. (j).

The evaluation must be expunged from the nurse's record if there is insufficient evidence to bring action against the nurse or applicant.

The BON has adopted these guidelines in Rule 213.33 (k),(l).

✔Shading Denotes More Important Practice-Related NPA Sections

✔Sec. 301.453. DISCIPLINARY AUTHORITY OF BOARD; METHODS OF DISCIPLINE. (a) If the board determines that a person has committed an act listed in Section 301.452(b), the board shall enter an order imposing one or more of the following:

(1) denial of the person's application for a license, license renewal, or temporary permit;

(2) issuance of a written warning;

(3) administration of a public reprimand;

(4) limitation or restriction of the person's license, including:

(A) limiting to or excluding from the person's practice one or more specified activities of nursing; or

(B) stipulating periodic board review;

(5) suspension of the person's license;

(6) revocation of the person's license; or

(7) assessment of a fine.

(b) In addition to or instead of an action under Subsection (a), the board, by order, may require the person to:

(1) submit to care, counseling, or treatment by a health provider designated by the board as a condition for the issuance or renewal of a license;

(2) participate in a program of education or counseling prescribed by the board, including a program of remedial education;

(3) practice for a specified period under the direction of a registered nurse or vocational nurse designated by the board; or

(4) perform public service the board considers appropriate.

(c) The board may probate any penalty imposed on a nurse and may accept the voluntary surrender of a license. The board may not reinstate a surrendered license unless it determines that the person is competent to resume practice.

(d) If the board suspends, revokes, or accepts surrender of a license, the board may impose conditions for reinstatement that the person must satisfy before the board may issue an unrestricted license; or

(5) abstain from the consumption of alcohol or the use of drugs and submit to random periodic screening for alcohol or drug use.

✔Sec. 301.4531. SCHEDULE OF SANCTIONS. (a) The board by rule shall adopt a schedule of the disciplinary sanctions that the board may impose under this chapter. In adopting the schedule of sanctions, the board shall ensure that the severity of the sanction imposed is appropriate to the type of violation or conduct that is the basis for disciplinary action.

(b) In determining the appropriate disciplinary action, including the amount of any administrative penalty to assess, the board shall consider:

(1) whether the person:

(A) is being disciplined for multiple violations of either this chapter or a rule or order adopted under this chapter; or

(B) has previously been the subject of disciplinary action by the board and has previously complied with board rules and this chapter;

(2) the seriousness of the violation;

(3) the threat to public safety; and

(4) any mitigating factors.

(c) In the case of a person described by:

(1) Subsection (b)(1)(A), the board shall consider taking a more severe disciplinary action, including revocation of the person's license, than the disciplinary action that would be taken for a single violation; and

This Sec. 301.453 gives the BON a broad range of enforcement options and significant flexibility in the penalties it can impose. In short, it gives the BON a wide range of options in order to impose "a penalty that fits the violation."

NPA Sec. 301.468 addresses procedures governing probation in more detail.

This Subsec. (d) allows the BON, at the time a license is suspended, revoked or surrendered, to impose conditions for reinstatement that must be satisfied before that license can be reinstated. This process prevents a nurse from simply "sitting out" a suspension.

BON Rule 213.33 (b) sets out a Disciplinary Matrix implementing this section. The matrix can be found on the BON website under the "Disciplinary Action" tab.

This Subsec. (b) sets out the factors the board must consider in determining the appropriate disciplinary action.

Multiple violations can result in a more severe sanction.

(2) Subsection (b)(1)(B), the board shall consider taking a more severe disciplinary action, including revocation of the person's license, than the disciplinary action that would be taken for a person who has not previously been the subject of disciplinary action by the board.

✔Sec. 301.4535 - REQUIRED SUSPENSION, REVOCATION, OR REFUSAL OF LICENSE FOR CERTAIN OFFENSES.

(a) The board shall suspend a nurse's license or refuse to issue a license to an applicant on proof that the nurse or applicant has been initially convicted of:

(1) murder under Section 19.02, Penal Code, capital murder under Section 19.03, Penal Code, or manslaughter under Section 19.04, Penal Code;

(2) kidnapping or unlawful restraint under Chapter 20, Penal Code, and the offense was punished as a felony or state jail felony;

(3) sexual assault under Section 22.011, Penal Code;

(4) aggravated sexual assault under Section 22.021, Penal Code;

(5) continuous sexual abuse of young child or children under Section 21.02, Penal Code, or indecency with a child under Section 21.11, Penal Code;;

(6) aggravated assault under Section 22.02, Penal Code;

(7) intentionally, knowingly, or recklessly injuring a child, elderly individual, or disabled individual under Section 22.04, Penal Code;

(8) intentionally, knowingly, or recklessly abandoning or endangering a child under Section 22.041, Penal Code;

(9) aiding suicide under Section 22.08, Penal Code, and the offense was punished as a state jail felony;

(10) an offense involving a violation of certain court orders or conditions of bond under Section 25.07, 25.071, or 25.072, Penal Code, punished as a felony;

(11) an agreement to abduct a child from custody under Section 25.031, Penal Code;

(12) the sale or purchase of a child under Section 25.08, Penal Code;

(13) robbery under Section 29.02, Penal Code;

(14) aggravated robbery under Section 29.03, Penal Code;

(15) an offense for which a defendant is required to register as a sex offender under Chapter 62, Code of Criminal Procedure; or

(16) an offense under the law of another state, federal law, or the Uniform Code of Military Justice that contains elements that are substantially similar to the elements of an offense listed in this subsection.

(a-1) An applicant or nurse who is refused an initial license or renewal of a license or whose license is suspended under Subsection (a) is not eligible for a probationary, stipulated, or otherwise encumbered license unless the board establishes by rule criteria that would permit the issuance or renewal of the license.

(b) On final conviction or a plea of guilty or nolo contendere for an offense listed in Subsection (a), the board, as appropriate, may not issue a license to an applicant, shall refuse to renew a license, or shall revoke a license.

(c) A person is not eligible for an initial license or for reinstatement or endorsement of a license to practice nursing in this state before the fifth anniversary of the date the person successfully completed and was dismissed from community supervision or parole for an offense described by Subsection (a).

✔Sec. 301.454. NOTICE AND HEARING. (a) Except in the case of a temporary suspension authorized under Section 301.455 or 301.4551 or an action taken in accordance with

This section makes the criminal offenses listed a bar to licensure as a nurse - both initial licensure and renewal. Other offenses would fall within the BON's current discretionary authority to take action against a nurse's license for criminal offenses. But with respect to the offenses listed in this section, the BON has no discretion. The offenses listed are serious offenses and ones in which it is hard to imagine what extenuating circumstances might justify the person becoming or remaining a nurse. However, mandatory revocation may still lead to what appear to be unfair results in specific situations. See annotations to Subdivisions (7) and (8) below.

Subdivisions (7) and (8) requiring loss of license for conviction of injuring or endangering a child can produce what appear to be unfair results in a particular situation. This is because some prosecutors have become much more aggressive in prosecuting parents who leave their child in a hot car, fail to know their child has wandered off, or drive while intoxicated with their child in the car. These cases often allege recklessly injuring or endangering a child. If the case results in a conviction or a guilty plea and the parent is a nurse, the BON will have no choice but to revoke her or his nursing license.

Felony offenses under Secs. 25.07, 25.071 and 25.072 involve multiple or serious violations of 1) protective court orders in domestic disputes or domestic violence situations (Sec. 25.07), 2) bias or prejudice ("hate crimes") (Sec. 25.071), or 3) family violence (Sec. 25.072).

The offenses requiring registration as a sex offender are quite broad.

A restricted license may be issued only if the BON adopts rules establishing criteria for doing so.

Crimes in which the nurse received deferred adjudications would also bar licensure.

The person is not eligible for licensure until 5 years after completion of probation. Since probation may be 5 or even 10 years for the types of crime covered by this section, the length of time before the person is eligible for re-licensure raises questions about the person's ability to maintain competency.

An applicant denied licensure or an RN or LVN subject to disciplinary action is entitled to notice and a hearing. The procedures for such hearings are set out in BON Rule §213.1 et seq.

an agreement between the board and a license holder, the board may not take any disciplinary action relating to a license unless:

(1) the board has served notice to the license holder of the facts or conduct alleged to warrant the intended action; and

(2) the license holder has been given an opportunity, in writing or through an informal meeting, to show compliance with all requirements of law for the retention of the license.

(b) If an informal meeting is held, a board member, staff member, or board representative who attends the meeting is considered to have participated in the hearing of the case for the purposes of ex parte communications under Section 2001.061, Government Code.

(c) A person is entitled to a hearing conducted by the State Office of Administrative Hearings if the board proposes to:

(1) refuse to admit the person to examination;

(2) refuse to issue a license or temporary permit;

(3) refuse to renew a license; or

(4) suspend or revoke the person's license or permit.

(d) The State Office of Administrative Hearings shall use the schedule of sanctions adopted by the board for any sanction imposed as the result of a hearing conducted by that office.

(e) Notwithstanding Subsection (a), a person is not entitled to a hearing on a refusal to renew a license if the person:

(1) fails to submit a renewal application; or

(2) submits an application that:

(A) is incomplete;

(B) shows on its face that the person does not meet the renewal requirements; or

(C) is not accompanied by the correct fee.

✔Sec. 301.455. TEMPORARY LICENSE SUSPENSION OR RESTRICTION. (a) The license of a nurse shall be temporarily suspended or restricted on a determination by a majority of the board or a three-member committee of board members designated by the board that, from the evidence or information presented, the continued practice of the nurse would constitute a continuing and imminent threat to the public welfare.

(b) A license may be temporarily suspended or restricted under this section without notice or hearing on the complaint if:

(1) institution of proceedings for a hearing before the State Office of Administrative Hearings is initiated simultaneously with the temporary suspension or determination to restrict; and

(2) a hearing is held as soon as possible under this chapter and Chapter 2001, Government Code.

(c) The State Office of Administrative Hearings shall hold a preliminary hearing not later than the 17th day after the date of the temporary suspension or restriction to determine whether probable cause exists that a continuing and imminent threat to the public welfare exists. The probable cause hearing shall be conducted as a de novo hearing.

(d) A final hearing on the matter shall be held not later than the 61st day after the date of the temporary suspension or restriction.

301.4551. TEMPORARY LICENSE SUSPENSION FOR DRUG OR ALCOHOL USE. (a) The board shall temporarily suspend the license of a nurse as provided by Section 301.455 if the nurse is under a board order prohibiting the use of alcohol or a drug or requiring the nurse to participate in a peer assistance program, and the nurse:

Additional information can also be found on the BON website under "Disciplinary Action."

Notice is considered to be given if mailed to the address that the nurse has on file with the BON. It is important that the nurse notify the board of any change of address as required by Rule 217.7.

A nurse does have a right to a formal hearing before an administrative law judge at the State Office of Administrative Hearings. See NPA Sec. 301.459 and Rule 213.22.

The administrative law judge must use the BON's schedule of sanctions.

The BON can refuse to renew a license without a hearing when the nurse fails to submit an application that meets the requirements for renewal or a completed application shows the nurse does not meet those requirements. An example of the latter would be an application showing insufficient continuing education hours.

The BON can immediately suspend or restrict the license of an RN or LVN whose continuing practice poses an immediate threat to the public. Immediate suspension is an extraordinary penalty since the nurse is removed from practice prior to a hearing. It is intended to be used only when the nurse's continuing to practice is an immediate threat to patient safety. A similar provision can be found in other health professional licensing acts. The BON's authority to impose restrictions on the nurse's practice gives the BON flexibility to protect the public without necessarily suspending the nurse's license.

If a nurse is under a board order to participate in peer assistance or not to use drugs, the BON may immediately suspend a nurse's license for a positive drug screen, refusal to be tested or failure to participate in peer assistance. This section makes action taken by BON consistent with the requirements of the Texas Peer Assistance Program for Nurses (TPAPN). Otherwise, a

(1) tests positive for alcohol or a prohibited drug;

(2) refuses to comply with a board order to submit to a drug or alcohol test; or

(3) fails to participate in the peer assistance program and the program issues a letter of dismissal and referral to the board for noncompliance.

(b) For the purposes of Section 301.455(c), proof of the elements required for the board to suspend a license under this section is proof that probable cause of a continuing and imminent threat to the public welfare exists.

Sec. 301.456. EVIDENCE. A certified copy of the order of the denial, suspension, or revocation or other action under Section 301.452(b)(8) is conclusive evidence of that action.

✔Sec. 301.457. COMPLAINT AND INVESTIGATION.

(a) The board or any person may initiate a proceeding under this subchapter by filing with the board a complaint against a nurse. The complaint must be in writing and signed by the complainant.

(b) Except as otherwise provided by this section, the board or a person authorized by the board shall conduct each investigation. Each complaint against a nurse that requires a determination of nursing competency shall be reviewed by a board member, consultant, or employee with a nursing background the board considers sufficient.

(c) On the filing of a complaint, the board:

(1) may conduct a preliminary investigation into the identity of the nurse named or described in the complaint;

(2) shall make a timely and appropriate preliminary investigation of the complaint; and

(3) may issue a warning or reprimand to the nurse.

(d) After any preliminary investigation to determine the identity of the subject of the complaint, unless it would jeopardize an investigation, the board shall notify the nurse that a complaint has been filed and the nature of the complaint. If the investigation reveals probable cause to take further disciplinary action, the board shall either attempt an informal disposition of the complaint or file a formal charge against the nurse stating the provision of this chapter or *situation can be created in which a nurse is dismissed from TPAPN, and is able to return to practice unmonitored during the period before the BON takes final action against the nurse.*

Sec. 301.452(b)(8) gives the BON the authority to take action against an RN's or LVN's license on the basis of action by another state.

The general process for filing, investigating and resolving complaints against nurses is set out below. The BON and nurse may settle the complaint by agreement at any point in the process as an agreed disposition under Sec. 301.463.

1. *complaint/report filed with BON*
2. *verification of nurse's identity*
3. *notification of nurse (Notice of Complaint)*
4. *initial investigation*
5. *either a) complaint dismissed or b) complaint settled or c) formal charges filed*

(Following occur only if not dismissed or settled; again can be settled at any point)

6. *additional investigation/discovery by both Board and nurse/nurse's attorney*
7. *hearing before administrative law judge*
8. *proposal for decision by administrative law judge*
9. *acceptance/modification of administrative law judge's proposal for decision*
10. *final order by BON*
11. *nurse accepts order or appeals Board order to courts*

The BON has adopted extensive rules governing the complaint process. See Rule §213. It also has guidelines for the nurse available on its website at www.bon.texas.gov.

Most complaints will be reports mandated under the mandatory reporting provisions of Subchapter I. However, complaints can come from other sources such as patients, their family, other practitioners, or the BON itself can initiate a complaint. Complaints must be in writing and signed.

A complaint involving professional competency must be reviewed by a nurse.

Since there are over 300,000 nurses licensed in Texas, the possibility of mistaken identity exists whenever a complaint or report is made to the Board. This section authorizes the BON to conduct a preliminary investigation to verify the nurse's identity before notifying the nurse that a complaint or report has been made against the nurse.

Once the BON has verified the identity of the nurse against whom the complaint was filed, it must notify the nurse of the complaint. This is referred to as a "Notice of Complaint." The only exception is if doing so would jeopardize the investigation.

board rule that is alleged to have been violated and a brief description of each act or omission that constitutes the violation.

(e) The board shall conduct an investigation of the complaint to determine:

(1) whether the nurse's continued practice of nursing poses a risk of harm to clients or other persons; and

(2) whether probable cause exists that a nurse committed an act listed in Section 301.452(b) or that violates other law.

(f) In making a determination under Subsection (e), the board shall review the evidence to determine the extent to which a deficiency in care by the registered nurse was the result of deficiencies in the registered nurse's judgment, knowledge, training, or skill rather than other factors beyond the nurse's control. A determination that a deficiency in care is attributable to a registered nurse must be based on the extent to which the registered nurse's conduct was the result of a deficiency in the registered nurse's judgment, knowledge, training, or skill.

(g) If the board determines after investigating a complaint under Subsection (e) that there is reason to believe that a nurse's deficiency in care was the result of a factor beyond the nurse's control, the board shall report that determination to the patient safety committee at the facility where the nurse's deficiency in care occurred, or if the facility does not have a patient safety committee, to the chief nursing officer.

Sec. 301.458. INITIATION OF FORMAL CHARGES; DISCOVERY. (a) Unless there is an agreed disposition of the complaint under Section 301.463, if probable cause is found under Section 301.457(e)(2), the board or the board's authorized representative shall file formal charges against the nurse.

(b) A formal charge must:

(1) be written;

(2) be specific enough to enable a person of common understanding to know what is meant by the formal charge; and

(3) contain a degree of certainty that gives the person who is the subject of the formal charge notice of each particular act alleged to violate a specific statute, board rule, or board order.

(c) A copy of the formal charge shall be served on the nurse or the nurse's counsel of record.

(d) The board shall adopt reasonable rules to promote discovery by each party to a contested case.

Sec. 301.459. FORMAL HEARING. (a) The board by rule shall adopt procedures under Chapter 2001, Government Code, governing formal disposition of a contested case. The State Office of Administrative Hearings shall conduct a formal hearing.

(b) In any hearing under this section, a nurse is entitled to appear in person or by counsel.

This Subsec. (f) requires the BON to consider the role of systems errors in investigating a nurse. Section 303.011 of the Nursing Peer Review Law imposes a similar requirement on nursing peer review committees. See Part IV (Nursing Peer Review) of this Guide. The intent of this subsection and Sec. 303.011 is to protect individual nurses from being held unjustifiably accountable for errors resulting from system inadequacies.

This Subsec. (g) is designed to help ensure that whenever a situation is identified in which a nursing error resulted from external factors that committees or individuals responsible for addressing those factors are notified. Otherwise, other nurses may be placed in a similar situation in which the lack of adequate systems makes the error more likely to reoccur.

Formal charges are filed only if the initial investigation shows probable cause that the nurse has violated the NPA or BON rules. The filing of formal charges can be considered as analogous to an indictment after a grand jury investigation. That is, the filing of formal charges doesn't mean that the nurse violated the NPA or BON rules. Rather, it means that the initial investigation justifies continuing the proceedings against the nurse, i.e., dismissal of the complaint is not justified.

Since formal charges indicate that there is probable cause to believe action against the RN's or LVN's license is justified, the RN or LVN has a right to know precisely what conduct he or she is alleged to have engaged in and what provisions of the NPA or BON rules that conduct violates. Only then can the nurse adequately prepare a defense.

The Board has adopted extensive rules governing administrative hearings. See Rule §213. The Administrative Procedures Act governs hearings before a state agency. Its purpose is to insure that cases are conducted fairly for all parties.

Administrative law judges are attorneys with special training in the hearing of cases before administrative agencies. Their role is very similar to a judge in a nonjury lawsuit. They will hear the evidence presented by both the BON and nurse's attorneys and then make a proposal for decision that will include findings of fact, conclusions of law and the recommended sanction. Basically, this means they will find what conduct the nurse engaged in, state if that conduct violates a provision of the NPA or BON rules and indicate what sanction they believe is appropriate. The proposal for decision goes to the BON which has authority under Sec. 2001.58 of the Government Code to change the findings of fact and conclusions of law only if it determines that 1) the administrative law judge (ALJ) did not properly apply or interpret applicable law, BON rules or policies, or prior administrative decisions, 2) a prior administrative decision on which the ALJ relied is incorrect or should be changed, or 3) a technical error in a finding of fact should be changed. It must state in writing the specific reason and legal basis for the change. See Rule 213.23. The BON also retains the authority to select the sanction that will be imposed on the

Sec. 301.460. ACCESS TO INFORMATION. (a) Except for good cause shown for delay and subject to any other privilege or restriction set forth by statute, rule, or legal precedent, the board shall, not later than the 30th day after the date the board receives a written request from a license holder who is the subject of a formal charge filed under Section 301.458 or from the license holder's counsel of record, provide the license holder with access to:

(1) all known exculpatory information in the board's possession; and

(2) information in the board's possession that the board intends to offer into evidence in presenting its case in chief at the contested hearing on the complaint.

(b) The board is not required to provide:

(1) board investigative reports or investigative memoranda;

(2) the identity of nontestifying complainants;

(3) attorney-client communications;

(4) attorney work product; or

(5) other materials covered by a privilege as recognized by the Texas Rules of Civil Procedure or the Texas Rules of Evidence.

(c) The provision of information under Subsection (a) does not constitute a waiver of privilege or confidentiality under this chapter or other applicable law.

Sec. 301.461. ASSESSMENT OF COSTS. The board may assess a person who is found to have violated this chapter the administrative costs of conducting a hearing to determine the violation.

Sec. 301.462. VOLUNTARY SURRENDER OF LICENSE. The board may revoke a nurse's license without formal charges, notice, or opportunity of hearing if the nurse voluntarily surrenders the nurse's license to the board and executes a sworn statement that the nurse does not desire to be licensed.

Sec. 301.463. AGREED DISPOSITION. (a) Unless precluded by this chapter or other law, the board may dispose of a complaint by:

(1) stipulation;

(2) agreed settlement;

(3) agreed order; or

(4) dismissal.

(b) An agreed disposition of a complaint is considered to be a disciplinary order for purposes of reporting under this chapter and an administrative hearing and proceeding by a state or federal regulatory agency regarding the practice of nursing..

(c) An agreed order is a public record.

(d) In civil or criminal litigation an agreed disposition is a settlement agreement under Rule 408, Texas Rules of Evidence.

Sec. 301.464. INFORMAL PROCEEDINGS. (a) The board by rule shall adopt procedures governing:

(1) informal disposition of a contested case under Section 2001.056, Government Code; and

nurse which may be the same or different from that recommended by the administrative law judge.

This section is designed to promote full disclosure of evidence so that the nurse can adequately prepare a defense. As indicated above, the purpose of a hearing is to get at the truth about what happened, not to spring surprises on either party.

Subsec. (b) imposes limitations on the information or evidence the Board must disclose.

This provision concerning not disclosing the complainant's identity is similar to the prohibition in Sec. 301.417 against disclosing the identity of a person reporting an RN or LVN to the BON. Disclosing the complainant's identity may have a chilling effect on filing a complaint. If the complainant (or person reporting the nurse) also testifies against the nurse, then his or her identity, as a witness, is disclosed. If a complainant also testifies, his or her identity must be disclosed at that time but not that was the person who filed complaint.

Many feel that if a nurse, in good faith, pursues her or his right to a hearing, then the costs of the disciplinary hearing should be paid through licensing fees and not imposed on the individual nurse. Otherwise, the nurse may be "discouraged" from exercising her or his right to due process.

Agreed deposition is an option at any point in the process.

An agreed disposition is still a disciplinary action.

The Rule 408 referred to precludes use of a settlement agreement to prove liability. This Sec. (b) would prevent an agreed disposition from being used against a nurse in a professional liability suit based on the same conduct. That is, a nurse can "agree" to a settlement without fear of its being used as evidence of negligence in a liability suit. The client is not precluded from suing the nurse for negligence - just from using the settlement to prove negligence.

Section 2001.056 authorizes agencies to dispose of cases informally by stipulation, agreed settlement, consent order, or default.

(2) an informal proceeding held in compliance with Section 2001.054, Government Code.

(b) Rules adopted under this section must:

(1) provide the complainant and the license holder an opportunity to be heard; and

(2) require the presence of a representative of the board's legal staff or of the attorney general to advise the board or the board's employees.

Sec. 301.465. SUBPOENAS; REQUEST FOR INFORMATION. (a) Notwithstanding Section 2001.089, Government Code, the board may request issuance of a subpoena to be served in any manner authorized by law, including personal service by a board investigator or by certified mail.

(b) Each person shall respond promptly and fully to a request for information by the board or to a subpoena issued by the board. A request or subpoena may not be refused, denied, or resisted unless the request or subpoena calls for information within the attorney-client privilege. No other privilege applies to a board proceeding.

(c) The board may pay a reasonable fee for photocopies subpoenaed at the board's request. The amount paid may not exceed the amount the board charges for copies of its records.

(d) The board shall protect, to the extent possible, the identity of each patient named in information received by the board.

Sec. 301.466. CONFIDENTIALITY. (a) A complaint and investigation concerning a nurse under this subchapter, all information and material compiled by the board in connection with the complaint and investigation, and the information described by Subsection (d) are:

(1) confidential and not subject to disclosure under Chapter 552, Government Code; and

(2) not subject to disclosure, discovery, subpoena, or other means of legal compulsion for release to anyone other than the board or a board employee or agent involved in license holder discipline.

(b) Notwithstanding Subsection (a), information regarding a complaint and an investigation may be disclosed to:

(1) a person involved with the board in a disciplinary action against the nurse;

(2) a nursing licensing or disciplinary board in another jurisdiction;

(3) a peer assistance program approved by the board under Chapter 467, Health and Safety Code;

(4) a law enforcement agency; or

(5) a person engaged in bona fide research, if all information identifying a specific individual has been deleted.

(c) The filing of formal charges against a nurse by the board, the nature of those charges, disciplinary proceedings of the board, and final disciplinary actions, including warnings and reprimands, by the board are not confidential and are subject to disclosure in accordance with Chapter 552, Government Code.

(d) Notwithstanding Subsection (c), if the board orders a nurse to participate in a peer assistance program approved by the board under Section 467.003, Health and Safety Code, the complaint, filing of formal charges, nature of those charges, final board order, and disciplinary proceedings are subject to disclosure:

(1) only to the same extent as information regarding a complaint is subject to disclosure under Subsection (b); or

(2) in a subsequent matter relating to the board order or a subsequent violation of this chapter or a board rule.

Section 2001.054 addresses actions against a license and requires that a licensee be notified of the conduct alleged to justify the proposed action and be given an opportunity to show compliance with the licensing law. These requirements are very similar to those set out in Sec. 301.454 relating to rights of nurses against whom a complaint is filed.

The BON has broad subpoena powers and the only basis for refusing a subpoena is the attorney-client privilege.

Complaints are confidential. The purpose is to protect the nurse until the BON has conducted its initial investigation to determine if there is probable cause to believe a violation of the NPA has occurred. However, if formal charges are filed, they are not confidential. See Subsection (c). The complaint itself may be disclosed for certain purposes. See Subsec. (b).

Once formal charges are filed, those charges are not confidential.

Orders sending nurses to an approved peer assistance program are confidential.

Sec. 301.467. REINSTATEMENT. (a) On application, the board may reinstate a license to practice professional nursing or vocational nursing to a person whose license has been revoked, suspended, or surrendered.

(b) An application to reinstate a revoked license:

(1) may not be made before the first anniversary of the date of the revocation; and

(2) must be made in the manner and form the board requires.

(c) If the board denies an application for reinstatement, it may set a reasonable waiting period before the applicant may reapply for reinstatement.

Sec. 301.468. PROBATION. (a) The board may determine that an order denying a license application or suspending a license be probated. A person subject to a probation order shall conform to each condition the board sets as the terms of probation, including a condition:

(1) limiting the practice of the person to, or excluding, one or more specified activities of professional nursing or vocational nursing; or

(2) requiring the person to submit to supervision, care, counseling, or treatment by a practitioner designated by the board.

(3) requiring the person to submit to random drug or alcohol tests in the manner prescribed by the board.

(b) At the time the probation is granted, the board shall establish the term of the probationary period.

(c) At any time while the person remains subject to the probation order, the board may hold a hearing and rescind the probation and enforce the board's original action in denying or suspending the license. The hearing shall be called by the presiding officer of the board, who shall issue a notice to be served on the person or the person's counsel not later than the 20th day before the date scheduled for the hearing that:

(1) sets the time and place for the hearing; and

(2) contains the charges or complaints against the probationer.

(d) Notice under Subsection (c) is sufficient if sent by registered or certified mail to the affected person at the person's most recent address as shown in the board's records.

(e) A hearing under this section is limited to a determination of whether the person violated the terms of the probation order under Subsection (a) and whether the board should:

(1) continue, rescind, or modify the terms of probation, including imposing an administrative penalty; or

(2) enter an order denying, suspending, or revoking the person's license.

(f) If one of the conditions of probation is the prohibition of using alcohol or a drug or participation in a peer assistance program, violation of that condition is established by:

(1) a positive drug or alcohol test result;

(2) refusal to submit to a drug or alcohol test as required by the board; or

(3) a letter of noncompliance from the peer assistance program.

Sec. 301.469. NOTICE OF FINAL ACTION. If the board takes a final disciplinary action, including a warning or reprimand, against a nurse under this subchapter, the board shall immediately send a copy of the board's final order to the nurse and to the last known employer of the nurse.

Sec. 301.470. REFUND. (a) Subject to Subsection (b), the board may order a license holder to pay a refund to a consumer as provided in an agreement resulting from an informal settlement conference instead of or in addition to imposing an administrative penalty under this chapter.

(b) The amount of a refund ordered as provided in an agreement resulting from an informal settlement conference may not exceed the amount the consumer paid to a nurse for a

The BON may reinstate a license after 1 year.

The BON has a right to probate any of its decisions. The Board will usually impose certain conditions that the nurse must comply with as a condition of probation. The Board has considerable discretion in what conditions it imposes. If the nurse does not meet these conditions, the BON can revoke the probation under Subsec. (c). See Rule 213.24.

The BON may revoke probation. A probation revocation hearing is required. See Rule 213.24.

This Subsec. (e) clarifies that a revocation of probation hearing is limited to a determination of the issue of whether the condition of probation has been violated. The original charges against the nurse are not subject to being re-litigated in a probation revocation hearing.

If a condition of probation that is alleged to have been violated involves not using drugs or participating in peer assistance, then the BON may prove that allegation as set out in this section.

Both the nurse and employer are notified of final actions against the nurse's license.

A refund to a patient is likely to be applicable only to APRNs and other nurses that directly bill patients.

service regulated by this chapter or the actual amount stolen or defrauded from a patient by the nurse. The board may not require payment of other damages or estimate harm in a refund order.

Sec. 301.471. EMERGENCY CEASE AND DESIST ORDER. (a) If it appears to the board that a person who is not licensed under this chapter is violating this chapter, a rule adopted under this chapter, or another state statute or rule relating to the practice of professional nursing or vocational nursing and the board determines that the unauthorized activity constitutes a clear, imminent, or continuing threat to the public health and safety, the board may:

(1) issue an emergency cease and desist order prohibiting the person from engaging in the activity; and

(2) report the activity to a local law enforcement agency or the attorney general for prosecution.

(b) An order issued under Subsection (a) must:

(1) be delivered on issuance to the person affected by the order by personal delivery or registered or certified mail, return receipt requested, to the person's last known address;

(2) state the acts or practices alleged to be an unauthorized activity and require the person immediately to cease and desist from the unauthorized activity; and

(3) contain a notice that a request for hearing may be filed under this section.

(c) Unless the person against whom the emergency cease and desist order is directed requests a board hearing in writing before the 11th day after the date it is served on the person, the order is final and nonappealable as to that person. A request for a board hearing must:

(1) be in writing and directed to the board; and

(2) state the grounds for the request to set aside or modify the order.

(d) On receiving a request for a hearing, the board shall serve notice of the time and place of the hearing by personal delivery or registered or certified mail, return receipt requested. The hearing must be held not later than the 10th day after the date the board receives the request for a hearing unless the parties agree to a later hearing date. A hearing under this subsection is subject to Chapter 2001, Government Code.

(e) After the hearing, the board shall affirm, modify, or set aside wholly or partly the emergency cease and desist order. An order affirming or modifying the emergency cease and desist order is immediately final for purposes of enforcement and appeal.

(f) An order under this section continues in effect unless the order is stayed by the board. The board may impose any condition before granting a stay of the order.

(g) The board may release to the public a final cease and desist order issued under this section or information regarding the existence of the order if the board determines that the release would enhance the effective enforcement of the order or will serve the public interest.

(h) A violation of an order issued under this section constitutes grounds for imposing an administrative penalty under this chapter.

SUBCHAPTER K.
ADMINISTRATIVE PENALTY

Cease and desist orders permit the BON to prevent the unauthorized practice of nursing by unlicensed persons.

An administrative penalty is normally used in situations in which the RN's or LVN's conduct is not practice-related and action against the nurse's license would not be the appropriate sanction. An example might be failure to notify the board of a change in address. See also Sec. 301.651 (Corrective Action) and Sec. 301.1607 (Deferred Disciplinary Action Pilot).

Sec. 301.507. OPTIONS FOLLOWING DECISION: PAY OR APPEAL
Sec. 301.508. COLLECTION OF PENALTY
Sec. 301.509. DETERMINATION BY COURT
Sec. 301.510. REMITTANCE OF PENALTY AND INTEREST
Sec. 301.511. ADMINISTRATIVE PROCEDURE

Sec. 301.501. IMPOSITION OF PENALTY. The board may impose an administrative penalty on a person licensed or regulated under this chapter who violates this chapter or a rule or order adopted under this chapter.

Sec. 301.502. AMOUNT OF PENALTY. (a) The amount of the administrative penalty may not exceed $5,000 for each violation. Each day a violation continues or occurs is a separate violation for purposes of imposing a penalty.

(b) The amount of the penalty shall be based on:

(1) the seriousness of the violation, including:

(A) the nature, circumstances, extent, and gravity of any prohibited acts; and

(B) the hazard or potential hazard created to the health, safety, or economic welfare of the public;

(2) the economic harm to property or the environment caused by the violation;

(3) the history of previous violations;

(4) the amount necessary to deter a future violation;

(5) efforts made to correct the violation; and

(6) any other matter that justice may require.

Sec. 301.503. REPORT AND NOTICE OF VIOLATION AND PENALTY. (a) If the executive director determines that a violation has occurred, the executive director may issue to the board a report stating:

(1) the facts on which the determination is based; and

(2) the director's recommendation on the imposition of the administrative penalty, including a recommendation on the amount of the penalty.

(b) Not later than the 14th day after the date the report is issued, the executive director shall give written notice of the report to the person on whom the penalty may be imposed. The notice may be given by certified mail. The notice must:

(1) include a brief summary of the alleged violation;

(2) state the amount of the recommended penalty; and

(3) inform the person of the person's right to a hearing on the occurrence of the violation, the amount of the penalty, or both.

Sec. 301.504. PENALTY TO BE PAID OR HEARING REQUESTED. (a) Not later than the 20th day after the date the person receives the notice, the person may:

(1) accept the executive director's determination and recommended administrative penalty in writing; or

(2) make a written request for a hearing on the occurrence of the violation, the amount of the penalty, or both.

(b) If the person accepts the executive director's determination and recommended penalty, the board by order shall approve the determination and impose the recommended penalty.

Sec. 301.505. HEARING. (a) If the person requests a hearing or fails to respond in a timely manner to the notice, the executive director shall set a hearing and give notice of the hearing to the person.

(b) An administrative law judge of the State Office of Administrative Hearings shall hold the hearing.

(c) The administrative law judge shall make findings of fact and conclusions of law and promptly issue to the board a proposal for decision as to the occurrence of the violation and the amount of any proposed administrative penalty.

Sec. 301.506. DECISION BY BOARD. (a) Based on the findings of fact, conclusions of law, and proposal for decision, the board by order may:

(1) find that a violation occurred and impose an administrative penalty; or

(2) find that a violation did not occur.

(b) The notice of the board's order given to the person under Chapter 2001, Government Code, must include a statement of the right of the person to judicial review of the order.

Sec. 301.507. OPTIONS FOLLOWING DECISION: PAY OR APPEAL. (a) Not later than the 30th day after the date the board's order becomes final, the person shall:

(1) pay the administrative penalty;

(2)pay the penalty and file a petition for judicial review contesting the occurrence of the violation, the amount of the penalty, or both; or

(3) without paying the penalty, file a petition for judicial review contesting the occurrence of the violation, the amount of the penalty, or both.

(b) Within the 30-day period, a person who acts under Subsection (a)(3) may:

(1) stay enforcement of the penalty by:

(A) paying the penalty to the court for placement in an escrow account; or

(B) giving to the court a supersedeas bond that is approved by the court and that:

(I) is for the amount of the penalty; and

(ii) is effective until judicial review of the board's order is final; or

(2) request the court to stay enforcement of the penalty by:

(A) filing with the court a sworn affidavit of the person stating that the person is financially unable to pay the penalty and is financially unable to give the supersedeas bond; and

(B) giving a copy of the affidavit to the executive director by certified mail.

(c) If the executive director receives a copy of an affidavit under Subsection (b)(2), the executive director may file with the court a contest to the affidavit not later than the fifth day after the date the copy is received.

(d) The court shall hold a hearing on the facts alleged in the affidavit as soon as practicable and shall stay the enforcement of the penalty on finding that the alleged facts are true. The person who files an affidavit has the burden of proving that the person is financially unable to pay the penalty and to give a supersedeas bond.

Sec. 301.508. COLLECTION OF PENALTY. If the person does not pay the penalty and the enforcement of the penalty is not stayed, the executive director may refer the matter to the attorney general for collection of the penalty.

Sec. 301.509. DETERMINATION BY COURT. (a) If a court sustains the determination that a violation occurred, the court may uphold or reduce the amount of the administrative penalty and order the person to pay the full or reduced penalty.

(b) If the court does not sustain the determination that a violation occurred, the court shall order that a penalty is not owed.

Sec. 301.510. REMITTANCE OF PENALTY AND INTEREST. (a) If after judicial review, the administrative penalty is reduced or not imposed by the court, the court shall, after the

A supersedeas bond means filing a bond with the court in order to "suspend" the board's order while it is being appealed. Such a bond can usually be purchased from certain insurance companies.

judgment becomes final:

(1) order that the appropriate amount, plus accrued interest, be remitted to the person if the person paid the penalty; or

(2) order the release of the bond in full if the penalty is not imposed or order the release of the bond after the person pays the penalty imposed if the person posted a supersedeas bond.

(b) The interest paid under Subsection (a)(1) is the rate charged on loans to depository institutions by the New York Federal Reserve Bank. The interest shall be paid for the period beginning on the date the penalty is paid and ending on the date the penalty is remitted.

Sec. 301.511. ADMINISTRATIVE PROCEDURE. A proceeding under this subchapter is subject to Chapter 2001, Government Code.

SUBCHAPTER L.
OTHER PENALTIES AND ENFORCEMENT PROVISIONS

Sec. 301.551. INJUNCTION. (a) In addition to any other action authorized by law, the board may institute an action in its name to enjoin a violation of this chapter or a board rule.

(b) To obtain an injunction under this section, it is not necessary to allege or prove that:

(1) an adequate remedy at law does not exist; or

(2) substantial or irreparable damage would result from the continued violation.

(c) Notwithstanding Subsection (b), in a proceeding for an injunction under Subsection (a), the defendant may assert and prove as a complete defense to the action that the board's actions or proceedings were:

(1) arbitrary or capricious;

(2) contrary to legal requirements; or

(3) conducted without due process of law.

(d) Either party to an action under Subsection (a) may appeal. The board is not required to give an appeal bond in a cause arising under this section.

Sec. 301.552. MONITORING OF LICENSE HOLDER. The board by rule shall develop a system for monitoring the compliance of license holders with the requirements of this chapter. Rules adopted under this section must include procedures to:

(1) monitor for compliance a license holder who is ordered by the board to perform certain acts; and

(2) identify and monitor each license holder who represents a risk to the public.

Sec. 301.553. CIVIL PENALTY. (a) A person who violates Section 301.451 or Section 301.251 is liable to the state for a civil penalty not to exceed $1,000 a day.

(b) The civil penalty may be collected in a suit initiated by the board.

This Subchapter addresses miscellaneous provisions relating to enforcement of the NPA.

An injunction is a court order directing an individual to refrain from some action. The BON would normally be requesting a court to order someone to refrain from engaging in the unauthorized practice of professional nursing.

The legal system considers an injunction to be an "extraordinary remedy" and normally not available unless it can be shown that no other remedy (e.g., monetary damages) would correct the alleged harm or that irreparable damage would occur if the injunction were not granted. The board is relieved from having to show these two things since no other relief is likely to protect the public from the unauthorized practice of professional nursing, and it is presumed that the public is harmed by such unauthorized practice.

Sec. 301.471 gives the BON cease and desist authority to permit the Board to stop immediately the unauthorized practice of nursing by unlicensed persons.

The BON is the agency primarily responsible for enforcing the NPA. Ensuring compliance by nurses is one of its main roles.

The practices prohibited by NPA Secs. 301.251 and 301.451 include practicing without a license, practicing with a fraudulently obtained or unlawfully obtained license or suspended or revoked license.

Sec. 301.554. CRIMINAL PENALTY. (a) A person commits an offense if the person violates Section 301.451 or Section 301.251.

(b) An offense under Subsection (a) is a Class A misdemeanor, except that if it is shown on the trial of the offense that the defendant has been previously convicted under Subsection (a), the offense is a felony of the third degree.

(c) Each day of violation constitutes a separate offense.

(d) On final conviction of an offense under Subsection (a), the defendant forfeits all rights and privileges conferred by a license issued under this chapter.

Sec. 301.555. APPEAL. (a) A person against whom the board has taken adverse action under this chapter may appeal to a district court in the county of the person's residence or in Travis County.

(b) The board's decision may not be enjoined or stayed except on application to the district court after notice to the board.

SUBCHAPTER M.
ANESTHESIA IN OUTPATIENT SETTING

Sec. 301.601. DEFINITION. In this subchapter, "outpatient setting" means a facility, clinic, center, office, or other setting that is not part of a licensed hospital or a licensed ambulatory surgical center.

Sec. 301.602. RULES. (a) The board by rule shall establish minimum standards for anesthesia services provided in an outpatient setting by a person licensed by the board.

(b) The rules adopted under this section must be designed to protect the health, safety, and welfare of the public and include requirements relating to:

(1) general anesthesia, regional anesthesia, and monitored anesthesia care;

(2) patient assessment, counseling, and preparation;

(3) patient monitoring to be performed and equipment to be used during a procedure and during post-procedure monitoring;

(4) emergency procedures, drugs, and equipment, including education, training, and certification of personnel, as appropriate, and including protocols for transfers to a hospital;

(5) the documentation necessary to demonstrate compliance with this subchapter; and

(6) the period in which protocols or procedures covered by rules of the board shall be reviewed, updated, or amended.

(c) The board shall cooperate with the Texas Medical Board in adopting rules under this subchapter to eliminate, to the extent possible, conflicts between the rules adopted by each board.

Sec. 301.603. APPLICABILITY. Rules adopted by the board under Section 301.602 do not apply to:

The practices prohibited by NPA Secs. 301.251 and 301.451 include practicing without a license, practicing with a fraudulently obtained or unlawfully obtained license or suspended or revoked license.

The nurse may appeal an adverse finding to the court system. The standard of review is "substantial evidence." This means that the court will not rehear all the evidence and decide the case from scratch but rather will review the record of the administrative hearing and decide whether there was substantial evidence to support the board's decision. The court can disagree with the decision and it still will not overrule the board unless it finds a lack of substantial evidence to support that decision. As long as the board's decision is a "reasonable" decision based on the evidence, the court will uphold it.

This provision was added as a result of a case involving use of defective in-office anesthesia equipment that resulted in a child's death. Prior to the passage of this legislation (1999) in-office anesthesia was unregulated. A similar provision governing physicians was added to the Medical Practice Act. Both the BON and Texas Medical Board have adopted rules implementing the legislation. See BON Rule 221.16.

(1) an outpatient setting in which only local anesthesia, peripheral nerve blocks, or both are used;

(2) a licensed hospital, including an outpatient facility of the hospital that is located separate from the hospital;

(3) a licensed ambulatory surgical center;

(4) a clinic located on land recognized as tribal land by the federal government and maintained or operated by a federally recognized Indian tribe or tribal organization as listed by the United States secretary of the interior under 25 U.S.C. Section 479a-1 or as listed under a successor federal statute or regulation;

(5) a facility maintained or operated by a state or local governmental entity;

(6) a clinic directly maintained or operated by the United States; or

(7) an outpatient setting accredited by:

(A) the Joint Commission on Accreditation of Healthcare Organizations relating to ambulatory surgical centers;

(B) the American Association for the Accreditation of Ambulatory Surgery Facilities; or

(C) the Accreditation Association for Ambulatory Health Care.

Sec. 301.604. REGISTRATION REQUIRED. (a) The board shall require each certified registered nurse anesthetist who provides anesthesia services in an outpatient setting to register biennially by applying to the board on a form prescribed by the board and paying to the board a fee in an amount established by the board.

(b) The board shall coordinate the registration required under this section with the license renewal requirements of Subchapter G so that the times of registration, payment, notice, and imposition of penalties for late payment are similar and provide a minimal administrative burden for the board and certified registered nurse anesthetists.

Sec. 301.605. COMPLIANCE WITH RULES. (a) A certified registered nurse anesthetist providing anesthesia services in an outpatient setting shall comply with the rules adopted by the board under Section 301.602.

(b) The board may require a certified registered nurse anesthetist to submit and comply with a corrective action plan to remedy or address any current or potential deficiencies with the nurse anesthetist's provision of anesthesia in an outpatient setting in accordance with this chapter or board rule.

Sec. 301.606. INSPECTIONS. (a) The board may conduct inspections to enforce this subchapter, including inspections of the equipment owned or leased by a certified registered nurse anesthetist and of documents of a certified registered nurse anesthetist's practice that relate to providing anesthesia in an outpatient setting. The board may contract with another state agency or qualified person to conduct these inspections.

(b) Unless it would jeopardize an ongoing investigation, the board must provide notice at least five business days before the date of conducting an on-site inspection under this section.

(c) This section does not require the board to make an on-site inspection of an outpatient setting in which a certified registered nurse anesthetist provides anesthesia.

Sec. 301.607. REQUESTS FOR INSPECTION AND ADVISORY OPINIONS. (a) The board may consider a request by a certified registered nurse anesthetist for an inspection of equipment owned or leased by the nurse anesthetist and of documents of the nurse anesthetist's practice that relate to the provision of anesthesia in an outpatient setting. The board, on payment of a fee set by the board, may conduct the requested inspection and issue an advisory opinion.

(b) An advisory opinion issued by the board under this section is not binding on the board. Except as provided by Subsection (c), the board may take any action under this chapter relating to the situation addressed by the advisory opinion as the board considers appropriate.

(c) A certified registered nurse anesthetist who requests and relies on a board advisory opinion may use the opinion as mitigating evidence in an action or proceeding by the board to impose an administrative penalty or to assess a fine under this chapter. On receipt of proof of reliance on an advisory opinion, the board shall consider the reliance and mitigate imposition of an administrative penalty or assessment of a fine accordingly.

SUBCHAPTER N.
CORRECTIVE ACTION PROCEEDING AND DEFERRED ACTION

Sec. 301.651. DEFINITIONS. In this subchapter:

(1) "Corrective action" means a fine or remedial education imposed under Section 301.652.

(2) "Deferred action" means an action against a person licensed or regulated under this chapter that is deferred by the board as provided by this subchapter.

Sec. 301.652. IMPOSITION OF CORRECTIVE ACTION.

(a) The board may impose a corrective action on a person licensed or regulated under this chapter who violates this chapter or a rule or order adopted under this chapter. The corrective action:

(1) may be a fine, remedial education, or any combination of a fine or remedial education;

(2) is not a disciplinary action under Subchapter J; and

(3) is subject to disclosure only to the extent a complaint is subject to disclosure under Section 301.466.

(b) The board by rule shall adopt guidelines for the types of violations for which a corrective action may be imposed.

This Subchapter N was added in 2009 as part of an initiative by the Texas Nurses Association begun in the 2007 legislative session to create a regulatory environment for nurses that focuses more on system deficiencies and less on assigning individual blame to nurses for making a mistake. Promoting such a regulatory environment was one of the recommendations coming out of the Institute of Medicine's reports To Err Is Human and Keeping Patients Safe: Transforming the Work Environment of Nurses. The subchapter was amended in 2013 to include deferred actions for which the BON only had pilot authority to take prior to the 2013 legislation.

The subchapter gives the BON additional options to address minor violations. Prior to enactment of this subchapter, the BON's option in addressing a minor violation was either to dismiss the complaint (even though the violation had occurred) or take permanent, public disciplinary action against the nurse's license. This subchapter gives the BON two additional options – corrective action and deferred action. Corrective action is nondisciplinary and confidential. It is limited to violations involving only a fine or remedial education. Deferred actions are for violations more serious than those for which corrective action might be appropriate. Deferred actions can be used for any actions in which the BON proposes to take action other than reprimand or a denial, suspension, or revocation of a license. Deferred actions are public for a period of time but then can be dismissed and become confidential.

See BON Rule 213.32 governing corrective actions. BON Rule 213.34 governs deferred actions but will need to be revised to reflect that the BON's authority has been converted from pilot to permanent authority.

This section describes a corrective action. BON Rule 213.32 sets out the types of violations eligible for corrective action.

Corrective actions are not disciplinary action.
Corrective actions are confidential.

Sec. 301.653. REPORT AND NOTICE OF VIOLATION AND CORRECTIVE ACTION. If the executive director determines that a person has committed a violation for which a corrective action may be imposed under the guidelines adopted under Section 301.652(b), the executive director may give written notice of the determination and recommendation for corrective action to the person subject to the corrective action. The notice may be given by certified mail. The notice must:

(1) include a brief summary of the alleged violation;

(2) state the recommended corrective action; and

(3) inform the person of the person's options in responding to the notice.

Sec. 301.654. RESPONSE. Not later than the 20th day after the date the person receives the notice under Section 301.653, the person may:

(1) accept in writing the executive director's determination and recommended corrective action; or

(2) reject the executive director's determination and recommended corrective action.

Sec. 301.655. ACTION FOLLOWING RESPONSE. (a) If the person accepts the executive director's determination and satisfies the recommended corrective action, the case is closed.

(b) If the person does not accept the executive director's determination and recommended corrective action as originally proposed or as modified by the board or fails to respond in a timely manner to the executive director's notice as provided by Section 301.654, the executive director shall:

(1) terminate corrective action proceedings; and

(2) dispose of the matter as a complaint under Subchapter J.

Sec. 301.6555. DEFERRED ACTION. (a) For any action or complaint for which the board proposes to impose on a person a sanction other than a reprimand or a denial, suspension, or revocation of a license, the board may:

(1) defer the final action the board has proposed if the person conforms to conditions imposed by the board, including any condition the board could impose as a condition of probation under Section 301.468; and

(2) if the person successfully meets the imposed conditions, dismiss the complaint.

(b) Except as provided by this subsection, a deferred action by the board is not confidential and is subject to disclosure in accordance with Chapter 552, Government Code. If the person successfully meets the conditions imposed by the board in deferring final action and the board dismisses the action or complaint, the deferred action of the board is confidential to the same extent as a complaint is confidential under Section 301.466.

Sec. 301.656. REPORT TO BOARD. The executive director shall report periodically to the board on the corrective or deferred actions imposed under this subchapter, including:

(1) the number of actions imposed; and

(2) the types of violations for which actions were imposed.

Sec. 301.657. EFFECT ON ACCEPTANCE OF CORRECTIVE OR DEFERRED ACTION. (a) Except to the extent provided by this section, a person's acceptance of a corrective

Corrective action is initiated by the BON's executive director.

The nurse can reject the offer of corrective action.

If the nurse accepts the offer of corrective action and satisfies any requirements (e.g., pays the fine), the case is closed.

If the nurse refuses the offer of corrective action, the case is converted to a regular complaint and disposed of as a disciplinary matter. The reference to "the corrective action as originally proposed or as modified by the board" is language from the bill as filed which provided for the BON 's reviewing the proposed corrective action before it was sent to the nurse. That process was amended out of the bill and the amendment inadvertently failed to delete this reference.

This Sec. 301.6555 describes the characteristics of deferred actions. BON Rule 213.34 governs deferred actions but will need to be revised to reflect that the BON's authority has been converted from pilot to permanent authority by legislation passed in 2013.

The BON proposed action is deferred while the nurse fulfills certain "probation" conditions. The deferred action is public during this time.

If the nurse successfully completes the "probation," the compliant is dismissed and becomes confidential.

Deferred actions are public record until the period of probation is successfully completed.

The executive director periodically reports to the BON about corrective and deferred action cases.

Acceptance of a corrective or deferred action is not an admission of a violation..

or deferred action under this subchapter does not constitute an admission of a violation but does constitute a plea of nolo contendere.

(b) The board may treat a person's acceptance of corrective or deferred action as an admission of a violation if the board imposes a sanction on the person for a subsequent violation of this chapter or a rule or order adopted under this chapter.

(c) The board may consider a corrective or deferred action taken against a person to be a prior disciplinary action under this chapter when imposing a sanction on the person for a subsequent violation of this chapter or a rule or order adopted under this chapter

The BON may consider a corrective or deferred action in any subsequent violation by the nurse.

PART II.

SELECTED RULES
OF THE
TEXAS BOARD OF NURSING

*NOTE: A **Cross Reference Index** listing all BON rules in numeric order and showing their location in this Guide can be found in Part XI (Indexes) of this Guide.*

RULES

The following are rules of the Texas Board of Nursing (BON) most directly affecting a nurse's practice. A complete copy of all of the BON's rules can be found on the BON website at www.bon.texas.gov or on Texas Legislature Online at www.legis.state.tx.us (Select Administrative Code, TAC viewer, Title 22 Examining Boards, and finally BON). The Texas Administrative Code sets out the official version of agency rules. Rule changes are normally posted within 10 days of adoption. The BON makes changes to its rules on an as-needed basis. Each state agency is also required to review its rules within four years of adoption or readoption to determine if the reason for adopting or readopting the rule continues to exist. The BON will frequently revise its rules as part of this review process. Because the BON is not restricted as to when it may amend its rules, nurses with an interest in a specific rule should verify that they have the most current version. The BON posts proposed rule changes in the Nursing Law and Rules section of its website. Proposed rules and newly adopted rules are also normally covered in the BON's quarterly newsletter and on its website in the About the Board section under News . The rules set out n this Part II are current through July 31, 2011.

The rules have been grouped by subject matter rather than simply being set out in numerical order. Part XI (Indexes) of this Guide includes a Cross-Reference Index listing all the BON Rules in numerical order and showing their location in this Guide. A number of rule headings have been added or edited to be more descriptive of content.

RULE CHANGES SINCE LAST EDITION

Since the last edition of this Guide was published in 2011, the BON has also amended several of its rules but has not made any major revisions. The Board will need to amend several of its rules to implement legislation passed by 2013 Legislature. The most significant will likely be its APRN Rule 221. The board is also expected to make changes to its rule relating to delegation in independent living environments (Rule 225) and to address its rules governing corrective and deferred action.

SUBPART A.
DEFINITIONS

DEFINITIONS FOR RULE 217 (LICENSURE AND PRACTICE)
DEFINITIONS FOR RULE 213 (DISCIPLINE AND PROCEDURE)

ANNOTATOR'S NOTES

1. All the terms defined are listed but definitions set out only for the more important terms. The definitions for the other terms can be found in Rules 217 and 213 which are on the BON website under Nursing Law and Rules.

2. ✔Shading denotes key definitions.

1. DEFINITIONS FOR RULE 217 (LICENSURE AND PRACTICE)

217.1. Definitions. The following words and terms, when used in this chapter, shall have the following meanings, unless the context clearly indicates otherwise:

(1) Academic course

ANNOTATIONS

The Nursing Practice Act (NPA), Sec. 301.151 gives the Texas Board of Nursing (BON) broad rule-making authority. Through rules, the BON can address issues in much more detail than is generally possible or feasible in the NPA itself. In fact, the agency rule-making process is frequently described as the filling in of the details of policies set by the Legislature in the statute. Through rule-making, the BON can apply the NPA to emerging practice settings. Two of the more important BON practice-related rules are those defining the standards of nursing practice and unprofessional conduct. Complaints filed against nurses are most frequently based on alleged violations of the Standards of Practice and Unprofessional Conduct Rules. The Table of Contents for this Part II set out on the previous page can serve as a quick reference to the BON's practice-related rules.

The BON rules are grouped by subject matter rather than in numerical order. The subject matter groupings are:

Subpart A. Definitions
Subpart B. Standards and Scope of Practice
Subpart C. Professional Responsibilities
Subpart D. Minor Incident Reporting
Subpart E. Nursing Peer Review
Subpart F. Fitness to Practice
Subpart G. Licensure-Initial, Renewals, Inactive and Retired
Subpart H. Disciplinary Process
Subpart I. Peer Assistance
Subpart J. Advanced Practice Registered Nursing
Subpart K. Deferred Disciplinary Action Pilot

The table of contents on the previous page lists the rules included in each group.

This Subpart A sets out definitions that apply to all BON rules numbered 213.__ or 217.___. Rules 213 and 217 each contain a set of definitions that apply to all sections of each rule. Since the rules in this Part II are grouped by subject matter and not in numerical order, the definitions are being set out as a separate subpart.

An attempt has been made in the annotations to individual rules to identify any definitions of special significance in understanding that rule.

These definitions apply to BON rules numbered "217.__." Some of the individual rules also have their own definitions. The more important definitions set out in this Rule include "Direct supervision," "Indirect supervision," "Impaired practice." and "Professional boundaries."

(2) Advanced practice nurse (APN)

(3) Applicant

(4) Approved

(6) Board --The Texas Board of Nursing.

(7) Credential Evaluation Services (CES).

(8) Declaratory order

(9) Delinquent license

✔(10) Direct supervision--Requires a nurse to be immediately available to coordinate, direct, and observe at firsthand another individual for whom the nurse is responsible.

(11) Eligibility order

(12) Endorsement

(13) First level, general nurse

(15) Graduate nurse (GN) --Graduates of approved professional nursing programs who are issued a permit to practice for a specific time period until they successfully meet all licensure requirements.

(16) Graduate vocational nurse (GVN) --Graduates of approved vocational nursing programs who are issued a permit to practice for a specific time period until they successfully meet all licensure requirements.

✔(17) Impaired practice--Practice in which the nurse's ability to perform the essential functions of a nurse is impaired by chemical dependency on drugs and/or alcohol or by mental illness.

✔(18) Indirect supervision--Requires a nurse to be readily available if needed for consultation to coordinate, direct, and observe another individual for whom the nurse is responsible.

(19) Jurisdiction

(21) Licensing authority

(22) National Council Licensure Examination for Practical Nurses (NCLEX-PN)

(23) National Council Licensure Examination for Registered Nurses (NCLEX-RN)

(24) Nurse--a person required to be licensed under Texas Occupations Code chapter 301 to engage in professional or vocational nursing.

(25) Nursing curriculum

(26) Nursing program

✔(27) Peer assistance program--An approved program designed for nurses whose nursing practice is or may be impaired by chemical dependency on drugs and/or alcohol or certain mental illnesses and which meets the minimum criteria established by the Texas Commission on on Alcohol and Drug Abuse and the additional criteria established by the Texas Board of Nursing.

(28) Practitioner

✔(29) Professional boundaries--The appropriate limits which should be established by the nurse in the nurse/client relationship due to the nurse's power and the patient's vulnerability. Refers to the provision of nursing services within the limits of the nurse/client relationship which promote the client's dignity, independence and best interests and refrain from inappropriate involvement in the client's personal relationships and/or the obtainment of the nurse's personal gain at the client's expense.

(30) Professional nursing education program (general)

✔(31) Professional nursing practice --The performance for compensation of an act that requires substantial specialized judgment and skill, the proper performance of which is based on knowledge and application of the principles of biological, physical, and social science as acquired by a completed course in an approved school of professional nursing.

(32) Program of study

(33) Radiologic procedure

(34) Reactivation

(35) Refresher course

(36) Registered nurse --A person currently licensed by the board to practice professional

Direct supervision requires the supervising nurse to be immediately available. See definition of "indirect supervision" below.

Impairment can be from prescription or nonprescription drugs.

Indirect supervision requires the supervising nurse to be readily available. See definition of "direct supervision" above.

Nurses should be familiar with this definition since not violating professional boundaries is one of the standards of practice set out in Rule 217.11.

This definition tracks definition in NPA Sec. 301.002 except that the requirement that the act be performed for compensation was deleted by the 2005 Legislature.

nursing.

(37) Registered nurse, retired --An individual on inactive status, 65 or older, who has met the requirements for using the title as stated in §217.9(b) of this title (relating to Inactive Status).

(38) Renewal period

(39) Second level nurses

✔(40) Shall, will and must--Mandatory requirements.

✔(41) Should--Denotes recommendations.

(42) State Board Test Pool Examination (SBTPE)

(44) Temporary license

(45) Temporary permit

(46) Vocational nurse --A person currently licensed by the board to practice vocational nursing.

(47) Vocational nurse, retired --An individual on inactive status, 65 or older, who has met the requirements for using the title as stated in §217.9(b) of this title (relating to Inactive Status); includes individuals formerly classified as Vocational nurse, emeritus.

✔(48) Vocational Nursing – Nursing other than professional nursing that generally requires experience and education in biological, physical, and social sciences sufficient to qualify as a licensed vocational nurse.

(49) Vocational Nursing Education Program

✔(50) Vocational Nursing Practice --The performance of services for compensation appropriate for Licensed Vocational Nurses employed in roles which fall within the scope of the definition of vocational nursing.

2. DEFINITIONS FOR RULE 213 (DISCIPLINE AND PROCEDURE)

§213.1.Definitions. The following words and terms, when used in this chapter, shall have the following meanings, unless the context clearly indicates otherwise:

(1) Act

(2) Address of record

(3) Administrative Law Judge or judge

✔(4) Adverse licensure action -- Adverse licensure action--Any action to fine, reprimand, warn, limit, probate, revoke, suspend, or otherwise discipline a license or multistate licensure privilege. The term includes an order accepting a voluntary surrender in lieu of disciplinary action.

(5) Answer

(6) APA

(7) Attorney of record

(8) Board

(9) Client

✔(10) Complaint – .Written accusations made by any person, or by the Board on its own initiative, alleging that a licensee's conduct may have violated the NPA.

(11) Contested case

✔(12) Conviction – The result of a criminal proceeding wherein an individual, based on a plea or verdict, is adjudged guilty of the offense charged, or has been placed on probation with or without an adjudication of guilt, or has received an order of deferred adjudication.

(13) Declaratory order -

✔(14) Default proceeding – -The issuance of a proposal for decision or an order in which the factual allegations against the respondent in a contested case are deemed admitted as true upon the respondent's failure to appear at a properly noticed hearing, or failure to file a response to the Formal Charges.

(15) Eligibility and Disciplinary Committee

(16) Eligibility matter

(17) Executive director

Note the difference between the "mandatory" meaning of "shall, will and must" and the "recommendation" meaning of "should" in the next definition.

The requirement that the act be compensated was not included in the definition of "vocational nursing" passed by the 2005 Legislature when it redefined "vocational nursing."

These definitions apply to BON rules numbered "213.__." Some of the individual rules also have their own definitions.

Conviction is defined to include deferred adjudication. NPA Sec. 301.452(b)(3).

✔(18) Formal charges – Pleading of the staff publicly alleging the reasons for disciplinary actions against a registered or vocational nurse created in accordance with Texas Occupations Code Annotated §301.458.

✔(19) Hearing – A public adjudicative proceeding at the State Office of Administrative Hearings.

✔(20) Informal conference --A non-public settlement meeting conducted by the executive director or designee to resolve a disciplinary or eligibility matter pending before the Board.

(21) Initial licensure

(22) License

(23) Licensee -

(24) Licensing

✔(25) Minor Incident – Conduct in violation of the Nursing Practice Act, which after a thorough evaluation of factors enumerated under §217.16 of this title (relating to Minor Incidents), indicates that the nurse's continuing to practice professional or vocational nursing does not pose a risk of harm to a client or other person and, therefore, does not need to be reported to the Board or peer review committee

(26) Multistate Licensure Privilege

(27) Order

(28) Party

(29) Patient

(30) Person

(31) Petitioner

(32) Pleading

(34) Respondent

(35) Rule

(36) SOAH *[State Office of Administrative Hearings]*

(37) Staff

(38) Technical error

SUBPART B.
STANDARDS AND SCOPE OF PRACTICE

Standards of Nursing Practice - Rule 217.11

Unprofessional Conduct - Rule 217.12

Titles and Nametags - Rule 217.10

Assignment and Delegation to Unlicensed Persons

- Assignment by LVNs - Rule 217.11(2)
- Delegation by RNs - Rules 224, 225

Assisting at Surgery - Rule 217.18

RNs Performing Radiologic Procedures - Rule 217.14

Advanced Practice Nursing - Rules 221, 222

NPA Sec. 301.401 defines "minor incident" as "conduct that does not indicate the continued practice of nursing by an affected nurse poses a risk of harm to a client or other person." The definition in this rule appears to require that the conduct positively indicate the nurse does not pose a risk of harm. The term is synonymous with "minor error" or "minor violation."

This Subpart B includes BON rules that establish standards and scope of practice for nurses. Standards and scope of practice are interrelated because one standard of practice is practicing within one's scope of practice. The definitions of "professional nursing" and "vocational nursing" in NPA Sec. 301.002 as well as Sec 301.353 (Supervision of LVNs) establish the legal scope of practice for RN and LVNs. See all BON Position Statements 15.27 (LVN Scope of Practice) and 15.28 (RN Scope of Practice) and the BON's Six-Step Decision Making Process. These documents are set out in Part III (Position Statements) of this Guide).

The rules included in this subpart are:

1. *Rule 217.11* — *Standards of Nursing Practice*
2. *Rule 217.12* — *Unprofessional Conduct*
3. *Rule 217.10* — *Titles and Nametags*
4. *Rules 224, 225* — *Delegation*
   - *224 Acute Care Settings or for Acute Conditions*
   - *225 Independent Living Environments for Stable Conditions*
5. *Rule 217.18* — *Assisting at Surgery*
6. *Rule 217.14* — *RNs Performing Radiologic Procedures*
7. *Rules 221, 222* — *Advanced Practice Nursing*

The BON also has adopted various Position Statements, Guidelines, Policy Statements and FAQs that clarify these rules or address specific nursing practice-related issues. See Parts III (Position Statements), V (Practice-Related Materials) and X (Appendices) of this Guide.

If a nurse believes she or he is being requested to engage in conduct that would violate any of the standards set out in these rules, the nurse should invoke the protections available such as

1. STANDARDS OF NURSING PRACTICE (RULE 217.11)

Rule 217.11. Standards of Nursing Practice

The Texas Board of Nursing is responsible for regulating the practice of nursing within the State of Texas for Vocational Nurses, Registered Nurses, and Registered Nurses with advanced practice authorization. The standards of practice establish a minimum acceptable level of nursing practice in any setting for each level of nursing licensure or advanced practice authorization. Failure to meet these standards may result in action against the nurse's license even if no actual patient injury resulted.

(1) Standards Applicable to All Nurses. All vocational nurses, registered nurses and registered nurses with advanced practice authorization shall:

(A) ***(Knowing/Conforming to Applicable Laws)*** Know and conform to the Texas Nursing Practice Act and the board's rules and regulations as well as all federal, state, or local laws, rules or regulations affecting the nurse's current area of practice;

(B) ***(Safe Practice Environment)*** Implement measures to promote a safe environment for clients and others;

safe harbor nursing peer review. See Part VI (Patient Advocacy Protections) of this Guide for a discussion of these protections.

NPA *Sec. 301.452(b)(3) makes it a ground for the BON to take action against a nurse's license if the nurse "fail[s] to conform to the minimum standards of acceptable nursing practice." This rule fills in the details by identifying specific standards of practice. These standards are the minimum acceptable standards expected of a nurse. All nurses are expected to practice in accordance with them and failure to do so is a basis for taking action against a nurse's license. A number of the standards reflect the fact that a nurse's duty is to her/his patient and not just to the employing institution, attending physician, etc. Simply following policies set by another practitioner or facility is not sufficient. One of the more significant Texas nursing court cases established this principle by recognizing that an independent nurse-patient relationship exists and that obligations of the nurse to the patient arise directly from that relationship. See* Lunsford v BON, *648 S.W.2d 391 (Tex. App. 1983) set out in the Appendices (Part X) of this Guide. This Rule along with Rule §217.12 (Unprofessional Conduct) also define a "nurse's duty to a patient" for the purposes of requesting safe harbor nursing peer review under Sec. 303.005 of the Occupations Code to determine if a nurse is being requested to engage in conduct that violates a nurse's duty to a patient. See Parts IV (Nursing Peer Review) and VI (Patient Advocacy Protections) of this Guide.*

The BON also has adopted various Position Statements, Interpretive Guidelines, Policy Statements and FAQs that clarify these standards or address specific nursing practice-related issues. See Parts III (Position Statements), V (Practice and Scope) and X (Appendices) of this Guide.

Actual injury to a patient is not required for a violation of a standard of practice to occur. Exposing a patient to risk of injury is sufficient. This is consistent with the role of licensing boards to protect, if possible, the public from ever being harmed. See Rule 217.12(4).

If a nurse believes she or he is being requested to engage in conduct that would violate any of the standards set out in this rule, the nurse should invoke the protections available such as safe harbor nursing peer review. See Part VI (Patient Advocacy Protections) of this Guide for a discussion of these protections.

Most standards of practice are applicable to all types of nurses (LVNs, RNs, APRNs) since they address general standards such as not accepting inappropriate assignments, proper documentation, etc. Some standards, however, are applicable to only one type of nurse such as delegation (RNs) or prescribing (APRNs). Others such as the "nursing process" may apply to all types but have a different meaning for LVNs and RNs. The standards set out in this Rule are divided into four subsections.

Subsec. (1) sets out standards applicable to all nurses
Subsec. (2) sets out additional standards applicable to LVNs
Subsec. (3) sets out additional standards applicable to RNs
Subsec. (4) sets out additional standards applicable to APRNs

In addition to being familiar with the NPA and rules of the BON, nurses are expected to know the various laws and regulations that affect their area of practice. These include such laws as patient bill of rights, abuse reporting laws, reimbursement fraud laws, patient consent laws, laws governing patient referrals, etc. The number of laws affecting any nurse's practice can be quite extensive and it may require substantial effort to identify all of the laws and rules involved. However, ignorance of a law is not an excuse for not complying. Also, violations of some of the laws carry substantial penalties -- both civil and criminal. See Part IX (Other Laws) of this Guide for examples of other such laws.

This standard most likely will involve institutional policies. However, it should be remembered that nurses owe a direct duty to the patient/client and following institutional policies

(C) ***(Rationale for Medications/Treatments)*** Know the rationale for and the effects of medications and treatments and shall correctly administer the same;

(D) ***(Documentation)*** Accurately and completely report and document:

(i) the client's status including signs and symptoms;

(ii) nursing care rendered;

(iii) physician, dentist or podiatrist orders;

(iv) administration of medications and treatments;

(v) client response(s); and

(vi) contacts with other health care team members concerning significant events regarding client's status;

(E) ***(Privacy/Confidentiality)*** Respect the client's right to privacy by protecting confidential information unless required or allowed by law to disclose the information;

(F) ***(Client Education/Counseling)*** Promote and participate in education and counseling to a client(s) and, where applicable, the family/significant other(s) based on health needs;

(G) ***(Obtaining Instruction/Supervision)*** Obtain instruction and supervision as necessary when implementing nursing procedures or practices;

(H) ***(Obtaining Orientation/Training)*** Make a reasonable effort to obtain orientation/training for competency when encountering new equipment and technology or unfamiliar care situations;

(I) ***(Leaving an Assignment)*** Notify the appropriate supervisor when leaving a nursing assignment;

(J) ***(Professional Boundaries)*** Know, recognize, and maintain professional boundaries of the nurse-client relationship

(K) ***(Reporting)*** Comply with mandatory reporting requirements of Texas Occupations Code Chapter 301 (Nursing Practice Act), Subchapter I, which include reporting a nurse:

(i) who violates the Nursing Practice Act or a board rule and contributed to the death or serious injury of a patient;

(ii) whose conduct causes a person to suspect that the nurse's practice is impaired by chemical dependency or drug or alcohol abuse;

(iii) whose actions constitute abuse, exploitation, fraud, or a violation of professional *is not a justification for nurses' not meeting their obligation to the patient.*

Since the nurse owes a duty directly to the patient, blindly relying on another practitioner's (e.g., a physician's) judgment is not permissible for a nurse. See Standard (N) below relating to clarifying orders.

This rule does not prevent correcting a client's record; however, corrections should be made in a way that reflects a correction was made.

Nurses should be aware that a patient's family or significant other does not automatically have a right to confidential information. This rule does recognize that in some cases the nurse can disclose confidential information. The nurse should also be aware that inadvertent disclosure is probably a greater risk than deliberate disclosure. Inadvertent disclosure can occur by casual conversation about a patient, leaving charts laying around, etc. Nurses need to be familiar with state and federal laws such as HIPAA governing confidentiality.

Nurses are responsible for requesting instruction and supervision when needed.

Nurses are responsible for keeping up with the rapid advances in new technology and equipment and not using new equipment and technology without proper orientation and training.

Nurses must notify a supervisor before leaving an assignment. The nurse's obligation is to the patient and to ensure the patient has coverage so reporting to the immediate supervisor is required. See BON Position Statement 15.6 (Patient Abandonment) and NPA Sec. 301.356 (Refusing Mandatory Overtime).

Rule 217.1 (Definitions) defines "professional boundaries" as:

> *(29) Professional boundaries--The appropriate limits which should be established by the nurse in the nurse/client relationship due to the nurse's power and the patient's vulnerability. Refers to the provision of nursing services within the limits of the nurse/client relationship which promote the client's dignity, independence and best interests and refrain from inappropriate involvement in the client's personal relationships and/or the obtainment of the nurse's personal gain at the client's expense.*

This standard addresses the nurse's mandatory duty to report under the NPA. See Part VII of this Guide for the NPA provisions and BON rules governing mandatory reporting.

boundaries; or

(iv) whose actions indicate that the nurse lacks knowledge, skill, judgment, or conscientiousness to such an extent that the nurse's continued practice of nursing could reasonably be expected to pose a risk of harm to a patient or another person, regardless of whether the conduct consists of a single incident or a pattern of behavior.

(v) except for minor incidents (Texas Occupations Code §§301.401(2), 301.419, 22 TAC §217.16), peer review (Texas Occupations Code §§301.403, 303.007, 22 TAC §217.19), or peer assistance if no practice violation (Texas Occupations Code §301.410) as stated in the Nursing Practice Act and Board rules (22 TAC Chapter 217).

(L) ***(Nondiscrimination in Care)*** Provide, without discrimination, nursing services regardless of the age, disability, economic status, gender, national origin, race, religion, health problems, or sexual orientation of the client served;

(M) ***(Nursing Intervention)*** Institute appropriate nursing interventions that might be required to stabilize a client's condition and/or prevent complications;

(N) ***(Clarifying Orders)*** Clarify any order or treatment regimen that the nurse has reason to believe is inaccurate, non efficacious or contraindicated by consulting with the appropriate licensed practitioner and notifying the ordering practitioner when the nurse makes the decision not to administer the medication or treatment;

(O) ***(Infection Control)*** Implement measures to prevent exposure to infectious pathogens and communicable conditions;

(P) ***(Collaboration)*** Collaborate with the client, members of the health care team and, when appropriate, the client's significant other(s) in the interest of the client's health care;

(Q) ***(Consultation/Referrals)*** Consult with, utilize, and make referrals to appropriate community agencies and health care resources to provide continuity of care;

(R) ***(Professional Growth)*** Be responsible for one's own continuing competence in nursing practice and individual professional growth;

(S) ***(Making Assignments)*** Make assignments to others that take into consideration client safety and that are commensurate with the educational preparation, experience, knowledge, and physical and emotional ability of the person to whom the assignments are made;

(T) ***(Accepting Assignments)*** Accept only those nursing assignments that take into consideration client safety and that are commensurate with the nurse's educational preparation, experience, knowledge, and physical and emotional ability;

(U) ***(Supervising)*** Supervise nursing care provided by others for whom the nurse is professionally responsible; and

NPA Sec. 301.410 limits alternate reporting to peer assistance to those situations in which no practice violation is involved.

The qualifier "without discrimination" is important since it permits differences in treatment for justified reasons. For example, a pregnant nurse may be justified in refusing to care for a patient who has a disease that could affect the fetus. However, the burden not to discriminate is on the nurse and the nurse's reasons for treating any patient differently must be clearly justified.

Appropriate intervention and stabilization is what a reasonable, prudent nurse would do under the same or similar circumstances. For example, referring a patient after an appropriate assessment may be what a reasonable, prudent nurse would do.

This rule addresses the nurse's duty to question an inappropriate order and requires the nurse to consult with an appropriate licensed practitioner (e.g., nursing supervisor) within the facility/agency and ultimately to notify the ordering practitioner if a decision is made to refuse to carry out an order. This standard reflects the principle that a nurse owes a duty directly to the patient. Facility/agency policies establishing procedures for questioning orders can minimize potential conflict between the nurse and prescribing practitioner in this situation.

This standard most likely will involve institutional policies. However, it should be remembered that nurses owe a direct duty to the client and following institutional policies is not a justification for nurses' not meeting their obligation to the patient.

Nurses normally practice as members of a health care team. They do have a duty to work collaboratively with other members of that team.

Nurses should be familiar with community resources available to the client.

Nurses are required to achieve/maintain national certification or complete at least 20 contact hours of continuing education each renewal period. This, however, is a minimum, and as professionals, nurses are responsible for maintaining a high level of professional competency.

Standards (S) - (U) address appropriate assignment and supervision. Standards (S) and (U) make the nurse (including the nurse supervisor/administrator) responsible for making appropriate assignments and for properly supervising assignments made. Standard (T) imposes a corresponding duty on nurses not to accept assignments for which they are not qualified.

Standards (G) and (H) above require nurses to seek appropriate supervision and instruction. If assignment to unlicensed persons is involved then LVNs must comply with Standard (2)(B) below and RNs with (3)(B) below.

A nurse must provide adequate supervision for any individual for which she or he is professionally responsible even if that individual is performing tasks assigned or delegated by another nurse or licensed practitioner. Standard (G) above requires nurses to obtain supervision when needed. See BON Delegation Rule 224.10.

(V) ***(License Verification)*** Ensure the verification of current Texas licensure or other Compact State licensure privilege and credentials of personnel for whom the nurse is administratively responsible, when acting in the role of nurse administrator.

(2) Standards Specific to Vocational Nurses. The licensed vocational nurse practice is a directed scope of nursing practice under the supervision of a registered nurse, advanced practice registered nurse, physician's assistant, physician, podiatrist, or dentist. Supervision is the process of directing, guiding, and influencing the outcome of an individual's performance of an activity. The licensed vocational nurse shall assist in the determination of predictable healthcare needs of clients within healthcare settings and:

(A) ***(Nursing Process for LVNs)*** Shall utilize a systematic approach to provide individualized, goal-directed nursing care by:

(i) collecting data and performing focused nursing assessments;

(ii) participating in the planning of nursing care needs for clients;

(iii) participating in the development and modification of the comprehensive nursing care plan for assigned clients;

(iv) implementing appropriate aspects of care within the LVN's scope of practice; and

(v) assisting in the evaluation of the client's responses to nursing interventions and the identification of client needs;

(B) ***(Assignment by LVNs)*** Shall assign specific tasks, activities and functions to unlicensed personnel commensurate with the educational preparation, experience, knowledge, and physical and emotional ability of the person to whom the assignments are made and shall maintain appropriate supervision of unlicensed personnel.

(C) ***(Scope of Practice for LVNs)*** May perform other acts that require education and training as prescribed by board rules and policies, commensurate with the licensed vocational nurse's experience, continuing education, and demonstrated licensed vocational nurse competencies.

(3) Standards Specific to Registered Nurses: The registered nurse shall assist in the determination of healthcare needs of clients and shall:

(A) ***(Nursing Process for RNs)*** Utilize a systematic approach to provide individualized, goal-directed, nursing care by:

The administrator doesn't have to personally verify licensure but is responsible for assuring that procedures are in place to verify credentials. Nurse administrators should know what information is available from the BON, what information is voluntarily disclosed, and what information is disclosed only if specifically requested. The BON website includes a section for employers.

Although most standards of practice are applicable to both LVNs and RNs, there are some that aren't. Standards applicable only to LVNs are set out in this Subsection (2).

LVNs are referred to as having a "directed practice." This means that they practice under the general supervision of another licensed health care practitioner – usually a registered nurse or physician. While this type of general supervision does not require the immediate presence of the supervising practitioner, it does require that the practitioner be readily available to the LVN for consultation and direction as needed. Directed practice also means that LVN practice deals with predictable health care needs of patients. See BON Position Statement 15.27 (LVN Scope of Practice) and Interpretive Guideline for LVN Scope of Practice in Part III of the Guide as well as definition of vocational nursing in NPA Sec. 301.002 and LVN supervision requirement in NPA Sec. 301.353.

While a nursing process applies to both LVNs and RNs, what is involved in that process differs for LVNs and RNs. The nursing process for LVNs reflects that theirs is a directed practice and involves clients with predictable health care needs. While this may mean that the LVN doesn't develop the patient care plan, its does not mean the LVN is not an active participant in the development of the plan as a member of the health care team.

While LVNs do not have the authority to delegate to unlicensed persons, they do have the authority to assign tasks to unlicensed persons who have the legal authority to perform those tasks. Usually that authority will come from delegation of the task by a registered nurse (normally the RN providing general supervision of the LVN) or possibly a physician. Once the RN delegates the legal authority to the unlicensed person to perform certain tasks, the LVN may assign such tasks to the unlicensed person. The LVN is then responsible for appropriate supervision. An example of this relationship between delegation and assignment is a nursing home. The RN will have delegated certain nursing tasks to the nurse aide but the LVN working the evening shift will be the nurse who assigns actual tasks to the nurse aide. The LVN has an independent duty to be sure the unlicensed person is competent to perform this task and also to supervise the aide's performance of the task.

See BON Position Statement 15.27 (LVN Scope of Practice) in Part III of the Guide as well as definition of vocational nursing in NPA Sec. 301.002 and LVN supervision requirement in NPA Sec. 301.353.

Although most standards of practice are applicable to both RNs and LVNs there are some that aren't. Standards applicable only to RNs are set out in this Subsection (3). See also BON Position Statement 15.28 (RN Scope of Practice).

While a nursing process applies to both LVNs and RNs, what is involved in that process differs for LVNs and RNs. The nursing process for RNs reflects that theirs is a more independent practice

(i) performing comprehensive nursing assessments regarding the health status of the client;

(ii) making nursing diagnoses that serve as the basis for the strategy of care;

(iii) developing a plan of care based on the assessment and nursing diagnosis;

(iv) implementing nursing care; and

(v) evaluating the client's responses to nursing interventions

(B) ***(Delegation by RNs)*** Delegate tasks to unlicensed personnel in compliance with 22 TEX. ADMIN. CODE chapter 224, relating to clients with acute conditions or in acute care environments, and chapter 225, relating to independent living environments for clients with stable and predictable conditions.

(4) Standards Specific to Registered Nurses with Advanced Practice Authorization: Standards for a specific role and specialty of advanced practice nurse supersede standards for registered nurses where conflict between the standards, if any, exist. In addition to subsections (1) and (3) above, a registered nurse who holds authorization to practice as an advanced practice nurse (APRN) shall:

(A) ***(Practice Within APRN Role)*** Practice in an advanced nursing practice role and specialty in accordance with authorization granted under Board Rule 221 (relating to practicing in an APRN role; 22 TAC ch. 221) and standards set out in that Rule.

(B) ***(Prescribing by APRNs)*** Prescribe medications in accordance with prescriptive authority granted under Board Rule 222 (relating to APRNs prescribing; 22 TAC ch. 222) and standards set out in that Rule and in compliance with state and federal laws and regulations relating to prescription of dangerous drugs and controlled substances.

2. UNPROFESSIONAL CONDUCT (RULE 217.12)

§217.12. Unprofessional Conduct.

The unprofessional conduct rules are intended to protect clients and the public from incompetent, unethical, or illegal conduct of licensees. The purpose of these rules is to identify unprofessional or dishonorable behaviors of a nurse which the board believes are likely to deceive, defraud, or injure clients or the public. Actual injury to a client need not be established. These behaviors include but are not limited to:

(1) ***(Unsafe Practice)*** Unsafe Practice - actions or conduct including, but not limited to:

(A) ***(Failure to comply with BON Standards)*** Carelessly failing, repeatedly failing or exhibiting an inability to perform vocational, registered, or advanced practice nursing, in conformity with the standards of minimum acceptable level nursing practice set out in Rule *compared to the directed practice of LVNs.*

RNs can delegate legal authority to unlicensed persons to perform certain nursing tasks. Depending on the practice setting, that delegation must comply with the requirements of either BON Rule 224 or Rule 225 governing delegation.

This Subsection (4) sets out standards applicable only to APRNs. APRNs as RNs are required to comply both with the standards applicable to all nurses set out in Subsection (1) and those applicable to RNs set out in Subsection (3). Additional standards for APRNs are set out in BON Rules 221 and 222 and this subsection establishes compliance with those rules as a standard of practice for APRNs. See BON website section on APRN practice.

Rule 221 governs the general practice of the APRN in an advanced practice role. An APRN must practice within the specialty role for which he or she was licensed as an APRN.

Rule 222 sets out specific standards for APRNs with prescriptive authority.

Sec. 301.452(b)(10) of the NPA makes it a ground for disciplinary action for a nurse to engage in "unprofessional or dishonorable conduct which, in the opinion of the board is likely to deceive, defraud, or injure patients or the public." This rule identifies conduct the BON considers to be unprofessional conduct. This Rule along with Rule §217.11 (Standards of Practice) also define a "nurse's duty to a patient" for the purposes of requesting safe harbor nursing peer review under Sec. 303.005 of the Nursing Peer Review Law (Occupations Code Chap. 303) to determine if a nurse is being requested to engage in conduct that violates a nurse's duty to a patient. See Part VI (Patient Advocacy Protections) of this Guide.

This rule is distinguishable from Rule 217.11 (Standards) by the fact that it places emphasis on blameworthy behavior and culpability rather than the nurse simply failing to comply with a standard of care. For example, Subsection (1)(A) makes "carelessly failing, repeatedly failing or inability" to practice nursing in accordance with nursing standards unprofessional conduct. Violating a standard of practice may simply reflect a mistake by the nurse. Unprofessional conduct would reflect conduct more blameworthy than a simple mistake.

The BON also has adopted various Position Statements, Guidelines and Policy Statements that clarify these rules or address specific nursing practice-related issues. See Parts III (Position Statements), V (Practice-Related Materials) and X (Appendices) of this Guide and BON website.

If a nurse believes she or he is being requested to engage in conduct prohibited by this rule, the nurse should invoke the protections available such as safe harbor nursing peer review. See Part VI (Patient Advocacy Protections) of this Guide for a discussion of these protections.

Failure to comply with the standards of practice set out in Rule 217.11 (Standards of Nursing Practice) may constitute unprofessional conduct if done carelessly, repeatedly or in a manner that exhibits an inability to practice in conformity with those standards.

217.11;

(B) ***(Failure to comply with Accepted Standards)*** Carelessly or repeatedly failing to conform to generally accepted nursing standards in applicable practice settings;

(C) ***(Improper record management)*** Improper management of client records;

(D) ***(Improper Assignment or Delegation)*** Delegating or assigning nursing functions or a prescribed health function when the delegation or assignment could reasonably be expected to result in unsafe or ineffective client care;

(E) ***(Improper Acceptance of Assignment)*** Accepting the assignment of nursing functions or a prescribed health function when the acceptance of the assignment could be reasonably expected to result in unsafe or ineffective client care;

(F) ***(Improper Supervision)*** Failing to supervise the performance of tasks by any individual working pursuant to the nurse's delegation or assignment; or

(G) ***(Improper Supervision by Faculty)*** Failure of a clinical nursing instructor to adequately supervise or to assure adequate supervision of student experiences.

(2) ***(Lack of Responsible Oversight by CNO)*** Failure of a chief administrative nurse to follow appropriate and recognized standards and guidelines in providing oversight of the nursing organization and nursing services for which the nurse is administratively responsible.

(3) ***(Failure to Comply with License Restrictions)*** Failure to practice within a modified scope of practice or with the required accommodations, as specified by the board in granting a coded license or any stipulated agreement with the board.

(4) ***(Endangering Patients)*** Careless or repetitive conduct that may endanger a client's life, health, or safety. Actual injury to a client need not be established.

(5) ***(Fitness for Duty)*** Inability to Practice Safely - demonstration of actual or potential inability to practice nursing with reasonable skill and safety to clients by reason of illness, use of alcohol, drugs, chemicals, or any other mood-altering substances, or as a result of any mental or physical condition.

(6) ***(Misconduct)*** Misconduct - actions or conduct that include, but are not limited to:

(A) ***(Falsifying Records)*** Falsifying reports, client documentation, agency records or other documents;

(B) ***(Failure to Cooperate)*** Failing to cooperate with a lawful investigation conducted by the board;

(C) ***(Patient Harm, Neglect or Abuse)*** Causing or permitting physical, emotional or verbal abuse or injury or neglect to the client or the public, or failing to report same to the employer, appropriate legal authority and/or licensing board;

(D) ***(Violating Professional Boundaries)*** Violating professional boundaries of the

In addition to the standards of practice set out in Rule 217.11, nurses must comply with generally accepted standards applicable to their practice setting. Nurses should be familiar with the standards for their specialty area of practice.

Subdivisions (D) - (G) address inappropriate assignments, delegation and supervision. See also Rules 217.11(2)(B) and 217.11(3)(B) setting standards for assignment by LVNs and delegation by RNs and Rules 224 and 225 governing delegation.

Inappropriate assignments, delegation or supervision may constitute unprofessional conduct if it could "reasonably be expected to result in unsafe or ineffective patient care." Hospital nurse staffing rules of the Texas Department of State Health Services set out standards for nurse staffing in hospitals. These rules are set out in Part IX (Other Laws) of this Guide.

This rule specifically addresses faculty supervision of students. The reference to "clinical experience" is designed to apply to situations such as preceptorships in which the instructor may not be directly supervising the student.

The chief nursing officer is responsible for providing adequate oversight of nursing services. This requirement is consistent with hospital nurse staffing rules of the Texas Department of State Health Services that make the CNO responsible for nursing services. This provision is analogous to Subsection (1)(B) requiring all nurses to comply with generally accepted standards of practice for their practice area.

This is a rather general catchall standard and would cover most instances of unprofessional conduct involving patient care. Again, note that it is unprofessional conduct only if done carelessly or repeatedly. Also, note that actual injury is not required. Exposing a patient to risk of injury is sufficient. This is consistent with the role of licensing boards to protect, if possible, the public from ever being harmed.

This Subsec. (5) would cover a nurse who practices when overly fatigued or with any physical or mental condition that makes the nurse unable to practice safely. See Subsec. (10) which addresses drug-related misconduct in more detail.

Subdivisions.(6)(A)-(J) set out specific types fo misconduct.

This rule does not prevent correcting a client's record; however, corrections should be made in a way that reflects a correction was made.

There are also a number of laws that specifically prohibit abuse of elderly, children, and mentally ill patients. Many of these are in the form of patient rights. There are also a number of abuse reporting laws. Nurses should be familiar with these laws.

Rule 217.1 (Definitions) defines "professional boundaries" as:

nurse/client relationship including but not limited to physical, sexual, emotional or financial exploitation of the client or the client's significant other(s);

(E) ***(Sexual Misconduct)*** Engaging in sexual conduct with a client, touching a client in a sexual manner, requesting or offering sexual favors, or language or behavior suggestive of the same;

(F) ***(Violent or Threatening Behavior)*** Threatening or violent behavior in the workplace;

(G) ***(Misappropriation)*** Misappropriating, in connection with the practice of nursing, anything of value or benefit, including but not limited to, any property, real or personal of the client, employer, or any other person or entity, or failing to take precautions to prevent such misappropriation;

(H) ***(Giving False Information)*** Providing information which was false, deceptive, or misleading in connection with the practice of nursing;

(I) ***(False Employment Information)*** Failing to answer specific questions or providing false or misleading answers that would have affected the decision to license, employ, certify or otherwise utilize a nurse; or

(J) ***(Improper Solicitation or Referral)*** Offering, giving, soliciting, or receiving or agreeing to receive, directly or indirectly, any fee or other consideration to or from a third party for the referral of a client in connection with the performance of professional services.

(7) ***(Failure to Repay Student Loan)*** Failure to repay a guaranteed student loan, as provided in the Texas Education Code §57.491, or pay child support payments as required by the Texas Family Code §232.001, et seq.

(8) ***(Diverting Narcotics)*** Drug Diversion - diversion or attempts to divert drugs or controlled substances.

(9) ***(Dismissal from Peer Assistance)*** Dismissal from a board-approved peer assistance program for noncompliance and referral by that program to the BON.

(10) ***(Drug Related Misconduct)*** Other Drug Related - actions or conduct that include, but are not limited to:

(29) Professional boundaries--The appropriate limits which should be established by the nurse in the nurse/client relationship due to the nurse's power and the patient's vulnerability. Refers to the provision of nursing services within the limits of the nurse/client relationship which promote the client's dignity, independence and best interests and refrain from inappropriate involvement in the client's personal relationships and/or the obtainment of the nurse's personal gain at the client's expense.

Patient exploitation is most likely to be an issue in private duty, home health or hospice settings. A number of the patient rights laws prohibit exploitation of patients.

As a practical matter, any sexual conduct with a patient/client, even if consensual, will almost certainly violate this subsection or some other law. This is particularly true of nurses in a counseling role. See BON Disciplinary Sanction Policies on the BON website for additional materials on sexual conduct with patients. There are also criminal laws relating to sexual conduct with patients. See Part X (Other Laws) of this Guide.

Violence in the workplace is unacceptable conduct.

To be a violation of this subsection, the misappropriation must occur in connection with the nurse's practice. The nurse does not have to be convicted of a crime for the BON to take disciplinary action based on this subsection. Misappropriation not in connection with the practice of nursing could lead to a criminal conviction for which the BON might take disciplinary action.

This rule would cover reimbursement fraud and similar activities.

This rule addresses what has to be disclosed to prospective employers. It places a significant burden on the employer to ask the appropriate questions rather than on the nurse's volunteering information. Note that a nurse has an affirmative duty not to provide misleading information.

The Legislature has adopted laws governing improper referrals. This rule appears to be somewhat more restrictive than those laws and to prohibit a nurse from receiving compensation from a third party, i.e., someone other than the client/patient, for any type of referral. See Part IX (Other Laws of this Guide).

This rule reflects a requirement passed by the Legislature.

Participating in a board-approved peer assistance program frequently occurs as an alternative to the BON's taking disciplinary action against the nurse. Making the nurse's subsequent failure to satisfactorily participate a basis for the BON to take action against the nurse's license avoids the board having to investigate the nurse's original conduct which may have happened several years earlier. See NPA Sec. 301.4551.

Subdivisions (11)(A)-(E) set out specific types of drug related misconduct.

(A) ***(Use on Duty or on Call)*** Use of any controlled substance or any drug, prescribed or unprescribed, or device or alcoholic beverages while on duty or on call and to the extent that such use may impair the nurse's ability to safely conduct to the public the practice authorized by the nurse's license;

(B) ***(Improper Record Keeping)*** Falsification of or making incorrect, inconsistent, or unintelligible entries in any agency, client, or other record pertaining to drugs or controlled substances;

(C) ***(Improper Medication Wastage)*** Failing to follow the policy and procedure in place for the wastage of medications at the facility where the nurse was employed or working at the time of the incident(s);

(D) ***(Positive Drug Screen)*** A positive drug screen for which there is no lawful prescription; or

(E) ***(Falsifying Prescriptions)*** Obtaining or attempting to obtain or deliver medication(s) through means of misrepresentation, fraud, forgery, deception and/or subterfuge.

(11) ***(Unlawful Practice)*** Unlawful Practice - actions or conduct that include, but are not limited to:

(A) ***(Aiding Unlawful Practice)*** Knowingly aiding, assisting, advising, or allowing an unlicensed person to engage in the unlawful practice of vocational, registered or advanced practice nursing;

(B) ***(Violating Laws or Board Orders)*** Violating an order of the board, or carelessly or repetitively violating a state or federal law relating to the practice of vocational, registered or advanced practice nursing, or violating a state or federal narcotics or controlled substance law;

(C) ***(Aiding Violation of Board Order)*** Knowingly aiding, assisting, advising, or allowing a nurse under Board Order to violate the conditions set forth in the Order; or

(D) ***(Violating Duty to Report)*** Failing to report violations of the Nursing Practice Act and/or the Board's rules and regulations.

(12) ***(Inappropriate Leaving of Assignment)*** Leaving a nursing assignment, including a supervisory assignment, without notifying the appropriate personnel.

(13) ***(Criminal Conduct)*** Criminal Conduct -- including, but not limited to, conviction or probation, with or without an adjudication of guilt, receipt of a judicial order involving a crime or criminal behavior or conduct that could affect the practice of nursing.

3. TITLES AND NAMETAGS (RULE 217.10)

217.10 Restrictions to Use of Designations for Licensed Vocational or Registered Nurse

(a) Use of title

(1) A person who holds a valid current license as a registered nurse under this chapter:

(A) is referred to as a registered nurse; and

(B) may use the abbreviation "R.N."

(2) A person who holds a valid current license as a vocational nurse under this

Violation of this Standard (10)(A) can occur even if the medication is prescribed or the nurse is only on call since impairment in either situation can put patients at risk.

Documentation must be accurate and intelligible. This rule does not prevent correcting a client's record; however, corrections should be made in a way that reflects a correction was made.

Following wastage policies helps prevent diversion of drugs.

Although this Standard (10)(D) is limited to nonprescription drugs, Standard 10)(A) above prohibits being on duty or on call while under the influence of a prescription drug that impairs the nurse's ability to practice safely. The board expects nurses to know the side effects of medications.

Subds. (A)-(D) set out specific types of unlawful practice.

See also Standard of Practice Rule 217.11(1)(A).

Failure to report violations.

Patient abandonment. See BON Position Statement 15.6 (Patient Abandonment).

The BON considers a broad range of crimes as affecting the practice of nursing. See BON Rule 213.28.

This Rule is based on NPA Sec. 301.351.

Use of "Registered Nurse" or "RN" title is limited to licensed RNs.

Use of "Licensed Vocational Nurse" or "LVN" title is limited to licensed LVNs. .

chapter:

(A) is referred to as a licensed vocational nurse or vocational nurse; and

(B) may use the abbreviation "L.V.N." or "V.N."

(3) An applicant for initial licensure by examination in Texas who has valid temporary authorizations to practice professional nursing as a graduate nurse pending the results of the licensing examination may use the initials "GN " or the title "graduate nurse."

(4) An applicant for initial licensure by examination in Texas who has valid temporary authorization to practice vocational nursing as a graduate vocational nurse pending the results of the licensing examination may use the initials "GVN" or the title "graduate vocational nurse."

(5) A person who is eligible for licensure by endorsement in Texas, holding a valid Texas temporary license to engage in professional nursing practice, may use the title "registered nurse" or "RN."

(6) A person who is eligible for licensure by endorsement in Texas, holding a valid Texas temporary license to engage in vocational nursing practice, may use the title "licensed vocational nurse," "vocational nurse," "LVN," and "VN."

(7) No other person, other than designated in paragraphs (1) - (6) of this section, may use, where applicable, titles or abbreviations with the word "nurse" such as office nurse, staff nurse, head nurse, charge nurse, school nurse, supervisor of nursing or nurses, or any other title tending to imply to the public that the person holds a license to practice nursing in Texas.

(8) Any person other than as permitted by law or rule who uses any of the above titles or abbreviations deemed by the board misleading or implying that the individual is a licensed nurse may be subject to potential violation or prosecution under the applicable law.

(9) If a nurse holds herself or himself out to the public as being engaged in the practice of nursing, or uses the designations "licensed vocational nurse," "vocational nurse," "LVN," "VN," "registered nurse," or "RN" or any combination or variation of those terms and abbreviations, alone or in combination with any other terms, then they must practice in accordance with the Nursing Practice Act and the Rules and Regulations Relating to Nurse Education, Licensure and Practice.

(10) Unless the person is practicing under the delegated authority of a registered nurse or is otherwise authorized by state or federal law, a person may not use, in connection with the person's name:

(A) the title "nurse aide," "nurse assistant," or "nurse technician" or any other similar title; and

(B) may not abbreviate the title to "nurse."

(b) Display of Designations.

(1) While interacting with the public in a nursing role, each licensed nurse shall wear a clearly legible insignia that:

(A) displays the nurse's name, but the manner in which the name appears, in reference to use of first name and/or last name, is the nurse's preference in accordance with facility policy, if applicable; and

(B) identifies the nurse as a registered nurse or vocational nurse according to licensure.

(2) Although the board does not require the inclusion of any other designations, with the exception of the specific authorization of advanced practice nurses, the insignia may not contain information other than:

(A) the registered nurse or licensed vocational nurse designation;

(B) the nurse's name, certifications, academic degrees, or practice position;

(C) the name of the employing facility or agency, or other employer; or

(D) a picture of the nurse.

(c) Duty to Document Designations. While functioning in a nursing role, each licensed nurse shall document in his/her written communications:

(1) the nurse's name, but the manner in which the name appears, in reference to use

Use of "Graduate Nurse" or "GN" title.

Use of "Graduate Vocational Nurse" or "GVN" title.

RNs seeking licensure by endorsement may use the "RN" title once they have received a temporary license.

LVNs seeking licensure by endorsement may use the "LVN" title once they have received a temporary license.

The use of generic "nurse" title is restricted to RNs and LVNs.

These are examples of misleading titles if used by individuals other than RNs, LVNs, GNs, and GVNs.

This rule is designed to address situations in which a nurse practices under another state certification (e.g., midwife) but continues to use the title RN or LVN. This rule provides that such LVNs or RNs must conform to the NPA and BON rules. RNs or LVNs who wish to have the benefit of using the "RN" or "LVN" titles must comply with the NPA and BON rules.

The titles "nurse aide," "nurse assistant," etc. may be used only by aides functioning under the delegated authority of an RN. See NPA Sec. 301.4515. Only RNs are referred to because LVNs are not authorized to delegate. While LVNs may make an assignment to an individual, they may not delegate legal authority to perform the act. See discussion of delegation and assignment in next Subdivision (Subdivision 4).

Nurses must wear insignia identifying themselves as nurses. This rule implements NPA Sec. 301.351.

The nurse's nametag or identifying insignia must include the nurse's name (first or last is sufficient) and the RN or LVN designation. For safety reasons, nurses may not want to display their full name in certain practice settings.

This Subdivision (2) limits the additional information that may appear on a nurse's nametag or identifying insignia. The reason is to assure readability. This subdivision does not require that all of the information be on the nametag.

When documenting, nurses must include their name (first or last is sufficient) and their RN or LVN designation.

of first name and/or last name, is the nurse's preference in accordance with facility policy, if applicable; and

(2) the nurse's designation as a registered nurse or vocational nurse according to licensure.

4. ASSIGNMENT AND DELEGATION TO UNLICENSED PERSONS

A. Assignment by LVNs

Rule 217.11(2)(B). Standards of Nursing Practice

(2) Standards Specific to Vocational Nurses. The licensed vocational nurse shall assist in the determination of predictable healthcare needs of clients within healthcare settings and:

(B) ***(Assignment by LVNs)*** Shall assign specific tasks, activities and functions to unlicensed personnel commensurate with the educational preparation, experience, knowledge, and physical and emotional ability of the person to whom the assignments are made and shall maintain appropriate supervision of unlicensed personnel.

B. Delegation by RNs

Rule 224. Delegation of Nursing Tasks by Registered Professional Nurses to Unlicensed Personnel for Clients with Acute Conditions or in Acute Care Environments §§224.1 - 224.11.

While LVNs do not have the authority to delegate to unlicensed persons, they do have the authority to assign tasks to unlicensed persons who have the legal authority to perform those tasks. Usually that authority will come from delegation of the task by a registered nurse (normally the RN providing general supervision of the LVN) or possibly a physician. Once the RN delegates the legal authority to the unlicensed person to perform certain tasks, the LVN may assign such tasks to the unlicensed person. The LVN is then responsible for appropriate supervision. An example of this relationship between delegation and assignment is a nursing home. The RN will have delegated certain nursing tasks to the nurse aide but the LVN working the evening shift will be the nurse who assigns actual tasks to the nurse aide. The LVN has an independent duty to be sure the unlicensed person is competent to perform this task and also to supervise the aide's performance of the task.

RN delegation to unlicensed persons is addressed in two Board rules.

- *Rule 224 addressing delegation in acute settings and for clients with conditions that are not stable and predictable; and*
- *Rule 225 addressing delegation in independent living environments for clients with stable and predictable conditions that can self direct their care.*

Rule 225 reflects the work of a task force which the BON was directed to establish by 2001 legislation (HB 456). The task force was to explore if health maintenance activities can be appropriately performed in independent living environments by unlicensed persons for clients with stable and predictable conditions.

Because of the complexity surrounding delegation, the Board has developed a Delegation Resource Packet for RNs. The packet is set out on the Board's website. It includes the following materials:

The Five Rights of Delegation
Delegation Don'ts
Rule 224 Flow Chart
Rule 225 Flow Chart
Rule 225 Professional Nursing Assessment Grid with examples
Rule 225 Quick Reference Guide
Delegation and the Advanced Practice Nurse
Links to Delegation Resources
Conflict Resolution Model

The BON also has entered into a memorandum of understanding (MOU) with the Department of Aging and Disability Services regarding certain tasks that can be performed by unlicensed personnel in community support agencies without RN delegation.

Legislation (HB 3611; SB 1857) passed in 2011 added Secs. 161.091-.096 to the Human Resources Code. These sections permit unlicensed persons to administer medications in certain practice settings providing care to persons with intellectual and developmental disabilities after being assessed by an RN.

This rule governs RN delegation to unlicensed persons in acute care settings and in other settings if the clients' condition is not stable and predictable.

An understanding of Rule 224's structure is helpful in understanding its content.

- *§224.1 (Application) and §224.2 (Exclusions) identify the settings in which this rule*

***ANNOTATOR'S NOTE:** The BON has developed a Delegation Resource Packet to assist the RN in making decisions about the appropriate utilizations of unlicensed persons in situations governed by Rule 224. The packet can be found on the BON website under the Practice Section and includes the following materials:*

Frequently Asked Questions
Links to Delegation Resources
Rule 224 Flow Chart

224.1. Application of Chapter.

This chapter applies to situations where:

(1) the client has an acute health condition that is unstable or unpredictable; or

(2) the client is in an acute care environment where nursing services are continuously provided including, but not limited to, hospitals, rehabilitation centers, skilled nursing facilities, clinics, and private practice physician offices.

224.2. Exclusions from Chapter.

This chapter does not apply to:

(1) tasks provided in compliance with Government Code §531.051(f) (relating to Voucher Program for Payment of Certain Services for Persons With Disabilities); or

(2) RNs who:

(A) supervise or instruct others in the gratuitous nursing care of the sick;

(B) are qualified nursing faculty or preceptors directly supervising or instructing nursing students in the performance of nursing tasks while enrolled in accredited nursing programs;

(C) instruct and/or supervise an unlicensed person in the proper performance of nursing tasks as a part of an education course designed to prepare persons to obtain a state license, certificate or permit that authorizes the person to perform such tasks; and

(D) assign tasks to or supervise LVNs or other licensed practitioners practicing within the scope of their license.

224.3. Purpose.

The Texas Board of Nursing (BON or Board) recognizes that changes in health care delivery have and will continue to influence the way nursing care is delivered. The Board believes that the registered nurse (RN) is in a unique position to develop and implement a nursing plan of care that incorporates a professional relationship between the RN and the client. The Board recognizes that the RN's responsibility may vary from that of the nurse providing care at the bedside of an acutely ill client to that of the nurse managing health care delivery in institutional and community settings. Assessment of the nursing needs of the client, the plan of nursing actions, implementation of the plan, and evaluation are essential components of professional nursing practice and are the responsibilities of the RN. The full utilization of the services of a RN may require delegation of selected nursing tasks to unlicensed personnel. The scope of delegation and the level of supervision by the RN may vary depending on the setting, the complexity of the task, the skills and experience of the unlicensed person, and the client's physical and mental status. The *applies.*

- *§224.3 (Purpose) and §224.4 (Definitions) set out general principles governing delegation and define key terms.*
- *§224.5 (Accountability) clarifies the RN's accountability for delegated tasks.*
- *§224.6 (General Criteria) and §224.7 (Supervision) set out general criteria that must always be met for delegation to be appropriate. Although an oversimplification, these two sections generally permit delegation only of those tasks that a reasonable, prudent nurse would find is within the scope of sound professional nursing judgment to delegate and only if the task is adequately supervised.*
- *§224.8 (Delegation of Specific Tasks) provides more specific guidance to the RN by indicating what tasks a reasonable, prudent RN would find to be within sound professional nursing judgment 1) to commonly delegate, 2) to delegate only under special circumstances, or 3) not to delegate.*
- *§§224.9-.10 addresses delegating to medication aides and supervising unlicensed persons performing tasks delegated by another practitioner.*
- *§224.11 (Other Laws) sets out guidelines for when more than a single law or rule applies to delegation.*

Since two rules govern delegation, RNs will need to know which rule applies. This Rule 224 applies to acute settings or acute conditions. It applies to any and all situations not governed by Rule 225 which applies only to clients with stable and predictable conditions in independent living environments. See Rule 225.1.

If an exclusion applies, then that situation is not governed by this rule. There may still be other rules that do apply. For example, both the BON's Unprofessional Conduct Rule and Standard of Practice Rule prohibit an RN from delegating or making assignments to persons without the necessary education, training and experience.

Nursing students performing tasks or functions performed as part of their educational program are excluded from the definition of unlicensed person in Rule 224.4(4).

RNs do not delegate tasks to LVNs but rather assign LVNs to perform tasks or functions that they are authorized to do by their LVN license. See definition of unlicensed person in 224.4.

This purpose statement recognizes that what is appropriate to delegate varies with the practice setting.

The appropriateness of delegation depends on a variety of factors.

following sections govern the RN in delegating nursing tasks to unlicensed personnel across a variety of settings where nursing care services are delivered.

224.4. Definitions.

The following words and terms, when used in this chapter, shall have the following meanings, unless the context clearly indicates otherwise.

(1) Activities of daily living--Limited to the following activities: bathing, dressing, grooming, routine hair and skin care, meal preparation, feeding, exercising, toileting, transfer/ambulation, positioning, and range of motion.

(2) Client-- the individual receiving care.

(3) Delegation--Authorizing an unlicensed person to provide nursing services while retaining accountability for how the unlicensed person performs the task. It does not include situations in which an unlicensed person is directly assisting a RN by carrying out nursing tasks in the presence of a RN.

(4) Unlicensed person--An individual, not licensed as a health care provider:

(A) who is monetarily compensated to provide certain health related tasks and functions in a complementary or assistive role to the RN in providing direct client care or carrying out common nursing functions;

(B) including, but is not limited to, nurse aides, orderlies, assistants, attendants, technicians, home health aides, medication aides permitted by a state agency, and other individuals providing personal care/assistance of health related services; or

(C) who is a professional nursing student, not licensed as a RN or LVN, providing care for monetary compensation and not as part of their formal educational program shall be considered to be unlicensed persons and must provide that care in conformity with this chapter.

224.5. RN Accountability for Delegated Tasks.

(a) The RN's accountability to the BON with respect to its taking disciplinary action against the RN's license is met when the delegating RN has complied with and can verify compliance with this chapter and specifically with §224.6 and §224.8(b)(1) of this title (relating to General Criteria for Delegation and Discretionary Delegation Tasks) as appropriate.

(b) This chapter does not change or apply to a RN's civil liability.

224.6. General Criteria for Delegation.

The following standards must be met before the RN delegates nursing tasks to unlicensed persons. These criteria apply to all instances of RN delegation. Additional criteria, if appropriate to the particular task being delegated, may also be found in §224.8(b)(1) of this title (relating to Discretionary Delegation Tasks).

(1) The RN must make an assessment of the client's nursing care needs. The RN should, when the client's status allows, consult with the client, and when appropriate the client's family and/or significant other(s), to identify the client's nursing needs prior to delegating nursing tasks.

(2) The nursing task must be one that a reasonable and prudent RN would find is within the scope of sound nursing judgment to delegate. The RN should consider the five rights of delegation: the right task, the right person to whom the delegation is made, the right

RNs should read these definitions carefully since how a term is defined can be crucial in understanding a rule. Normally, only the most important terms are defined.

Delegation confers legal authority on individuals to perform tasks that they would otherwise not have the legal authority to perform. It differs from "assigning" which is administratively directing a person to perform a task that she/he already has legal authority to perform. For example, RNs may assign tasks to LVNs but would not normally delegate tasks to them if they are otherwise legally authorized to perform those tasks. LVNs have no authority to delegate tasks to unlicensed persons but may assign tasks to them. Defining "delegation" as not including "assisting" means that the latter is not governed by these rules. Note that assisting must occur in the presence of the RN.

This definition does not include other licensed practitioners such as LVNs. Licensed practitioners operate under the authority of their own license and delegation is not required for them to perform tasks falling within the scope of their license. Delegation normally occurs only with respect to unlicensed persons. One might look at delegation as "loaning one's license." RNs don't need to loan their license to someone (e.g., an LVN) who has a license. Delegation would still be required for tasks outside the scope of the other practitioner's license. As a practical matter, any task outside the scope of the other practitioner's (e.g., LVN's) license is unlikely to be a task that can be delegated under these rules.

Nursing students performing tasks as part of their educational program are exempted under §224.2(2)(C) from the application of these delegation rules. When nursing students perform nursing tasks outside of their educational program they are in fact functioning as unlicensed persons.

An RN delegating in accordance with this rule will not be subject to disciplinary action by the BON even if the unlicensed person makes a mistake. This is the case because any RN complying with these rules will be acting in a way that the BON has indicated is appropriate conduct for an RN. However, the RN may still be liable in a professional liability suit for any injury to a patient on a theory of vicarious liability. This is the case because the unlicensed person will be performing under the authority of the RN's license and legally as the RN's agent.

This section sets out the criteria that must always be met if delegation is to be appropriate in situations governed by this Rule 224. Other sections may clarify or add to these criteria but do not replace them. If the criteria set out in this section are not met, the task is not one that can be delegated in acute care settings or for acute conditions.

The RN must make an assessment before delegating. Without an initial assessment, the RN has no basis for deciding what can be delegated safely.

This is an objective standard. If a reasonable, prudent RN wouldn't delegate the task then it cannot be delegated. What a reasonable, prudent RN would do is normally determined by expert testimony.

circumstances, the right direction and communication by the RN, and the right supervision as determined by the RN.

(3) The nursing task must be one that, in the opinion of the delegating RN, can be properly and safely performed by the unlicensed person involved without jeopardizing the client's welfare.

(4) The nursing task must not require the unlicensed person to exercise professional nursing judgment; however, the unlicensed person may take any action that a reasonable, prudent non-health care professional would take in an emergency situation.

(5) The unlicensed person to whom the nursing task is delegated must be adequately identified. The identification may be by individual or, if appropriate, by training, education, and/or certification/permit of the unlicensed person.

(6) The RN shall have either instructed the unlicensed person in the delegated task, or verified the unlicensed person's competency to perform the nursing task. The verification of competence may be done by the RN making the decision to delegate or, if appropriate, by training, education, experience and/or certification/permit of the unlicensed person.

(7) The RN shall adequately supervise the performance of the delegated nursing task in accordance with the requirements of §224.7 of this title (relating to Supervision).

(8) If the delegation continues over time, the RN shall periodically evaluate the delegation of tasks. For example, the evaluation would be appropriate when the client's Nursing Care Plan is reviewed and revised. The RN's evaluation of a delegated task(s) will be incorporated into the client's Nursing Care Plan.

224.7. Supervision.

The registered professional nurse shall provide supervision of all nursing tasks delegated to unlicensed persons in accordance with the following conditions. These supervision criteria apply to all instances of RN delegation for clients with acute conditions or in acute care environments.

(1) The degree of supervision required shall be determined by the RN after an evaluation of appropriate factors involved including, but not limited to, the following:

(A) the stability of the client's status in relation to the task(s) to be delegated;

(B) the training, experience, and capability of the unlicensed person to whom the nursing task is delegated;

(C) the nature of the nursing task being delegated; and

(D) the proximity and availability of the RN to the unlicensed person when the nursing task will be performed.

(2) The RN or another equally qualified RN shall be available in person or by telecommunications, and shall make decisions about appropriate levels of supervision using the following examples as guidelines:

(A) In situations where the RN's regularly scheduled presence is required to provide nursing services, including assessment, planning, intervention and evaluation of the client whose health status is changing and/or to evaluate the client's health status, the RN must be readily available to supervise the unlicensed person in the performance of delegated tasks. Settings include, but are not limited to acute care, long term care, rehabilitation centers, and/or clinics providing public health services.

(B) In situations where nursing care is provided in the client's residence but the client's status is unstable and unpredictable and the RN is required to assess, plan, intervene, and evaluate the client's unstable and unpredictable status and need for skilled nursing services, the

This is a subjective standard requiring that the delegating RN believe the task being delegated can be performed safely by the unlicensed person. Obviously, there must be some reasonable basis for the RN's opinion.

If nursing judgment and nursing intervention could be routinely delegated, the unlicensed personnel would become a nursing substitute.

To know if a a task can be safely delegated, the RN needs to know who will be performing the task. Delegating to a completely unknown individual is not permitted. This rule does permit delegation to a person identified in terms of training, certification, etc. The RN should have a basis for knowing that a person with that training, education or certification can perform the task being delegated.

This subsection is also designed to ensure that the RN knows the unlicensed person can safely perform the task delegated.

The RN must adequately supervise any delegated task. The next section (§224.7) sets out in more detail what constitutes adequate supervision.

Periodically, the RN must evaluate the delegation to assure it remains appropriate and safe.

This section defines what constitutes adequate supervision of the unlicensed person by the RN.

The degree of supervision required depends on a number of factors and therefore will vary from case to case. The factors listed are ones that the RN must consider.

Supervision can be provided by an RN (if equally qualified) other than the delegating RN. An RN does have to be available to the unlicensed person. Subsecs. (A) and (B) provide additional guidance as to the required availability of the supervising RN.

This Subdivision (A) would apply to most cases and to all cases when care is being provided outside the client's residence or independent living environment. Acute care, long-term care and public health clinics are all governed by this subsection. The supervising RN must be "readily available" (either in person or by telecommunications) but that term is not defined.

If care is provided in the client's residence and the client's condition is unstable, the RN must make a supervisory visit at least every two weeks. If the client's condition is stable and predictable then Rule 225 most likely would apply rather than this Rule 224.

RN shall make supervisory visits at least every fourteen calendar days. The RN shall assess the relationship between the unlicensed person and the client to determine whether health care goals are being met. Settings include, but are not limited to group homes, foster homes and/or the client's residence.

224.8. Delegation of Tasks.

(a) Tasks Which are Most Commonly Delegated. By way of example, and not in limitation, the following nursing tasks are ones that are most commonly the type of tasks within the scope of sound professional nursing practice to be considered for delegation, regardless of the setting, provided the delegation is in compliance with §224.6 of this title (relating to General Criteria for Delegation) and the level of supervision required is determined by the RN in accordance with §224.7 of this title (relating to Supervision):

(1) non-invasive and non-sterile treatments;

(2) the collecting, reporting, and documentation of data including, but not limited to:

(A) vital signs, height, weight, intake and output, capillary blood and urine test for sugar and hematest results;

(B) environmental situations;

(C) client or family comments relating to the client's care; and

(D) behaviors related to the plan of care;

(3) ambulation, positioning, and turning;

(4) transportation of the client within a facility;

(5) personal hygiene and elimination, including vaginal irrigations and cleansing enemas;

(6) feeding, cutting up of food, or placing of meal trays;

(7) socialization activities;

(8) activities of daily living; and

(9) reinforcement of health teaching planned and/or provided by the registered nurse.

(b) Discretionary Delegation Tasks.

(1) In addition to General Criteria for Delegation outlined in §224.6 of this title, the nursing tasks which follow in paragraph (2) of this subsection may be delegated to an unlicensed person only:

(A) if the RN delegating the task is directly responsible for the nursing care given to the client;

(B) if the agency, facility, or institution employing unlicensed personnel follows a current protocol for the instruction and training of unlicensed personnel performing nursing tasks under this subsection and that the protocol is developed with input by registered nurses currently employed in the facility and includes:

This Sec.224.8 addresses what tasks can and cannot be delegated.

This Subsec. (a) identifies tasks that a reasonable, prudent RN would normally find to be within the scope of sound professional nursing judgment to delegate. This only means that the one requirement of being within sound practice to delegate set out in Subsec. (2) of §224.6 (General Criteria for Delegation) has been met. The delegating RN still needs to be sure the other seven criteria listed in §224.6 are met -- that the task can be safely delegated in the particular circumstances, that supervision is adequate, etc.

This Subdivision (9) permits delegation <u>only</u> of reinforcement of health teaching done by the RN. See Paragraph (c)(4) [Nursing Tasks Prohibited from Delegation] below which prohibits RNs' delegating responsibility for health teaching.

This Subsec. (b) may be one of the more difficult sections of the delegation rules to understand. It identifies tasks which a reasonable, prudent RN would not usually find to be within the scope of sound professional judgment to delegate but would so find under special circumstances, i.e., tasks that can be delegated but normally would not be. The subsection in essence puts the RN on notice to be very careful in delegating any of the tasks identified in (b)(2) since they are not usually tasks that could be delegated.

To help assure such delegation is safe, this Paragraph (1) sets out additional conditions that must be met. An RN delegating any of the tasks in Paragraph (b)(2) should be sure not only that these special conditions are met, but also all the other general criteria for delegation set out in §224.6, although there is some duplication.

The delegating RN must be an RN directly responsible for the client's nursing care, i.e., these tasks may not be delegated by a nursing supervisor who does not have direct patient care responsibility. It is only the RN caring for the patient who can know if these tasks can be safely delegated.

The facility or institution must have a training protocol in place that complies with this subsection.

(i) the manner in which the instruction addresses the complexity of the delegated task;

(ii) the manner in which the unlicensed person demonstrates competency of the delegated task;

(iii) the mechanism for reevaluation of the competency; and

(iv) an established mechanism for identifying those individuals to whom nursing tasks under this subsection may be delegated; and

(C) if the protocol recognizes that the final decision as to what nursing tasks can be safely delegated in any specific situation is within the specific scope of the RN's professional judgment.

(2) the following are nursing tasks that are not usually within the scope of sound professional nursing judgment to delegate and may be delegated only in accordance with, §224.6 of this title and paragraph (1) of this subsection. These types of tasks include:

(A) sterile procedures--those procedures involving a wound or an anatomical site which could potentially become infected;

(B) non-sterile procedures, such as dressing or cleansing penetrating wounds and deep burns;

(C) invasive procedures--inserting tubes in a body cavity or instilling or inserting substances into an indwelling tube; and

(D) care of broken skin other than minor abrasions or cuts generally classified as requiring only first aid treatment.

(c) Nursing Tasks Prohibited from Delegation. By way of example, and not in limitation, the following are nursing tasks that are not within the scope of sound professional nursing judgment to delegate:

(1) physical, psychological, and social assessment which requires professional nursing judgment, intervention, referral, or follow-up;

(2) formulation of the nursing care plan and evaluation of the client's response to the care rendered;

(3) specific tasks involved in the implementation of the care plan which require professional nursing judgment or intervention;

(4) the responsibility and accountability for client health teaching and health counseling which promotes client education and involves the client's significant others in accomplishing health goals; and

(5) administration of medications, including intravenous fluids, except by medication aides as permitted under §224.9 of this title (relating to The Medication Aide Permit Holder).

224.9. The Medication Aide Permit Holder.

(a) A RN may delegate to medication aides the administration of medication to clients in long term care facilities and home health agencies if:

(1) the medication aide holds a valid permit issued by the appropriate state agency to administer medications in that facility or agency;

(2) the RN assures that the medication aide functions in compliance with the laws and regulations of the agency issuing the permit; and

(3) the route of administration is oral, via a permanently placed feeding tube, sublingual or topical including eye, ear or nose drops and vaginal or rectal suppositories.

(b) The following tasks may not be delegated to the Medication Aide Permit Holder unless allowed and in compliance with Chapter 225 of this title (relating to RN Delegation to Unlicensed Personnel and Tasks not Requiring Delegation in Independent Living Environments for Clients with Stable and Predictable Conditions):

The protocol must explicitly give the delegating RN ultimate authority over the decision as to what tasks can be safely delegated.

This Paragraph (2) lists the tasks that may be delegated if, and only if, the requirements of Subsection (a) have been met. These are tasks an RN should be careful in delegating and be sure the conditions of Paragraph (b)(1) and the general criteria of Sec. 224.6 have been met.

This Subsec. (c) identifies tasks that a reasonable, prudent RN would not find to be within the scope of sound nursing judgment to delegate. Since Subsec. (2) of §224.6 (General Criteria for Delegation) permits delegation only if a reasonable, prudent RN would make such a finding, none of the tasks identified here can meet all the criteria for delegation and therefore cannot be delegated. No task involving the exercise of professional nursing judgment can be delegated.

See Paragraph(a)(9) above which does permit the delegation of the reinforcement of health teaching.

The administration of medications cannot be delegated except as specifically permitted by §224.9.

This section permits the delegation of medication administration to medication aides in long-term care and to home health medication aides in community settings if the conditions listed are met. Neither of these aides function in hospitals so delegation of the administration of medications in hospital settings is not permitted. Rules of the Texas Department of Aging and Disabilities Services govern medication aides in long-term care and home health medication aides and address the types of medications that these aides can administer.

Legislation (HB 3611; SB 1857) passed in 2011 added Secs. 161.091-.096 to the Human Resources Code. These sections permit unlicensed persons to administer medications in certain practice settings providing care to persons with intellectual and developmental disabilities after being assessed by an RN.

This Subsec. (b) identifies what tasks may not be delegated to medication aides.

(1) calculation of any medication doses except for measuring a prescribed amount of liquid medication and breaking a tablet for administration, provided the RN has calculated the dose;

(2) administration of the initial dose of a medication that has not been previously administered to the client;

(3) administration of medications by an injectable route except as permitted for administration of insulin under §225.11 of this title (relating to Delegation of Administration of Medications From Pill Reminder Container and Administration of Insulin);

(4) administration of medications used for intermittent positive pressure breathing or other methods involving medication inhalation treatments except as permitted in §225.10(10)(E) of this title (relating to Tasks That May Be Delegated).

(5) administration of medications by way of a tube inserted in a cavity of the body except as stated in §225.11 of this title.

(6) responsibility for receiving verbal or telephone orders from a physician, dentist, or podiatrist; and

(7) responsibility for ordering a client's medication from the pharmacy.

224.10. Supervising Unlicensed Personnel Performing Tasks Delegated by Other Practitioners.

(a) The following applies to the registered professional nurse who practices in a collegial relationship with another licensed practitioner who has delegated tasks to an unlicensed person over whom the RN has supervisory responsibilities. The RN's accountability to the BON, with respect to its taking disciplinary action against the RN's license, is met if the RN:

(1) verifies the training of the unlicensed person;

(2) verifies that the unlicensed person can properly and adequately perform the delegated task without jeopardizing the client's welfare; and

(3) adequately supervises the unlicensed person.

(b) If the RN cannot verify the unlicensed person's capability to perform the delegated task, the RN must communicate this fact to the licensee who delegated the task.

224.11. Application of Other Laws and Regulations.

BON §217.11(1) of this title (relating to Standards of Professional Nursing Practice) requires RNs to know and conform to all laws and regulations affecting their area of practice. The RN delegating tasks to an unlicensed person should be aware that, in addition to this chapter, various laws and regulations may apply to, including but not limited to, laws and regulations governing home and community support services agencies, Medicare and Medicaid regulations, and Medication Aide regulations. In situations where a RN's practice is governed by multiple laws and regulations that impose different requirements, the RN must comply with them all and if inconsistent, the most restrictive requirement(s) governs. For example, if one regulation requires an RN to make a supervisory visit every 14 days and another leaves it to the RN's professional judgment, the RN would have to visit at least every 14 days or more frequently, if that is what the RN's professional judgment indicated.

Rule 225. RN Delegation to Unlicensed Personnel and Tasks Not Requiring Delegation in Independent Living Environments for Clients with Stable and Predictable Conditions. §§225.1 - 225.14

ANNOTATOR'S NOTE 1: *The BON is currently in process of considering revisions to this Rule 225 and is expected to propose amendments by late 2013 or early 2014.*

ANNOTATOR'S NOTE 2: *The BON has developed a Delegation Resource Packet to assist*

An RN may be called on to supervise unlicensed persons performing tasks delegated by another provider. This rule identifies the RN's responsibilities in this situation. It should be noted that this rule appears not to prevent an RN from supervising the performance of a task (e.g., administration of medications) that the RN cannot delegate. Many RNs think this should not be the case and reason that if it is not safe for an RN to delegate a task, it should not be safe for an unlicensed person to perform that task under RN supervision. If it is safe for RNs to supervise tasks they cannot safely delegate themselves, the other practitioner's involvement should add something that transforms the situation from an unsafe to a safe one.

Laws and regulations other than the BON's delegation rules may apply to the delegation of tasks to unlicensed persons. Complying with the BON rules does not guarantee compliance with these other rules. Conversely, complying with those other laws and regulations does not assure compliance with the BON rules. As a general rule, when two or more laws or rules apply, the RN must follow both and if the two are inconsistent, the more restrictive of the two.

This Rule 225 governs delegation in independent living environments for clients with stable and predictable conditions. Texas has been one of the more progressive states in developing a delegation model that will assist clients with functional disabilities to maintain independence. Board rules governing delegation of tasks for this client population were first adopted in 1990 and have been significantly modified at least three times. Current Rule 224 reflects the work of a task force mandated by 2001 legislation (HB 456). That legislation charged the BON to appoint a task force to "review and make recommendations regarding the provision of health maintenance tasks to persons with functional disabilities in independent living environments including analysis of when delegation and assignment by RNs is appropriate and safe."

the RN in making decisions about the appropriate utilizations of unlicensed persons in situations governed by Rule 225. The packet includes the following materials:

Frequently Asked Questions
Links to Delegation Resources
Rule 225 Conflict Resolution Model
Rule 225 Professional Nursing Assessment Grid with examples
Rule 225 Quick Reference Guide
Rule 225 Flow Chart

These are set out in the Appendices to this Guide and also are on the BON website.

225.1. Application of Chapter.

(a) This chapter applies only to situations meeting the following criteria:

(1) the client is in an independent living environment;

(2) the client, if 16 or older, or client's responsible adult is willing and able to participate in decisions about the overall management of the client's health care; and

(3) the task is for a stable, predictable condition as defined by §225.4 of this title (relating to Definitions).

(b) If the situation does not meet the above criteria in subsection (a) of this section, any delegation of nursing tasks by the RN to an unlicensed person must comply with BON Chapter 224 of this title (relating to Delegation of Tasks Relating to Acute Conditions or Settings Other Than Independent Living Environments).

(c) Should a client develop an acute condition that is unstable or unpredictable, this chapter may still be applicable to tasks that relate solely to the client's stable and predictable condition(s) and not to the acute condition(s).

A key aspect of the rule is the dividing of tasks performed by unlicensed persons in the independent living environment into three categories or levels:

1. *Activities of daily living (ADLs);*
2. *Health maintenance activities (HMAs); and*
3. *Nursing tasks requiring delegation.*

Another important aspect of the rule is that it is designed for what is sometimes referred to as consumer-directed care. More specifically, the rule applies only to situations meeting the following three criteria:

1. *Is an independent living environment;*
2. *The client (or client's responsible adult) is able to participate in decisions about the client's care; and*
3. *The client's condition is stable and predictable.*

An understanding of Rule 225's structure is helpful in understanding its content.

- *§225.1 (Application) and §225.2 (Exclusions) identify the settings in which this rule applies.*
- *§225.3 (Purpose) and §225.4 (Definitions) set out general principles governing delegation and define key terms.*
- *§225.5 (Accountability) clarifies the RN's accountability for delegated tasks.*
- *§225.6 (Assessment) addresses the client assessment the RN must perform.*
- *§225.7 (ADLs) and §225.8 (HMAs) address activities of daily living and health maintenance activities.*
- *§225.9 - §225.12 address delegation.*
- *§225.13 addresses supervising unlicensed persons performing tasks delegated by another practitioner.*
- *§225.14 (Other Laws) sets out guidelines for when more than a single law or rule applies to delegation.*

The BON also has entered into a memorandum of understanding with the Department of Aging and Disability Services regarding certain tasks that can be performed by unlicensed personnel in community support agencies without RN delegation.

Legislation (HB 3611; SB 1857) passed in 2011 added Secs. 161.091-.096 to the Human Resources Code. These sections permit unlicensed persons to administer medications in certain practice settings providing care to persons with intellectual and developmental disabilities after being assessed by an RN.

Since two rules govern delegation, RNs will need to know which rule applies. This Rule 225 applies only to situations that meet all three of the following criteria:

1. *independent living environments (see definition in §225.4);*
2. *the client (or client's responsible adult) must be able to participate in decisions about the client's care (see definition of "client's responsible adult" in §225.4); and*
3. *client's condition is stable and predictable (see definition of "stable and predictable" in §225.4).*

Rule 224 applies to all other situations. In short, Rule 224 applies to all delegation not specially allowed under this Rule 225. See Rule 224.1.

If a situation does not meet the three criteria set out in Subsec. (a), then Rule 224 applies.

Just because a client covered by this rule develops an acute condition does not mean this rule does not continue to govern the stable, predictable condition. For example, if a client with a functional disability develops the flu, tasks performed by unlicensed persons for the flu would be governed by Rule 224 but this Rule 225 would still apply to tasks performed for conditions related to the functional disability.

225.2. Exclusions from Chapter.

This chapter does not apply to:

(1) tasks performed for acute, unstable, or unpredictable conditions;

(2) settings where nursing services are continuously provided;

(3) tasks provided in compliance with Government Code §531.051(f) (relating to certain tasks performed for clients under certain state-funded programs not constituting practice of professional nursing);

(4) RNs who:

(A) supervise or instruct others in the gratuitous nursing care of the sick;

(B) are qualified nursing faculty or preceptors directly supervising or instructing nursing students in the performance of nursing tasks while enrolled in accredited nursing programs;

(C) instruct and/or supervise an unlicensed person in the proper performance of nursing tasks as a part of an education course designed to prepare persons to obtain a state license, certificate or permit that authorizes the person to perform such tasks; and

(D) assign tasks to or supervise LVNs or other licensed practitioners practicing within the scope of their license.

225.3. Purpose.

(a) The Texas Board of Nursing(BON or Board) recognizes that public preference in the provision of health care services includes a greater opportunity for clients to share with the RN in the choice and control for delivery of services in the community based setting. The Board also appreciates that the provision of health care is dynamic in nature and continually evolving. As professional nurses, regardless of practice setting, RNs are obligated to assess the nursing needs of the client, develop a plan of nursing actions, implement this plan, and evaluate the outcome. These are essential components of RN practice that identify professional nursing as a process discipline. Professional nursing while inclusive of tasks is not focused on tasks but rather on interventions or client-centered actions initiated to assist the client in accomplishing the goals defined in the nursing care plan.

(b) In the independent living environment, RNs encounter clients across the spectrum of health to illness. The primary goal is to assist the choice of the client to achieve the most integrated setting/least restrictive environment throughout the life span. This is regularly accomplished, in part, through the assistance of unlicensed personnel who work with the client to complete a variety of tasks on a daily basis. Some tasks that are considered nursing tasks in the acute care setting are considered support services necessary to assist the client to maintain client health, and thus the highest degree of independence and quality of life possible, in the independent living environment.

(c) The purpose of this chapter is to provide guidance to RNs practicing in independent living environments in incorporating the use of unlicensed personnel to achieve optimal health benefits for the client. Clients in these settings have needs that may be categorized as activities of daily living (ADLs), health maintenance activities (HMAs), or nursing tasks. For some clients, ADLs and HMAs may be of a routine and supportive nature that minimizes the need for RN involvement.

(d) The RN shall collaborate with the client and/or the client's responsible adult in pursuit

If an exclusion applies then that situation is not governed by these delegation rules. There may still be other rules that do apply. For example, both the BON's Unprofessional Conduct Rule and Standard of Practice Rule prohibit an RN from delegating or making assignments to persons without the necessary education, training and experience.

Exclusions (1) and (2) mirror the three criteria that must be met for this Rule 225 to apply.

The reference to Section 531.051(f) should be to (e) and (f). It exempts from the practice of nursing certain health maintenance tasks performed for clients with disabilities in what is referred to as the "consumer-directed service option." Sec. 531.051(e)-(f) is set out in Part IX (Other Laws) of this Guide.

Legislation (HB 3611; SB 1857) passed in 2011 added Secs. 161.091-.096 to the Human Resources Code. These sections permit unlicensed persons to administer medications in certain practice settings providing care to persons with intellectual and developmental disabilities after being assessed by an RN.

Nursing students performing tasks or functions as part of their educational program are excluded from definition of unlicensed person in Rule 225.4(12).

RNs do not delegate tasks to LVNs but rather assign LVNs to perform tasks or functions they are authorized to do by their LVN license. See the definition of "unlicensed person" in 225.4.

This purpose statement specifically addresses the needs of clients in independent living environments with stable, predictable conditions who (or a responsible adult) can participate in decisions about management of their care.

The primary goal of nursing care by unlicensed persons for clients in this setting is to promote the client's independence.

Tasks may be described differently in this setting than they would be in an acute care setting.

The RN should collaborate with the client or client's responsible adult in decisions about the of the highest possible degree of independent living for the client. By adequately and accurately assessing the needs of the client in this setting, and considering the inter-related factors impacting the client's environment, the RN can effectively make decisions in utilizing unlicensed personnel to accomplish quality supportive services and care.

225.4. Definitions.

The following words and terms, when used in this chapter, shall have the following meanings, unless the context clearly indicates otherwise.

(1) Activities of daily living (ADLs)--limited to the following activities: bathing, dressing, grooming, routine hair and skin care, meal preparation, feeding, exercising, toileting, transfer/ambulation, positioning, range of motion, and assistance with self administered medications. The term does not include more specific tasks defined as health maintenance activities under paragraph (8) of this section (relating to Health Maintenance Activities).

(2) Administration of Medications--removal of an individual/unit dose from a previously dispensed, properly labeled container; verifying it with the medication order; giving the correct medication and the correct dose to the proper client at the proper time by the proper route; and accurately recording the time and dose given.

(3) Assistance with self-administered medication--any needed ancillary aid provided to a client in the client's self-administered medication or treatment regimen, such as reminding a client to take a medication at the prescribed time, opening and closing a medication container, pouring a predetermined quantity of liquid to be ingested, returning a medication to the proper storage area, and assisting in reordering medications from a pharmacy.

(4) Client--the individual receiving care.

(5) Client's Responsible Adult--an individual, 18 or older, normally chosen by the client, who is willing and able to participate in decisions about the overall management of the client's health care and to fulfill any other responsibilities required under this chapter for care of the client. The term includes but is not limited to parent, foster parent, family member, significant other, or legal guardian.

(6) Delegation--authorizing an unlicensed person to provide nursing services while retaining accountability for how the unlicensed person performs the task. It does not include situations in which an unlicensed person is directly assisting a RN by carrying out nursing tasks in the presence of a RN.

(7) Functional Disability--a mental, cognitive, or physical disability that precludes the physical performance of self-care tasks, including health maintenance activities and ADLs.

(8) Health Maintenance Activities (HMAs)--limited to the following tasks that enable the client to remain in an independent living environment and that go beyond ADLs because of the higher skill level required to perform:

(A) administering oral medications that are normally self-administered, including administration through a permanently placed feeding tube with irrigation;

(B) the administering of a bowel and bladder program, including suppositories, enemas, manual evacuation, intermittent catheterization, digital stimulation associated with a *client's health care.*

RNs should read these definitions carefully since how a term is defined can be crucial in understanding a rule. Normally, only the most important terms are defined. Some of the key terms defined are:

- *Activities of daily living (ADLs)*
- *Assistance with self-administered medications*
- *Client's responsible adult*
- *Delegation*
- *Functional disability*
- *Health maintenance activities (HMAs)*
- *Not requiring delegation*
- *Stable and predictable*

This is a traditional definition but note that it does not include HMAs as defined below. The distinction between ADLs and HMAs is important because unlicensed persons can perform the former in more situations than the latter. See Rules 225.7 and 225.8.

Assisting with self-medications is defined as an ADL and can be routinely performed by an unlicensed person without being delegated. The client does need to have the mental capacity to be able to be aware of what is occurring. Otherwise it is not assisting but administering.

This is a new term introduced in this rule. It is important because the rule applies not only to when the client can manage her or his care, but also when the client's responsible adult can.

Delegation confers legal authority on individuals to perform tasks that they would otherwise not have the legal authority to perform. It differs from "assigning" which is administratively directing a person to perform tasks that they already have legal authority to perform. For example, RNs may assign tasks to LVNs but would not normally delegate tasks to them. LVNs have no authority to delegate tasks to unlicensed persons but may assign tasks to them. Defining "delegation" as not including "assisting" means the latter is not governed by these rules. Note that assisting must occur in the presence of the RN.

"Health Maintenance Activities (HMAs)" is also a new terminology introduced in this rule. It denotes a level of task higher than ADLs but still at a level below delegation. See Rule 225.8.

bowel program, tasks related to external stoma care including but not limited to pouch changes, measuring intake and output, and skin care surrounding the stoma area;

(C) routine care of a Stage 1 decubitus;

(D) feeding and irrigation through a permanently placed feeding tube inserted in a surgically created orifice or stoma; and

(E) such other tasks as the Board may designate.

(9) Independent living environment--A client's individual residence which may include a home or homelike setting such as the client's home, an entity licensed or regulated by a state or federal agency or exempt from such licensure or regulation, (such as a group home, foster home, or assisted living facility), and includes where the client works, attends school, or engages in other community activities. The term does not include settings in which nursing services are continuously provided.

(10) Not Requiring Delegation--a determination by a RN that the performance of an ADL or HMA for a particular client does not constitute the practice of professional nursing based on criteria established by the Board/this chapter.

(11) Stable and predictable--a situation where the client's clinical and behavioral status is determined to be non-fluctuating and consistent. A stable/predictable condition involves long term health care needs which are not recuperative in nature and do not require the regularly scheduled presence of a registered nurse or licensed vocational nurse. Excluded by this definition are situations where the client's clinical and behavioral status is expected to change rapidly or in need of the continuous/continual assessment and evaluation of a registered nurse or licensed vocational nurse. The condition of clients receiving hospice care in an independent living environment where deterioration is predictable shall be deemed to be stable and predictable.

(12) Unlicensed person--an individual, not licensed as a health care provider:

(A) who is monetarily compensated to provide certain health related tasks and functions in a complementary or assistive role to the RN in providing direct client care or carrying out common nursing functions;

(B) who provides those tasks and functions as a volunteer but does not qualify as a friend providing gratuitous care for the sick under §301.004(1) of the Nursing Practice Act;

(C) including, but not limited to, nurse aides, orderlies, assistants, attendants, technicians, home health aides, medication aides permitted by a state agency, and other individuals providing personal care/assistance of health related services; or

(D) who is a professional nursing student, not licensed as a RN or LVN, providing care for monetary compensation and not as part of their formal educational program shall be considered to be unlicensed persons and must provide that care in conformity with this chapter.

225.5. RN Accountability.

(a) The RN is responsible for proper performance of the assessment required by §225.6 of this title (relating to RN Assessment of the Client) and for the RN's decisions made as a result of that assessment including determining that performance of a particular ADL or HMA for a particular client qualifies as not requiring delegation.

(b) The RN is not accountable for an unlicensed person's actual performance of ADLs or HMAs not requiring delegation.

(c) The RN's accountability to the BON with respect to its taking disciplinary action against the RN's license is met when the RN can verify compliance with this chapter.

(d) This chapter does not change a RN's civil liability.

225.6. RN Assessment of the Client.

(a) The RN, in consultation with the client if 16 or older, and when appropriate the client's

Independent living environment is broadly defined to include locations in addition to the client's residence.

The BON sets the criteria for when a task does not require delegation because it does not constitute the practice of nursing. The individual RN applies these criteria to the specific situation to determine if the task in this situation constitutes the practice of nursing.

"Stable and predictable" is another key term in this Rule 224 since the rule applies only when the client's condition is stable and predictable. See Rule 225.1 and .2.

"Unlicensed persons" do not include other licensed practitioners such as LVNs. Licensed practitioners operate under the authority of their own license and delegation is not required for them to perform tasks falling within the scope of their license. Delegation normally occurs only with respect to unlicensed persons. One might look at delegation as "loaning one's license." RNs don't need to loan their license to someone (e.g., an LVN) who has a license. Delegation would still be required for tasks outside the scope of the other practitioner's license. As a practical matter, any task outside the scope of the other practitioner's (e.g., LVN's) license is unlikely to be a task that can be delegated under these rules.

Nursing students performing tasks as part of their educational program are exempted under §225.2(4)(C) from the application of these delegation rules. When nursing students perform nursing tasks outside of their educational program they are in fact functioning as unlicensed persons.

An RN delegating in accordance with this rule will not be subject to disciplinary action by the BON even if the unlicensed person makes a mistake. This is the case because any RN complying with these rules will be acting in a way that the BON has indicated is appropriate conduct for an RN.

Because ADLs and HMAs not requiring delegation do not constitute the practice of nursing, the RN is not accountable for actual performance of the task. Note that Subsec. (a) makes the RN accountable for the decision that the task was an ADL or HMA not requiring delegation and the assessment on which that decision is based.

The RN may still be liable in a professional liability lawsuit for any injury to a patient on a theory of vicarious liability. This is the case because the unlicensed person will be performing under the authority of the RN's license and legally as the RN's agent.

The client assessment required by this Rule 225.6is a crucial component of the process by which the RN decides what tasks the unlicensed person can perform. The assessment results in responsible adult, must make an assessment to determine if the care:

(1) qualifies as an ADL or HMA not requiring delegation;

(2) can be delegated to an unlicensed person; or

(3) should not be delegated.

(b) In making this determination, the RN shall consider each of the following elements of assessment to develop an overall picture of the client's health status:

(1) the ability of the client or client's responsible adult to participate in the health care decision and ability and willingness to participate in the management and direction of the task;

(2) the adequacy and reliability of support systems available to the client or client's responsible adult;

(3) the degree of the stability and predictability of the client's health status relative to which the task is performed;

(4) the knowledge base of the client or client's responsible adult about the client's health status;

(5) the ability of the client or client's responsible adult to communicate with an unlicensed person in traditional or non-traditional ways; and

(6) how frequently the client's status shall be reassessed.

(c) While each element must be assessed, strength in one factor may compensate/offset a weakness in another factor. The assessment under this section does not require the RN to know either the specific unlicensed person who will perform the tasks or the specific qualifications of the unlicensed person who will perform the tasks, thus the RN is not required to determine the competency of the unlicensed person.

225.7. Activities of Daily Living Not Requiring Delegation.

(a) Activities of daily living (ADLs), as defined in this chapter, that do not fall within the practice of professional nursing may be performed by an unlicensed person in accordance with this section without being delegated. The Board has determined that in situations governed by this chapter ADLs do not fall within the practice of professional nursing when:

(1) performed for a person with a functional disability and the client would perform the task(s) but for the functional disability; and

(2) the RN determines, based on an assessment under §225.6 of this title (relating to RN Assessment of the Client) that the task(s) is such that it could be performed by any unlicensed person without RN supervision.

(b) If the above criteria cannot be met, an ADL may still be performed as a delegated task if it meets the criteria of §225.9 of this title (relating to Delegation Criteria).

225.8. Health Maintenance Activities Not Requiring Delegation.

(a) Health Maintenance Activities (HMAs), as defined in this chapter that do not fall within the practice of professional nursing, may be performed by an unlicensed person in accordance with this section without being delegated. The Board has determined that in situations governed by this chapter HMAs do not fall within the practice of professional nursing when:

(1) performed for a person with a functional disability;

(2) in addition to the client assessment under §225.6 of this title (relating to RN Assessment of the Client), a RN determines all of the following conditions exist:

(A) the client would perform the task(s) but for her/his functional disability;

(B) the task(s) can be directed by the client or client's responsible adult to be performed by an unlicensed person without RN supervision;

(C) the client or client's responsible adult is able, and has agreed in writing, to *a decision in how to classify the tasks as an ADL, HMA or nursing task requiring delegation. What additional assessment is required before the unlicensed person performs the task will depend on how the task is classified. See Rules 225.7, 225.8 and Rule 225.9.*

This initial assessment required by this rule is an assessment of the six factors listed.

This is not the frequency of supervisory visits of the tasks (which may not be required for ADLs or HMAs) but rather the frequency of reassessment of the client and situation to determine if the tasks being performed by the unlicensed person continue to be appropriately classified as ADLs, HMAs or nursing tasks.

No one factor is determinative. Rather, it is the factors considered in their totality that the RN considers. The assessment under this Rule is of the client and client's situation and not of the competency of a particular unlicensed person who will perform the task. Who will perform the task may not be known at the time of the assessment or may subsequently change. Additional assessment is required by other sections of this rule for particular types of tasks. See Rules 225.7, 225.8 and Rule 225.9.

Activities of daily living (ADLs) normally do not constitute nursing tasks and therefore normally do not require the RN to delegate in order to be performed by an unlicensed person.

The RN applies the criteria listed to determine if the ADL is one that does not constitute the practice of nursing and therefore does not require delegation. The RN's decision is to determine if these BON-developed criteria apply.

The RN may not know who the unlicensed person is. It is assumed that the client will select a person competent to perform the task.

If the RN determines delegation is required, then the RN looks to Rule 225.9 to determine if delegation is appropriate.

Though a higher level of task than ADLs, health maintenance activities (HMAs) may also not constitute nursing tasks and therefore may not require delegation in order to be performed by an unlicensed person.

The RN applies the criteria listed to determine if the HMA is one that does not constitute the practice of nursing and therefore does not require delegation. The RN's decision is to determine if these BON-developed criteria apply.

participate in directing the unlicensed person's actions in carrying out the HMA; and

(D) Either

(i) the client is willing and able to train the unlicensed person in the proper performance of the HMA, or

(ii) the client's responsible adult is capable of training the unlicensed person in the proper performance of the task and

(I) will be present when the task is performed, or

(II) if not present, will have observed the unlicensed person perform the task at least once to assure he/she can competently perform the task and will be immediately accessible in person or by telecommunications to the unlicensed person when the task is performed.

(b) If the above criteria cannot be met, an HMA may still be performed as a delegated task if it meets the criteria of §225.9 of this title (relating to Delegation Criteria).

225.9. Delegation Criteria.

(a) When determining whether to delegate a nursing task or those ADLs or HMAs requiring delegation, the RN, in addition to the assessment under §225.6 of this title (relating to RN Assessment of the Client), shall:

(1) determine that the task does not require the unlicensed person to exercise nursing judgment;

(2) verify the experience and competency of the unlicensed person to perform the task, including the unlicensed person's ability to recognize and inform the RN of client changes related to the task. The RN must have either:

(A) instructed the unlicensed person in the delegated task; or

(B) verified the unlicensed person's competency to perform the nursing task based on personal knowledge of the training, education, experience and/or certification/permit of the unlicensed person.

(3) determine, in consultation with the client or the client's responsible adult, the level of supervision and frequency of supervisory visits required, taking into account:

(A) the stability of the client's status;

(B) the training, experience and capability of the unlicensed person to whom the nursing task is delegated;

(C) the nature of the nursing task being delegated;

(D) the proximity and availability of the RN to the unlicensed person when the nursing task will be performed; and

(E) the level of participation of client or client's responsible adult; and

(4) consider whether the five rights of delegation can be met: the right task; the right person to whom the delegation is made; the right circumstances; the right direction and communication by the RN; and the right supervision.

(b) The RN or another RN qualified to supervise the unlicensed person shall be available, in person or by telecommunications when the unlicensed person is performing the task.

(c) If the RN is employed, the employing entity must have a written policy acknowledging that the final decision to delegate shall be made by the RN in consultation with client or client's responsible adult.

225.10. Tasks That May Be Delegated.

A RN may delegate the following tasks unless the RN's assessment under §225.6 of this title (relating to RN Assessment of the Client) and §225.9 of this title (relating to Delegation Criteria) determines that the task is not a task a reasonable and prudent nurse would delegate. Tasks include:

(1) an ADL the RN has determined requires delegation under §225.7 of this title (relating to Activities of Daily Living Not Requiring Delegation);

If the client's responsible adult will be the person to train the unlicensed person to perform the task, then he or she must be present or be immediately accessible at least by telecommunications when the unlicensed person performs the task.

If the RN determines an HMA does constitute the practice of nursing, the unlicensed person may still be able to perform it as a delegated task under Rule 225.9.

Nursing tasks can be delegated if the additional criteria of this rule are met as well as any additional criteria that may be applicable under Rules 225.10 and 225.11. Rule 225.12 sets out tasks that may not be delegated.

The RN must assess the four factors listed to determine if a nursing task can be delegated. The assessment of these factors is in addition to the assessment required under Rule 225.6. It should be noted that this rule applies to ADLs and HMAs if, and only if, the RN has determined the ADL or HMA requires delegation. Applying the criteria set out in Rules 225.7 and 225.8, the RN usually will determine that ADLs, and in many situations HMAs, are not nursing tasks. In short, delegation of ADLs and HMAs is likely to be the exception rather than the rule.

No preset frequency of supervisory visits is required. The factors listed are what the RN and client consider in deciding how frequently the RN should visit.

The RN or another qualified RN must be available to supervise the unlicensed person.

If the RN is employed, the employer must have a written policy acknowledging that the RN makes the final decision as to the appropriateness of delegation. The RN cannot simply say that she or he delegated the task because that is what the employer wanted.

This rule lists nursing tasks that it is presumed a reasonable, prudent RN would delegate in the absence of some contra-indicating factor identified as a result of the assessments required by Rules 225.6 and 225.9.

ANNOTATOR'S NOTE

The BON is currently in process of considering revisions to Rule 225 and will likely review this list of tasks. The board is expected to propose amendments by late 2013 or early 2014.

(2) a HMA the RN has determined requires delegation under §225.8 of this title (relating to Health Maintenance Activities Not Requiring Delegation);

(3) non-invasive and non-sterile treatments with low risk of infection;

(4) the collecting, reporting, and documentation of data including, but not limited to

(A) vital signs, height, weight, intake and output, capillary blood and urine test for sugar and hematest results,

(B) environmental situations/living conditions that affect the client's health status,

(C) client or significant other's comments relating to the client's care, and

(D) behaviors related to the plan of care;

(5) reinforcement of health teaching provided by the registered nurse;

(6) inserting tubes in a body cavity or instilling or inserting substances into an indwelling tube limited to the following:

(A) insertion and/or irrigation of urinary catheters for purpose of intermittent catheterization; and

(B) irrigation of an indwelling tube such as a urinary catheter or permanently placed feeding tube;

(7) tracheal care to include instilling normal saline and suctioning of a tracheostomy with routine supplemental oxygen administration;

(8) care of broken skin with low risk of infection;

(9) sterile procedures those procedures involving a wound or an anatomical site that could potentially become infected;

(10) administration of medications that are administered:

(A) orally or via permanently placed feeding tube inserted in a surgically created orifice or stoma;

(B) sublingually;

(C) topically;

(D) eye and ear drops; nose drops and sprays;

(E) vaginal or rectal suppositories;

(F) unit dose medication administration by way of inhalation for prophylaxis and/or maintenance; and

(G) oxygen administration for the purpose of non-acute respiratory maintenance.

(11) administration of oral unit dose medications from the client's daily reminder pill container in accordance with §225.11(a) of this title (relating to Delegation of Administration of Medications From Pill Reminder Container and Administration of Insulin);

(12) administration of insulin subcutaneously, nasally, or via insulin pump in accordance with §225.11(b) of this title; and

(13) other such tasks as the Board may designate.

225.11. Delegation of Administration of Medications From Pill Reminder Container and Administration of Insulin.

(a) In addition to complying with all previous criteria listed, when delegating the administration of oral unit dose medications from the client's daily pill reminder container, the RN must:

(1) ensure that the unit dose medication(s) are placed in the client's daily reminder pill container, from properly dispensed prescription bottle(s), by the RN or a person mutually agreed upon by the RN and client or client's responsible adult who has demonstrated the ability to complete the task properly;

(2) instruct the client or client's responsible adult and the unlicensed person involved in such delegation activity about each medication placed in such a container with regard to

The BON may add to this list of tasks but has not done so.

This rule provides additional guidance to the RN when delegating either 1) the administration of medications from a pill reminder container or 2) the administration of insulin.

Subsection (a) addresses delegation of medications from a pill reminder container.

distinguishing characteristics of each medication, proper time, dose, route and adverse effects which may be associated with the medication;

(3) provide to the client, client's responsible adult if applicable, and the unlicensed person(s) instructions to contact the RN before the medication is administered when there are questions concerning the medications or changes in the client's status related to the medication being given. An example is when the medications appear to be rearranged or missing.

(4) make supervisory visits in the event there are changes in the client's status related to the medication being given and determine the frequency of supervisory visits in consultation with the client or the client's responsible adult to assure that safe and effective services are being provided; and

(5) ensure the client or client's responsible adult acknowledges in writing that the administration of medication(s) under this section will be delegated to an unlicensed person.

(b) In addition to complying with all previous criteria listed, when delegating administration of insulin subcutaneously, nasally, or via insulin pump the RN must:

(1) arrange for a RN to be available on call for consultation/intervention 24 hours each day;

(2) provide teaching of all aspects of insulin administration, subcutaneously, nasally, or via insulin pump to the client and the unlicensed person to include, but not limited to proper technique for determination of the client's blood sugar prior to each administration of insulin, proper injection technique, risks, side effects and the correct response(s). The RN must leave written instructions for the performance of the administration of insulin subcutaneously, nasally, or via insulin pump, including a copy of the physician's order or instructions, for the unlicensed person, client, or client's responsible adult to use as a reference.

(3) delegate the administration of insulin subcutaneously, nasally, or via insulin pump to an unlicensed person, specific to one client. The RN must teach that the administration of insulin subcutaneously, nasally, or via insulin pump is to be performed only for the patient for whom the instructions are provided and instruct the unlicensed person that the task is client specific and not transferable to other clients or providers;

(4) delegate the administration of insulin subcutaneously, nasally, or via insulin pump to additional unlicensed persons providing care to the specific client provided the registered nurse limits the number of unlicensed persons to the number who will remain proficient in performing the task and can be safely supervised by the registered nurse;

(5) make supervisory visits to the client's location at least 3 times within the first 60 days (one within the first two weeks, one within the second two weeks and one in the last 30 days) to evaluate the proper medication administration of insulin by the unlicensed person(s). After the initial 60 days, the RN, in consultation with the client or client's responsible adult, shall determine the frequency for supervisory visits to assure the proper and safe administration of insulin by the unlicensed person(s). Separate visits shall be made for each unlicensed person administering insulin;

(6) make supervisory visits in the event there are changes in the client's status; and

(7) ensure that the client or client's responsible adult acknowledges in writing that the administration of medication(s) under this section will be delegated to an unlicensed person.

225.12. Tasks Prohibited From Delegation.

The following are nursing tasks that are not within the scope of sound professional nursing judgment to delegate:

(1) physical, psychological, and social assessment, which requires professional nursing judgment, intervention, referral, or follow-up;

(2) formulation of the nursing care plan and evaluation of the client's response to the care rendered;

(3) specific tasks involved in the implementation of the care plan that require professional nursing judgment or intervention;

(4) the responsibility and accountability for client or client's responsible adult health

Subsection (b) addresses delegation of the administration of insulin.

Supervisory visits are required.

This rule sets out what tasks may <u>not</u> be delegated.

teaching and health counseling which promotes client or client's responsible adult education and involves the client's responsible adult in accomplishing health goals; and

(5) the following tasks related to medication administration:

(A) calculation of any medication doses except for measuring a prescribed amount of liquid medication and breaking a tablet for administration, provided the RN has calculated the dose;

(B) administration of medications by an injectable route except for subcutaneous injectable insulin as permitted by §225.11(b) of this title (relating to Delegation of Administration of Medications From Pill Reminder Container and Administration of Insulin);

(C) administration of medications by way of a tube inserted in a cavity of the body except as permitted by §225.10(10) of this title (relating to Task That May Be Delegated);

(D) responsibility for receiving or requesting verbal or telephone orders from a physician, dentist, or podiatrist; and

(E) administration of the initial dose of a medication that has not been previously administered to the client unless the RN documents in the client's medical record the rationale for authorizing the unlicensed person to administer the initial dose.

225.13. Supervising Unlicensed Personnel Performing Tasks Delegated by Other Practitioners.

(a) The following applies to the registered nurse who practices in a collegial relationship with another licensed practitioner who has delegated tasks to an unlicensed person over whom the RN has supervisory responsibilities. The RN's accountability to the BON, with respect to its taking disciplinary action against the RN's license, is met if the RN:

(1) verifies the training of the unlicensed person;

(2) verifies that the unlicensed person can properly and adequately perform the delegated task without jeopardizing the client's welfare; and

(3) adequately supervises the unlicensed person.

(b) If the RN cannot verify the unlicensed person's capability to perform the delegated task, the RN must communicate this fact to the licensee who delegated the task.

225.14. Application of Other Laws and Regulations.

BON §217.11(1) of this title (relating to Standards of Professional Nursing Practice) requires RNs to know and conform to all laws and regulations affecting their area of practice. The RN authorizing an unlicensed person to perform tasks in independent living environments should be aware to that, in addition to this chapter, various laws and regulations may apply including, but not limited to, laws and regulations governing home and community support service agencies and Medicare and Medicaid regulations. In situations where a RN's practice is governed by multiple laws and regulations that impose different requirements, the RN must comply with them all and if inconsistent, the most restrictive requirement(s) governs. For example, if one regulation requires a RN to make a supervisory visit every 14 days and another leaves it to the RN's professional judgment, the RN would have to visit at least every 14 days or more frequently, if that is what the RN's professional judgment indicated.

5. ASSISTING AT SURGERY (RULE 217.18)

Rule 217.18. Assisting at Surgery

(a) Nurse First Assistants.

(1) A registered nurse who wishes to function as a first assistant (RNFA) in surgery shall meet the following requirements :

(A) Current licensure as a registered nurse in the State of Texas or a current, valid registered nurse license with a multi-state privilege in a party state;

Certain tasks related to medication administration may not be delegated.

An RN may be called on to supervise unlicensed persons performing tasks delegated by another provider. This rule identifies the RN's responsibilities in this situation. It should be noted that this rule appears not to prevent an RN from supervising the performance of a task (e.g., administration of medications) that the RN cannot delegate. Many RNs think this should not be the case and reason that if it is not safe for an RN to delegate a task, it should not be safe for an unlicensed person to perform that task under RN supervision. If it is safe for RNs to supervise tasks they cannot safely delegate themselves, the other practitioners' involvement should add something that transforms the situation from an unsafe to a safe one.

Laws and regulations other than the BON's delegation rules may apply to the delegation of tasks to unlicensed persons. Complying with the BON rules does not guarantee compliance with these other rules. Conversely, complying with those other laws and regulations does not assure compliance with the BON rules. As a general rule, when two or more laws or rules apply, the RN must follow both and if the two are inconsistent, follow the more restrictive of the two.

This rule implements NPA Sec. 301.353. This rule addresses both RNs who practice as nurse first assistants (RNFAs) and other nurses (RNs and LVNs) who may otherwise assist in the performance of surgery. See Part IX (Other Laws) for laws and rules governing the Circulating RN role or position.

(B) Completion of a nurse first assistant educational program approved or recognized by an organization recognized by the Board; and

(C) Is either:

(i) currently certified in perioperative nursing by an organization recognized by the board (CNOR certification in perioperative nursing); or

(ii) currently recognized by the board as an advanced practice nurse and qualified by education, training, or experience to perform the tasks involved in perioperative nursing.

(2) When collaborating with other health care providers, the RNFA shall be accountable for knowledge of the statutes and rules relating to RNFAs and function within the scope of the registered nurse. Advanced practice nurses functioning as first assistants under the authority of (a)(1)(C)(ii) of this subsection shall function within the scope of the advanced role and specialty for which they hold authorization to practice from the board.

(3) A registered nurse (including an advanced practice nurse) functioning as a first assistant in surgery shall comply with the standards set forth by the AORN.

(b) Assisting at Surgery by Other Nurses.

(1) A nurse who is not a nurse first assistant as defined in subsection (a) of this section may assist a physician, podiatrist, or dentist in the performance of surgery if the nurse:

(A) Has current licensure as a nurse in the State of Texas or a current, valid nursing license with a multi-state privilege in a party state;

(B) Assists under the direct personal supervision and in the physical presence of the physician, podiatrist, or dentist;

(C) Is in the same sterile field as the physician, podiatrist, or dentist;

(D) Is employed by:

(i) the physician, podiatrist, or dentist;

(ii) a group to which the physician, podiatrist, or dentist belongs; or

(iii) a hospital licensed or owned by the state; and

(E) Is qualified by education, training, or experience to perform the tasks assigned to the nurse.

(2) A nurse assisting in the performance of surgery under this subsection shall not use:

(A) The title "nurse first assistant" or "registered nurse first assistant,"

(B) The abbreviation "R.N.F.A.," or

(C) Any other title or abbreviation that implies to the public that the person is qualified as a nurse first assistant under subsection (a) of this section.

6. RNS PERFORMING RADIOLOGIC PROCEDURES (RULE 217.14)

217.14. Registered Nurses Performing Radiologic Procedures.

(a) A registered nurse who performs radiologic procedures other than in a hospital that participates in the federal Medicare program or that is accredited by The Joint Commission shall submit an application for registration to the board and shall submit evidence including, but not limited to, the following:

(1) current licensure as a registered nurse in the State of Texas; and

(2) the name and business address of the practitioner or director of radiological services under whose instruction or direction the radiologic procedures are performed.

(b) After review by the board, notification of registration shall be mailed to the registered nurse informing him/her that the registration with the board has been completed.

(c) The registered nurse who is registered to perform radiologic procedures pursuant to subsection (a) of this section shall notify the board within 30 days of any changes that would render the information on the nurse's application incorrect, including but not limited to any changes in the identity of the practitioner or director of radiological procedures under whose

The only nurses who may practice as "nurse first assistants" or "RNFAs" are RNs who 1) are CNOR certified or APRNs and 2) have completed a nurse first assistant program recognized by the BON.

APRNs who qualify to first assist only in their APRN role may first assist only in that role. Some APRNs will qualify through the CNOR route and these may first assist in any role.

Nurses (RNs and LVNs) who are not nurse first assistants or RNFAs may still assist in the performance of surgery in a more limited way. They may not use the term "nurse first assistant" or "RNFA." See Subsection (b)(2) below. NPA Sec. 301.353(e) also prohibits these nurses from separately billing for assisting.

Only RNs who qualify to first assist as CNOR certified or APRN under subsection (a) may call themselves "nurse first assistants" or "RNFAs."

The Health and Safety Code gives the Texas Department of State Health Services (DSHS) authority 1) to require anyone not certified as a radiologic technologist to complete minimum training standards set by the Department, and 2) to identify dangerous/hazardous procedures that noncertified persons cannot perform. This would include RNs but the Department was given explicit authority to take into account the education that an RN has both 1) when setting the education required for RNs to perform radiologic procedures, and 2) when identifying what dangerous/hazardous procedures may not be performed by noncertified persons. The Department has adopted rules establishing a minimum training program for RNs and identifying dangerous/hazardous procedures. DSHS Rules 25 TAC §§140.516-.517 are set out in Part X (Other Laws) of this Guide.. RNs performing radiologic procedures should be familiar with and must comply with these rules.

The law governing radiologic technologists recognizes the BON retains certain authority over RNs performing radiologic procedures and requires certain of them to register with the BON. The BON's rule governing RN's performing radiologic procedures is set out here. However, RNs must still comply with the rules of the Texas Department of State Health Services.

See the definitions of "practitioner" and "radiologic procedure" in BON Rule 217.1. For instruction or direction the radiologic procedures are performed.

(d) The registered nurse whose functions include radiologic procedures must act within the scope of the Texas Nursing Practice Act and the Board's rules and shall comply with the training requirements and limitations of the Medical Radiologic Technologist Certification Act and the Texas Department of State Health Services rules, 25 TAC §§140.517 - 140.522. In addition, the registered nurse must be in compliance with the Texas Medical Practice Act, the Texas Pharmacy Act, and any applicable laws of the State of Texas.

(e) Any nurse who violates these rules shall be subject to disciplinary action by the board under the Occupations Code Chapter 301 and the Board's rules.

7. ADVANCED PRACTICE NURSING (RULES 221, 222)

ANNOTATOR'S NOTE: *Rules 217.11(4), Rule 221 and Rule 222 govern APRN standards and scope of practice and are set out in Subpart J below.*

A. Rule 217.11(4). Standards of Practice Applicable to APRNs
[See Subpart J]

B. Rule 221. Advanced Practice Nurses
[See Subpart J]

C. Rule 222. APRNs with Prescriptive Authority
[See Subpart J]

SUBPART C
PROFESSIONAL RESPONSIBILITIES

CHANGE OF NAME OR ADDRESS - RULE 217.7
REPLACING LICENSE - RULE 217.8
COPYING LICENSE - RULE 217.15
CONTINUING COMPETENCY - RULE 216

1. CHANGE OF NAME OR ADDRESS (RULE 217.7)

217.7. Change of Name and/or Address.

(a) A nurse/applicant for licensure shall notify the board in writing within ten days of a change of name by submitting a legal document reflecting this name change.

(b) A nurse/applicant for licensure shall notify the board in writing within 10 days of a change of address, providing the new address and his or her license number.

2. REPLACING LICENSE (RULE 217.8)

217.8. Duplicate or Substitute Credentials.

(a) A nurse whose original certificate of registration or wallet-sized license is lost or destroyed may obtain a duplicate by filing a form containing identifying information, notarized affidavit, and paying a non- refundable fee.

(b) A nurse who wants to change his/her name on the original certificate of registration or current wallet-sized license must submit:

purposes of this Rule 217.14, "practitioners" include only physicians, podiatrists, chiropractors and dentists. "Radiologic procedures" is defined quite broadly.

This Subpart C includes BON rules relating to a nurse's responsibilities as a licensed health care professional. That responsibility includes maintaining professional competency. The rules set out in this subpart are:

1. *Rule 217.7 Change of Address*
2. *Rule 217.8 Replacing License*
3. *Rule 217.15 Copying License*
4. *Rule 216 Continuing Competency*

It is important that a nurse maintain a current address with the BON. The Board is usually required to send notices only to the address that the nurse has on file with the Board and the nurse is assumed to have been given proper notice even if she/he never actually received it. For example, the Board is required to send any notice of a complaint against a nurse to the address the nurse has on file with the Board. The Board may take a default judgment against a nurse who doesn't respond to the complaint even though the nurse never received the complaint because she/he had not notified the BON of a change of address.

(1) a duly executed affidavit;
(2) the required non-refundable fee; and
(3) a copy of the legal document reflecting this name change

3. COPYING LICENSE (RULE 217.15)

217.15. Copying the License/Permit/Permanent Certificate of a Licensed Vocational Nurse or Registered Nurse/Graduate Nurse/Advanced Practice Nurse.

(a) The licensee or permit holder has the responsibility to protect his or her license/permit/permanent certificate from loss and potential fraudulent or unlawful use.

(b) A licensee or permit holder shall only allow his or her license/permit certificate to be copied for the purpose of licensure verification by employers, licensing boards, professional organizations, nursing programs, and third party payors for credentialing and reimbursement purposes. Other persons and/or agencies may contact the board's office in writing or by phone to verify licensure.

4. CONTINUING COMPETENCY (RULE 216)

216.1. Definitions.

The following words and terms, when used in this chapter, shall have the following meanings, unless the context clearly indicates otherwise:

(1) Academic course--A specific set of learning experiences offered in an accredited school, college or university. Academic credit will convert on the following basis: One academic quarter hour = 10 contact hours; one academic semester hour = 15 contact hours.

(2) Advanced Practice Registered Nurse (APRN)--A nurse anesthetist, nurse practitioner, nurse midwife, or clinical nurse specialist approved by the board to practice as an advanced practice registered nurse based on completion of an advanced educational program

The situations in which a nurse's license can be copied are limited. . Licenses can be verified online on the Board's website so verifying a license is easily done..

Nurses may demonstrate continuing competency in two ways - 1) taking a minimum number of CNE in their area of practice or 2) maintaining national certification in their area of practice. When the Board published proposed rules adding certification as an option, it described the change as follows:

> *Traditionally, continuing competency has been demonstrated primarily through the completion of continuing education courses. However, based upon the recommendations of the Task Force [Texas Nurses Association Competency Task Force] and the Texas Competency Consortium and the studies conducted by the NCSBN [National Council of State Board of Nursing] over the last five to ten years, the Board is proposing a departure from this approach by authorizing nurses to utilize other methods of demonstrating continuing competency. Under the proposed new chapter, a nurse is authorized to demonstrate continuing competency through the achievement, maintenance, or renewal of an approved national nursing certification in the nurse's area of practice, as well as through the completion of continuing education courses. Recognizing this additional method of compliance provides nurses with the option of pursuing and maintaining a certification in a specific area of practice. The additional education and training associated with obtaining and maintaining such a certification serves the purpose of the proposed new chapter, which is to protect the public health, safety, and welfare by ensuring that nurses stay abreast of current industry practices, enhance their professional competence, learn about new technology and treatment regimens, and update their clinical skills.*
>
> 34 *TexReg 2866 (5/15/09)*

The BON publishes a document explaining the continued competency requirements for license renewal. It is set out on the BON's website.

acceptable to the board.

(3) Approved--Recognized as having met established standards and predetermined criteria of the:

(A) credentialing agencies recognized by the board (applies to providers and programs); and

(B) certifying bodies accredited by a national certification accreditation body recognized by the board.

(4) Area of Practice--Any activity, assignment, or task in which the nurse utilized nursing knowledge, judgment, or skills during the licensure renewal cycle. If a nurse does not have a current area of practice, the nurse may refer to his or her last area of practice or most recent area of practice.

(5) Audit--A random sample of licensees taken to verify satisfactory completion of the board's requirements for continuing competency during a biennial license renewal period.

(6) Authorship--Development and publication of a manuscript related to nursing and health care.

(7) Certification--Nursing certification from an approved certifying body accredited by a national accreditation body recognized by the board.

(8) Classroom instruction--Workshops, seminars, institutes, conferences or short term courses which the individual attends which may be acceptable for continuing education credit.

(9) Clinical learning experiences--Faculty-planned and guided learning experiences designed to assist students to meet the course objectives and to apply nursing knowledge and skills in the direct care of patients/clients. This includes laboratories, acute care facilities, extended care facilities, and other community resources.

(10) Competency--The application of knowledge and the interpersonal decision making, and psychomotor skills expected for the nurse's practice role, within the context of public health, safety, and welfare.

(11) Contact hour--Sixty consecutive minutes of participation in a learning activity.

(12) Continuing Education (CE)--Programs beyond the basic preparation which are designed to promote and enrich knowledge, improve skills, and develop attitudes for the enhancement of nursing practice, thus improving health care to the public.

(13) Continuing education program--An organ0ized educational activity, e.g, self paced (online), classroom, approved through an external review process based on a predetermined set of criteria. The review is conducted by an organization(s) recognized by the board to approve programs and providers.

(14) Credentialing agency--An organization recognized by the board as having met nationally predetermined criteria to approve programs and providers of CE.

(15) Prescriptive Authority--Authorization granted to an advanced practice registered nurse who meets the requirements to carry out or sign a prescription drug order.

(16) Program number--A unique number assigned to a program upon approval which shall identify it regardless of the number of times it is presented.

(17) Provider--An individual, partnership, organization, agency or institution approved by an organization recognized by the board which offers continuing education programs.

(18) Provider number--A unique number assigned to the provider upon approval by the credentialing agency or organization.

216.2. Purpose.

The purpose of continuing competency is to ensure that nurses stay abreast of current industry practices, enhance their professional competence, learn about new technology and treatment regimens, and update their clinical skills. Continuing education in nursing includes programs beyond the basic preparation which are designed to promote and enrich knowledge, improve skills and develop attitudes for the enhancement of nursing practice, thus improving health care to the public. Nursing certification is another method of demonstrating continuing competence. Pursuant to authority set forth in the Occupations Code §301.303, the board requires

"Area of practice" is broadly defined. Rule 216.3(a) requires that CNE for license renewal be in the nurse's area of practice. An example of a nurse who does not have a current area of practice might be a nurse attorney.

Certification to satisfy continued competency for license renewal must be by a certifying body recognized by the BON.

A "contact hour" is 60 minutes.

Credentialing agencies must be recognized by the BON.

Purpose of requiring nurses to demonstrate continuing competency as part of license renewal is to ensure nurses keep their nursing knowledge and skills current.

participation in continuing competency activities for license renewal. The procedures set forth in these rules provide guidance to fulfilling the continuing competency requirement. The board encourages nurses to choose continuing education courses that relate to their work setting and area of practice or to attain, maintain, or renew an approved national nursing certification in their practice area, which benefits the public welfare.

216.3. Requirements.

(a) A nurse must meet either the requirements of this subsection or subsection (b) of this section. A nurse may choose to complete 20 contact hours of continuing education within the two years immediately preceding renewal of registration in his or her area of practice. These hours shall be obtained by participation in programs approved by a credentialing agency recognized by the board. A list of these agencies/organizations may be obtained from the board's office or web site.

(b) A nurse must meet either the requirements of this subsection or subsection (a) of this section. A nurse may choose to demonstrate the achievement, maintenance, or renewal of an approved national nursing certification in the nurse's area of practice. A list of approved national nursing certification criteria may be obtained from the board's office or web site.

(c) Requirements for the Advanced Practice Registered Nurse. The licensee authorized by the board as an advanced practice registered nurse (APRN) is required to obtain 20 contact hours of continuing education or attain, maintain or renew the national certification recognized by the board as meeting the certification requirement for the advanced practice registered nurse's role and population focus area of licensure within the previous two years of licensure. National certification as discussed in this section will only meet the requirement for licensure renewal.

(1) The required hours are not in addition to the requirements of subsection (a) or (b) of this section.

(2) The 20 contact hours of continuing education must be appropriate to the advanced specialty area and role recognized by the board.

(3) The APRN who holds prescriptive authority must complete, in addition to the requirements of this subsection, at least five additional contact hours of continuing education in pharmacotherapeutics.

(4) Category I Continuing Medical Education (CME) contact hours will meet requirements as described in this chapter.

(d) Forensic Evidence Collection.

(1) Each nurse licensed in Texas and employed in an emergency room (ER) setting on or after September 1, 2006 shall complete a minimum of two hours of continuing education relating to forensic evidence collection, as required by the Occupations Code §301.306 and this subsection:

(A) by September 1, 2008 for nurses to whom this requirement applies who are employed in an ER setting on or before September 1, 2006; or

(B) within two years of the initial date of employment in an ER setting. This requirement may be met through completion of approved continuing education activities, as set forth in §216.4 of this chapter (relating to Criteria for Acceptable Continuing Education Activity).

(2) This requirement shall apply to nurses who work in an ER setting that is:

(A) the nurse's home unit;

(B) an ER unit to which the nurse "floats" or schedules shifts; or

(C) a nurse employed under contractual, temporary, per diem, agency, traveling, or other employment relationship whose duties include working in an ER.

(3) A licensed nurse in Texas who would otherwise be exempt from CE requirements

A nurse can demonstrate continued competency either by:

1) Completing 20 contact hours of CNE (must in the nurse's area of practice) approved by a credentialing agency recognized by the BON; or

2) obtaining or maintaining national certification in the nurse's area of practice.

Special requirements apply to APRNs.

Like other nurses, APRNs can meet the continuing competency requirement either by CNE or national certification. However, APRNs with prescriptive authority will still need to take the 5 hours in pharmacotherapeutics.

CNE must be appropriate to their advanced practice specialty area.

APRNs with prescriptive authority must have 5 contact hours in pharmacotherapeutics.

***ANNOTATOR's NOTE**: In the 8/9/13 issue of the Texas Register, the BON issued proposed rules to require APRNs who prescribe controlled substances to complete an additional three hours of CNE relating to prescribing of controlled substances.*

APRNs may take Category I Continuing Medical Education.

Subsection (d) implements NPA Sec. 301.306. The forensic evidence collection CNE is a one time requirement and applies only to nurses practicing in an ER setting. All nurses practicing in ER must take the two hours even if otherwise exempt from taking CNE.

Nurses have two years to complete the CNE from when they begin practicing in an ER setting.

This Subdivision (2) describes in more detail the nurse to whom the requirement applies.

Even if a nurse is exempt from the general CNE requirement, the nurse still must complete the during the nurse's initial licensure or first renewal periods under §216.8(b) or (c) of this chapter (relating to Relicensure Process) shall comply with the requirements of this section. This is a one-time requirement for each nurse employed in an ER setting. In compliance with §216.7(b) of this chapter (relating to Responsibilities of Individual Licensee), each licensee is responsible for maintaining records of CE attendance. Validation of course completion in Forensic Evidence Collection should be retained by the nurse indefinitely, even if a nurse changes employment.

(4) The minimum 2 hours of continuing education requirement shall include information relevant to forensic evidence collection and age or population-specific nursing interventions that may be required by other laws and/or are necessary in order to assure evidence collection that meets requirements under the Government Code §420.031 regarding use of a service-approved evidence collection kit and protocol. Content may also include but is not limited to documentation, history-taking skills, use of sexual assault kit, survivor symptoms, and emotional and psychological support interventions for victims.

(5) The required hours under this subsection are included in the continuing education requirements for nurses.

(e) A nurse who is 65 years old or older and who holds or is seeking to hold a valid volunteer retired (VR) nurse authorization in compliance with the Occupations Code §112.051 and §217.9(d) of this title (relating to Inactive Status):

(1) Must have completed at least 10 hours of continuing education as defined in this chapter during the previous biennium, unless the nurse also holds valid recognition as an advanced practice registered nurse or is a Volunteer Retired Registered Nurse (VR-RN) with advanced practice authorization in a given role and specialty in the State of Texas.

(2) Must have completed at least 20 hours of CE as defined in this chapter if authorized by the board in a specific advanced practice role and specialty. The 20 hours of CE must meet the same criteria as APRN CE defined under subsection (c) of this section. An APRN authorized as a VR-RN with APRN authorization may not hold prescriptive authority. This does not preclude a registered nurse from placing his/her APRN authorization on inactive status and applying for authorization only as a VR-RN.

(3) Is exempt from fulfilling targeted CE requirements except as required for volunteer retired advanced practice registered nurses.

(f) Tick-Borne Diseases. An APRN, whose practice includes the treatment of tick-borne diseases, is encouraged to participate in continuing education relating to the treatment of tick-borne diseases. The continuing education course(s) should contain information relevant to treatment of the disease within the role and population focus area applicable to the APRN and may represent a spectrum of relevant medical clinical treatment relating to tick-borne disease. Completion of continuing medical education in the treatment of tick-borne disease that meets the requirements of this subsection shall be credited as continuing education under this chapter.

216.4. Criteria for Acceptable Continuing Education Activity.

Continuing Education programs must be approved by a credentialing agency or an affiliated entity of one of these agencies. Proof of successful completion shall contain the name of the provider; the program title, date, and location; number of contact hours; provider number; and credentialing agency.

two hours of forensic evidence collection if she/he practices in an ER setting. This is a one time requirement.

Subsection (e) implements Texas Occupations Code Sec. 112.051 addressing retired nurses (and other health care professionals) who want to continue to practice but only by providing charity care. That section provides, in part:

> *Sec. 112.051. REDUCED LICENSE REQUIREMENTS FOR RETIRED HEALTH CARE PRACTITIONERS PERFORMING CHARITY WORK.*
>
> *(a) Each licensing entity shall adopt rules providing for reduced fees and continuing education requirements for a retired health care practitioner whose only practice is voluntary charity care.*
>
> *(b) The licensing entity by rule shall define voluntary charity care.*

This subsection requires volunteer retired nurses to complete 10 hours of CNE per license renewal period. Volunteer retired nurses will have a special license. See also Rule 217.4(d) relating to licensing of Volunteer Retired RNs or LVNs.

Legislation (SB 193) passed in 2011 authorizes the BON to make the option of taking "retired" status available to nurses under 65 years old.

ANNOTATOR'S NOTE: *Legislation (SB 1058) was passed in 2013 requiring all nurses to take CNE in jurisprudence/ethics and nurses caring for older adults or geriatrics to take CNE in that area. The BON is expected to issue proposed rules implementing this legislation in late 2013 or early 2014.*

Any CNE that satisfies the license renewal requirement must be approved by a credentialing agency recognized by the BON. Nurses need to be sure they receive their record of attendance and that it is accurate. The nurse is responsible for maintaining a record of CNE taken for a minimum of four years. Having these records is critical if the nurse is audited by the BON for compliance with CNE requirements. The BON has recognized the following as approved credentialing agencies:

American Nurses Credentialing Center (ANCC)

216.5. Additional Criteria for Specific Continuing Education Programs.

In addition to those programs reviewed by a board-approved entity, a licensee may attend an academic course that meets the following criteria:

(1) The course shall be within the framework of a curriculum that leads to an academic degree in nursing or any academic course relevant to nursing practice.

(2) Participants, upon audit by the board, shall be able to present an official transcript indicating completion of the course with a grade of "C" or better, or a "Pass" on a Pass/Fail grading system.

216.6. Activities Which Are Not Acceptable as Continuing Education.

The following activities do not meet continuing education requirements for licensure renewal.

(1) Basic Life Support (BLS) or cardiopulmonary resuscitation (CPR) courses.

(2) In service programs. Programs sponsored by the employing agency to provide specific information about the work setting and orientation or other programs which address the institution's philosophy, policies and procedures; on-the-job training; basic CPR; and equipment demonstration are not acceptable for CE credit.

(3) Nursing refresher courses. Programs designed to update knowledge or current nursing theory and clinical practice, which consist of a didactic and clinical component to ensure entry level competencies into nursing practice are not accepted for CE credit.

(4) Orientation programs. A program designed to introduce employees to the philosophy, goals, policies, procedures, role expectations and physical facilities of a specific work place are not acceptable for CE credit.

(5) Courses which focus upon self-improvement, changes in attitude, self therapy, self-awareness, weight loss, and yoga.

(6) Economic courses for financial gain, e.g., investments, retirement, preparing resumes, and techniques for job interview.

(7) Courses which focus on personal appearance in nursing.

(8) Liberal art courses in music, art, philosophy, and others when unrelated to patient/client care.

(9) Courses designed for lay people.

(10) Self-directed study--An educational activity wherein the learner takes the initiative and the responsibility for assessing, planning, implementing and evaluating the activity including, but not limited to:

(A) academic courses that are audited, or that are healthcare-related courses but

*(**Annotator Note**: Texas Nurses Assn is the ANCC approver unit in Texas)*
American Academy of Nurse Practitioners (AANP)
American Association of Critical-Care Nurses (AACN)
American Association of Nurse Anesthetists (AANA)
American College of Nurse Midwives (ACNM)
Emergency Nurses Association (ENA)
Category 1 Continuing Medical Education (for APRNs only)
National Association of Practical Nurse Education and Service (NAPNES)
National Federation of Licensed Practical Nurses (NFLPN)
National Association of Pediatric Nurse Associates and Practitioners (NAPNAP)
Colleges and Universities
Other State Boards of Nursing

In additional, the Board recognizes Licensed Vocational Nurses Association of Texas (LVNAT) and Texas League of Vocational Nurses (TLVN) as providers of CE for LVNs.

Academic courses may qualify as approved CNE if the conditions listed are met.

This section lists activities that will <u>not</u> qualify for CNE.

BLS CPR does not qualify as CNE.

Inservice does not qualify as CNE.

Refresher courses do not qualify as CNE.

Orientation programs do not qualify as CNE.

Self-improvement courses don't qualify.

Personal economic courses don't qualify.

Personal appearance focused courses don't qualify.

Liberal arts courses don't qualify.

Courses designed for lay people don't qualify.

Self-directed study doesn't qualify.

not part of a nursing degree program, or that are prerequisite courses such as mathematics, physiology, biology, government, or other similar courses are not acceptable;

(B) authorship; and

(C) program development and presentation.

216.7. Responsibilities of Individual Licensee.

(a) It shall be the licensee's responsibility to select and participate in continuing competency activities that will meet the criteria listed in this chapter.

(b) The licensee shall be responsible for maintaining a record of CE activities. These records shall document attendance as evidenced by original certificates of attendance, contact hour certificates, academic transcripts, or grade slips and copies of these shall be submitted to the board upon audit.

(c) These records shall be maintained by the licensee for a minimum of two consecutive renewal periods or four years.

216.8. Relicensure Process.

(a) Renewal of license.

(1) Upon renewal of the license, the licensee shall sign a statement attesting that the CE or approved national nursing certification requirements have been met.

(2) The contact hours must have been completed in the biennium immediately preceding the license renewal. CE contact hours from a previous renewal period will not be accepted. Additional contact hours earned may not be used for subsequent renewal periods.

(b) Persons licensed by examination. A candidate licensed by examination shall be exempt from the CE or approved national nursing certification requirement for issuance of the initial license and for the immediate renewal period following licensure.

(c) Persons licensed by endorsement. An applicant licensed by endorsement shall be exempt from the CE or approved national nursing certification requirement for the issuance of the initial Texas license and for the immediate renewal period following initial Texas licensure.

(d) Delinquent license.

(1) A license that has been delinquent for less than four years may be renewed by the licensee showing evidence of having completed 20 contact hours of acceptable continuing education or an approved national nursing certification within two years immediately preceding the application for relicensure and by meeting all other board requirements. A licensee shall be exempt from the continuing education requirement for the immediate renewal period following renewal of the delinquent license.

(2) A license that has been delinquent for four or more years may be renewed upon completion of requirements listed in §217.6 of this title (relating to Failure to Renew License).

(e) Reactivation of a license.

(1) A license that has been inactive for less than four years may be reactivated by the licensee submitting verification of having completed at least 20 contact hours of continuing education or a current approved national nursing certification in their current or prior area of practice within the past two years immediately prior to application for reactivation.

(2) A license that has been inactive for four or more years may be reactivated upon completion of requirements in §217.9 of this title (relating to Inactive Status).

(f) Reinstatement of a license. A licensee whose license has been revoked and subsequently applies for reinstatement must show evidence that the continuing competency requirement and other board requirements have been met prior to reinstatement of the license by the board.

216.9. Audit Process.

The board shall select a random sample of licensees 90 days prior to each renewal month. Audit forms shall be sent to selected licensees to substantiate compliance with the continuing competency requirements.

This section sets out the responsibilities of the individual nurse and every nurse should be familiar with them. The nurse is responsible for seeing that any continued competency activities taken meet the criteria to be used for license renewal.

The nurse must maintain records in the way required by the BON.

Records must be kept for two license renewal periods or four years.

At the time of licensure renewal, nurses must certify they have met either the 20 CNE contact hours or the national certification requirement. Falsifying such certification is a basis for action against the nurse's license.

CNE contact hours cannot be carried forward from one license renewal period to another.

Initial licensees are exempt from the continuing competency requirement during the first two-year license renewal period.

Random audits are conducted to verify compliance. A nurse who is audited and cannot verify compliance is subject to action. against her or his license.

(1) Within 30 days following notification of audit, these selected licensees shall submit an audit form and:

(A) documentation as specified in §216.4 and §216.5 of this chapter (relating to Criteria for Acceptable Continuing Education Activity and Additional Criteria for Specific Continuing Education Programs) and any additional documentation the board deems necessary to verify compliance with continuing education requirements for the period of licensure being audited; or

(B) a copy of the current approved national nursing certification and any additional documentation the board deems necessary to verify compliance with continuing competency requirements for the period of licensure being audited.

(2) Failure to notify the board of a current mailing address will not absolve the licensee from audit requirements.

(3) Pursuant to this section, an audit shall be automatic for a licensee who has been found noncompliant in an immediately preceding audit.

(4) Failure to complete the audit satisfactorily or falsification of records shall constitute unprofessional conduct and provide grounds for disciplinary action.

216.10. Appeals.

(a) Any individual who wishes to appeal a determination of non-compliance with continuing competency requirements must submit a letter of appeal within 20 days of notification of the audit results.

(b) The board or its designee shall conduct a review in which the appellant may appear in person to present reasons why the audit decision should be set aside or modified.

(c) The decision of the board after the appeal shall be considered final and binding.

216.11. Consequences of Non-Compliance.

Failure to comply with the board's continuing competency requirements will result in the denial of renewal.

SUBPART D
MINOR INCIDENT REPORTING

ANNOTATOR'S NOTE: Rule 217.16 relating to reporting of minor incidents is set out in Part VII (Mandatory Reporting) of this Guide.

217.16. Minor Incidents.

[See Part VII (Mandatory Reporting) of this Guide]

SUBPART E
NURSING PEER REVIEW

ANNOTATOR'S NOTE: Rules relating to nursing peer review are set out in Parts IV (Nursing Peer Review) and VI (Patient Advocacy Protections) of this Guide.

1. 217.19 Incident-based Nursing Peer Review

[See Part IV (Peer Review) of this Guide]

2. 217.20 Safe Harbor Nursing Peer Review

Failure to comply with continuing competency requirements constitutes unprofessional conduct.

Nurses not complying with continued competency requirements are subject to disciplinary action by the board.

Rule 217.16 (Minor Incidents) and other provisions relating to mandatory reporting are set out in Part VII (Mandatory Reporting) of this Guide.

Two BON Rules relate to Nursing Peer Review:

1. *Rule 217.19 Incident-based Nursing Peer Review*
2. *Rule 217.20 Safe Harbor Nursing Peer Review*

Rule 217.19 is set out in Part IV (Nursing Peer Review) of this Guide and Rule 217.20 is set out in Part VI (Patient Advocacy Protections) of this Guide.

[See Part VI (Patient Advocacy Protections) of this Guide]

SUBPART F
FITNESS TO PRACTICE

GOOD PROFESSIONAL CHARACTER - RULE 213.27
CRIMINAL CONVICTIONS - RULE 213.28
INTEMPERATE USE AND MENTAL ILLNESS - RULE 213.29

1. RULE 213.27 GOOD PROFESSIONAL CHARACTER

§213.27. Good Professional Character.

(a) Good professional character is the integrated pattern of personal, academic and occupational behaviors which, in the judgment of the Board, indicates that an individual is able to consistently conform his or her conduct to the requirements of the Nursing Practice Act, the Board's rules and regulations, and generally accepted standards of nursing practice including, but not limited to, behaviors indicating honesty, accountability, trustworthiness, reliability, and integrity.

(b) Factors to be used in evaluating good professional character in eligibility and disciplinary matters are:

(1) Good professional character is determined through the evaluation of behaviors demonstrated by an individual in his or her personal, academic and occupational history. An individual's age, education, and experience necessarily affect the nature and extent of behavioral history; and, therefore, shall be considered in each evaluation.

(2) A person who seeks to obtain or retain a license to practice professional nursing shall provide evidence of good professional character which, in the judgment of the Board, is sufficient to insure that the individual can consistently act in the best interest of patients/clients and the public in any practice setting. Such evidence shall establish that the person:

(A) is able to distinguish right from wrong;

(B) is able to think and act rationally;

(C) is able to keep promises and honor obligations;

(D) is accountable for his or her own behavior;

(E) is able to practice nursing in an autonomous role with patients/clients, their families, significant others, and members of the public who are or who may become physically, emotionally, or financially vulnerable;

(F) is able to recognize and honor the interpersonal boundaries appropriate to any therapeutic relationship or health care setting; and

(G) is able to promptly and fully self-disclose facts, circumstances, events, errors, and omissions when such disclosure could enhance the health status of patients/clients or the public or could protect patients/clients or the public from unnecessary risk of harm.

(3) Any conviction for a felony or for a misdemeanor involving moral turpitude or order of probation with or without an adjudication of guilt for an offense that would be a felony or misdemeanor involving moral turpitude if guilt were adjudicated.

(4) Any revocation, suspension, or denial of, or any other adverse action relating to, the person's license or privilege to practice nursing in another jurisdiction.

(c) The following provisions shall govern the determination of present good professional character and fitness of a Petitioner, Applicant, or Licensee who has been convicted of a felony in Texas or placed on probation for a felony with or without an adjudication of guilt in Texas, or who has been convicted or placed on probation with or without an adjudication of guilt in another

This Subpart F includes BON rules relating to a nurse's fitness to practice and to be issued a license. These rules address such issues as professional character, criminal convictions, intemperate use, and mental illness. The rules set out in this Subpart are:

1. *Rule 213.27 Good Professional Character*
2. *Rule 213.28 Criminal Convictions*
3. *Rule 213.29 Intemperate Use and Mental Illness*

Sec. 301.252 of the NPA requires applicants for licensure to demonstrate "good professional character" as a condition of licensure. This rule defines what constitutes "good professional character."

Subsection (b) lists the factors the board will generally consider in evaluating good professional character. Subsections (c) and (d) address the specific situations in which the nurse has committed a felony or been disciplined by another nursing board. The board may utilize psychological evaluations in determining "good professional character" and "fitness to practice." See Rule 213.33(k)-(l) and BON Guidelines for Physical and Psychological Evaluations.

Note that an actual or final conviction is not required. The BON also considers deferred adjudication in evaluating good professional character. Deferred adjudication is the judicial process that permits a defendant to accept guilt and be put on probation without an actual formal adjudication of guilt (final conviction) being entered. If the person successfully completes the probation, a final conviction is never entered. If the person does not successfully complete the probation, the court will enter a final conviction without any further testimony or evidence.

This Subsection (c) sets out how the BON will determine the presence of "good professional character" when a nurse has been involved in a felony.

jurisdiction for a crime which would be a felony in Texas. A Petitioner, Applicant, or Licensee may be found lacking in present good professional character and fitness under this rule based on the underlying facts of a felony conviction or deferred adjudication, as well as based on the conviction or probation through deferred adjudication itself.

(1) The record of conviction or order of deferred adjudication is conclusive evidence of guilt.

(2) In addition to the disciplinary remedies available to the Board pursuant to Tex. Occ. Code Ann. §301.452(b)(3) and (4), Texas Occupations Code chapter 53, and §213.28, a licensee guilty of a felony under this rule is conclusively deemed to have violated Tex. Occ. Code Ann. §3 01.452(b)(10) and is subject to appropriate discipline, up to and including revocation.

(d) The following provisions shall govern the determination of present good professional character and fitness of a Petitioner, Applicant, or Licensee who has been licensed to practice professional nursing in any jurisdiction and has been disciplined, or allowed to voluntarily surrender in lieu of discipline, in that jurisdiction.

(1) A certified copy of the order, judgment of discipline, or order of adverse licensure action from the jurisdiction is prima facie evidence of the matters contained in such order, judgment, or adverse action and is conclusive evidence that the individual in question has committed professional misconduct as alleged in such order of judgment.

(2) An individual disciplined for professional misconduct in the course of practicing professional nursing in any jurisdiction or an or an individual who resigned in lieu of disciplinary action (disciplined individual) is deemed not to have present good professional character and fitness and is, therefore, ineligible to file an Application for Endorsement to the Texas Board of Nursing during the period of such discipline imposed by such jurisdiction, and in the case of revocation or surrender in lieu of disciplinary action, until the disciplined individual has filed an application for reinstatement in the disciplining jurisdiction and obtained a final determination on that application.

(3) The only defenses available to a Petitioner, Applicant, or Licensee under section (d) are outlined below and must be proved by clear and convincing evidence:

(A) The procedure followed in the disciplining jurisdiction was so lacking in notice or opportunity to be heard as to constitute a deprivation of due process.

(B) There was such an infirmity of proof establishing the misconduct in the other jurisdiction as to give rise to the clear conviction that the Board, consistent with its duty, should not accept as final the conclusion on the evidence reached in the disciplining jurisdiction.

(C) The deeming of lack of present good professional character and fitness by the Board during the period required under the provisions of section (d) would result in grave injustice.

(D) The misconduct for which the individual was disciplined does not constitute professional misconduct in Texas.

(4) If the Board determines that one or more of the foregoing defenses has been established, it shall render such orders as it deems necessary and appropriate.

(e) An individual who applies for initial licensure, reinstatement, renewal, or endorsement to practice professional nursing in Texas after the expiration of the three-year period in subsection (f) of this section, or after the completion of the disciplinary period assessed or ineligibility period imposed by any jurisdiction under subsection (d) of this section shall be required to prove, by a preponderance of the evidence:

(1) that the best interest of the public and the profession, as well as the ends of justice, would be served by his or her admission to practice professional nursing; and

(2) that (s)he is of present good professional character and fitness.

(f) An individual who applies for initial licensure, reinstatement, renewal, or endorsement to practice professional nursing in Texas after a negative determination based on a felony conviction, felony probation with or without an adjudication of guilt, or professional misconduct, or voluntary surrender in lieu of disciplinary action and whose application or petition is denied and not appealed is not eligible to file another petition or application for licensure until after the

This Subsection (d) sets out how the BON will determine the presence of "good professional character" when a nurse has been the subject of disciplinary action by another nursing board.

This Subsection (e) sets out the criteria that a nurse must establish when seeking to return to practice after a previous finding of a lack of professional character because she or he was involved in a felony or disciplined by another nursing board.

expiration of three years from the date of the Board's order denying the preceding petition for licensure.

(g) The following disciplinary and eligibility sanction policies and guidelines shall be used by the Executive Director, the State Office of Administrative Hearings (SOAH), or the Board in evaluating good professional character in eligibility and disciplinary matters:

(1) Disciplinary Sanctions for Fraud, Theft and Deception approved by the Board and published on February 22, 2008 in the Texas Register (33 TexReg 1646) and available on the Board's website at http://www.bon.state.tx.us/disciplinaryaction/dsp.html.

(2) Disciplinary Sanctions for Lying and Falsification approved by the Board and published on February 22, 2008 in the Texas Register (33 TexReg 1647) and available on the Board's website at http://www.bon.state.tx.us/disciplinaryaction/dsp.html.

(3) Disciplinary Sanctions for Sexual Misconduct approved by the Board and published on February 22, 2008 in the Texas Register (33 TexReg 1649) and available on the Board's website at http://www.bon.state.tx.us/disciplinaryaction/dsp.html.

(4) Eligibility and Disciplinary Sanctions for Nurses with Substance Abuse, Misuse, Substance Dependency, or other Substance Use Disorder and published on February 22, 2008 in the Texas Register (33 TexReg 1651) and available on the Board's website at http://www.bon.state.tx.us/disciplinaryaction/dsp.html.

(5) Disciplinary Guidelines for Criminal Conduct approved by the Board and published on May 17, 2013, in the Texas Register (38 TexReg 3152) and available on the Board's website at http://www.bon.texas.gov/disciplinaryaction/discp-guide.html.

2. RULE 213.28 CRIMINAL CONVICTIONS

§213.28. Licensure of Persons with Criminal Convictions. (a) This section sets out the considerations and criteria in determining the effect of criminal offenses on the eligibility of a person to obtain a license and the consequences that criminal offenses may have on a person's ability to retain or renew a license as a registered nurse or licensed vocational nurse. The Board may refuse to approve persons to take the licensure examination, may refuse to issue or renew a license or certificate of registration, or may refuse to issue a temporary permit to any individual that has been convicted of or received a deferred disposition for a felony, a misdemeanor involving moral turpitude, or engaged in conduct resulting in the revocation of probation.

(b) The practice of nursing involves clients, their families, significant others and the public in diverse settings. The registered and vocational nurse practices in an autonomous role with individuals who are physically, emotionally and financially vulnerable. The nurse has access to personal information about all aspects of a person's life, resources and relationships. Therefore, criminal behavior whether violent or non-violent, directed against persons, property or public order and decency is considered by the Board as highly relevant to an individual's fitness to practice nursing. The Board considers the following categories of criminal conduct to relate to and affect the practice of nursing:

(1) offenses against the person similar to those outlined in Title 5 of the Texas Penal Code.

(A) These offenses include, but are not limited to, the following crimes, as well as any crime that contains substantially similar or equivalent elements under another state or federal law:

(i) Abandonment/Endangerment of a Child {TPC §22.041}

The BON has developed disciplinary and eligibility sanction policies in four areas:

1. *Fraud, Theft and Deception*
2. *Lying and Falsification*
3. *Sexual Misconduct*
4. *Substance Abuse, Misuse, Substance Dependency or Other Substance Disorder*

The policies can be found on the BON's website.

The BON Guidelines for how criminal convictions will be handled can be found on its website.

This rule governs board action based on criminal convictions or deferred adjudication. Sec. 301.452(b)(3) of the NPA makes conviction of a felony or a misdemeanor involving moral turpitude a basis for denying a person a nursing license or for taking disciplinary action against a nurse. Misdemeanors involving moral turpitude are crimes that although misdemeanors, indicate moral depravity in some way. For example, theft is a crime of moral turpitude even if a misdemeanor. NPA Sec. 301.4535 sets out certain serious crimes that require suspension, revocation or denial of a license. NPA Sec. 301.1545 directs the BON to list the offenses that constitute grounds for the board to take disciplinary action or deny a license. This rule identifies the offenses or crimes that relate to the practice of nurses and states the BON's rationale for considering them to be related to the practice of nursing.

See BON's Disciplinary Guidelines for Criminal Convictions on its website.

This Subsection (b) explains why a criminal conviction is relevant to a person's ability to practice professional nursing. It lists five categories of criminal offenses and then states the reasons why each type relates to and affects the practice of nursing. The five types are:

1. *offenses against the person*
2. *offenses against property*
3. *offenses involving fraud or deception*
4. *offenses involving lying and falsification*
5. *offenses involving drugs*

The format of each Subd. (b)(1-(5) is to list the type of offense and then list the reasons that type of offense relates to or affects the practice of nursing.

Offenses against persons.

(ii) Agree to Abduct Child for Remuneration: Younger than Eighteen {TPC §25.031}

(iii) Aiding Suicide: Serious Bodily Injury/Death {TPC §22.08}

(iv) Assault, Aggravated {TPC §22.02}

(v) Capital Murder {TPC §19.03}

(vi) Child Pornography, Possession or Promotion {TPC §43.26(a), (e) (Texas Rules of Criminal Procedure Ch. 62)}

(vii) Indecency with a Child {TPC §21.11(TRCP Ch. 62)}

(viii) Indecent exposure (2 or more counts and/or required to register as sex offender) {TPC §21.08 (TRCP Ch. 62)}

(ix) Injury to Child, Elderly, Disabled {TPC §22.04}

(x) Kidnapping {TPC §20.03, §20.04 (TRCP Ch. 62)}

(xi) Manslaughter {TPC §19.04}

(xii) Murder {TPC §19.02}

(xiii) Online Solicitation of a Minor {TPC §33.021(b), (c), (f); (TRCP Ch. 62)}

(xiv) Prostitution, Compelling {TPC §43.05 (TRCP Ch. 62)}

(xv) Protective Order, Violation {TPC §25.07, §25.071}

(xvi) Sale or Purchase of a Child {TPC §25.08}

(xvii) Sexual Assault {TPC §22.011 (TRCP Ch. 62)}

(xviii) Sexual Conduct, Prohibited {TPC §25.02 (TRCP Ch. 62)}

(xix) Sexual Assault, Aggravated {TPC §22.021 (TRCP Ch. 62)}

(xx) Sexual Performance by Child {TPC §43.24 (d), §43.25(b) (TRCP Ch. 62)}

(xxi) Unlawful Restraint {TPC §20.02}

(xxii) Assault {TPC §22.01(a)(1), (b), (c)}

(xxiii) Criminally negligent homicide {TPC §19.05}

(xxiv) Improper Relationship between Educator and Student {TPC §21.12}

(xxv) Improper photography {TPC §21.15}

(xxvi) Obscenity, Wholesale promotion {TPC §43.23(a), (h)}

(xxvii) Prostitution (3 or more counts) or Aggravated Promotion {TPC §43.02, §43.04}

(xxviii) Resisting Arrest, Use of Deadly Weapon {TPC §38.03(d)}

(xxix) Stalking {TPC §42.072(b)}

(xxx) Harassment {TPC §42.07}

(xxxi) Prostitution or Promotion of {TPC §43.02}

(xxxii) Protective Order, Violation {TPC §25.07, §38.112}

(xxxiii) Resisting Arrest {TPC §38.03(a)}

(xxxiv) Deadly conduct {TPC §22.05(a)}

(xxxv) Obscenity, Participates {TPC §43.23(c), (h)}

(xxxvi) Terroristic Threat {TPC §22.07}

(xxxvii) Criminal Attempt or Conspiracy {TPC §15.01, §15.02}

(B) These types of crimes relate to the practice of nursing because:

(i) nurses have access to persons who are vulnerable by virtue of illness or injury and are frequently in a position to be exploited;

(ii) nurses have access to persons who are especially vulnerable including the elderly, children, the mentally ill, sedated and anesthetized patients, those whose mental or cognitive ability is compromised and patients who are disabled or immobilized and may be subject to harm by similar criminal behavior;

(iii) nurses are frequently in situations where they provide intimate care to patients or have contact with partially clothed or fully undressed patients who are vulnerable to exploitation both physically and emotionally;

(iv) nurses are in the position to have access to privileged information

Reasons why these crimes (offenses against persons) relate to or affect the practice of nursing.

and opportunity to exploit patient vulnerability; and

(v) nurses who commit these crimes outside the workplace raise concern about the nurse's propensity to repeat that same misconduct in the workplace and raises concerns regarding the individual's ability to provide safe, competent care to patients.

(2) offenses against property, e.g., robbery, burglary and theft, etc.

(A) These offenses include, but are not limited to, the following crimes, as well as any crime that contains substantially similar or equivalent elements under another state or federal law:

(i) Burglary (if punishable under Penal Code §30.02(d)) {TRCP Ch. 62 (§62.001(5)(D))}

(ii) Robbery {TPC §29.02}

(iii) Robbery, Aggravated {TPC §29.03}

(iv) Arson {TPC §28.02(d)}

(v) Burglary {TPC §30.02}

(vi) Criminal Mischief {TPC §28.03}

(vii) Money Laundering >= $1500 {TPC §34.02(e)(1)-(4)}

(viii) Theft >= $1500 {TPC §31.03(e)(4)-(7)}

(ix) Theft < 9 {TPC §31.03(e)(1)-(3)}

(x) Vehicle, Unauthorized Use {TPC §31.07}

(xi) Criminal Trespass {TPC §30.05(a),(d)}

(xii) Cruelty to Animals {TPC §42.091}

(xiii) Criminal Attempt or Conspiracy {TPC §15.01, §15.02}

(B)These types of crimes relate to the practice of nursing because:

(i) nurses have access to persons who are vulnerable by virtue of illness or injury and are frequently in a position to be exploited;

(ii) nurses have access to persons who are especially vulnerable including the elderly, children, the mentally ill, sedated and anesthetized patients, those whose mental or cognitive ability is compromised and patients who are disabled or immobilized and may provide easy opportunity to be victimized;

(iii) nurses have access to persons who frequently bring valuables (medications, money, jewelry, items of sentimental value, checkbook, or credit cards) with them to a health care facility with no security to prevent theft or exploitation;

(iv) nurses frequently provide care in private homes and home-like settings where all of the patient's property and valuables are accessible to the nurse;

(v) nurses frequently provide care autonomously without direct supervision and may have access to and opportunity to misappropriate property; and

(vi) nurses who commit these crimes outside the workplace raise concern about the nurse's propensity to repeat that same misconduct in the workplace and, therefore, place patients' property at risk.

(vii) certain crimes involving property, such as cruelty to animals and criminal trespass, may also concern the safety of persons and, as such, raise concerns about the propensity of the nurse to repeat similar conduct in the workplace, placing patients at risk.

(3) offenses involving fraud or deception.

(A) These offenses include, but are not limited to, the following crimes, as well as any crime that contains substantially similar or equivalent elements under another state or federal law:

(i) Attempt, Conspiracy, or Solicitation of Ch. 62 offense {TRCP Ch. 62}

(ii) Tampering with a Government Record {TPC §37.10}

(iii) Insurance Fraud: Intent to Defraud {TPC §35.02(a-1), (d)}

(iv) Insurance Fraud: Claim > $500 {TPC §35.02(c)}

(v) Insurance Fraud: Claim < 0 {TPC §35.02 (c)(1)-(3)}

Offenses against property.

The reference to "Theft <9"in (ix) probably means "Theft <$1500" to be consistent with the "Theft >=$1500" in (viii).

Reasons why these crimes (offenses against property) relate to or affect the practice of nursing.

Offenses involving fraud and deception.

"Claim <0" in (v) probably means "Claim <= $500" to agree with (iv).

(vi) Medicaid Fraud > $1500 {TPC §35A.02(b)(4)-(7)}

(vii) Medicaid Fraud < $1500 {TPC §35A.02(b)(2)-(3)}

(viii) Criminal Attempt or Conspiracy {TPC §15.01, §15.02}

(B) These types of crime relate to the practice of nursing because:

(i) nurses have access to persons who are vulnerable by virtue of illness or injury and are frequently in a position to be exploited;

(ii) nurses have access to persons who are especially vulnerable including the elderly, children, the mentally ill, sedated and anesthetized patients, those whose mental or cognitive ability is compromised and patients who are disabled or immobilized;

(iii) nurses are in the position to have access to privileged information and opportunity to exploit patient vulnerability;

(iv) nurses are frequently in situations where they must report patient condition, record objective/subjective information, provide patients with information, and report errors in the nurse's own practice or conduct;

(v) the nurse-patient relationship is of a dependent nature; and

(vi) nurses who commit these crimes outside the workplace raise concern about the nurse's propensity to repeat that same misconduct in the workplace and, therefore, place patients at risk.

(4) offenses involving lying and falsification.

(A) These offenses include, but are not limited to, the following crimes, as well as any crime that contains substantially similar or equivalent elements under another state or federal law:

(i) False Report or Statement {TPC §32.32, §42.06}

(ii) Forgery {TPC §32.21(c), (d), (e)}

(iii) Tampering with a Governmental Record {TPC §37.10}

(B) These crimes are related to nursing because:

(i) nurses have access to persons who are vulnerable by virtue of illness or injury;

(ii) nurses have access to persons who are especially vulnerable including the elderly, children, the mentally ill, sedated and anesthetized patients, those whose mental or cognitive ability is compromised and patients who are disabled or immobilized;

(iii) nurses are frequently in situations where they must report patient condition, record objective/subjective information, provide patients with information, and report errors in the nurse's own practice or conduct;

(iv) honesty, accuracy and integrity are personal traits valued by the nursing profession, and considered imperative for the provision of safe and effective nursing care;

(v) falsification of documents regarding patient care, incomplete or inaccurate documentation of patient care, failure to provide the care documented, or other acts of deception raise serious concerns whether the nurse will continue such behavior and jeopardize the effectiveness of patient care in the future;

(vi) falsification of employment applications and failing to answer specific questions that would have affected the decision to employ, certify, or otherwise utilize a nurse raises concerns about a nurse's propensity to lie and whether the nurse possesses the qualities of honesty and integrity;

(vii) falsification of documents or deception/lying outside of the workplace, including falsification of an application for licensure to the Board, raises concerns about the person's propensity to lie, and the likelihood that such conduct will continue in the practice of nursing; and

(viii) a crime of lying or falsification raises concerns about the nurse's propensity to engage in similar conduct while practicing nursing and place patients at risk.

(5) offenses involving the delivery, possession, manufacture, or use of, or dispensing

Reasons why these crimes (offenses involving fraud and deception) relate to or affect the practice of nursing.

Offenses involving lying and falsification.

Reasons why these crimes (offenses involving lying and falsification) relate to or affect the practice of nursing.

Offenses involving drugs.

or prescribing a controlled substance, dangerous drug, or mood-altering substance.

(A) These offenses include, but are not limited to, the following crimes, as well as any crime that contains substantially similar or equivalent elements under another state or federal law:

(i) Drug Violations under Health and Safety Code Chs. 481, 482, 483; or

(ii) Driving While Intoxicated (2 or more counts) {TPC §49.09}

(B) These crimes relate to the practice of nursing because:

(i) nurses have access to persons who are vulnerable by virtue of illness or injury;

(ii) nurses have access to persons who are especially vulnerable including the elderly, children, the mentally ill, sedated and anesthetized patients, those whose mental or cognitive ability is compromised and patients who are disabled or immobilized;

(iii) nurses provide care to critical care, geriatric, and pediatric patients who are particularly vulnerable given the level of vigilance demanded under the circumstances of their health condition;

(iv) nurses are able to provide care in private homes and home-like setting without supervision;

(v) nurses who are chemically dependent or who abuse drugs or alcohol may have impaired judgment while caring for patients and are at risk for harming patients; and

(vi) an offense regarding delivery, possession, manufacture, or use of, or dispensing , or prescribing a controlled substance, dangerous drug or mood altering drug raises concern about the nurse's propensity to repeat that same misconduct in the workplace.

(vii) DWI offenses involve the use and/or abuse of mood altering drugs while performing a state licensed activity affecting public safety; repeated violations suggest a willingness to continue in reckless and dangerous conduct, or an unwillingness to take appropriate corrective measures, despite previous disciplinary action by the state.

(c) In considering whether a criminal offense renders the individual ineligible for licensure or renewal of licensure as a registered or vocational nurse, the Board shall consider:

(1) the knowing or intentional practice of nursing without a license issued under the NPA;

(2) any felony or misdemeanor involving moral turpitude;

(3) the nature and seriousness of the crime;

(4) the relationship of the crime to the purposes for requiring a license to engage in nursing practice;

(5) the extent to which a license might offer an opportunity to engage in further criminal activity of the same type as that in which the person previously had been involved; and

(6) the relationship of the crime to the ability, capacity, or fitness required to perform the duties and discharge the responsibilities of nursing practice;

(7) whether imprisonment followed a felony conviction, felony community supervision revocation, revocation of parole or revocation of mandatory supervision; and

(8) conduct that results in the revocation of probation imposed because of conviction for a felony or for a misdemeanor involving moral turpitude.

(d) Crimes listed under subsections (b)(1)(A)(i)-(xxi), (b)(2)(A)(i)-(iii), and (b)(3)(A)(i) of this section are offenses identified under §301.4535 of the NPA. As such, these offenses require the board to suspend a nurse's license, revoke a license, or deny issuing a license to an applicant upon proof of initial conviction.

(e) In addition to the factors that may be considered under subsection (c) of this section, the Board, in determining the present fitness of a person who has been convicted of or received a deferred order for a crime, shall consider:

(1) the extent and nature of the person's past criminal activity;

Reasons why these crimes (offenses involving drugs) relate to or affect the practice of nursing.

Subsection (c) sets out the factors the board will consider in evaluating whether a criminal conviction is a reason to deny a license or to take action against an existing license. Rule 213.33 sets out the factors the board considers in imposing sanctions in disciplinary action. Subsection. (f) of that Rule permits the board to request a forensic evaluation by a forensic psychologist or psychiatrist when the nurse has a criminal history. NPA Sec. 301.4535 sets out certain serious crimes that require automatic suspension, revocation or denial of a license.

NPA §301.4535 requires the BON to deny a license and revoke a current license for certain very serious crimes. Subsection (d) identifies these crimes.

This Subsec. (e) sets out additional factors the board considers in evaluating criminal offenses.

(2) the age of the person when the crime was committed;

(3) the amount of time that has elapsed since the person's last criminal activity;

(4) the conduct and work activity of the person before and after the criminal activity;

(5) evidence of the person's rehabilitation or rehabilitative effort while incarcerated or after release; and

(6) other evidence of the person's present fitness, including letters of recommendation from: prosecutors and law enforcement and correctional officers who prosecuted, arrested, or had custodial responsibility for the person; the sheriff or chief of police in the community where the person resides; and any other persons in contact with the convicted person.

(f) It shall be the responsibility of the applicant, to the extent possible, to obtain and provide to the Board the recommendations of the prosecution, law enforcement, and correctional authorities as required under this Act. The applicant shall also furnish proof in such form as may be required by the Board that he or she has maintained a record of steady employment and has supported his or her dependents and has otherwise maintained a record of good conduct and has paid all outstanding court costs, supervision fees, fines, and restitution as may have been ordered in all criminal cases in which he or she has been convicted or received a deferred order.

(g) If requested by staff, it shall be the responsibility of the individual seeking licensure to ensure that staff is provided with legible, certified copies of all court and law enforcement documentation from all jurisdictions where the individual has resided or practiced as a licensed health care professional. Failure to provide complete, legible and accurate documentation will result in delays prior to licensure or renewal of licensure and possible grounds for ineligibility.

(h) The fact that a person has been arrested will not be used as grounds for disciplinary action. If, however, evidence ascertained through the Board's own investigation from information contained in the arrest record regarding the underlying conduct suggests actions violating the Nursing Practice Act or rules of the Board, the board may consider such evidence as a factor in its deliberations regarding any decision to grant a license, restrict a license, or impose licensure discipline.

(i) Behavior that would otherwise bar or impede licensure may be deemed a "Youthful Indiscretion" as determined by an analysis of the behavior using the factors set out in §213.27 of this title (relating to Good Professional Character), subsections (a) - (e) of this section and at least the following criteria:

(1) age of 22 years or less at the time of the behavior;

(2) absence of criminal plan or premeditation;

(3) presence of peer pressure or other contributing influences;

(4) absence of adult supervision or guidance;

(5) evidence of immature thought process/judgment at the time of the activity;

(6) evidence of remorse;

(7) evidence of restitution to both victim and community;

(8) evidence of current maturity and personal accountability;

(9) absence of subsequent undesirable conduct;

(10) evidence of having learned from past mistakes;

(11) evidence of current support structures that will prevent future criminal activity; and

(12) evidence of current ability to practice nursing in accordance with the Nursing Practice Act, Board rules and generally accepted standards of nursing.

(j) With respect to a request to obtain a license from a person who has a criminal history, the executive director is authorized to close an eligibility file when the applicant has failed to respond to a request for information or to a proposal for denial of eligibility within 60 days thereof.

See Subsection (i) below addressing behaviors attributable to "youthful indiscretion."

It is the applicant's responsibility to collect and provide the necessary information to the BON.

Although an arrest itself cannot be used by the BON to take disciplinary action, the BON may initiate an investigation because of an arrest and any evidence that investigation produces may be used in the BON's deliberations.

This Subsec. (i) addresses behavior attributable to "youthful indiscretion." Under Subsec. (e)(2) the age of the person is one of the factors considered by the board in determining if behavior will be a bar or impediment to licensure. This subsection sets out factors BON will consider in determining if behavior resulted from youthful indiscretion.

(k) The board shall revoke a license or authorization to practice as an advanced practice nurse upon the imprisonment of the licensee following a felony conviction or deferred adjudication, or revocation of felony community supervision, parole, or mandatory supervision.

(l) The board shall revoke or deny a license or authorization to practice as an advanced practice nurse for the crimes listed in Texas Occupations Code §301.4535.

(m) The following disciplinary and eligibility sanction policies and guidelines shall be used by the Executive Director, the State Office of Administrative Hearings (SOAH), or the Board in evaluating the impact of criminal conduct on nurse licensure in eligibility and disciplinary matters:

(1) Disciplinary Sanctions for Fraud, Theft and Deception approved by the Board and published on February 22, 2008 in the Texas Register (33 TexReg 1646) and available on the Board's website at http://www.bon.state.tx.us/disciplinaryaction/dsp.html.

(2) Disciplinary Sanctions for Lying and Falsification approved by the Board and published on February 22, 2008 in the Texas Register (33 TexReg 1647) and available on the Board's website at http://www.bon.state.tx.us/disciplinaryaction/dsp.html.

(3) Disciplinary Sanctions for Sexual Misconduct approved by the Board and published on February 22, 2008 in the Texas Register (33 TexReg 1649) and available on the Board's website at http://www.bon.state.tx.us/disciplinaryaction/dsp.html.

(4) Eligibility and Disciplinary Sanctions for Nurses with Substance Abuse, Misuse, Substance Dependency, or other Substance Use Disorder and published on February 22, 2008 in the Texas Register (33 TexReg 1651) and available on the Board's website at http://www.bon.state.tx.us/disciplinaryaction/dsp.html.

(5) Disciplinary Guidelines for Criminal Conduct approved by the Board and published on May 17, 2013 in the Texas Register (38 TexReg 3152) and available on the Board's website at http://www.bon.texas.gov/disciplinaryaction/discp-guide.html

3. RULE 213.29 INTEMPERATE USE AND LACK OF FITNESS

§213.29. Criteria and Procedure Regarding Intemperate Use and Lack of Fitness in Eligibility and Disciplinary Matters.

(a) A person desiring to obtain or retain a license to practice professional or vocational nursing shall provide evidence of current sobriety and fitness consistent with this rule.

(b) Such person shall provide a sworn certificate to the Board stating that he/she has read and understands the requirements for licensure as a registered or vocational nurse and that he/she has not:

(1) within the past five years, become addicted to or treated for the use of alcohol or any other drug; or

(2) within the past five years, been diagnosed with, treated or hospitalized for schizophrenia and/or other psychotic disorders, bi-polar disorder, paranoid personality disorder, antisocial personality disorder or borderline personality disorder.

(c) If a registered or vocational nurse is reported to the Board for intemperate use, abuse of drugs or alcohol, or diagnosis of or treatment for chemical dependency; or if a person is unable to sign the certification in subsection (b) of this section, the following restrictions and requirements apply:

(1) Any matter before the Board that involves an allegation of chemical dependency, or misuse or abuse of drugs or alcohol, will require at a minimum that such person obtain for

The BON has developed disciplinary and eligibility sanction policies in four areas:

1. *Fraud, Theft and Deception*
2. *Lying and Falsification*
3. *Sexual Misconduct*
4. *Substance Abuse, Misuse, Substance Dependency or Other Substance Disorder*

The policies can be found on the BON's website.

BON Guidelines for how it will handle criminal convictions can be found on its website.

Secs. 301.452(b)(9) and (12) of the NPA make intemperate use and lack of fitness grounds for denying a license or disciplining a nurse. Sec. 301.452(a) defines "intemperate use to being on duty or on call while under the influence." This rule describes how the BON will address nurses or applicants for licensure whose ability to practice professional nursing may be impaired by mental illness or chemical dependency. Participation by the nurse or applicant in a board-approved peer assistance program may be an option. The Texas Peer Assistance Program for Nurses is the only program approved by the board. See also BON Rules 217.12(5) and (10)(A).

This sworn certification is required as part of the licensing and license renewal process.

The board considers problems with mental illness or chemical dependency over the past five years.

This Subsection (c) sets out requirements for licensure when use of drugs is involved.

Professional evaluation is required. See Rule 213.33(k),(l).

Board review an evaluation that meets the criteria of §213.33 of this chapter (relating to Factors Considered for Imposition of Penalties/Sanctions and/or Fines);

(2) Those persons who have become addicted to or treated for alcohol or chemical dependency will not be eligible to obtain or retain a license to practice as a nurse unless such person can demonstrate sobriety and abstinence for the preceding twelve consecutive months through verifiable and reliable evidence, or can establish eligibility to participate in a peer assistance program created pursuant to Chapter 467 of the Health and Safety Code;

(3) Those persons who have become addicted to or treated for alcohol or chemical dependency will not be eligible to obtain or retain an unencumbered license to practice nursing until the individual has attained a five-year term of sobriety and abstinence or until such person has successfully completed participation in a board-approved peer assistance program created pursuant to Chapter 467 of the Health and Safety Code.

(4) Those persons who have been diagnosed with, treated, or hospitalized for the disorders mentioned in subsection (b) of this section shall execute an authorization for release of medical, psychiatric, and treatment records.

(d) It shall be the responsibility of those persons subject to this rule to submit to and pay for an evaluation that meets the criteria of §213.33 of this chapter.

(e) Prior intemperate use, mental illness, or diminished mental capacity is relevant only so far as it may indicate current intemperate use or lack of fitness.

(f) With respect to chemical dependency in eligibility and disciplinary matters, the executive director is authorized to:

(1) review submissions from a movant, materials and information gathered or prepared by staff, and identify any deficiencies in file information necessary to determine the movant's request;

(2) close any eligibility file in which the movant has failed to respond to a request for information or to a proposal for denial of eligibility within 60 days thereof;

(3) approve eligibility, enter eligibility orders and approve renewals, without Board ratification, when the evidence is clearly insufficient to prove a ground for denial of licensure; and

(4) propose conditional orders in eligibility, disciplinary and renewal matters for individuals who have experienced chemical/alcohol dependency within the past five years provided:

(A) the individual presents reliable and verifiable evidence of having functioned in a sober/abstinent manner for the previous twelve consecutive months; and

(B) licensure limitations/stipulations and/or peer assistance program participation can be implemented which will ensure that patients and the public are protected until the individual has attained a five-year term of sobriety/abstinence.

(g) With respect to mental illness or diminished mental capacity in eligibility, disciplinary, and renewal matters, the executive director is authorized to propose conditional orders for individuals who have experienced mental illness or diminished mental capacity within the past five years provided:

(1) the individual presents reliable and verifiable evidence of having functioned in a manner consistent with the behaviors required of nurses under the Nursing Practice Act and Board rules for at least the previous twelve consecutive months; and

(2) licensure limitations/stipulations and/or peer assistance program participation can be implemented which will ensure that patients and the public are protected until the individual has attained a five-year term of controlled behavior and consistent compliance with the requirements of the Nursing Practice Act and Board rules.

(h) In renewal matters involving chemical dependency use, mental illness, or diminished mental capacity, the executive director shall consider the following information from the preceding renewal period:

(1) evidence of the licensee's safe practice;

(2) compliance with the NPA and Board rules; and

Twelve months of sobriety or eligibility to participate in a board-approved peer assistance program is required to practice.

Five years or successful completion of a board-approved peer assistance program is required to get an unencumbered license.

Prior intemperate use or mental illness is relevant only to the extent it may indicate current problems. See Rule 213.33(k),(l).

This Subsec. (f) addresses chemical dependency.

The BON can impose stipulations on the license and may require participation in a peer assistance program. Five years of sobriety are required to remove stipulations.

This Subsec. (g) addresses mental illness.

The BON can impose stipulations on the license and may require participation in a peer assistance program. Five years of demonstrated mental stability are required to remove stipulations.

(3) written verification of compliance with any treatment.

(i) Upon receipt of items (h)(1) - (3) of this section, the executive director may renew the license.

(j) The following disciplinary and eligibility sanction policies and guidelines shall be used by the Executive Director, the State Office of Administrative Hearings (SOAH), or the Board in evaluating the appropriate licensure determination or sanction in eligibility and disciplinary matters:

(1) Eligibility and Disciplinary Sanctions for Nurses with Substance Abuse, Misuse, Substance Dependency, or other Substance Use Disorder and published on February 22, 2008 in the Texas Register (33 TexReg 1651) and available on the Board's web site at http://www.bon.state.tx.us/disciplinaryaction/dsp.html.

(2) Disciplinary Guidelines for Criminal Conduct approved by the Board and published on May 17, 2013 in the Texas Register (38 TexReg 3152) and available on the Board's website at http://www.bon.texas.gov/disciplinaryaction/discp-guide.html.

SUBPART G.
LICENSURE - INITIAL, RENEWAL, INACTIVE & RETIRED

ANNOTATOR'S NOTE: *Only selected rules relating to initial licensure are being set out because the BON has extensive materials on initial licensure on its website including online applications. Most individuals seeking licensure will rely on these materials if they have questions about the process.*

1. RULE 213.30 DECLARATORY ORDERS OF ELIGIBILITY

§213.30. Declaratory Order of Eligibility for Licensure.

(a) For purposes of this section only, "petitioner" means an individual who:

(1) is enrolled or planning to enroll in an educational nursing program that prepares individuals for initial licensure as a registered or vocational nurse;

(2) seeks licensure by endorsement pursuant to §217.5 of this title (relating to Temporary License and Endorsement); or

(3) seeks licensure by examination pursuant to §217.2 (relating to Licensure by Examination for Graduates of Nursing Education Programs Within the United States, its Territories, or Possessions) or §217.4 (relating to Requirements for Initial Licensure by Examination for Nurses Who Graduate From Nursing Education Programs Outside of United States' Jurisdiction) of this title.

(b) An individual who has reason to believe that he or she may be ineligible for initial licensure or licensure by endorsement may petition the Board for a declaratory order as to his or her eligibility.

(c) A petitioner must submit a petition on forms provided by the Board, which includes:

Two of the BON's disciplinary and eligibility sanction policies and guidelines are particularly relevant:

1. *Substance Abuse, Misuse, Substance Dependency or Other Substance Disorder*
2. *Disciplinary Guidelines for Criminal Conduct*

These can be found on the BON's website.

This Subpart G addresses the BON rules relating to the requirements and processes relating to licensure - both initial and renewal.

1. *Rule 213.30 Declaratory Orders of Eligibility for Licensure*
2. *Rule 217.2 Licensure by Examination for US Graduates*
3. *Rule 217.3 Temporary Permits for US Graduates*
4. *Rule 217.4 Licensure of Foreign Graduates*
5. *Rule 217.5 Licensure by Endorsement*
6. *Rule 217.6 Renewing an Expired License*
7. *Rule 217.9 Inactive and Retired Status*

This rule implements Sec. 301.257 of the NPA. It provides a process for individuals that have reason to believe they may be ineligible for licensure to request the BON to make a determination of that issue. The purpose of that provision is to avoid individuals' investing 1 to 4 years in their nursing education only to find they are ineligible for licensure. Its purpose is also to avoid the program using its resources to educate persons not eligible for licensure. A frequent reason for seeking such a determination is a prior criminal conviction. The declaratory order process is also available to nurses seeking licensure by endorsement. Nursing programs are required to notify students of eligibility requirements by BON Rules 215.8(b) and (f)(2) [RN programs] and 214.8(b) and (f)(2) [LVN programs] which are set out below following this Rule 213.30.

(1) a statement by the petitioner indicating the reason(s) and basis of potential ineligibility;

(2) if the potential ineligibility is due to criminal conduct and/or conviction, any court documents including, but not limited to: indictments, orders of deferred adjudication, judgments, probation records, and evidence of completion of probation, if applicable;

(3) if the potential ineligibility is due to mental illness, evidence of an evaluation that meets the criteria of §213.33 of this chapter (relating to Factors Considered for Imposition of Penalties/Sanctions) and evidence of treatment;

(4) if the potential ineligibility is due to chemical dependency, including alcohol, evidence of an evaluation that meets the criteria of §213.33 of this chapter and treatment, after care, and support group attendance; and

(5) the required fee, which is not refundable.

(d) Once the Board has received all necessary information, including the information required by subsection (c) of this section, an investigation of the petition and the petitioner's eligibility shall be conducted.

(e) The petitioner or the Board may amend the petition to include additional grounds for potential ineligibility at any time before a final determination is made.

(f) If an individual seeking licensure by endorsement pursuant to §217.5 of this title has been licensed to practice professional or vocational nursing in any jurisdiction and has been disciplined in that jurisdiction or allowed to surrender in lieu of discipline in that jurisdiction, the following provisions shall govern the eligibility of the petitioner with regard to §213.27 of this title (relating to Good Professional Character).

(1) A certified copy of the order or judgment of discipline from the jurisdiction is prima facie evidence of the matters contained in such order or judgment, and a final adjudication in the jurisdiction that the individual has committed professional misconduct is conclusive of the professional misconduct alleged in such order or judgment.

(2) An individual who is disciplined for professional misconduct in the course of nursing in any jurisdiction or who resigned in lieu of disciplinary action is deemed to not have present good professional character under §213.27 of this title, and is therefore ineligible to seek licensure by endorsement under §217.5 of this title during the period of discipline imposed by such jurisdiction, and in the case of revocation or surrender in lieu of disciplinary action, until the individual has filed a petition for reinstatement in the disciplining jurisdiction and obtained a final determination on that petition.

(g) If a petitioner's potential ineligibility is due to criminal conduct and/or conviction, including deferred adjudication, the following provisions shall govern the eligibility of the petitioner with regard to §213.28 of this title (relating to Licensure of Persons with Criminal Convictions).

(1) The record of conviction, guilty plea, or order of deferred adjudication is conclusive evidence of guilt.

(2) Upon proof that a felony conviction or felony order of probation, with or without adjudication of guilt, has been set aside or reversed, the petitioner shall be entitled to a new hearing before the Board for the purpose of determining whether, absent the record of conclusive evidence of guilt, the petitioner possesses present good professional character and fitness.

(h) If the Executive Director proposes to find the petitioner ineligible for licensure, the petitioner may obtain a hearing before the State Office of Administrative Hearings (SOAH). The Executive Director shall have discretion to set a hearing and give notice of the hearing to the petitioner. The hearing shall be conducted in accordance with §213.22 of this chapter (relating to Formal Proceedings) and the rules of SOAH. When in conflict, SOAH's rules of procedure will prevail. The decision of the Board shall be rendered in accordance with §213.23 of this chapter (relating to Decision of the Board).

(i) A final Board order is issued after an appeal results in a Proposal for Decision from SOAH. The Board's final order must set out each basis for potential ineligibility and the Board's determination as to eligibility. In the absence of new evidence not disclosed by the petitioner or

Rule 213.33(k),(l) permits psychological evaluations. See also the BON's Guidelines for Physical and Psychological Evaluations.

not reasonably available to the Board at the time the order is issued, the Board's ruling determines the petitioner's eligibility with respect to the grounds for potential ineligibility as set out in the order. An individual whose petition is denied by final order of the Board may not file another petition or seek licensure by endorsement or examination until after the expiration of three years from the date of the Board's order denying the petition. If the petitioner does not appeal or request a formal hearing at SOAH after a letter proposal to deny eligibility made by the Eligibility and Disciplinary Committee of the Board or the Executive Director, the petitioner may re-petition or seek licensure by endorsement or examination after the expiration of one year from the date of the proposal to deny eligibility, in accordance with this section and the Occupations Code §301.257.

(j) The Disciplinary Matrix and factors set forth in §213.33(b) and (c) of this chapter and the following disciplinary and eligibility sanction policies and guidelines shall be used by the Executive Director and SOAH when recommending a declaratory order of eligibility, and the Board in determining the appropriate declaratory order in eligibility matters:

(1) Disciplinary Sanctions for Fraud, Theft and Deception approved by the Board and published on February 22, 2008 in the Texas Register (33 TexReg 1646) and available on the Board's website at http://www.bon.state.tx.us/disciplinaryaction/dsp.html.

(2) Disciplinary Sanctions for Lying and Falsification approved by the Board and published on February 22, 2008 in the Texas Register (33 TexReg 1647) and available on the Board's website at http://www.bon.state.tx.us/disciplinaryaction/dsp.html.

(3) Disciplinary Sanctions for Sexual Misconduct approved by the Board and published on February 22, 2008 in the Texas Register (33 TexReg 1649) and available on the Board's website at http://www.bon.state.tx.us/disciplinaryaction/dsp.html.

(4) Eligibility and Disciplinary Sanctions for Nurses with Substance Abuse, Misuse, Substance Dependency, or other Substance Use Disorder and published on February 22, 2008 in the Texas Register (33 TexReg 1651) and available on the Board's website at http://www.bon.state.tx.us/disciplinaryaction/dsp.html.

(5) Disciplinary Guidelines for Criminal Conduct approved by the Board and published on May 17, 2013 in the Texas Register (38 TexReg 3152) and available on the Board's website at http://www.bon.texas.gov/disciplinaryaction/discp-guide.html.

(k) If an individual seeking licensure by endorsement under §217.5 of this title or licensure by examination under §217.2 or §217.4 of this title should have had an eligibility issue settled pursuant to the Occupations Code §301.257, the filed application will be treated and processed as a petition for declaratory order under this section, and the individual will be treated as a petitioner under this section and will be required to pay the non-refundable fee required by this section.

(l) This section implements the requirements of the Occupations Code Chapter 53 Subchapter D and the Occupations Code §301.257.

Rule 215.8, Subsecs. (b) and (f)(2) (Professional Nursing Education)

(b) Individuals enrolled in approved professional nursing educational programs preparing students for initial licensure shall be provided verbal and written information regarding conditions that may disqualify graduates from licensure and of their rights to petition the Board for a Declaratory Order of Eligibility. Required eligibility information includes:

(1) Texas Occupations Code §§301.252, 301.257 and 301.452 - 301.469; and

(2) Sections 213.27 - 213.30 of this title (relating to Good Professional Character, Licensure of Persons with Criminal Offenses, Criteria and Procedure Regarding Intemperate Use and Lack of Fitness in Eligibility and Disciplinary Matters, Declaratory Order of Eligibility for Licensure).

(f)(2) The program shall maintain evidence of student receipt of the Board's license eligibility information as specifically outlined in subsection (b) of this section.

In terms of when an applicant/petitioner may re-petition an adverse decision, the BON distinguishes between those applicants/petitioners who seek an SOAH hearing and those who don't. The former must wait three years and the latter one year.

The BON has developed disciplinary and eligibility sanction policies and guidelines:

1. *Fraud, Theft and Deception*
2. *Lying and Falsification*
3. *Sexual Misconduct*
4. *Substance Abuse, Misuse, Substance Dependency or Other Substance Disorder*
5. *Disciplinary Guidelines for Criminal Convictions*

These can be found on the BON's website.

Chapter 53 relates to effect of criminal convictions on professional licensure generally.

ANNOTATOR'S NOTE*: Legislation (SB 1058) passed in 2013 requires the BON conduct criminal background checks of students and authorizes the board to self-initiate a declaratory order based on a positive background check. See NPA Secs. 301.2511(c) and 301.257(j). This rule will need to be amended to reflect this legislation.*

Sec. 301.257 of the NPA permits the BON to collect information from students to determine if they are aware of what might disqualify them from licensure upon graduation and of their right to seek a declaratory order. This subsection implements that provision. The school only provides the student with the information and makes documentation that the student received the information. It does not collect the information regarding the student's potential disqualification. Secttion 301.257 requires the BON to notify the school if it determines a student is disqualified. See also BON Rule 213.30.

Rule 214.8, Subsecs. (b) and (f)(2) (Vocational Nursing Education)

(b) Individuals enrolled in approved vocational nursing education programs preparing students for licensure shall be provided verbal and written information regarding conditions that may disqualify graduates from licensure and of their rights to petition the Board for a Declaratory Order of Eligibility. Required eligibility information includes:

(1) Texas Occupations Code §§301.252, 301.257, and 301.452-.469; and

(2) Sections §§213.27 - 213.30 of the Texas Administrative Code (relating to Good Professional Character, Licensure of Persons with Criminal Offenses, Criteria and Procedure Regarding Intemperate Use and Lack of Fitness in Eligibility and Disciplinary Matters, and Declaratory Order of Eligibility for Licensure).

(f)(2) The program shall maintain evidence of student receipt of the criteria regarding eligibility for licensure, as specifically outlined in subsection (b) of this section.

2. INITIAL LICENSURE AND RENEWING AN EXPIRED LICENSE

217.2 Licensure by Examination for Graduates of Nursing Education Programs Within the United States, its Territories , or Possessions.
217.3. Temporary Authorization to Practice/Temporary Permit.
217.4. Requirements for Initial Licensure by Examination for Nurses Who Graduate from Nursing Programs Outside of United States' Jurisdictions.
217.5. Temporary License and Endorsement.
217.6 Renewing an Expired License
217.17. Jurisprudence Exam

3. RULE 217.9 INACTIVE AND RETIRED STATUS

§217.9. Inactive and Retired Status.

(a) A nurse may change his/her licensure status from "active" to "inactive" status by:

(1) submitting a written request to the Board prior to the expiration of his/her license; or

(2) designating "inactive" on the renewal form, if at the time of renewal.

(b) A nurse may change his/her licensure status from "active" or "inactive" to "retired" or "volunteer retired" status. A nurse who elects to change his/her licensure status from "active" or "inactive" to "retired" or "volunteer retired" status may do so only if he/she is in good standing with the Board. For purposes of this section, good standing means that the nurse's license is not in delinquent status and that there is no current disciplinary action, disciplinary probation, or pending investigation/s on his/her nursing license/s or authorization/s. A nurse will not be eligible for "retired" or "volunteer retired" status until all outstanding disciplinary issues have been resolved. Further, a nurse who wishes to change his/her licensure status from "inactive" to "retired" or "volunteer retired" status may do so only if his/her license was in good standing with the Board on the date his/her license became inactive.

(c) Retired Status. A nurse who wishes to change his/her licensure status to "retired" status and is eligible to do so under subsection (b) of this section must submit the following information to the Board:

(1) a written request to use one of the following titles:

(A) "Licensed Vocational Nurse, Retired"; "LVN, Retired"; "Vocational Nurse, Retired"; or "VN, Retired";

***ANNOTATOR'S NOTE**: Legislation (SB 1058) passed in 2013 requires the BON conduct criminal background checks of students and authorizes the board to self-initiate a declaratory order based on a positive background check. See NPA Secs. 301.2511(c) and 301.257(j). This rule will need to be amended to reflect this legislation.*

Sec. 301.257 of the NPA permits the BON to collect information from students to determine if they are aware of what might disqualify them from licensure upon graduation and of their right to seek a declaratory order. This subsection implements that provision. The school only provides the student with the information and makes documentation that the student received the information. It does not collect the information regarding the student's potential disqualification. Sec. 301.257 requires the BON to notify the school if it determines a student is disqualified. See also Rule 213.30.

***ANNOTATOR'S NOTE**: The rules relating to initial licensure and renewing an expired license are not being set out because the BON has extensive materials on initial licensure on its website including online applications. Most individuals seeking licensure will rely on these materials if they have questions about the process. These rules can also be accessed through the BON's website.*

The requirements for renewing an expired license vary with the length of time expired and whether the nurse has practiced in another state.

This rule governs nurses who voluntarily elect inactive status as opposed to those who simply fail to renew their license.

An LVN or RN retireing or leaving nurisng in good standing may qualify for the special status of "LVN Retired" or "RN Retired." NPA Sec. 301.261(e) on which this rule is based was amended in 2011 (SB 193) to permit nurses younger than 65 to qualify for "retired" status.

Process for applying for "retired" status.

(B) "Registered Nurse, Retired" or "RN, Retired"; or

(C) "RN, Nurse Anesthetist, Retired"; "RN, Nurse-Midwife, Retired"; "RN, Nurse Practitioner, Retired"; or "RN, Clinical Nurse Specialist, Retired"; and

(2) the required, non-refundable fee.

(d) A nurse whose license is in "retired" status may not practice as a nurse for compensation (monetary or non-monetary benefits).

(e) Volunteer Retired Authorization. In compliance with the Occupations Code §112.051, the Board shall adopt rules providing for reduced fees and continuing education requirements for retired health care practitioners whose only practice is voluntary charity care. The Board shall also define voluntary charity care.

(1) A nurse who wishes to change his/her licensure status to "volunteer retired" status and is eligible to do so under subsection (b) of this section must request authorization from the Board. The nurse must meet the following criteria:

(A) Must claim Texas as the nurse's Primary State of Residence in accordance with the Occupations Code Chapter 304, Nurse Licensure Compact, and Chapter 220 of this title; and

(B) If applying as a vocational or registered nurse, must have completed at least 10 contact hours of continuing education as required by Chapter 216 of this title during the previous biennium. If applying as a registered nurse with advanced practice recognition, must meet the continuing education requirements of §216.3(c).

(2) Application. An applicant for "volunteer retired" authorization must complete and submit to the Board an application requesting "volunteer retired" authorization as a vocational nurse, registered nurse, or registered nurse with advanced practice authorization in a given role and population focus area.

(3) Scope of Authorization for LVN or RN. A nurse holding "volunteer retired" authorization may only practice nursing at the level for which he/she formerly held an active/unencumbered license to practice nursing. To qualify as volunteer practice, such practice must be without compensation or expectation of compensation as a direct service volunteer of a charitable organization. When engaging in practice as a volunteer retired nurse, the nurse must comply with the Nursing Practice Act (NPA) and Board rules in their entirety.

(4) Scope of Authorization for APRN. A nurse who has authorization in an advanced practice role and population focus area at the time of application for "volunteer retired" authorization must continue to practice in collaboration/supervision with a physician qualified in the APRN's role and population focus area, as well as in compliance with all other laws applicable to the APRN's practice setting, both within the NPA and Board rules, as well as other applicable laws.

(5) Charitable Organization. A charitable organization is defined in §84.003 of the Texas Civil Practice and Remedies Code and includes any bona fide charitable, religious, prevention of cruelty to children or animals, youth sports and youth recreational, neighborhood crime prevention or patrol, or educational organization (excluding fraternities, sororities, and secret societies), or other organization promoting the common good and general welfare for the people in a community, including these types of organizations with a §501(c)(3) or (4) exemption from federal income tax, some chambers of commerce, and volunteer centers certified by the Department of Public Safety.

(6) Renewal. A nurse's "volunteer retired" authorization expires on the same date as the nurse's regular license previously expired. Each volunteer retired nurse seeking to renew his/her "volunteer retired" authorization must meet all of the requirements of this section, including the continuing education requirements set forth in this section for the applicable renewal period.

(7) Penalty. A nurse whose license is in "volunteer retired" status shall not receive compensation (monetary or non-monetary benefits) for the practice of nursing. To do so would constitute the practice of vocational, professional, or advanced practice nursing (as applicable)

An "LVN Retired" or "RN Retired" may not practice nursing for compensation.

Volunteer Retired Nurse Authorization. Subsection (d) implements Texas Occupations Code Sec. 112.051 which addresses retired nurses (and other health care professionals) who want to continue to practice but only to provide charity care. That section provides, in part:

> *Sec. 112.051. REDUCED LICENSE REQUIREMENTS FOR RETIRED HEALTH CARE PRACTITIONERS PERFORMING CHARITY WORK.*
>
> *(a) Each licensing entity shall adopt rules providing for reduced fees and continuing education requirements for a retired health care practitioner whose only practice is voluntary charity care.*
>
> *(b) The licensing entity by rule shall define voluntary charity care.*

Volunteer retired nurses will have a special license. Volunteer retired nurses must limit their practice to charity care as set out in this subsection. This subsection sets out how the BON will license volunteer retired nurses. Volunteer retired nurses need to complete 10 hours of CNE per license renewal period. See also Rule 216.3(7) relating to CNE requirements for Volunteer Retired RNs or LVNs.

Scope of authorization/practice for a "Volunteer Retired" RN or LVN.

Scope of authorization/practice for a "Volunteer Retired" APRN.

Definition of a charitable organization.

Renewal of "Volunteer Retired" status

A "retired volunteer" nurse who takes compensation would be considered to have engaged in the unauthorized practice of nursing.

without a license and will subject the volunteer retired nurse to the penalties imposed for this violation.

(8) Titles. A nurse holding "volunteer retired" authorization may hold him/herself out as and may use one of the titles specified in subsection (c) of this section to reflect the individual nurse's "volunteer retired" authorization. Titles representing to the public that a nurse holds "volunteer retired" authorization are protected in the same manner as titles listed in the Occupations Code §301.351 and §217.10 of this chapter.

(9) Authorization Verification. Authorization verification may be accomplished by accessing the Board's web page at http://www.bon.texas.gov/.

(f) A nurse who has not practiced nursing in Texas and whose license has been in an inactive status for less than four years may reactivate the license by completing the reactivation application form, paying the required reactivation fee and the current licensure fee which are non-refundable, and submitting verification of completion of 20 contact hours of continuing education that meets the requirements of Chapter 216 of this title (relating to Continuing Competency) within the two years immediately preceding the application for reactivation.

(g) A nurse who has not practiced nursing and whose license has been in an inactive status for four or more years must submit to the Board:

(1) a completed reactivation application;

(2) verification of successful completion of a refresher course, extensive orientation to the practice of nursing, or a nursing program of study that meets the requirements prescribed by the Board. The nurse must submit an application to the Board for a temporary permit for the limited purpose of completing a refresher course, extensive orientation to the practice of nursing, or a nursing program of study;

(3) evidence of completion of 20 contact hours of acceptable continuing education for the two years immediately preceding the application for reactivation that meets the requirements of Chapter 216 of this title;

(4) a successful course completion form from one of the following:

(A) the online Texas Board of Nursing Jurisprudence Prep Course;

(B) the Texas Board of Nursing Jurisprudence and Ethics Workshop; or

(C) a Texas Board of Nursing approved Nursing Jurisprudence and Ethics course;

(5) a certificate of successful completion from the Texas Nursing Jurisprudence Exam; and

(6) the required reactivation fee, plus the current licensure fee, which are non-refundable.

(h) The Board adopts by reference the following forms, which comprise the instructions and requirements for a refresher course, extensive orientation to the practice of nursing, and a nursing program of study required by this section, and which are available at http://www.bon.state.tx.us/olv/forms.html:

(1) Application for Six Month Temporary Permit (RN); and

(2) Application for Six Month Temporary Permit (LVN).

(i) A nurse whose license has been in an inactive status for four years or more and who is licensed and has practiced in another state during the previous four years preceding the application for reactivation in Texas must comply with the requirements of subsection (g)(1) and (3) - (6) of this section.

Returning to active status. A nurse on inactive status for less than four years may reactivate her/his license by paying a fee and completing 20 hours of CNE within the 2 years preceding reactivation. The reactivation fee is considerably less than the fee to renew an expired license.

A nurse on inactive status who has not practiced nursing for more than four years must take a refresher course and meet other requirements to reactivate her or his inactive license.

Reactivation of license inactive for more than four years by a nurse who has practiced in another state during the past four years.

SUBPART H
DISCIPLINARY PROCESS

1. RULE 213.31. RIGHTS OF LICENSEES IN DISCIPLINARY MATTERS

§213.31. Cross-Reference of Rights and Options Available to Licensees and Petitioners.
Licensees subject to disciplinary action and petitioners seeking a determination of licensure eligibility have certain rights and options available to them in connection with these mechanisms. For example, licensees or petitioners have the right to request information in the Board's possession, including information favorable to licensee or petitioner, and the option to be represented by an attorney at their own expense. The following is a list of references to provisions of the Nursing Practice Act (Texas Occupations Code Annotated Chapter 301) and the Board's rules addressing these rights and options and related matters. Persons with matters before the Board should familiarize themselves with these provisions:

(1) Section 301.257--Declaratory Order of License Eligibility;
(2) Section 301.203--Records of Complaints;
(3) Section 301.204--General Rules Regarding Complaint Investigation and Disposition;
(4) Section 301.464--Informal Proceedings;
(5) Section 301.552--Monitoring of License Holder;
(6) Section 301.452--Grounds for Disciplinary Action;
(7) Section 301.453--Disciplinary Authority of Board; Methods of Discipline;
(8) Section 301.457--Complaint and Investigation;
(9) Section 301.159--Board Duties Regarding Complaints;
(10) Section 301.463--Agreed Disposition;
(11) Section 301.462--Voluntary Surrender of License;
(12) Section 301.454--Notice and Hearing;
(13) Section 301.458--Initiation of Formal Charges; Discovery;
(14) Section 301.459--Formal Hearing;
(15) Section 301.460--Access to Information;
(16) Section 301.352--Protection for Refusal to Engage in Certain Conduct;
(17) Section 301.455--Temporary License Suspension;
(18) Section 217.11--Standards of Nursing Practice;
(19) Section 217.12--Unprofessional Conduct; and
(20) Sections 213.1 - 213.33--Practice and Procedure.

2. RULES 213.1- 213.26. DISCIPLINARY PROCEEDINGS

> ***ANNOTATOR'S NOTE**: BON Rules 213.1-.26 deal primarily with procedure and many are fairly technical, e.g., deadlines to file documents. Nurses normally will not need to be familiar with these rules unless they have had a complaint against them, and if they retain an attorney, he or she will do that. Consequently, only a few of these rules are being set out in full. The remainder will simply be listed.*

This Subpart H includes BON rules governing the BON's taking disciplinary action against a nurse. The rules set out are:

Rule 213.31	*Rights of Nurse in Disciplinary Matters*
Rule 213.1-213.26	*Disciplinary Proceedings*
Rule 213.33	*Factors Considered by BON for Imposition of Penalties/Sanctions*
Rule 213.34	*Deferred Disciplinary Action Pilot Program*

Certain provisions of the NPA and BON rules relate primarily to nurses who have complaints filed against them or who otherwise appear before the board for disciplinary reasons. Some of these provisions give important rights to these nurses. This rule identifies the more important of these provisions.

This group of rules governs the processes and procedures when nurses have complaints filed against them . The factors the BON considers in imposing penalties and sanctions are in Rule §213.33 set out in Subpart H below.

The BON has adopted Disciplinary Sanction Policies that are set out on the BON website at www.bon.texas.gov. The website also has information about the disciplinary process.

§213.1. Definitions.

§213.2. Construction.

§213.3. Pleading.

§213.4. Representation.

(a) A person may represent himself/herself or be represented by an attorney licensed to practice law in Texas.

(b) A party's attorney of record shall remain the attorney of record in the absence of a formal request to withdraw and an order of the judge approving the request.

(c) Notwithstanding the above, a party may expressly waive the right to assistance of counsel.

§213.5. Appearance.

§213.6. Agreements in Writing.

§213.7. Final Disposition.

§213.8. Filing of Documents.

§213.9. Computation of Time.

§213.10. Notice and Service.

(a) Notice must be in writing and addressed to the party. Notice to a licensee is effective and service is complete when sent by certified or registered mail, return receipt requested, to the licensee's address of record at the time of the mailing.

(b) Notice to a party holding a multistate licensure privilege is effective and service is complete when sent by certified or registered mail, return receipt requested, to the privilege holder's address of record maintained with the home state nurse licensing agency at the time of the mailing.

(c) Notice to a non-licensee is effective and service is complete when sent by certified or registered mail, return receipt requested, to the person's address as stated on his/her petition, application, or other pleading.

(d) Notice to any person other than the Board is effective and service is complete when sent by certified or registered mail, return receipt requested, to the person's attorney of record.

(e) Notice of a hearing in a contested case must comply with Texas Government Code §2001.052 (Texas Administrative Procedure Act). Service is complete when made pursuant to 1 TAC §155.25 (SOAH).

§213.11. Non-SOAH Motion for Continuance.

§213.12. Witness Fees and Expenses.

§213.13. Complaint Investigation and Disposition.

(a) Complaints shall be submitted to the Board in writing and should contain at least the following information: Nurse/Respondent Name, License Number, Social Security Number, Date of Birth, Employer, Dates of Occurrence(s), Description of Facts or Conduct, Witnesses, Outcome,

Rule 213.1 (Definitions) is set out in Subpart A(2) above. Those definitions apply not only to Rules 213.1-.26 but to all of Rule 213.

Addresses how the rules will be construed, e.g, words will be read in context.

Addresses form and content of pleading both by the board and the nurse.

When a nurse appears before the board, she or he is entitled to be represented by an attorney or the nurse may represent her or himself.

Addresses prefiling of written testimony and filing of amicus ("friend of the court") briefs by third parties.

Requires agreements be in writing.

Requires all final orders be approved by the board itself unless NPA or rules specifically provide otherwise.

Addresses how and where documents should be filed.

Addresses how time periods and deadlines are calculated and extensions for deadlines.

Any notice to the nurse is effective when mailed to the nurse's address on file at the BON – regardless of whether the nurse actually receives the notice. This is why it is important that nurses notify the BON of any address change. As long as the notice is sent to the address on file, the board may proceed with disciplinary action against the nurse including taking of a default judgment. See Rules 213.16, 213.22 and 213.33(m) below.

Addresses seeking and granting of motions for continuance for cases not before the State Office of Administrative Hearings (SOAH).

Provides for payment and reimbursement of expenses for subpoenaed witnesses.

Complaints must be in writing.

Complainant Identification (Name, Address, and Telephone Number), and Written Instructions For Providing Information to the Board. Complaints may be made on the agency's complaint form.

(b) A preliminary investigation shall be conducted to determine the identity of the person named or described in the complaint.

(c) Complaints shall be assigned a priority status:

(1) Priority 1--those indicating that credible evidence exists showing a guilty plea, with or without an adjudication of guilt, or conviction of a serious crime involving moral turpitude; a violation of the NPA involving actual deception, fraud, or injury to clients or the public or a high probability of immediate deception, fraud or injury to clients or the public;

(2) Priority 2--those indicating that credible evidence exists showing a violation of the NPA involving a high probability of potential deception, fraud, or injury to clients or the public;

(3) Priority 3--those indicating that credible evidence exists showing a violation of the NPA involving a potential for deception, fraud, or injury to clients or the public; and

(4) Priority 4--all other complaints.

(d) Not later than the 30th day after a complaint is received, the staff shall place a time line for completion, not to exceed one year, in the investigative file and notify all parties to the complaint. Any change in time line must be noted in the file and all parties notified of the change not later than seven days after the change was made. For purposes of this rule, completion of an investigation in a disciplinary matter occurs when:

(1) staff determines insufficient evidence exists to substantiate the allegation of a violation of the NPA, Board's rules, or a Board order; or

(2) staff determines sufficient evidence exists to demonstrate a violation of the NPA, Board's rules, or a Board order and drafts proposed formal charges.

(e) Staff shall conduct a criminal background search of the party described in the complaint.

(f) The staff shall provide summary data of complaints extending beyond the complaint time line to the executive director.

§213.14. Preliminary Notice to Respondent in Disciplinary Matters.

(a) Except for proceedings conducted pursuant to the authority of Texas Occupations Code Annotated §301.455 (Temporary Suspensions) or unless it would jeopardize the investigation, prior to commencing disciplinary proceedings under §213.15 of this title (relating to Commencement of Disciplinary Proceedings), the staff shall serve the respondent with written notice in accordance with Texas Government Code §2001.054(c).

(b) Such notice shall contain a statement of the facts or conduct alleged to warrant an adverse licensure action. The notice shall invite the respondent to show compliance with all requirements of the law for retention of the license.

(c) Respondent shall file a written response within 20 days after service of the notice specified in subsection (a) of this section.

§213.15. Commencement of Disciplinary Proceedings.

(a) If a complaint is not resolved informally, the staff may commence disciplinary proceedings by filing formal charges.

(b) The formal charges shall contain the following information:

(1) the name of the respondent and his or her license number;

(2) a statement alleging with reasonable certainty the specific act or acts relied on by the Board to constitute a violation of a specific statute, Board rule, or Board order; and

(3) a reference to the section of the Act or to the Board's rule, regulation, or order which respondent is alleged to have violated.

The board conducts a preliminary investigation of a complaint to be sure it identifies the right person. This investigation occurs before any notices are sent out. Once it is determined that the nurse has been correctly identified, the nurse is notified that a complaint has been filed against her/him.

The board assigns a priority to the complaints it receives and conducts its investigations based on these priorities. The priorities are based on danger to patients.

The nurse is notified when a complaint is filed against her/him. The board may conduct a preliminary investigation to be sure the correct nurse has been identified before sending out notice. The nurse may also not be notified if doing so would undermine the investigation. It would be an unusual situation in which this would be the case.

The nurse has 20 days to respond. If necessary, the nurse may request an extension from the board, but normally a nurse should be able to respond within 20 days.

The board normally attempts to resolve a complaint informally, i.e., by agreement. Informal conferences are governed by Rule §217.20 below. If the complaint cannot be resolved informally, the board files formal charges against the nurse and the matter is set for a hearing before an Administrative Law Judge. Administrative Law Judges are attorneys who are employed by the State Office of Administrative Hearings to conduct hearings for cases before administrative agencies such as the BON.

(c) When formal charges are filed, the executive director shall serve respondent with a copy of the formal charges. The notice shall state that respondent shall file a written answer to the formal charges that meets the requirements of §213.16 of this title (relating to Respondent's Answer in a Disciplinary Matter).

(d) The staff may amend the formal charges at any time permitted by the APA. A copy of any formal amended charges shall be served on the respondent. The first charges filed shall be entitled "formal charges," the first amended charges filed shall be entitled "first amended formal charges," and so forth.

(e) Formal charges may be resolved by agreement of the parties at any time.

§213.16. Respondent's Answer in a Disciplinary Matter.

(a) The respondent in a disciplinary matter shall file an answer to the formal charges and to every amendment thereof.

(b) The answer shall admit or deny each of the allegations in the charges or amendment thereof. If the respondent intends to deny only a part of an allegation, the respondent shall specify so much of it is true and shall deny only the remainder. The answer shall also include any other matter, whether of law or fact, upon which respondent intends to rely for his or her defense.

(c) If the Respondent fails to file a response to the Formal charges, the matter will be considered as a default case

(d) In a case of default, the Respondent will be deemed to have

(1) admitted all the factual allegations in the Formal charges;

(2) waived the opportunity to show compliance with the law;

(3) waived the opportunity for a hearing on the Formal charges; and

(4) waived objection to the recommended sanction in the Formal charges.

(e) The Executive Director may recommend that the Board enter a default order, based upon the allegations set out in the Formal charges, that adopts the sanction that was recommended in the Formal charges.

(f) Upon consideration of the case, the Board may:

(1) enter a default order under §2001.056 of the APA; or

(2) order the matter to be set for a hearing at SOAH.

(g) The respondent may amend his or her answer at any time permitted by the APA or SOAH rules.

(h) The first answer filed shall be entitled "answer," the first amended answer filed shall be entitled "first amended answer," and so forth.

(i) Any default judgment granted under this section will be entered on the basis of the factual allegations in the formal charges contained in the notice, and upon proof of proper notice to the Respondent. For purposes of this section, proper notice means notice sufficient to meet the provisions of the Texas Government Code §2001.054 and §213.10 of this title (relating to Notice and Service). Such notice shall also include the following language in capital letters in 12 point boldface type: FAILURE TO FILE A WRITTEN ANSWER TO THE FORMAL CHARGES, EITHER PERSONALLY OR BY LEGAL REPRESENTATIVE, WILL RESULT IN THE ALLEGATIONS CONTAINED IN THE FORMAL CHARGES BEING ADMITTED AS TRUE AND THE PROPOSED RECOMMENDATION OF STAFF SHALL BE GRANTED BY DEFAULT.

(j) A motion for rehearing which requests that the Board vacate its default order under this section shall be granted if movant proves by the preponderance of the evidence that the failure to answer the formal charges was not intentional or the result of conscious indifference, but due to accident or mistake--provided that movant has a meritorious defense to the factual allegations contained in the formal charges and the granting thereof will occasion no delay or otherwise work an injury to the Board.

§213.17. Discovery.

If the nurse fails to respond, the board may take a default judgment against the nurse.

A default can be overturned but the burden of proof is high.

Addresses how discovery generally will be done.

§213.18. Depositions.

§213.19. Subpoenas.

§213.20. Informal Proceedings and Alternate Dispute Resolution (ADR).

(a) The Board's policy is to encourage the resolution and early settlement of internal and external disputes, including contested cases, through voluntary settlement processes such as informal proceedings or alternative dispute resolution. Any matter within the Board's jurisdiction may be resolved informally by stipulation, agreed settlement, agreed order, dismissal, or default. These matters may also be resolved using any ADR procedure or combination of procedures described by Chapter 154, Civil Practice and Remedies Code.

(b) In disciplinary matters, the Board shall offer the complainant and the licensee the opportunity to be heard. The offer may be made at any time prior to disposition and may be included on the Board's complaint form, on any notice required by statute or these rules, or otherwise.

(c) Informal proceedings may be conducted in person, by attorney, or by electronic, telephonic, or written communication.

(d) Informal proceedings shall be conducted pursuant to the following procedural standards:

(1) Respondent shall have a right to be represented by an attorney of record. At any time, should respondent choose to obtain representation by an attorney and advises staff of such choice, the conference will be discontinued;

(2) Respondent will be expected to answer questions concerning the allegations contained in notice of complaint or formal charges, but may decline to answer any questions posed during the conference;

(3) Respondent and staff participation in the conference is voluntary and may be terminated by either party without prejudicing the right to proceed with a contested case. Respondent will be expected to cooperate fully with the Enforcement Staff to ensure that it has all pertinent information relating to the complaint or formal charges against respondent; and

(4) Although, a verbatim transcript is not being kept of the informal conference, party admissions and outline notes may be used at a formal hearing if this matter is docketed as a formal complaint at the State Office of Administrative Hearings.

(e) Informal conferences may be conducted at any time by the executive director or designee.

(f) The Board's counsel or assistant attorney general shall participate in informal proceedings.

(g) Disposition of matters considered informally may be made at any time in an agreed order containing such terms as the executive director may deem reasonable and necessary. Except as to matters delegated to the executive director for ratification, said agreed order shall not be final and effective until the Board, or an eligibility and disciplinary committee, votes to accept the proposed disposition.

(h) Referral to peer assistance after report to the Board.

(1) A nurse required to be reported under Texas Occupations Code Annotated §§301.401 - 301.409, may obtain informal disposition through referral to a peer assistance program as specified in Texas Occupations Code Annotated §301.410, as amended, if the nurse:

(A) makes a written stipulation of the nurse's impairment by dependency on chemicals or by mental illness;

(B) makes a written waiver of the nurse's right to administrative hearing and judicial review of:

(i) all matters contained in the stipulation of impairment;

(ii) any future modification or extension of the peer assistance contract;

(iii) the future imposition of sanctions under Texas Occupations Code

Addresses process for taking of depositions.

Addresses the issuing of subpoenas by the board. The NPA gives the BON broad subpoena powers. See NPA Sec. 301.465.

The board has authority to settle a complaint through informal proceedings without having a formal hearing. The nurse has the option of rejecting any settlement offered by the board in an informal proceeding. If the matter is not resolved in informal proceedings, formal charges are filed and the matter will be set for formal hearing before an Administrative Law Judge.

Information from the informal hearing may be used if the case is not resolved at the informal hearing stage and goes to formal hearing.

Peer assistance referrals.

Nurses experiencing problems with chemical dependency or mental illness may be referred to peer assistance in lieu of continuation of the disciplinary action against them. The only board-approved peer assistance program is the Texas Peer Assistance Program for Nurses. As a condition of referral, the nurse must agree to certain stipulations.

Annotated §301.453 in the event the executive director should determine the nurse has failed to comply with the requirements of the peer assistance program; and

(C) makes a written contract with the Texas Board of Nursing through its executive director promising to:

(i) undergo and pay for such physical and mental evaluations as the peer assistance program determines to be reasonable and necessary to evaluate the nurse's impairment; to plan, implement and monitor the nurse's rehabilitation; and, to determine if, when and under what conditions the nurse can safely return to practice;

(ii) sign a participation agreement with the peer assistance program;

(iii) comply with each and every requirement of the peer assistance program in full and timely fashion for the duration of the contract and any extension(s) thereof; and

(iv) waive confidentiality and privilege and authorize release of information about the nurse's impairment and rehabilitation to the peer assistance program and the executive director of the Texas Board of Nursing.

(2) Disposition of a complaint by referral to a peer assistance program is not a finding which requires imposition of a sanction under Texas Occupations Code Annotated §301.453.

(3) In the event the nurse fails to comply with the nurse's contract with the Texas Board of Nursingor the nurse's participation agreement with the peer assistance program, such non-compliance will be considered by the executive director at an informal proceeding after notice to the nurse of the non-compliance and opportunity to respond. At the informal proceeding, the executive director may consider facts relevant to the alleged non- compliance, modify or extend the contract or participation agreement, declare the contract satisfied or impose §301.453 sanctions on the nurse which will result in public discipline and reporting to the National Council of State Boards of Nursing's Disciplinary Data Bank.

(i) ADR shall be conducted pursuant to the following procedural standards:

(1) Any ADR procedure used to resolve disputes before the Board shall comply with the requirements of the NPA, chapter 2009 of the Government Code, and any model guidelines for the use of ADR issued by the State Office of Administrative Hearings, which may be found at: http://www.soah.state.tx.us.

(2) The Board's general counsel or his designee shall be the Board's dispute resolution coordinator (DRC). The DRC shall perform the following functions, as required:

(A) coordinate the implementation of the Board's ADR policy;

(B) serve as a resource for any staff training or education needed to implement the ADR procedures; and

(C) collect data to evaluate the effectiveness of ADR procedures implemented by the Board.

(3) The Board, a committee of the Board, a respondent in a disciplinary matter pending before the Board, the executive director, or a Board employee engaged in a dispute with the executive director or another employee, may request that the contested matter be submitted to ADR. The request must be in writing, be addressed to the DRC, and state the issues to be determined. The person requesting ADR and the DRC will determine which method of ADR is most appropriate. If the person requesting ADR is the respondent in a disciplinary proceeding, the executive director shall determine if the Board will participate in ADR or proceed with the Board's normal disciplinary processes. The matter may be submitted to ADR only upon approval by all concerned parties.

(4) Any costs associated with retaining an impartial third party mediator, moderator, facilitator, or arbitrator, shall be borne by the party requesting ADR.

(5) Agreements of the parties to ADR must be in writing and are enforceable in the same manner as any other written contract. Confidentiality of records and communications related to the subject matter of an ADR proceeding shall be governed by §154.073 of the Civil Practice and Remedies Code.

(6) If the ADR process does not result in an agreement, the matter shall be referred to the Board for other appropriate disposition.

If the nurse fails to successfully complete the peer assistance program, the BON can proceed with disciplining the nurse.

Procedures for alternate dispute resolution(ADR).

(j) If eligibility matters are not resolved informally, the petitioner may obtain a hearing before SOAH by submitting a written request to the staff.

(k) If disciplinary matters are not resolved informally, formal charges may be filed in accordance with §213.15 of this title (relating to Commencement of Disciplinary Proceedings) and the case may be set for a hearing before SOAH in accordance with §213.22 of this title (relating to Formal Proceedings).

(l) Pre-docketing conferences may be conducted by the executive director prior to SOAH acquiring jurisdiction over the contested case. The executive director, unilaterally or at the request of any party, may direct the parties, their attorneys or representatives to appear before the executive director at a specified time and place for a conference prior to the hearing for the purpose of:

(1) simplifying the issues;

(2) considering the making of admissions or stipulations of fact or law;

(3) reviewing the procedure governing the hearing;

(4) limiting the number of witnesses whose testimony will be repetitious; and

(5) doing any act that may simplify the proceedings, and disposing of the matters in controversy, including settling all or part of the issues in dispute pursuant to §213.20 and §213.21 of this title (Informal Proceedings and Agreed Disposition).

§213.21. Agreed Disposition.

Informal proceedings, complaints and formal charges may be resolved by stipulation, agreed settlement, agreed order, or dismissal pursuant to Texas Occupations Code Annotated §301.463.

§213.22. Formal Proceedings.

§213.23. Decision of the Board.

(a) Except as to those matters expressly delegated to the executive director for ratification, either the Board or the Eligibility and Disciplinary Committee, may make final decisions in all matters relating to the granting or denial of a license or permit, discipline, temporary suspension, or administrative and civil penalties.

(b) Prior to the issuance of a proposal for decision, a party may submit proposed findings of fact and conclusions of law to the judge. The judge shall issue a ruling on each proposed finding of fact and conclusion of law and shall set forth the specific reason for not adopting a particular proposed finding of fact or conclusion of law.

(c) Any party of record who is adversely affected by the proposal for decision of the judge shall have the opportunity to file with the judge exceptions to the proposal for decision and replies to exceptions to the proposal for decision in accordance with 1 TAC §155.507. The proposal for decision may be amended by the judge in accordance with 1 TAC §155.507 without again being served on the parties.

(d) The proposal for decision may be acted on by the Board or the Eligibility and Disciplinary Committee, in accordance with this section, after the expiration of 10 days after the filing of replies to exceptions to the proposal for decision or upon the day following the day exceptions or replies to exceptions are due if no such exceptions or replies are filed.

If a case is not resolved informally, the nurse may request a hearing before the State Office of Administrative Hearings.

If a case is not resolved informally, formal charges are likely to be filed and the case goes to formal hearing.

A case can normally be settled by agreement at any point in the process.

Addresses procedures for formal proceedings. Formal hearings are very much like a trial except that the procedures and rules of evidence are not quite as strict. They are governed by the Administrative Procedures Act and rules of the State Office of Administrative Hearings. Formal hearings are conducted by Administrative Law Judges who are attorneys employed by the State to conduct such hearings.

Failure to appear at a hearing will normally result in a default judgment being taken against the nurse. The board can proceed as long as it has mailed notice to the address the nurse has on file with the board, regardless of whether the nurse actually received the notice. In a default judgment, the allegations set out in the formal charges will be deemed to be true.

This Rule 213.23 sets out how the BON order is developed and finally approved when a formal hearing is involved. The first step is for the nurse's and board's attorneys to submit the proposed findings of fact and conclusion of law to the Administrative Law Judge. The judge then prepares a Proposal for Decision. Both the nurse and board may file exceptions (i.e., request changes). The Administrative Law Judge reviews these and issues a final Proposal for Decision. Both the nurse's and board's attorneys may file exceptions with the board (i.e., request baord to make changes before issues its final order). The board's authority to change a Proposal for Decision is limited.

(e) Following the issuance of a proposal for decision, parties shall have an opportunity to file written exceptions and/or briefs with the Board concerning a proposal for decision. An opportunity shall be given to file a response to written exceptions and/or briefs. The following requirements govern the submission of written exceptions and/or briefs to the Board:

(1) Individuals wishing to file written exceptions and/or briefs with the Board, but not wishing to make an oral presentation to the Board concerning a proposal for decision. A Respondent wishing to file written exceptions and/or briefs with the Board concerning a proposal for decision must do so no later than 10 days prior to the date of the next regularly scheduled Board meeting where the Board will deliberate on the proposal for decision. The Board will not consider any written exceptions and/or briefs submitted in violation of this requirement.

(2) Individuals wishing to make an oral presentation to the Board concerning a proposal for decision. An individual wishing to make an oral presentation to the Board must file written exceptions and/or briefs with the Board. If no modification is proposed to the proposal for decision, an individual must file written exceptions and/or briefs with the Board at least 21 days prior to the date of the next regularly scheduled Board meeting where the Board will deliberate on the proposal for decision. If a modification is proposed to the proposal for decision, an individual must file a written response to the proposed modification, written exceptions, and/or briefs with the Board at least 10 days prior to the date of the regularly scheduled Board meeting where the Board will deliberate on the proposal for decision. An individual will not be permitted to make an oral presentation to the Board if the individual does not comply with these requirements.

(f) It is the policy of the Board to change a finding of fact or conclusion of law in a proposal for decision or to vacate or modify the proposed order of a judge when, the Board determines:

(1) that the judge did not properly apply or interpret applicable law, agency rules, written policies provided by staff or prior administrative decisions;

(2) that a prior administrative decision on which the judge relied is incorrect or should be changed; or

(3) that a technical error in a finding of fact should be changed.

(g) If the Board modifies, amends, or changes the recommended proposal for decision or order of the judge, an order shall be prepared reflecting the Board's changes as stated in the record of the meeting and stating the specific reason and legal basis for the changes made according to subsection (f) of this section.

(h) An order of the Board shall be in writing and may be signed by the executive director on behalf of the Board.

(i) A copy of the order shall be mailed to all parties and to the party's last known employer as a nurse.

(j) The decision of the Board is immediate, final, and appealable upon the signing of the written order by the executive director on behalf of the Board where:

(1) the Board finds and states in the order that an imminent peril to the public health, safety, and welfare requires immediate effect of the order; and

(2) the order states it is final and effective on the date rendered.

(k) A motion for rehearing shall not be a prerequisite for appeal of the decision where the order of the Board contains the finding set forth in subsection (j) of this section.

(l) Motions for rehearing under this section are controlled by Texas Government Code §2001.145.

§213.24. Rescission of Probation.

§213.25. Monitoring.

(a) The Board shall identify and monitor licensees who present a risk to the public and who are subject to Board orders. The monitoring system shall track at least the name, license

The nurse may appear before the BON to make an oral presentation on why her or his requested changes to the Proposal for Decision should be granted.

Even though the Administrative Law Judge issues findings of fact and conclusions of law in his/her proposal for decision, the BON has the authority to modify that decision. This section sets out the conditions under which the board may change the Administrative Law Judges's recommended order.

"Technical error" is defined in Rule §213.1 as "an ALJ's misinterpretation or misapplication of sound nursing principles or minimum nursing practice standards in a proposal for decision that must be corrected to sufficiently protect the public."

Addresses the circumstances under which the BON may rescind probation and the process for rescinding.

The board can monitor nurses to ensure compliance with board orders.

number, address, employer, and any other information necessary to demonstrate compliance or non-compliance with an order of the Board.

(b) Monitored licensees will pay a monthly fee as stated in the Board order. Said fee shall be paid on or before the 5th of each month.

§213.26. Reissuance of a License.

3. RULE 213.33. FACTORS CONSIDERED FOR IMPOSITION OF PENALTIES/ SANCTIONS

§213.33. Factors Considered for Imposition of Penalties/Sanctions.

(a) The Board and the State Office of Administrative Hearings (SOAH) shall utilize the Disciplinary Matrix set forth in subsection (b) of this section in all disciplinary and eligibility matters.

(b) The Disciplinary Matrix is as follows:

Attached Graphic

(c) The Board and SOAH shall consider the following factors in conjunction with the Disciplinary Matrix when determining the appropriate penalty/sanction in disciplinary and eligibility matters. The following factors shall be analyzed in determining the tier and sanction level of the Disciplinary Matrix for a particular violation or multiple violations of the Nursing Practice Act (NPA) and Board rules:

(1) evidence of actual or potential harm to patients, clients, or the public;

(2) evidence of a lack of truthfulness or trustworthiness;

(3) evidence of misrepresentation(s) of knowledge, education, experience, credentials, or skills which would lead a member of the public, an employer, a member of the health-care team, or a patient to rely on the fact(s) misrepresented where such reliance could be unsafe;

(4) evidence of practice history;

(5) evidence of present fitness to practice;

(6) whether the person has been subject to previous disciplinary action by the Board or any other health care licensing agency in Texas or another jurisdiction and, if so, the history of compliance with those actions;

(7) the length of time the person has practiced;

(8) the actual damages, physical, economic, or otherwise, resulting from the violation;

(9) the deterrent effect of the penalty imposed;

(10) attempts by the licensee to correct or stop the violation;

(11) any mitigating or aggravating circumstances, including those specified in the Disciplinary Matrix;

(12) the extent to which system dynamics in the practice setting contributed to the problem;

(13) whether the person is being disciplined for multiple violations of the NPA or its derivative rules and orders;

(14) the seriousness of the violation;

(15) the threat to public safety;

(16) evidence of good professional character as set forth and required by §213.27 of this chapter (relating to Good Professional Character); and

(17) participation in a continuing education course described in §216.3(f) of this title (relating to Requirements) completed not more than two years before the start of the Board's investigation, if the nurse is being investigated by the Board regarding the nurse's selection of clinical care for the treatment of tick-borne diseases; and

Addresses reinstatement of a revoked, suspended or surrendered license. A revoked license cannot be reinstated for at least one year.

This rule sets out the factors the BON will consider in determining the appropriate penalty/sanction to impose on a nurse in a disciplinary case. The BON 2007 Sunset legislation added NPA Sec. 301.4531 requiring the BON to consider factors similar to those that were already set out in this rule. Subsecs. (k) and (l) address evaluations by a psychologist or psychiatrist to determine present fitness to practice.

The board utilizes a Disciplinary Matrix in determining what penalty or sanction to impose. The matrix is on the board's website.

The Disciplinary Matrix is set out on the board's website under the "Disciplinary Action" tab. Factors that will be considered in applying the Disciplinary Matrix.

(18) any other matter that justice may require. The presence of mitigating factors does not constitute a requirement of dismissal of a violation of the NPA and/or Board rules.

(d) Each specific act or instance of conduct may be treated as a separate violation.

(e) The Board may, upon the finding of a violation, enter an order imposing one or more of the following disciplinary actions, with or without probationary stipulations:

(1) Denial of the person's application for a license; license renewal; reinstatement of a revoked, suspended, or surrendered license; or temporary permit;

(2) Approval of the person's application for a license; license renewal; reinstatement of a revoked, suspended, or surrendered license; or temporary permit, with reasonable probationary stipulations as a condition of issuance, renewal, or reinstatement of the license or temporary permit. Additionally, the Board may determine, in accordance with §301.468 of the NPA, that an order denying a license application, license renewal, license reinstatement, or temporary permit be probated. Reasonable probationary stipulations may include, but are not limited to:

(A) submit to care, supervision, counseling, or treatment by a health provider designated by the Board as a condition for the issuance, renewal, or reinstatement of the license or temporary permit;

(B) submit to an evaluation as outlined in subsections (k) and (l) of this section or pursuant to the Occupations Code §301.4521;

(C) participate in a program of education or counseling prescribed by the Board;

(D) limit specific nursing activities and/or periodic Board review;

(E) practice for a specified period under the direction of a registered nurse or vocational nurse designated by the Board;

(F) abstain from unauthorized use of drugs and alcohol to be verified by random drug testing conducted through urinalysis; or

(G) perform public service which the Board considers appropriate;

(3) Issuance of a Warning. The issuance of a Warning shall include reasonable probationary stipulations which may include, but are not limited to, one or more of the following:

(A) submit to care, supervision, counseling, or treatment by a health provider designated by the Board;

(B) submit to an evaluation as outlined in subsections (k) and (l) of this section or pursuant to the Occupations Code §301.4521;

(C) participate in a program of education or counseling prescribed by the Board;

(D) limit specific nursing activities and/or periodic Board review;

(E) practice for a specified period of at least one year under the direction of a registered nurse or vocational nurse designated by the Board;

(F) abstain from unauthorized use of drugs and alcohol to be verified by random drug testing conducted through urinalysis; or

(G) perform public service which the Board considers appropriate;

(4) Issuance of a Reprimand. The issuance of a Reprimand shall include reasonable probationary stipulations which may include, but are not limited to, one or more of the following:

(A) submit to care, supervision, counseling, or treatment by a health provider designated by the Board;

(B) submit to an evaluation as outlined in subsections (k) and (l) of this section or pursuant to the Occupations Code §301.4521;

(C) participate in a program of education or counseling prescribed by the Board;

(D) limit specific nursing activities and/or periodic Board review;

(E) practice for a specified period of at least two years under the direction of a

Each instance of conduct can be treated as a separate violation.

This Subsec. (e) sets out the range of penalties or sanctions that the board can impose on a nurse. It has a broad range of options.

Deny the license, license renewal or license reactivation.

Approve the license, license renewal or license reactivation but do so with stipulations.

Issue a warning.

Issue a reprimand.

registered nurse or vocational nurse designated by the Board;

(F) abstain from unauthorized use of drugs and alcohol to be verified by random drug testing conducted through urinalysis; or

(G) perform public service which the Board considers appropriate;

(5) Limitation or restriction of the person's license, including limits on specific nursing activities or periodic Board review;

(6) Suspension of the person's license. The Board may determine that the order of suspension be enforced and active for a specific period and/or probated with reasonable probationary stipulations as a condition for lifting or staying the order of suspension. Reasonable probationary stipulations may include, but are not limited to, one or more of the following:

(A) submit to care, supervision, counseling, or treatment by a health provider designated by the Board;

(B) submit to an evaluation as outlined in subsections (k) and (l) of this section or pursuant to the Occupations Code §301.4521;

(C) participate in a program of education or counseling prescribed by the Board;

(D) limit specific nursing activities and/or periodic Board review;

(E) practice for a specified period of not less than two years under the direction of a registered nurse or vocational nurse designated by the Board;

(F) abstain from unauthorized use of drugs and alcohol to be verified by random drug testing conducted through urinalysis; or

(G) perform public service which the Board considers appropriate;

(7) Remit payment of the administrative penalty, fine, or assessment of hearing costs;

(8) Acceptance of a Voluntary Surrender of a nurse's license(s);

(9) Revocation of the person's license;

(10) Require participation in remedial education course or courses prescribed by the Board which are designed to address those competency deficiencies identified by the Board;

(11) Assessment of a fine as set forth in §213.32 of this chapter (relating to Corrective Action Proceedings and Schedule of Administrative Fines);

(12) Assessment of costs as authorized by the Occupations Code §301.461 and the Government Code §2001.177; or

(13) Require successful completion of a Board approved peer assistance program.

(f) Every disciplinary order issued by the Board shall require the person subject to the order to participate in a program of education or counseling prescribed by the Board, which at a minimum, will include a review course in nursing jurisprudence and ethics.

(g) The following disciplinary and eligibility sanction policies and guidelines shall be used by the Board and SOAH when determining the appropriate penalty/sanction in disciplinary and eligibility matters:

(1) Disciplinary Sanctions for Fraud, Theft, and Deception approved by the Board and published on February 22, 2008 in the Texas Register (33 TexReg 1646) and available on the Board's website at http://www.bon.state.tx.us/disciplinaryaction/dsp.html.

(2) Disciplinary Sanctions for Lying and Falsification approved by the Board and published on February 22, 2008 in the Texas Register (33 TexReg 1647) and available on the Board's website at http://www.bon.state.tx.us/disciplinaryaction/dsp.html.

(3) Disciplinary Sanctions for Sexual Misconduct approved by the Board and published on February 22, 2008 in the Texas Register (33 TexReg 1649) and available on the Board's website at http://www.bon.state.tx.us/disciplinaryaction/dsp.html.

(4) Eligibility and Disciplinary Sanctions for Nurses with Substance Abuse, Misuse, Substance Dependency, or other Substance Use Disorder and published on February 22, 2008 in the Texas Register (33 TexReg 1651) and available on the Board's website at http://www.bon.state.tx.us/disciplinaryaction/dsp.html.

(5) Disciplinary Guidelines for Criminal Conduct approved by the Board and published on May 17, 2013 in the Texas Register (38 TexReg 3152) and available on the Board's website at http://www.bon.texas.gov/disciplinaryaction/discp-guide.html.

Place restrictions on the license.

Suspend the license.

Subdivisions (7)-(13) list other options the BON has.

Education or counseling is required in every case and will include a jurisprudence review course.

The board has licensure eligibility and disciplinary sanction policies it follows. These can be found on the board's website.

The BON also has disciplinary guidelines it follows for criminal conduct.

(h) To the extent that a conflict exists between the Disciplinary Matrix and a disciplinary and eligibility sanction policy described in subsection (g) of this section, the Disciplinary Matrix controls.

(i) Unless otherwise specified, fines shall be payable in full by cashier's check or money order not later than the 45th day following the entry of an Order.

(j) The payment of a fine shall be in addition to the full payment of all applicable fees and satisfaction of all other applicable requirements of the NPA and the Board's rules.

(k) If the Board has probable cause to believe that a person is unable to practice nursing with reasonable skill and safety because of physical impairment, mental impairment, chemical dependency, or abuse of drugs or alcohol, the Board may require an evaluation that meets the following standards:

(1) The evaluation must be conducted by a Board-approved addictionologist, addictionist, medical doctor, neurologist, doctor of osteopathy, psychologist, neuropsychologist, advanced practice registered nurse, or psychiatrist, with credentials appropriate for the specific evaluation, as determined by the Board. In all cases, the evaluator must possess credentials, expertise, and experience appropriate for conducting the evaluation, as determined by the Board. The evaluator must be familiar with the duties appropriate to the nursing profession.

(2) The evaluation must be designed to determine whether the suspected impairment prevents the person from practicing nursing with reasonable skill and safety to patients. The evaluation must be conducted pursuant to professionally recognized standards and methods. The evaluation must include the utilization of objective tests and instruments with valid and reliable validity scales designed to test the person's fitness to practice. The evaluation may include testing of the person's psychological or neuropsychological stability only if the person is suspected of mental impairment, chemical dependency, or drug or alcohol abuse. If applicable, the evaluation must include information regarding the person's prognosis and medication regime.

(3) The person subject to evaluation shall sign a release allowing the evaluator to review the file compiled by the Board staff and a release that permits the evaluator to release the evaluation to the Board. The person subject to evaluation should be provided a copy of the evaluation upon completion by the evaluator; if not, the Board will provide the person a copy.

(l) When determining evidence of present fitness to practice because of known or reported unprofessional conduct, lack of good professional character, or prior criminal history:

(1) The Board may request an evaluation conducted by a Board-approved forensic psychologist, forensic psychiatrist, or advanced practice registered nurse who:

(A) evaluates the behavior in question or the prior criminal history of the person;

(B) seeks to predict:

(i) the likelihood that the person subject to evaluation will engage in the behavior in question or criminal activity again, which may result in the person committing a second or subsequent reportable violation or receiving a second or subsequent reportable adjudication or conviction; and

(ii) the continuing danger, if any, that the person poses to the community;

(C) is familiar with the duties appropriate to the nursing profession;

(D) conducts the evaluation pursuant to professionally recognized standards and methods; and

(E) utilizes objective tests and instruments, as determined and requested by the Board, that are designed to test the psychological or neuropsychological stability, fitness to practice, professional character, and/or veracity of the person subject to evaluation.

(2) The person subject to evaluation shall sign a release allowing the evaluator to review the file compiled by Board staff and a release that permits the evaluator to release the

Subsections (k) and (l) address the BON's requesting the nurse submit to a physical or psychological evaluation. These subsections implement NPA Sec. 301.4521.

Subsection (k) addresses when the board may require psychological and physical evaluations and the standards for such evaluations. See Guidelines for Physical and Psychological Evaluations on the board's website. This subsection implements NPA Sec. 301.4521

Evaluator's qualifications.

Content of evaluation.

Subsection. (l) addresses when the board may request a physical or psychological evaluation, but the nurse has a right to refuse. See Guidelines for Physical and Psychological Evaluations on the board's website. This subsection implements NPA Sec. 301.4521

What the evaluation is designed to determine.

The reference to testing for veracity permits the use of polygraphs for certain purposes.

evaluation to the Board.

(3) The person subject to evaluation should be provided a copy of the evaluation upon completion by the evaluator; if not, the Board will provide the person a copy.

(m) Notwithstanding any other provision herein, a person's failure to appear in person or by attorney on the day and at the time set for hearing in a contested case shall entitle the Board to revoke the person's license.

4. RULE 213.32. CORRECTIVE ACTION PROCEEDINGS AND SCHEDULE OF FINES

§213.32. Corrective Action Proceedings and Schedule of Administrative Fine(s).

A corrective action may be imposed by the Board as specified in the following circumstances.

(1) For purposes of this section only, corrective action has the meaning assigned by the Occupations Code §301.651. A corrective action imposed under this section is not a disciplinary action under the Occupations Code Chapter 301, Subchapter J.

(2) Pursuant to the Occupations Code §301.652, the Board may impose a corrective action for the first occurrence of each of the following violations:

(A) practice on a delinquent license for more than six months but less than one year;

(B) failure to comply with continuing competency requirements;

(C) failure to assure licensure/credentials of personnel for whom the nurse is administratively responsible;

(D) failure to provide employers, potential employers, or the Board with complete and accurate answers to either oral or written questions on subject matters including, but not limited to: employment history, licensure history, and criminal history;

(E) failure to comply with Board requirements for change of name/address;

(F) failure to develop, maintain, and implement a peer review plan according to statutory peer review requirements; and

(G) failure of an advanced practice registered nurse to register for prescriptive authority in an additional role and population focus area, where the advanced practice registered nurse otherwise meets all requirements for prescriptive authority as specified in Chapter 222 of this title (relating to Advanced Practice Nurses With Prescriptive Authority).

(3) An individual will not be eligible for a corrective action if the individual has committed more than one of the violations listed in paragraph (2) of this section. If a fine is imposed by the Board as part of a corrective action under paragraph (2) of this section, the amount of the fine shall be $500.

(4) The opportunity to enter into an agreed corrective action order is at the sole discretion of the Executive Director and is not available as a result of a contested case proceeding conducted pursuant to the Government Code Chapter 2001.

(5) A fine, with or without remedial education stipulations, may be imposed in a disciplinary matter for the following violations in the following amounts:

(A) practice on a delinquent license for more than six months but less than two years:

(i) first occurrence: $250; (ii) subsequent occurrence: $500;

(B) practice on a delinquent license for two to four years:

(i) first occurrence: $500; (ii) subsequent occurrence: $1,000;

(C) practice on a delinquent license more than four years: $1,000 plus $250 for each year over four years;

Failure to appear for any hearing may result in revocation of the nurse's license.

***ANNOTATOR'S NOTE**: A BON task force recently completed a review of the BON's deferred action pilot which resulted in the board's pilot authority being converted to permanent authority by legislation (HB 1058) passed in 2013. See NPA Section 301.651-.567. The task force also identified some possible changes to corrective actions. The BON is expected to review this corrective action rule within the next year.*

This Rule 213.32 implements corrective action provisions of NPA Secs.301.651-.657. Corrective action is a confidential, non-disciplinary action designed for minor violations. Unlike a disciplinary action, it is not posted on the Board's website as an action against the nurse's license and is not reported to the National Practitioner Data Bank. The addition of corrective action to the NPA is part of an ongoing initiative by the Texas Nurses Association to create less punitive regulatory systems, as recommended by the Institute of Medicine in its reports TO ERR IS HUMAN AND KEEPING PATIENTS SAFE. See also Rule 213.34 below relating to a deferred actions.

Violations for which corrective action can be applied.

The amount of any fine imposed as part of corrective action is $500.

Subdivision (5) sets out the BON schedule of administrative fines (other than corrective action). Even though a fine is assessed, there may be other violations of the NPA or BON rules that result in disciplinary action against the person's license. For example, a nurse practicing with an expired license may also have engaged in conduct violating the BON's rules, e.g., failed to administer a medication correctly.

(D) failure to comply with continuing competency requirements:

(i) first occurrence: $250; (ii) subsequent occurrence: $500;

(E) failure to comply with mandatory reporting requirements:

(i) first occurrence: $250-$500; (ii) subsequent occurrence: $500-$1,000;

(F) failure to assure licensure/credentials of personnel for whom the nurse is administratively responsible:

(i) first occurrence: $250-$500; (ii) subsequent occurrence: $500-$1,000;

(G) failure to provide employers, potential employers, or the Board with complete and accurate answers to either oral or written questions on subject matters including but not limited to: employment history, licensure history, criminal history:

(i) first occurrence: $250-$800; (ii) second occurrence: $500-$1000;

(H) failure to report unauthorized practice:

(i) first occurrence: $250-$500; (ii) subsequent occurrence: $500-$1,000;

(I) failure to comply with Board requirements for change of name/address:

(i) first occurrence: $250; (ii) subsequent occurrence: $300;

(J) failure to develop, maintain and implement a peer review plan according to statutory peer review requirements:

(i) first occurrence: $250-$1,000; (ii) subsequent occurrence: $500-$1,000;

(K) failure to file, or cause to be filed, complete, accurate and timely reports required by Board order: $250 for first occurrence;

(L) failure to make complete and timely compliance with the terms of any stipulation contained in a Board order: $250 for first occurrence;

(M) failure to report patient abuse to the appropriate authority of the State of Texas, including but not limited to, providing inaccurate or incomplete information when requested from said authorities:

(i) first occurrence: $500; (ii) second occurrence: $1000 - $5000; and

(N) other non-compliance with the NPA, Board rules or orders which does not involve fraud, deceit, dishonesty, intentional disregard of the NPA, Board rules, Board orders, harm or substantial risk of harm to patients, clients or the public:

(i) first occurrence: $250-$500; (ii) subsequent occurrence: $500-$1,000.

(6) The following violations may be appropriate for disposition by fine in conjunction with one or more of the penalties/sanctions contained elsewhere in the Board's rules:

(A) violations other than those listed in paragraphs (2) and (5) of this section:

(i) first occurrence: $250-$1,000; (ii) subsequent occurrence: $500-$1,000; and

(B) a cluster of violations listed in paragraphs (2) and (5) of this section: $250 - $5,000.

(7) The executive director is authorized to dispose of violations listed in paragraphs (2) and (5) of this section without ratification by the Board. The executive director shall report such cases to the Board at its regular meetings.

5. RULE 213.34. DEFERRED DISCIPLINARY ACTION PILOT PROGRAM

§213.34. Deferred Disciplinary Action Pilot Program

(a) This section implements the deferred disciplinary action pilot program authorized by the Occupations Code §301.1607. The pilot program will commence on February 1, 2011, and will conclude no later than January 1, 2014.

(b) The purpose of the pilot program is to evaluate the efficacy and effect of Board deferral of final disciplinary actions against individuals for violations of the Nursing Practice Act and/or Board rules.

(c) The opportunity to enter into a deferred disciplinary order under the pilot program is at the sole discretion of the Executive Director.

(d) A deferred disciplinary action under the pilot program will be available:

ANNOTATOR'S NOTE: *In fall 2012, a BON task force completed a review of the BON's deferred action pilot. Based on the task force's recommendation, legislation (HB 1058) was passed in 2013 converting the board's pilot authority to imposed deferred action to permanent authority. See NPA Sections 301.651-.567. The BON will need to amend this Rule 213.34 in light of this legislation since the rule implemented NPA Sec. 301.1607 (deferred action pilot) which was repealed by the 2013 legislation. The rule is being set out because much of the substance of the rule is expected to be maintained by the BON. However, based on the task force's recommendations, the BON is expected to make some changes which are expected to be proposed in late 2013 or early 2014.*

Both corrective action (see Rule 213.33 above)and the deferred action are part of an ongoing initiative by the Texas Nurses Association to create less punitive regulatory systems, as recommended by the Institute of Medicine in its reports TO ERR IS HUMAN and KEEPING PATIENTS

(1) for individuals with no prior disciplinary history with the Board;

(2) for violations of the Nursing Practice Act and/or Board rules that are proposed for resolution through the issuance of a Warning, a Warning with Stipulations, a Warning with Stipulations and a Fine, a Warning with a Fine, Remedial Education, Remedial Education with a Fine, or a Fine;

(3) only as a condition of settlement by agreement prior to the initiation of proceedings before the State Office of Administrative Hearings;

(4) only if the probationary stipulations outlined in the deferred disciplinary order are designed to address an individual's practice deficit, knowledge deficit, or lack of situational awareness; and

(5) for violations of the Nursing Practice Act and/or Board rules that were pending with the Board on September 1, 2009, or after.

(e) Violations involving sexual misconduct, criminal conduct, intentional acts, falsification, deception, chemical dependency, or substance abuse will not be eligible for resolution through a deferred disciplinary action under the pilot program.

(f) A deferred disciplinary action under the pilot program will not be available to:

(1) an individual who files a petition for declaratory order under §213.30 of this title (relating to Declaratory Order of Eligibility for Licensure);

(2) an individual whose application under §217.2 (relating to Licensure by Examination for Graduates of Nursing Education Programs Within the United States, its Territories, or Possessions), §217.4 (relating to Requirements for Initial Licensure by Examination for Nurses Who Graduate From Nursing Education Programs Outside of United States' Jurisdiction), or §217.5 of this title (relating to Temporary License and Endorsement) is treated as a petition for declaratory order under §213.30 of this title; or

(3) an individual who is practicing nursing in Texas on a nurse licensure compact privilege.

(g) A deferred disciplinary order will be available to the public for a minimum of five years and until such time as an individual successfully completes all of the probationary stipulations required by the deferred disciplinary order and the originating complaint is dismissed by the Board. After such time, the deferred disciplinary order will not be available to the public.

(h) If an individual fails to comply with a probationary stipulation required by a deferred disciplinary order or if a subsequent complaint is filed against an individual during the pendency of the deferred disciplinary order, the Board will stay the dismissal of the originating complaint pending the resolution of the subsequent complaint. If the subsequent complaint is proposed for resolution through a disciplinary action under the Occupations Code Subchapter J, the Board will not dismiss the originating complaint, and the Board may treat the deferred disciplinary action as prior disciplinary action when considering the imposition of a disciplinary sanction.

(i) The outcome and effectiveness of the pilot program will be evaluated by the Board on a regular basis.

SUBPART I
PEER ASSISTANCE

PEER ASSISTANCE PROGRAMS - RULE 217.13.

217.13. Peer Assistance Programs.

(a) A peer assistance program for nurses approved by the Board under chapter 467, Health and Safety Code, will identify, monitor, and assist with locating appropriate treatment for those nurses whose practice is impaired or suspected of being impaired by chemical dependency, mental illness or diminished mental capacity so that they may return to practice safe nursing.

(b) Role of the Board of Nursing and Peer Assistance Program.

SAFE.

This Subpart I includes only Rule 217.13 governing operations of a board-approved peer assistance program. Since this rule focuses on requirements that must be met by programs, it has little direct interest for the individual nurse.

This rule governs board-approved peer assistance programs. The Texas Peer Assistance Program for Nurses (TPAPN) is the only board-approved program for nurses in Texas. Nurses whose practice is suspected of being impaired by chemical dependency or mental illness can be reported to TPAPN, if no practice violation is involved.

(1) The Board of Nursing will retain the sole and exclusive authority to discipline a nurse who has committed a practice violation under §301.452(b) of the Nursing Practice Act regardless of whether such violation was influenced by chemical dependency, mental illness, or diminished mental capacity. The Board will balance the need to protect the public and the need to ensure the nurse seeks treatment in determining whether the nurse is appropriate for participation in an approved peer assistance program.

(2) The program shall report to the board, in accordance with policies adopted by the board, a nurse reported to the program who is impaired or suspected of being impaired for chemical dependency, mental illness, or diminished mental capacity if the nurse was reported to the program by third party. A third party report is a report concerning a nurse suspected of chemical dependency, mental illness, or diminished mental capacity that comes to the attention of the program through any source other than a self report.

(c)-(d) omitted

(e) Participants entering the approved peer assistance program for chemical dependency or chemical abuse must agree to the following minimum conditions:

(1) The nurse shall undergo, as appropriate, a physical and/or psychosocial evaluation before entering the approved monitoring program. This evaluation will be performed by health care professional(s) with expertise in chemical dependency.

(2) The nurse shall enter into a contract with the approved peer assistance program to comply with the requirements of the program which shall include, but not be limited to:

(A) The nurse will undergo recommended substance abuse treatment by an appropriate treatment facility or provider.

(B) The nurse will agree to remain free of all mind-altering substances including alcohol except for medications prescribed by an authorized prescriber for legitimate medical purposes and approved by the program.

(C) The nurse must complete the prescribed aftercare, if any, which may include individual and/or group psychotherapy.

(D) The nurse will submit to random and "for cause" drug screening as specified by the approved monitoring program.

(E) The nurse will attend support groups as specified by the contract.

(F) The nurse will comply with specified employment conditions and restrictions as defined by the contract.

(G) The nurse shall sign a waiver allowing the approved peer assistance program to release, to the extend permitted by federal or state law, information to the Board if the nurse does not comply with the requirements of this contract.

(3) The nurse may be subject to disciplinary action by the Board if the nurse does not participate in the approved peer assistance program, does not comply with specified employment restrictions, or does not successfully complete the program.

(f) Referral to Board of Noncompliance with Peer Assistance Program.

(1) A participant may be terminated from the program for the following causes:

(A) Noncompliance with any aspect of the program agreement;

(B) Receipt of information by the board which, after investigation, results in disciplinary action by the board; or

(C) Being unable to practice according to acceptable and prevailing standards of safe nursing care.

(2) The program shall contact the board in accordance with board policies if a nurse under contract fails to comply with the terms of the program agreement or evidences conduct that indicates an inability or unwillingness to comply with the program.

(g) Eligibility for Program Participation.

(1) The program shall contact the board if it receives a third-party referral for a nurse who may have been impaired or suspected of being impaired and who may have failed to comply

Under BON policies, all third-party referrals are shared with the board to determine if the nurse is appropriate for peer assistance.

Nurses in a board-approved peer assistance program must agree to certain conditions of participation.

Noncompliance and dismissal from the program will result in a referral to BON.

This Subsec. (g) addresses nurses' eligibility to participate in a board-approved peer assistance program.

Under BON policies, all third-party referrals are shared with the board to determine if the nurse is appropriate for peer assistance.

with the minimum standards of nursing (22 TAC §217.11) and/or committed an act constituting unprofessional conduct (22 TAC §217.12). The program shall send that report to the Board. The Board will balance the need to protect the public and the need to ensure the impaired nurse seeks treatment in determining the whether the nurse is appropriate for participation in an approved peer assistance program.

(2) An individual may not participate in the program if the information reviewed in conjunction with the report indicates to the board that the individual's compliance with the program may not be effectively monitored while participating in the program. This information includes, but is not limited to, the following:

(A) The individual is not currently licensed as a registered nurse or licensed vocational nurse;

(B) The individual is currently using or being prescribed a drug normally associated with chemical dependency or abuse;

(C) The individual has a medical and/or psychiatric condition, diagnosis, or disorder, other than chemical dependency, in which the manifest symptoms are not adequately controlled;

(D) The individual has attempted or completed two or more chemical dependency monitoring programs as of the date of the application, notwithstanding the individual's current chemical dependency treatment plan and related treatment currently submitted for purposes of program eligibility;

(E) The board has taken action against the individual's license to practice nursing as either a registered nurse or a licensed practical nurse in Texas within the last 5 years;

(F) The individual has been convicted of a felony, placed on probation or received deferred adjudication relating to a felony, or felony charges are currently pending, or is currently being investigated for a felony; or

(G) The individual has been convicted or registered as a sex offender.

(h) Successful Completion of the Program. A participant successfully completes the program when the participant fully complies with all of the terms of the program agreement for the period as specified in the agreement. When a participant successfully completes the program, the program shall notify the participant of the successful completion in writing. Once the participant receives this written notification of successful completion of the program, the participant shall no longer be required to comply with the program agreement. The program shall notify the board when a nurse who the board has ordered to attend or referred to the program successfully completes the peer assistance contract.

SUBPART J
ADVANCED PRACTICE REGISTERED NURSING

SCOPE OF PRACTICE
CONTINUING COMPETENCY ADVANCED PRACTICE REGISTERED NURSES - RULE 216.3
EDUCATIONAL PROGRAMS FOR ADVANCED PRACTICE REGISTERED NURSES - RULE 219
ADVANCED PRACTICE REGISTERED NURSES - RULE 221
PRESCRIPTIVE AUTHORITY - RULE 222

1. SCOPE OF PRACTICE FOR APRNS

Rule 217.11(4). Standards of Nursing Practice

(4) Standards Specific to Registered Nurses with Advanced Practice Authorization:

Nurses not eligible to participate.

Successful completion of program.

This Subpart J includes rules relating to advanced practice registered nurses. These rules only partially define the APRN's practice since rules of the Texas Medical Board and Pharmacy Board are also relevant – particularly with respect to prescriptive authority. The rules set out are:

1. Rule 217.11(4)	*Standards of Nursing Practice*
2. Rule 216.3	*Continuing Competency Requirements*
3. Rule 219	*APRN Education*
4. Rule 221	*Advanced Practice Registered Nurses*
5. Rule 222	*Prescriptive Authority*

The BON's website (www.bon.texas.gov) has a special section devoted to advanced practice nursing. The Texas Medical Board's rules relating to delegation of prescriptive authority to APRNs are set out in Part IX (Other Laws) of this Guide.

Rule 217.11(4) sets out standards of practice applicable only to APRNs. APRNs as RNs are

Standards for a specific role and specialty of advanced practice nurse supersede standards for registered nurses where conflict between the standards, if any, exist. In addition to subsections (1) and (3) above, a registered nurse who holds authorization to practice as an advanced practice nurse (APN) shall:

(A) ***(Practice Within APN Role)*** Practice in an advanced nursing practice role and specialty in accordance with authorization granted under Board Rule 221 (relating to practicing in an APN role; 22 TAC ch. 221) and standards set out in that Rule.

(B) ***(Prescribing by APNs)*** Prescribe medications in accordance with prescriptive authority granted under Board Rule 222 (relating to APNs prescribing; 22 TAC ch. 222) and standards set out in that Rule and in compliance with state and federal laws and regulations relating to prescription of dangerous drugs and controlled substances.

2. CONTINUING COMPETENCY FOR ADVANCED PRACTICE REGISTERED NURSES

Rule 216.3(c). Continuing Competency Requirements.

(c) Requirements for the Advanced Practice Registered Nurse. The licensee authorized by the board as an advanced practice registered nurse (APRN) is required to obtain 20 contact hours of continuing education or attain, maintain or renew the national certification recognized by the board as meeting the certification requirement for the advanced practice registered nurse's role and population focus area of licensure within the previous two years of licensure. National certification as discussed in this section will only meet the requirement for licensure renewal.

(1) The required hours are not in addition to the requirements of subsection (a) or (b) of this section.

(2) The 20 contact hours of continuing education must be appropriate to the advanced specialty area and role recognized by the board.

(3) The APRN who holds prescriptive authority must complete, in addition to the requirements of this subsection, at least five additional contact hours of continuing education in pharmacotherapeutics.

(4) Category I Continuing Medical Education (CME) contact hours will meet requirements as described in this chapter.

3. EDUCATIONAL PROGRAMS FOR ADVANCED PRACTICE REGISTERED NURSES - RULE 219

> ***ANNOTATOR'S NOTE:*** *Rule 219 governing APRN educational programs are not included in this Guide. Persons needing this rule can obtain them from the BON website at www.bon.texas.gov.*

4. ADVANCED PRACTICE REGISTERED NURSES - RULE 221

> ***ANNOTATOR'S NOTE 1:*** *Because of legislation (SB 406) passed in 2013 expanding prescriptive authority for APRNs, the BON will be extensively revising its Rule 222. Once that is completed, the BON will probably need to amend this Rule 221 to be consistent.*

required to comply both with the standards applicable to all nurses set out in Subsection (1) and those applicable to RNs set out in Rule 217.11(3). Additional standards for APRNs are set out in BON Rules 221 and 222.

Rule 221 governs the general practice of the APRN in an advanced practice role. An APRN must practice within the specialty role for which he or she was licensed as an APRN.

Rule 222 sets out specific standards for APRNs with prescriptive authority.

With the exceptions noted, APRNs have the same continuing competency requirements as other RNs -- 1) 20 contact hours of CNE or 2) attaining, maintaining or renewing the APRN's national certification. National certification does not satisfy the 5 hours of pharmacotherapeutics required to maintain prescriptive authority. See Subsec. (c)(3).

The national certification must be the certification recognized by the BON as meeting the certification requirement for the APRN's role and population focus area of licensure.

CNE must be appropriate to the APRNs' advanced practice specialty area and role.

APRNs with prescriptive authority must have 5 contact hours in pharmacotherapeutics in addition to the 20 hours or national certification needed to renew the APRN license.

APRNs may count Category I Continuing Medical Education to meet the 20 hours of CNE.

ANNOTATOR'S NOTE: *In the 8/9/13 Texas Register, the BON published proposed rules to require APRNs prescribing controlled substances to complete 3 hours of CNE related to prescribing controlled substances each renewal period.*

RNs practicing as Advanced Practice Registered Nurses (APRNs) must be licensed by the BON as APRNs. This rule establishes the licensing process for Advanced Practice Registered Nurses as well as sets out the general conditions of APRN practice.

***ANNOTATOR'S NOTE 2**: The terminology "Advanced Practice Nurse (APN)" has been changed to "Advanced Practice Registered Nurse (APRN)," and "authorization to practice" to "licensure." The terminology change will be incorporated in the rules as they are amended.*

Rule 221.1. Definitions. The following words and terms, when used in this chapter, shall have the following meanings unless the context clearly indicates otherwise:

(1) Accredited program--A program which has been deemed to have met certain standards set by the board or by a national accrediting body recognized by the board.

(2) Advanced educational program--A post-basic advanced practice nurse program at the certificate, master's degree, or higher level. Beginning January 1, 2003, a minimum of a master's degree in the advanced practice role and population focus area will be required for recognition as an Advanced Practice Registered Nurse.

(3) Advanced practice nurse--A registered nurse approved by the board to practice as an advanced practice nurse based on completing an advanced educational program acceptable to the board. The term includes a nurse practitioner, nurse-midwife, nurse anesthetist, and a clinical nurse specialist. The advanced practice nurse is prepared to practice in an expanded role to provide health care to individuals, families, and/or groups in a variety of settings including but not limited to homes, hospitals, institutions, offices, industry, schools, community agencies, public and private clinics, and private practice. The advanced practice nurse acts independently and/or in collaboration with other health care professionals in the delivery of health care services.

(4) Authorization to practice--The process of reviewing the educational, licensing, certification and other credentials of the registered nurse to determine compliance with the board's requirements for approval as an advanced practice nurse.

(5) Board--The Texas Board of Nursing.

(6) Current certification--Initial certification and maintenance of certification by national certifying bodies recognized by the board.

(7) Current practice--Maintaining competence as an advanced practice nurse by practicing in the advanced role and specialty in the clinical setting, practicing as an educator in the clinical and/or didactic portion of an advanced educational program of study, or practicing as a consultant or an administrator within the advanced specialty and role.

(8) Graduate advanced practice nurse--A registered nurse who has completed an advanced educational program of study and has been granted provisional or interim authorization by the board to practice in the advanced specialty and role.

(9) Monitored anesthesia care--refers to situations where a patient undergoing a diagnostic or therapeutic procedure receive doses of medication that create a risk of loss of normal protective reflexes or loss of consciousness and the patient remains able to protect the airway for the majority of the procedure. If, for an extended period of time, the patient is rendered unconscious and/or loses normal protective reflexes, then anesthesia care shall be considered a general anesthetic.

(10) Outpatient setting--Any facility, clinic, center, office, or other setting that is not a part of a licensed hospital or a licensed ambulatory surgical center with the exception of all of the following:

(A) clinic located on land recognized as tribal land by the federal government and maintained or operated by a federally recognized Indian tribe or tribal organization as listed under 25 U.S.C. Section 479-1 or as listed under a successor federal statute or regulation;

(B) a facility maintained or operated by a state or governmental entity;

(C) a clinic directly maintained or operated by the United States or by any of its departments, officers, or agencies; and

(D) an outpatient setting accredited by either the Joint Commission on Accreditation of Healthcare Organizations relating to ambulatory surgical centers, the American Association for the Accreditation of Ambulatory Surgery Facilities, or the Accreditation Association for Ambulatory Health Care.

APRNs are prepared to practice in an expanded role to provide care to a variety of patient populations in a variety of settings.

APRNs practice in both independent and collaborative roles.

"Authorization to practice" terminology has been replaced by "licensure" terminology.

(11) Party state--Any state that has entered into the Nurse Licensure Compact.

(12) Protocols or other written authorization--Written authorization to provide medical aspects of patient care which are agreed upon and signed by the advanced practice nurse and the physician, reviewed and signed at least annually, and maintained in the practice setting of the advanced practice nurse. Protocols or other written authorization shall be defined to promote the exercise of professional judgment by the advanced practice nurse commensurate with his/her education and experience. Such protocols or other written authorization need not describe the exact steps that the advanced practice nurse must take with respect to each specific condition, disease, or symptom and may state types or categories of drugs which may be prescribed rather that just list specific drugs.

(13) Shall and must--Mandatory requirements

(14) Should--A recommendation

(15) Unencumbered--A license to practice registered nursing which does not have stipulations against the license.

Rule 221.2 Authorizations and Restrictions to Use of Advanced Practice Titles

(a) Effective January 1, 2006, a registered nurse holding him or herself out to be an advanced practice nurse shall be authorized to practice and hold a title in the following categories:

(1) nurse anesthetist;

(2) nurse-midwife;

(3) nurse practitioner in the following specialties:

(A) Acute Care Adult;

(B) Acute Care Pediatric;

(C) Adult;

(D) Family;

(E) Gerontological;

(F) Neonatal;

(G) Pediatric;

(H) Psychiatric/Mental Health;

(I) Women's Health; and/or

(4) clinical nurse specialist in the following specialties:

(A) Adult Health/Medical-Surgical Nursing;

(B) Community Health Nursing;

(C) Critical Care Nursing;

(D) Gerontological Nursing;

(E) Pediatric Nursing; and

(F) Psychiatric/ Mental Health Nursing.

(b) A registered nurse who holds current authorization to practice as an advanced practice nurse issued by the board in any of the categories indicated in the previous subsection shall use that title when functioning in the advanced practice role. A registered nurse who was granted authorization to practice in an advanced role and specialty not indicated in the previous subsection prior to January 1, 2006, may continue to use the advanced practice title approved by the Board provided all requirements for maintenance of advanced practice authorization are met. "Advanced practice nurse" shall not be used as a title.

(c) Unless authorized as an advanced practice nurse by the board as provided for by §§221.4 - 221.8 of this chapter (relating to Full Authorization, Provisional Authorization; Interim Approval; Petitions for Waiver; and Maintaining Active Authorization as an Advanced Practice Nurse), a registered nurse shall not:

(1) claim to be an advanced practice nurse or hold himself/herself out to be an advanced practice nurse in this state; and/or

(2) use a title or any other designation tending to imply that the person is authorized as an advanced practice nurse.

This definition of protocol as authorization to initiate medical aspects of care is a legal definition for purposes of these rules. As such, the definition may differ from the definition commonly associated with the term. APRNs need to be aware of whether the term is being used in its legal or popular usage sense.

Protocols are to be jointly developed and reviewed at least annually. If the carrying out or signing of prescription drug orders is involved, then the protocols must be reviewed at least annually. See also the definition of protocol in Texas Medical Board Rule §193.2 (Definitions) in Part IX (Other Laws) of this Guide. Protocols should promote the exercise of professional judgment by APRNs. They don't need to take a cookbook approach. The drugs that an APRN is authorized to prescribe may be described by category. APRNs should remember that the term "protocol" is a legal term defined by the BON and Texas Medical Board rules and provides the legal authorization for APRNs to perform certain delegated medical acts. As indicated when used in this sense, the term may not have the meaning that is commonly associated with it.

Since January 1, 2006, the number of APRN titles that the BON recognizes has been limited to the titles listed. The change to fewer titles produced considerable public comment at the state level and a similar discussion occurred at the national level about the appropriate regulation of APRN titles. The result at the national level was the adoption of the Consensus Model for APRN Regulation. APRNs recognized before 1/1/2006 will be able to continue to use that title as long as they meet all requirements. See Subsec. (b) of this rule. The BON also has a limited waiver for applicants to be recognized in a category of title that is not recognized in this rule. See Rule 221.7(e) below.

APRNs will continue to be permitted to use the APRN title for which they were recognized even if it is not a title the BON will continue to recognize under Subsection (a).

The term "APRN" is not itself a title. Rather the APRN should use the specific title such as NP, CNS, PNP, etc.

This rule is what is referred to as a "title-control" rule in that it prohibits the use of the "APRN" title or holding oneself out as an APRN unless she/he complies with the requirements of this rule. Only RNs licensed by the Board as APRNs may hold themselves out as APRNs. Using any of the titles NP, CNS, NM, NA will be considered to be holding oneself out as an APRN. An RN who is not an APRN may perform functions (not all, e.g., prescribing) that APRNs perform so long as the RN is qualified by education and experience. Because of the specialized education of

(d) A registered nurse who violates subsection (c) of this section may be subject to an administrative penalty under §301.501 of the Nursing Practice Act.

Rule 221.3 Education
Rule 221.4 Advanced Practice Registered Nurse Licensure
Rule 221.5. *[Repealed Fall 2008]*
Rule 221.6. Interim Approval
Rule 221.7 Petitions for Waiver

Rule 221.8 Maintaining Active Authorization as an Advanced Practice Nurse

(a) In conjunction with RN license renewal, the advanced practice nurse seeking to maintain active advanced practice authorization(s) shall:

(1) attest on forms provided by the board to maintaining current national certification by the appropriate certifying body recognized by the board. This requirement shall apply to advanced practice nurses who:

(A) completed an advanced educational program on or after January 1, 1996, or

(B) were authorized as advanced practice nurses based upon obtaining national certification.

(2) attest, on forms provided by the board, to having a minimum of 400 hours of current practice within the preceding biennium;

(3) attest, on forms provided by the board, to having obtained 20 contact hours of continuing education in the advanced specialty area and role within the preceding biennium. Continuing education in the advanced practice specialty and role must meet requirements of Chapter 216 of this title (relating to Continuing Education). The 20 contact hours required for RN licensure may be met by the 20 hours required by this subsection; and

(4) submit the required fee, which is not refundable.

(b) Failure to renew the registered nurse license or to provide the required fee and documentation for maintaining authorization shall result in expiration of the board's authorization as an advanced practice nurse and limited prescriptive authority where applicable. The individual whose advanced practice authorization has expired may not practice as or use titles to imply that he/she is an advanced practice nurse.

Rule 221.9 Inactive Status
Rule 221.10 Reinstatement or Reactivation of Advanced Practice Nurse Status

Rule 221.11 Identification. When providing advanced practice nursing care to patients, the advanced practice nurse shall wear clear identification which indicates the individual is a registered nurse with the appropriate advanced practice designation authorized by the board.

Rule 221.12 Scope of Practice. The advanced practice nurse provides a broad range of health services, the scope of which shall be based upon educational preparation, continued advanced practice experience and the accepted scope of professional practice of the particular specialty area. Advanced practice nurses practice in a variety of settings and, according to their practice specialty and role, they provide a broad range of health care services to a variety of patient populations.

(1) The scope of practice of particular specialty areas shall be defined by national professional specialty organizations or advanced practice nursing organizations recognized by the Board. The advanced practice nurse may perform only those functions which are within that scope

APRNs, there are nursing tasks that only APRNs can perform.

ANNOTATOR'S NOTE: *Rules 221.3-.7 relating to education preparation and initial licensure are not being set out since the BON has extensive materials on its website under Advanced Practice. Most individuals seeking licensure will rely on these materials if they have questions about the process. These rules can also be accessed through the BON's website.*

APRN approval must be renewed every two years in conjunction with renewal of the APRN's basic RN license.

The renewal requirement of current national certification applies only to APRNs who graduated after 1/1/96 or who were authorized as APRNs based on certification.

Current practice is required for APRN renewal. See definition of "current practice" in Rule 221.1 above.

CNE in an APRN specialty area and role is required for APRN renewal. Continuing Medical Education can be used to meet requirement. See BON Rule 216.3 above. The 20 hours required for renewal of APRN approval also satisfies the 20 hours needed to renew the RN license. This rule does not reflect the change to §216.3(c) permitting national certification as an alternate means to demonstrate continuing competency. See Rule 216.3(c).

ANNOTATOR'S NOTE: *The rules relating to inactive status and related materials can be found on the BON website under Advanced Practice. Most individuals seeking licensure will rely on these materials if they have questions about the process. These rules can also be accessed through the BON's website.*

In addition to complying with the NPA requirement that RNs providing patient care wear an insignia identifying themselves as RNs, APRNs must identify the APRN category for which they have been approved. The "APRN" designation itself is not a title and may not be used as a title. See §221.2(b).

This rule elaborates on the scope of practice for APRNs. Ultimately, the scope of practice of APRNs is determined by the definition of professional nursing in the NPA, and this rule must be applied to be consistent with that definition. However, that definition provides little detailed guidance, so scope of practice questions do arise.

While scope of practice is set by national professional associations, APRNs must still practice within the authority of the NPA and other applicable laws. The Medical Practice Act, Pharmacy Act and Drug Laws are the primary ones. Relevant rules are those of the BON, TMB and of practice and which are consistent with the Nursing Practice Act, Board rules, and other laws and regulations of the State of Texas.

(2) The advanced practice nurse's scope of practice shall be in addition to the scope of practice permitted a registered nurse and does not prohibit the advanced practice nurse from practicing in those areas deemed to be within the scope of practice of a registered nurse.

Rule 221.13 Core Standards for Advanced Practice

(a) The advanced practice nurse shall know and conform to the Texas Nursing Practice Act; current board rules, regulations, and standards of professional nursing; and all federal, state, and local laws, rules, and regulations affecting the advanced role and specialty area. When collaborating with other health care providers, the advanced practice nurse shall be accountable for knowledge of the statutes and rules relating to advanced practice nursing and function within the boundaries of the appropriate advanced practice category.

(b) The advanced practice nurse shall practice within the advanced specialty and role appropriate to his/her advanced educational preparation.

(c) The advanced practice nurse acts independently and/or in collaboration with the health team in the observation, assessment, diagnosis, intervention, evaluation, rehabilitation, care and counsel, and health teachings of persons who are ill, injured or infirm or experiencing changes in normal health processes; and in the promotion and maintenance of health or prevention of illness.

(d) When providing medical aspects of care, advanced practice nurses shall utilize mechanisms which provide authority for that care. These mechanisms may include, but are not limited to, Protocols or other written authorization. This shall not be construed as requiring authority for nursing aspects of care.

(1) Protocols or other written authorization shall promote the exercise of professional judgment by the advanced practice nurse commensurate with his/her education and experience. The degree of detail within protocols/policies/practice guidelines/clinical practice privileges may vary in relation to the complexity of the situations covered by such Protocols, the advanced specialty area of practice, the advanced educational preparation of the individual, and the experience level of the individual advanced practice nurse.

(2) Protocols or other written authorization:

(A) should be jointly developed by the advanced practice nurse and the appropriate physician(s),

(B) shall be signed by both the advanced practice nurse and the physician(s),

(C) shall be reviewed and re-signed at least annually,

(D) shall be maintained in the practice setting of the advanced practice nurse, and

(E) shall be made available as necessary to verify authority to provide medical aspects of care.

(e) The advanced practice nurse shall retain professional accountability for advanced practice nursing care.

Rule 221.14 Nurse-Midwives Providing Controlled Substances

(a) In this section "provide" means to supply, for a term not to exceed 48 hours, one or more unit doses of a controlled substance for the immediate needs of a patient;

(b) An advanced practice nurse recognized by the board as a nurse-midwife may provide one or more unit doses of a controlled substance during intra-partum or immediate post-partum care subject to the following conditions:

(1) Physician delegation of authority to provide controlled substances must be made through a physician's order, medical order, standing delegation order, or protocol that requires adequate and documented availability for access to medical care. Delegation may not include the use of a prescription sticker or the use or issuance of an official prescription form under §481.075, Health and Safety Code;

(2) The nurse-midwife's protocols or other orders must require the reporting of or monitoring of each patient's progress, including complications of pregnancy and delivery and the

Pharmacy Board.

Most activities, e.g., assessments, which APRNs perform, fall within the scope of their professional nursing license and can be done without physician delegation. Also, the APRN may practice collaboratively with other practitioners.

Protocols, policies or other physician orders are necessary only if the APRN will be carrying out delegated medical acts (e.g., prescribing medications). APRNs wishing to exercise limited prescriptive authority must comply with Rule §222 (Relating to Prescriptive Authority) as well as applicable rules of the Texas Medical Board. The protocols/policies should reflect what constitutes good nursing and medical practice under the circumstances in which they will be used. For example, a recently graduated APRN may need more detailed instructions than an experienced APRN.

Protocols and orders authorizing the medical aspects of care should be developed jointly and signed by the APRN and physician.

This rule tracks the language of Sec. 157.059 of Medical Practice Act which gives CNMs authority to administer and provide controlled substances (i.e., narcotics) to their patients under limited circumstances. It does not give CNMs authority to prescribe controlled substances. If a CNM wishes to prescribe, she/he must qualify in the same manner as other APRNs. The CNM's prescriptive authority (ability to write prescriptions) will be subject to the same limitation on that authority as other APRNs, namely, to prescribing dangerous drugs and controlled substances Schedules III-V but not Schedule II.

administration and provision of controlled substances to the patient;

(3) delegation is limited to three full-time equivalent nurse-midwives at the designated facility where the nurse-midwife practices; and

(4) the controlled substance must be supplied in a suitable container that is labeled in compliance with the applicable drug laws and must include:

(A) the patient's name and address;

(B) the drug to be provided;

(C) the name, address, and telephone number of the physician;

(D) the name, address, and telephone number of the nurse-midwife; and

(E) the date.

Rule 221.15 Provision of Anesthesia Services by Nurse Anesthetists in Licensed Hospitals or Ambulatory Surgical Centers

(a) In a licensed hospital or ambulatory surgical center, consistent with facility policy or medical staff bylaws, a nurse anesthetist may select, obtain, and administer drugs including determination of appropriate dosages, techniques and medical devices for their administration and in maintaining the patient in sound physiologic status pursuant to a physician's order for anesthesia or an anesthesia-related service. This order need not be drug specific, dosage specific, or administration-technique specific.

(b) Pursuant to a physician's order for anesthesia or an anesthesia-related service, the nurse anesthetist may order anesthesia-related medications during perianesthesia periods in the preparation for or recovery from anesthesia. Another RN may carry out these orders.

(c) In providing anesthesia or an anesthesia-related service, the nurse anesthetist shall select, order, obtain and administer drugs which fall within categories of drugs generally utilized for anesthesia or anesthesia-related services and provide the concomitant care required to maintain the patient in sound physiologic status during those experiences.

Rule 221.16 Provision of Anesthesia Services by Nurse Anesthetists in Outpatient Settings

Rule 221.17 Enforcement

(a) The board may conduct an audit to determine compliance with §221.4 of this chapter (relating to Requirements for Full Authorization to Practice), §221.8 of this chapter (relating to Maintaining Active Authorization as an Advanced Practice Nurse), and §221.16 of this chapter (relating to Provision of Anesthesia Services by Nurse Anesthetists in Outpatient Settings).

(b) Any nurse who violates the rules set forth in this chapter shall be subject to disciplinary action and/or termination of the authorization by the board under Texas Occupations Code, §301.452.

5. PRESCRIPTIVE AUTHORITY - RULE 222

***ANNOTATOR'S NOTE**: Rule 222 is not being set out. Because of the passage of legislation (SB 406) in 2013, Rule 222 will need to be extensively rewritten. In the 8/9/13 Texas Register, the BON published a proposed revised rule. There will be 30-day public comment period. The BON is expected to adopt final rules at its October meeting. Set out in the ANNOTATIONS column is the preamble published with the proposed revision.*

This rule tracks the language of Sec. 157.058 of the Medical Practice Act. The provision was designed to codify current practice of CRNAs. If a CRNA wishes to prescribe, she/he must qualify the same as other APRNs. The CRNA's prescriptive authority (ability to write prescriptions) will be subject to the same limitation on that authority as other APRNs, namely, to prescribing dangerous drugs and controlled substances Schedules III-V but not Schedule II. CRNAs' administering anesthesia ordered by a surgeon does not constitute prescribing.

In June 1998, the BON requested a Texas Attorney General Opinion as to the correctness of the BON's long standing interpretation that the administration of anesthesia by Certified Registered Nurse Anesthetists constituted the practice of professional nursing. The Texas Attorney General issued Opinion JC-0117 (1999) responding to that request. The opinion held that while the provision of anesthesia services was a delegated medical act, CRNAs performing such delegated medical acts are engaged in the practice of professional nursing and subject to regulation by the BON. The opinion also held that §157.058 of the Medical Practice Act permitted delegation to CRNAs to occur through physician orders and did not require physician supervision of CRNAs. The opinion has had little effect on CRNA practice.

RNs may administer medications selected by a CRNA pursuant to the physician's order to the CRNA to provide anesthesia and anesthesia-related services. See the BON's website for position statements regarding RNs carrying out orders of APRNs.

***ANNOTATOR'S NOTE**: Because of the length of this rule and its narrow application, this rule is not being set out. The rule can be found on the BON website at www.bon.texas.gov or at Texas Legislature Online at www.legis.state.tx.us -- select Administrative Code, TAC Viewer, Title 22 Examining Boards, and then BON.*

***ANNOTATOR'S NOTE 1**: Rule 222 is not being set out. Because of the passage of legislation (SB 406) in 2013, Rule 222 will need to be extensively rewritten. In the 8/9/13 Texas Register, the BON published a proposed revised rule. There will be 30-day public comment period. The BON is expected to adopt final rules at its October meeting. Set out below is the preamble published with the proposed revision.*

Rule 222 -- APRN Prescriptive Authority.

***ANNOTATOR'S NOTE 2**: Prescriptive authority will continue to require physician delegation, so this BON Rule 222 only partially implements prescriptive authority for APRNs, since the Medical Practice Act and Texas Medical Board (TMB) rules will also govern over physician delegation. The relevant provisions of the Medical Practice Act and Medical Board rules are set out in Part X (Other Laws) of this Guide.*

PREAMBLE TO BON PROPOSED RULE 222 AS PUBLISHED IN TEXAS REGISTER.

Introduction. The Texas Board of Nursing (Board) proposes new Chapter 222, §§222.1 -222.10, concerning Advanced Practice Registered Nurses with Prescriptive Authority, in conjunction with a proposed repeal of existing Chapter 222, also concerning Advanced Practice Registered Nurses with Prescriptive Authority. The proposed repeal of Chapter 222 is being published elsewhere in this issue of the Texas Register.

The new chapter is proposed under the authority of the Occupations Code Chapter 157 and §§301.151, 301.152, 301.452, 301.453, and 301.4531 and is necessary to implement Senate Bill (SB) 406, which was enacted by the 83rd Texas Legislature, Regular Session, effective November 1, 2013. The proposed new chapter also includes provisions that are consistent with the Advanced Practice Registered Nurse Consensus Model of the National Council of State Boards of Nursing; clarifies the Board's endorsement and enforcement processes; and requires advanced practice registered nurses (APRNs) who prescribe controlled substances to complete an additional 3 hours of continuing education related to prescribing controlled substances each biennium. Although the Board is proposing the adoption of a new chapter, many of the provisions of existing Chapter 222 are incorporated into the proposed new chapter and remain unchanged from their current structure. The Board has chosen to repeal existing Chapter 222 and propose a new chapter for adoption primarily because of the many organizational changes to the chapter.

Background
Many of the changes in the proposed new chapter result from the enactment of SB 406. SB 406 was intended to improve the process by which physicians delegate and supervise the prescribing and/or ordering of drugs to APRNs and physician assistants. Further, SB expands the scope of APRNs by authorizing APRNs to prescribe and/or order Schedule II controlled substances in certain practice settings. SB 406 also eliminates alternate practice site and primary practice site requirements. In addition to prescribing new terminology for use throughout the Occupations Code Chapter 157, SB 406 also authorizes the use of a prescriptive authority agreement for physician delegation of ordering and/or prescribing drugs and devices. Further, SB 406 continues to recognize the use of protocols or other written authorization for physician delegation of ordering and/or prescribing drugs and devices in facility-based practice settings. Finally, SB 406 requires collaboration among the Board, the Texas Medical Board, and the Texas Physician Assistant Board regarding the sharing of disciplinary information and maintaining public lists of practitioners who have entered into prescriptive authority agreements.

Collaboration
The proposed new provisions were considered by the Advanced Practice Nursing Advisory Committee (Committee) on May 31, 2013. The Committee reviewed SB 406 and considered its impact on the prescriptive authority of APRNs in this state. Following its discussions of the proposed new chapter and SB 406, the Committee voted to approve the proposed new provisions and recommended their adoption to the Board, with one exception. Instead of requiring additional continuing education for APRNs who prescribe controlled substances, the Committee voted to recommend that the Board encourage, but not require, APRNs who prescribe controlled substances to complete pharmacotherapeutics continuing education activities related to controlled substances.

Board Staff also met with Staff of the Texas Medical Board to discuss the provisions of SB 406 and their implication. Following preliminary discussions, Board Staff felt that the provisions of the proposed new chapter were consistent with the Texas Medical Board's interpretation and projected implementation of SB 406. As a result, Staff recommended the adoption of the proposed new requirements to the Board at its July 2013 meeting. The Board considered the proposed new requirements, the Committee's recommendations, and Staff's recommendations at its July 2013 meeting. Following discussion and deliberation, the Board determined that it was appropriate to require additional continuing education for APRNs who prescribe controlled substances. The Board then voted to approve the publication of the proposed new chapter in the Texas Register.

Proposed new Chapter 222

Proposed new §222.1 sets forth definitions of the terms to be used throughout the new chapter. The proposed new definitions are consistent with the definitions and terminology used in SB 406. Also consistent with SB 406, the terms "alternate site", "eligible sites", "health manpower shortage area", "medically underserved area (MUA)", "physician's primary practice site", and "site serving a medically underserved population" have been removed from the proposed new chapter, and the term "prescriptive authority agreement" has been added.

Proposed new §222.2 sets forth the requirements that an APRN must meet in order to receive a prescription authorization number. The requirements in proposed new §222.2 are similar to the existing provisions of Chapter 222, with the exception that the requirements related to practice sites have been eliminated for consistency with the provisions of SB 406. Proposed new §222.4 addresses the minimum standards applicable to an APRN who orders drugs and/or devices pursuant to physician delegation. SB 406 authorizes the use of a prescriptive authority agreement to effectuate such delegation in all settings except for certain facility-based practices. In facility-based practices, SB 406 continues to recognize the use of protocols or other written authorization for physician delegation, provided that a physician does not delegate at more than 1 hospital or more than 2 long-term care facilities. Consistent with the bill's requirements, the proposed provisions of §222.4 require the use of a prescriptive authority agreement in all settings, except for facility-based practices, where either a prescriptive authority agreement or protocols or other written authorization may be used for physician delegation.

In settings where a prescriptive authority agreement is utilized by a physician and an APRN, SB 406 prescribes the particular requirements that the prescriptive authority agreement must meet. In addition to several other requirements, SB 406 requires periodic face to face meetings between a physician who delegates the act of prescribing and/or ordering drugs and devices to an APRN through a prescriptive authority agreement. Proposed new §222.4 makes clear that an APRN must comply with the requirements of SB 406 that relate to chart review and periodic face to face meetings. Further, for an APRN who orders and/or prescribes drugs or devices under facility-based protocols or other written authorization, proposed new §222.4 clarifies that the APRN must also comply with any requirements set forth in the protocols or other written authorization. Also pursuant to SB 406, proposed new §222.4 requires an APRN to cooperate with Board representatives or representatives from the Texas Medical Board during any audit or inspection relating to the operation and implementation of a prescriptive authority agreement.

The remaining provisions of proposed new §222.4 contain essentially the same requirements as existing Chapter 222 regarding prescription information, generic substitution, off label use, and prescribing medications for sexually transmitted diseases for partners of an established patient.

Proposed new §222.5 contains the requirements applicable to a prescriptive authority agreement. A prescriptive authority agreement is a mechanism by which an APRN is delegated the authority to order and/or prescribe drugs or devices by a physician. in all practice settings, except for facility-based practices where protocols or other written authorization are utilized instead. SB 406 sets forth specific requirements that apply to the use of a prescriptive authority agreement. Consistent with the provisions of SB 406, proposed new §222.5 sets forth the minimum requirements that a prescriptive authority agreement must meet and requires an APRN to be in good standing with the Board in order to enter into a prescriptive authority agreement with a physician. "Good standing" under proposed new §222.5 means that the APRN's license is not in delinquent status and that there is no current disciplinary action, disciplinary probation, or pending investigation of the APRN's nursing license and/or authorization.

Although a prescriptive authority agreement must meet the requirements of proposed new §222.5, the agreement may also include additional provisions or information agreed to by the delegating physician and APRN, including any provisions that may have been previously included in protocols or other written authorization. Thus, under proposed new §222.5, a prescriptive authority agreement may be utilized in a facility-based practice if the parties to the agreement choose to do so in lieu of utilizing protocols or other written authorization for physician delegation. The parties, however, are not required to do so, and SB 406, as well as the proposed new chapter, recognizes the continued use of protocols or other written authorization for physician delegation in such practice settings.

The provisions of proposed new §222.6 are consistent with the proposed provisions of §222.5 as they relate to the use of a prescriptive authority agreement in a facility-based practice. As previously stated, both SB 406 and the proposed new chapter authorize the use of either a prescriptive authority agreement or protocols or other written authorization for physician delegation in a facility-based practice. The provisions of proposed new §222.6 set forth the requirements applicable to the use of either mechanism in a facility-based practice.

Proposed new §222.7 clarifies that APRNs with a valid prescription authorization number are eligible to order or prescribe non-prescription drugs, dangerous drugs, and devices, including durable medical equipment. However, in order for an APRN to be eligible to also order and/or prescribe controlled substances, the APRN must meet the applicable requirements of the proposed new chapter.

Proposed new §222.8 sets forth the requirements that apply to ordering and/or prescribing controlled substances. Consistent with the existing provisions of Chapter 222, an APRN may order and/or prescribe controlled substances in Schedules III through V, pursuant to certain limitations. First, the prescription may not exceed a 90 day supply, including a refill of the prescription. The proposed new section does not alter this existing limitation. However, the proposed new section clarifies that this limitation applies to a prescription, either in the form of a new prescription or in the form of a refill, for the same controlled substance that a patient has been previously issued within a 90 day time period. Therefore, an APRN may not circumvent the limitations of this section by writing a new prescription for the same controlled substance for longer than 90 days without consulting with the APRN's delegating physician and documenting the consultation in the patient's chart. Limitations relating to the prescription of a controlled substance for a child less than two years of age remain unchanged from the current provisions of Chapter 222.

SB 406 authorizes APRNs to prescribe Schedule II controlled substances in certain circumstances. Consistent with this expanded authority, proposed new §222.8 authorizes APRNs to prescribe Schedule II controlled substances in a hospital facility-based practice for a patient who has been admitted to the hospital for an intended length of stay of 24 hours or greater or is receiving services in the emergency department of the hospital or as part of the plan of care for a patient

who is receiving hospice treatment from a qualified hospice provider.

Proposed new §222.9 contains substantially similar requirements as current Chapter 222, with slight modifications made to incorporate the use of prescriptive authority agreements.

The remaining provisions of the proposed new chapter are necessary for consistency with the provisions of the Advanced Practice Registered Nurse Consensus Model of the National Council of State Boards of Nursing; to clarify the Board's endorsement and enforcement processes, and to require APRNs who prescribe controlled substances to complete additional continuing education requirements each biennium.

Proposed new §222.1(4) includes a new definition of the term "advanced practice registered nurse (APRN)", which is consistent with the definition of "APRN" in the Occupations Code §301.152 and the provisions of the Advanced Practice Registered Nurse Consensus Model of the National Council of State Boards of Nursing.

Proposed new §222.2 clarifies that an APRN applying for prescriptive authority in this state based upon his/her advanced practice licensure and prescriptive authority issued in another state (by endorsement) must provide evidence to the Board that all education requirements for prescriptive authority in this state have been met.

Proposed new §222.3 requires an APRN who prescribes controlled substances to complete 3 additional contact hours of continuing education related to prescribing controlled substances each biennium. The Board has determined that this additional continuing education is reasonably related to the expanded scope authorized by SB 406 with regard to the prescription of Schedule II controlled substances and is necessary to ensure that APRNs who prescribe controlled substances stay abreast of current industry practices, enhance their professional competence, learn about new treatment regimens, and continually update their clinical skills. The proposed new requirement permits an APRN to complete the additional continuing education in any area related to prescribing controlled substances. Thus, the Board anticipates that many different types of continuing education courses could meet this proposed new requirement. For instance, courses in pain management, content related to recognition of patients with addictions/pseudo addictions, and medical management of patients with conditions such as Attention Deficit Hyperactivity Disorder could appropriately meet the proposed new requirements. So long as the content of a course relates to the prescription of controlled substances in a meaningful way, the Board anticipates that the course would be sufficient to meet the new proposed continuing education requirements.

Finally, new proposed §222.10 clarifies that an APRN may be subject to disciplinary action by the Board for ordering and/or prescribing in a manner that is inconsistent with the standard of care and/or for violating a provision of the proposed new chapter. Further, the proposed new section outlines examples of behavior that may subject an APRN to discipline and identifies the procedures that will be followed if an APRN becomes the subject of a Board investigation and/or receives a disciplinary order from the Board.

Section-by-Section Overview.

[Remainder of Preamble Is Not Set out.]

PART III.

BON POSITION STATEMENTS, GUIDELINES, FAQs AND OTHER PRACTICE-RELATED POLICIES

POSITION STATEMENTS AND GUIDELINES

In addition to rules, the Texas Board of Nursing (BON) from time to time will adopt position statements and guidelines relating to a specific issue -- usually a practice issue. These position statements and guidelines can be seen as the Board's "interpretations" of how the Nursing Practice Act (NPA) and Board rules apply to particular practice questions. They provide direct guidance to the nurse as to what the BON believes is permissible (or impermissible) conduct for nurses in a particular situation. The BON's webpage setting out its positions statements states:

> *Board Position Statements do not have the force of law, but are a means of providing direction for nurses on issues of concern to the Board relevant to protection of the public. Board position statements are reviewed annually for relevance and accuracy to current practice, the Nursing Practice Act, and Board rules.*

BON staff have further characterized position statements as:

> *Staff would also like to emphasize that Board Position Statements and Guidelines are not state laws or agency rules. Position statements, guidelines, and other board documents are intended to offer guidance to nurses in how to determine their individual scopes of practice, and how to determine what "best practice" is for given situations.*

Although position statements and interpretive guidelines are not BON rules and don't carry the legal force of laws or rules, they should be viewed as setting standards for practice. An RN or LVN violating them is certainly at risk of being found as not having acted as a reasonable, prudent nurse -- particularly if there is a bad patient outcome.

Since position statements and guidelines are not statutes or rules, they can be written in a less formal way. Consequently, nurses are likely to find them easier to read and understand than the NPA and BON rules. Reflective of this fact, the annotations for them are less extensive than those provided for the NPA and BON rules. Also, because there is less need for annotations to facilitate understanding, only a sampling of position statements and guidelines are included in this Guide. The others can be found on the BON's website.

ANNOTATOR'S NOTE

To assist nurses in identifying which position statement or guideline is most applicable to their practice, the position statements are listed on the facing page grouped by subject matter addressed.

On the following page, is a table prepared by the BON that list the position statements in numerical order with a brief synopsis of each statement.

SUBPART A.
POSITION STATEMENTS AND GUIDELINES BY TOPIC

ANNOTATOR'S NOTE: *The following is a list BON Position Statements and Guidelines grouped by subject matter. Only those listed under General Topics and Scope of Practice are included in this Guide. Copies of all Position Statements and Guidelines can be found on the BON's website.*

SUBPART B.
TEXAS BOARD OF NURSING
POSITION STATEMENT SYNOPSIS 2013

***ANNOTATORS NOTE:** The following Note and Table were prepared by BON and can be found on the BON website.*

Note: The following information is a brief summary of Position Statement content, and does not capture all details contained in each statement. There are additional guidelines, interpretive statements, and other information, along with the full text of the Position Statements, on the BON's web site at www.bon.texas.gov in "Nursing Practice." Nurses are strongly encouraged to review this information in its entirety.

#	Abbreviated Title	Description Summary
15.1	**Nurses Carrying out Orders from Physician's Assistants**	Nurses may carry out physician orders relayed by a PA and/or which originate from a protocol between the PA and the physician. The nurse is expected to clarify any order he/she questions by communicating with the PA or the physician.
15.2	**Role of the Licensed Vocational Nurse in the Pronouncement of Death**	Laws regarding the pronouncement of death are not in the NPA or Board Rules. LVNs cannot pronounce death. LVNs must initiate CPR in the absence of a clear do-not-resuscitate (DNR) order. The LVN may accept a physician's order regarding post-mortem care, but cannot accept a verbal order to pronounce death.
15.3	**LVNs Engaging in IV Therapy, Venipuncture, or PICC Lines**	LVN must complete post-licensure training to engage in IV Therapy/Venipuncture (not typically included in LVN curriculum). Insertion of PICC lines is beyond the scope of practice for LVN.
15.4	**Educational Mobility**	The Board supports educational mobility for nurse's prepared at LVN, ADN, Diploma, and BSN levels without needless repetition of clinical experiences or time penalties.
15.5	**Nurses with Responsibility for Initiating Physician Standing Orders**	Nurses may initiate physician's standing medical orders or standing delegation orders by selecting specific tasks or functions for patient management. The nurse is accountable to assure his/her actions are within the NPA and Board Rules, including that the standing orders do not require the nurse to engage in independent medical judgment. ***NOTE:** RN's who lack Advanced Practice authorization and LVNs may not utilize "protocols" intended for use by APRN's or PA's (see definitions of protocols from the Texas Medical Board in this position statement).*
15.6	**Board Rules Associated with Alleged Patient "Abandonment"**	This position statement differentiates employment vs. licensure issues; addresses relevant Board rules when a nurse engages in unprofessional conduct with regard to being unavailable to provide care to assigned patients (such as sleeping on the job).

15.7	**The Role of LVNs & RNs in Management and/or Administration of Medications via Epidural or Intrathecal Catheter Routes**	LVNs may provide nursing care to patients with epidural or intrathecal catheters, but should not be responsible for catheter management, including administration of drugs via these routes. Epidural & Intrathecal catheter management is within the RN's scope of practice if the RN has current competency in both the knowledge and skills required, with certain limitations recommended in the Obstetrical setting. Appropriate nursing policies and procedures must also be in place.
15.8	**The Role of the Nurse in Moderate Sedation**	LVNs cannot administer to or monitor patients receiving moderate sedation. The administration of drugs and monitoring of patients for moderate sedation can be within the RN's scope of practice. If an RN elects to engage in administration of pharmacologic agents classified as "anesthetic" agents to induce moderate sedation, the RN should either be skilled in, or have immediate availability of other practitioners skilled in advanced airway management along with appropriate equipment that might be necessary to rescue a patient from unintended deep sedation. The facility or physician's office needs to have policies and procedures to guide the RN. See evidencebased practice standards of professional anesthesia association guidelines listed in the position statement.
15.9	**Performance of Laser Therapy by RN's or LVNs**	A nurse must have the appropriate education, knowledge, and experience to engage in laser therapy. There are criteria to be followed by the nurse who accepts physician delegation in the use of nonablative laser therapy.
15.10	**Continuing Education: Limitations for Expanding Scope of Practice**	Clarifies that expansion of an individual nurse's scope of practice has licensure-related limitations. Informal continuing education or on-thejob training cannot be substituted for formal education leading to the next level of practice/licensure or authorization.
15.11	**Delegated Medical Acts**	Specifies criteria which must be met for a nurse to carry out a delegated medical act. This includes documentation of individual training and competency, procedures to be performed, physician order to initiate, and appropriate medical and nursing back up.
15.12	**Use of American Psychiatric Association Diagnoses by LVN, RNs, or APNs**	LVNs and RNs cannot determine Medical Diagnoses. Use of these multi-disciplinary psychiatric diagnoses is permitted by advanced practice nurses designated as Clinical Nurse Specialists (CNS) or Nurse Practitioners (NP's) whose specialty area is psych/mental health. Patient problems beyond the scope of training and education
15.13	**Role of LVNs & RNs As School Nurse**	Establishes, through the NPA and Board Rules, that a nurse has a responsibility and duty to a client/patient to provide and coordinate the delivery of safe, effective nursing care. This duty supersedes any facility policy or physician order.
15.14	**Duty of a Nurse in Any Practice Setting**	Establishes, through the NPA and Board Rules, that a nurse has a responsibility and duty to a client/patient to provide and coordinate the delivery of safe, effective nursing care. This duty supersedes any facility policy or physician order.

15.15	**Board's Jurisdiction Over A Nurse's Practice in Any Role and Use of the Nursing Title*** *New Title to Position Statement January 2013	If a RN or LVN functions in role of lower than that which for which each is licensed, or in another area with an overlapping scope of practice, the nurse is still held to the level of education and competency of their highest licensure. Also restricts use of the titles LVN or RN or any designation implying nursing licensure by nonnurses (Rule 217.10 and NPA Section 301.351)
15.16	**Development of Nursing Education Programs**	Judicious development of new nursing programs is urged as adding programs alone will not address the growing nursing shortage. Key considerations are delineated.
15.17	**BON/ Board of Pharmacy Joint Position Statement on Medication Errors**	Stresses the current trend to look at "systems" and not just "individual competency" in determining root causes of medication errors and implementing strategies to effectively reduce errors, thus better protecting the public.
15.18	**Nurses Carrying Out Orders from Advanced Practice Registered Nurses (APRN)**	As in PS 15.1, nurses may carry out orders issued by APRN's as long as the orders are within the APRN's scope of practice in their role and specialty. The nurse is expected to question orders they believe are non-efficacious or contraindicated by consulting with the APRN or the physician.
15.19	**Nurses Carrying Out Orders from Pharmacists for Drug Therapy Management**	There are current rules that permit pharmacists to write orders for Drug Therapy Management (DTM) while working under physician delegation. A nurse may carry out these orders provided the orders originate from a written protocol authorized by a physician. The nurse is responsible and accountable for his/her actions as with any physician order.
15.20	**Registered Nurses in the Management of an Unwitnessed Arrest in a Resident in a Long Term Care Facility**	Guidance is provided concerning the appropriateness of initiating cardiopulmonary resuscitation (CPR) when the RN encounters an unwitnessed resident arrest without a do not resuscitate (DNR) order in the long term care setting. Presumptive and conclusive signs of death are delineated, to assist the RN in making a decision that CPR would be futile. Documentation, RN obligation to the patient, care planning/advanced directives, and RN pronouncement of death are also discussed.
15.21	*Deleted 01/2005*	
15.22	**APRNs Providing Medical Aspects of Care for Themselves or Others with Whom There is a Close Personal Relationship**	The BON is concerned that when APRNs provide medical aspects of care for themselves or other individuals with whom they have a close personal relationship the APRNs risk allowing their personal feelings to cloud their professional judgment. Thus APRNs should not provide medical treatment or prescribe medications for themselves or any other individual with whom they have a close personal relationship.
15.23	**The RN's Use of Complementary Modalities**	Regardless of practice setting, RNs who incorporate complementary modalities into their practice are accountable and responsible for adherence to the NPA and BON Rules and Regulations. Specific regulations of particular relevance are identified in the position statement, including a reference to the BON's Six Step Decision- Making Model for Determining Nursing Scope of Practice. Also, a list of criteria is included in order for RNs to show accountability for the care they provide.

		Lastly, RNs are accountable to hold proper credentials (e.g., license, certification, registration) to safely engage in specific practices, where applicable.
15.24	**Nurses Engaging In Reinsertion of Permanently Placed Feeding Tubes**	LVNs & RNs should receive post-licensure training and demonstrate competency in reinsertion of a displaced permanently placed feeding tube prior to engaging in this activity. Verification of correct placement is essential to prevent life-threatening complications. Reinsertion by a nurse is not recommended prior to 8-12 weeks postinitial insertion; specific physician orders must be obtained regarding reinsertion by a nurse.
15.25	**Administration of Medication & Treatments by LVNs**	LVNs are educationally prepared to administer medications and treatments as ordered by a physician, podiatrist, dentist or any practitioner legally authorized to prescribe the ordered medication. LVNs may administer medications and treatments ordered by physician assistants (PS 15.1) and advanced practice registered nurses (PS 15.18). Also see NPA 301.002 (5), the definition of vocational nursing.
15.26	**Simulation in Prelicensure Nursing Education**	While the benefits of simulation are known, limitations to simulation do exist. Guidance is provided to clarify the role and limitation of simulation in prelicensure nursing education programs (Rule §214 and Rule §215). BON recommends adherence to the guidelines contained in the position statement to ensure that students receive optimal learning experiences.
15.27	**The Licensed Vocational Nurse Scope of Practice**	The LVN scope of practice is a directed scope of practice and requires appropriate supervision. The LVN is responsible for providing safe, compassionate and focused nursing care to assigned patients with predictable health care needs
15.28	**The Registered Nurse Scope of Practice**	The RN takes responsibility and accepts accountability for practicing within the legal scope of practice and is prepared to work in all health care settings, and may engage in independent nursing practice without supervision by another health care provider. The RN is responsible for providing safe, compassionate, and comprehensive nursing care to patients and their families with complex healthcare needs.
15.29	**Use of Social Media by Nurses**	The use of social media can be of tremendous benefit to nurses and patients alike. However, nurses must be aware of the potential consequences of disclosing patient-related information via social media. Nurses must always maintain professional standards, boundaries, and compliance with state and federal laws as stated in Board Rule 217.11(A). All nurses have an obligation to protect their patient's privacy and confidentiality [as required by Board Rule 217.11(E)] which extends to all environments, including the social media environment.

SUBPART C.
GENERAL TOPIC RELATED POSITION STATEMENTS

POSITION STATEMENT 15.14. DUTY OF A NURSE IN ANY PRACTICE SETTING

In a time when cost consciousness and a drive for increasing productivity have brought about the reorganization and restructuring of health care delivery systems, the effects of these new delivery systems on the safety of clients/patients have placed a greater burden on the licensed vocational nurse (LVN) and the registered professional nurse (RN) to consider the meaning of licensure and assurance of quality care that it provides.

In the interest of fulfilling its mission to protect the health, safety, and welfare of the people of Texas through the regulation of nurses, the Texas Board of Nursing (BON), through the Nursing Practice Act and Board Rules, emphasizes the nurse's responsibility and duty to the client/patient to provide safe, effective nursing care.

Specifically, the following portions of the Board Rules and supporting documents underscore the duty and responsibilities of the LVN and/or the RN to the client/patient:

1. The Standards of Nursing Practice differentiate the roles of the LVN and the RN in accepting nursing care assignments, assuring a safe environment for patients, and obtaining instruction and supervision as needed (Rule 217.11); and
2. In *Lunsford v. Board of Nurse Examiners*, 648 S.W. 2d 391 (Tex. App.--Austin, 1983), the court in affirming the disciplinary action of the Board, held that a nurse has a duty to the patient which cannot be superseded by hospital policy or physician's order.
    3. This landmark case involved a gentleman who arrived to a rural hospital via private vehicle. The gentleman was experiencing severe chest pain, nausea, and sweating—all hallmark symptoms of myocardial infarction (heart attack). Nurse Lunsford was summoned to the ER waiting room by this gentleman's friend. Upon seeing the acute distress the man was experiencing and hearing his symptoms, she instructed his friend to drive the man to the nearest facility equipped to handle heart attack victims. This facility was 24 miles away. The man succumbed to the heart attack 5 miles away from the small hospital.
    4. When the Board sought to sanction the nurse's license, the nurse maintained that the ER physician (who never saw the man) told her the man needed to be transported to the larger facility. The facility policy was also to transfer patients experiencing heart attacks (via ambulance) to the larger facility that was equipped to provide the broad range of therapies that might be needed.
    5. The court sided with the BON and agreed that the nurse had the knowledge, skills and abilities to recognize the life-threatening nature of the man's symptoms. Because of this knowledge, the court maintained that it was the nurse's duty to act in the best interest of the client by assessing the man, taking measures to stabilize him and to prevent complications, and communicating his condition to other staff (such as the MD) in order to enlist appropriate medical care.

- The Board's Disciplinary Sanction Policies discuss expectations of all nurses regarding

ANNOTATIONS

The two position statements set out in this Subpart A address issues applicable to most aspects of nursing practice.

As discussed, although BON position statements and guidelines don't carry the legal force of rules, they still should be viewed as setting out "best practices" in certain situations. A nurse who violates them is certainly at risk of not having acted as a reasonable, prudent nurse.

This position statement is designed to provide guidance to nurses who may be faced with difficult practice decisions because of changes currently occurring in the health care delivery system. NPA Secs. 301.352 (Part 1 of Guide) and Nursing Peer Review Law Sec. 303.005 (Part VI) provide protections to the nurse who feels that she or he is being requested to engage in actions believed to violate the NPA or BON rules.

The nurse's ultimate responsibility is to the client/patient. This principle of the nurse's duty to the public and her/his patient was clearly established in the Lunsford case described in this position statement. A copy of the case is set out in Part X (Appendices) of this Guide.

This is a listing of BON rules and other resources that the Board believes to be particularly significant for nurses in fulfilling their duty and responsibility to patients.

Standard of Practice set out in Rule 217.11. See Part II (Rules) of this Guide

The Lunsford court case held that nurses have a direct duty to patients and that hospital policies do not supersede the nurse's duty to the client/patient.

Disciplinary Sanction Policies.

behaviors that are consistent with the Board's rules on Good Professional Character, §§213.27-213.29. These policies explain the client's vulnerability and the nurse's "power" differential over the client by virtue of the client's status (with regard to age, illness, mental infirmity, etc) and by the nature of the nurse:client relationship (where the client typically defers decisions to the nurse, and relies on the nurse to protect the client from harm).

- The delegation rules guide the RN in delegation of tasks to unlicensed assistive personnel who are utilized to enhance the contribution of the RN to the client's/patient's well being. When performing nursing tasks, the unlicensed person cannot function independently and functions only under the RN's delegation and supervision. Through delegation the RN retains responsibility and accountability for care rendered (Rules 224 and 225). The Board may take disciplinary action against the license of a RN or RN administrator for inappropriate delegation
- RNs with advanced practice authorization from the Board must comply with the same rules applicable to other RNs. In addition, rules specific to advanced practice nursing Chapters 221 & 222, as well as laws applicable to the APRN's practice setting that are outside of the BON's jurisdiction must also be followed.
- Each nurse must be able to support how his/her clinical judgments and nursing actions were aligned with the NPA and Board Rules. The Board recommends nurses use the Six-Step Decision-Making Model for Determining Nursing Scope of Practice when trying to determine if a given task is within the individual nurse's abilities. Congruence with standards adopted by national nursing specialty organizations may further serve to enhance and support the nurse's decision to perform a particular task.

The nurse, by virtue of a rigorous process of education and examination leading to either LVN or RN licensure, is accountable to the Board to assure that nursing care meets standards of safety and effectiveness.

Therefore, it is the position of the Board that each licensed nurse upholds his/her duty to maintain client safety by practicing within the parameters of the NPA and Board Rules as they apply to each licensee.

(Adopted 01/2005; revised 01/2007); (Reviewed - 01/2009)

BON FAQ: When Does A Nurse's Duty to Patient Begin and End

Annotator's Note: The FAQ is set out in the Appendices of this Guide.

Position Statement 15.6. Board Rules Associated With Alleged Patient "Abandonment"

The Texas Board of Nursing (BON or Board), in keeping with its mission to protect the public health, safety, and welfare, holds nurses accountable for providing a safe environment for clients and others over whom the nurse is responsible [Rule 217.11(1)(B)]. Though the Nursing Practice Act (NPA) and Board Rules do not define the term "*abandonment*," the Board has investigated and disciplined nurses in the past for issues surrounding the concept of *abandonment* as it relates to *the nurse's duty to the patient*. The Board's position applies to licensed nurses (LVNs and RNs), including RN's with advanced practice authorization (Nurse Practitioners, Clinical Nurse Specialists, Nurse Midwives, and Certified Registered Nurse Anesthetists) in Texas.

Nurse's Duty To A Patient

All nurses, regardless of practice setting or position title/role, are required to adhere to the NPA and Board Rules. The "core" rules relating to nursing practice, however, are Rules 217.11, Standards of Nursing Practice, and 217.12, Unprofessional Conduct. The standard upon which other standards are based is 217.11(1)(B) "...promote a safe environment for clients and others." This standard supersedes any physician's order or facility's policy, and has previously been upheld

Delegation rules for RNs.

APRNs.

Six-Step Decision Process. A copy is set out in Part X (Appendices) of this Guide.

This FAQ address questions the BON staff receive about when a nurse's duty to the patient begins. Its content supplements Position Statement 15.14 set out above.

Nurses may be "threatened" with allegations that they are abandoning their patients if they don't accept an assignment. While not accepting an assignment would not normally constitute "abandonment," nurses need to know what does and does not constitute "abandonment" of patients. This position statement attempts to clarify this issue.

Nurses have a duty directly to patients and that duty cannot be overridden by hospital policies or physicians' orders.

in a landmark case, *Lunsford v. Board of Nurse Examiners*, 648 S.W. 2d 391 (Tex. App. -- Austin 1983). The concept of the nurse's duty to promote client safety also serves as the basis for behavior that could be considered unprofessional conduct by a nurse.

Patients under the care of a nurse are vulnerable by virtue of illness, injury, and/or the dependent nature and unequal power base of the nurse-patient relationship. Persons who are especially vulnerable include the elderly, children, the mentally ill, sedated and anesthetized patients, those whose mental or cognitive ability is compromised, and patients who are physically disabled, immobilized, restrained, or secluded. It is this dual-vulnerability (client status and nurse's power base) that creates the nurse's duty to protect the client. The distinction between a nurse leaving employment versus a nurse violating a duty to a patient through leaving an assignment is often confused. The first is an employment issue, the other is potentially a licensure issue.

There is also no routine answer to the question, *"When does the nurse's duty to a patient begin?"* The nurse's duty is not defined by any single event such as clocking in or taking report. From a BON standpoint, the focus for disciplinary sanctions is on the relationship and responsibility of the nurse to the patient, not to the employer or employment setting.

Employment Issues

Though the Board has no jurisdiction over employers or employment-related issues, other laws regulating facility licensure may apply certain responsibilities to the employer for provision of client safety, such as development of effective patient care systems or provision of adequate numbers of qualified staff. Specific requirements for a given facility may be obtained by contacting the applicable licensing authority for the institution.

The Board believes that the following additional examples of employment issues would not typically involve violations of the NPA or Board Rules:

- Resignation without advance notice, assuming the nurse's current patient care assignment and/or work shift has been completed.
- Refusal to work additional shifts, either "doubles" or extra shifts on days off.
- Other work-related issues, such as frequent absenteeism or tardiness, or conflicts between staff/employees.

The Board believes nurses should be vigilant and exercise good professional judgment when accepting assignments that may be requested by employers who need nurses to fill vacant shifts for licensed nursing staff, or other staffing-related situations. *Clear communication* between staff and supervisors is essential to arrive at solutions that best focus on patient care needs without compromising either patient safety or a nurse's license.

Licensure Issues

As previously noted, the rules most frequently applied to nursing practice concerns are Rule 217.11 *Standards of Nursing Practice*, and Rule 217.12 *Unprofessional Conduct*. In relation to questions of "abandonment," standard 217.11(1)(I) holds the nurse responsible to "notify the appropriate supervisor when leaving a nursing assignment." This standard should not be mis-interpreted to mean that the nurse may simply notify the supervisor that he/she is leaving the premises, regardless of whether or not another qualified licensed nurse is available to assume care of the nurse's patients. Specific procedures to follow in a given circumstance (nurse becomes ill, family emergency, etc.) should be delineated in facility policies (over which the Board has no jurisdiction).

Some actions may be more obvious examples of unprofessional conduct that could result in sanctions on the nurse's license. Examples of conduct that could lead to Board action on the nurse's license may include:

- Sleeping on the job, which effectively makes the nurse unavailable to observe the patient or respond to the patient's needs, even though the nurse is physically present.
- Simply walking off the job in mid-shift without notifying anyone, and without regard for patient safety;
- Failing to initiate or complete an agreed assignment when the nurse is the sole care provider, and/or the nurse is a consultant or supervisor in a home or homelike setting;

Confusion can exist between a "nurse leaving employment" versus "abandoning a patient."

Like many practice issues, there is not a "bright line" answer. The crucial issue is the nurse's relationship to the patient and not some arbitrary event.

Examples of when "not accepting an assignment" is unlikely to violate any duty a nurse has to a patient.

See NPA Sec. 301.356, which provides that a refusal to work illegal mandatory overtime does not constitute patient abandonment.

What actions the nurse takes can be crucial to whether abandonment occurs.

Examples of conduct involving assignments that would likely violate a nurse's duty to a patient.

and/or failing to notify a supervisor in a timely manner that the assignment will not be done, and/or falsifying records to the effect that the missed nursing visit was indeed completed ; and/or
- Leaving the assigned patient care area and remaining gone/unavailable for a period of time such that the care of any/all patients may be compromised due to lack of available licensed staff.

The Board may impose sanctions on a nurse's license for actions that potentially place patients at risk for harm, or when harm has resulted because a nurse violated his/her duty to the client by leaving a patient care assignment in a manner inconsistent with the Board Rules.

Board Disciplinary Actions

Complaints of "patient abandonment" when it is obvious from the allegation that it is an employment issue will not be investigated by the Board. In these circumstances, however, both parties (the nurse and the employer) may be advised to strive for alternate solutions to avoid similar situations in the future.

Some general factors that would be considered in investigating a complaint of leaving an assignment by a nurse would include, but not be limited to:

- the extent of dependency or disability of the patient;
- stability of the patient;
- the length of time the patient was deprived of care;
- any harm to the patient/level of risk of harm to the patient;
- steps taken by the nurse to notify a supervisor of the inability to provide care;
- previous history of leaving a patient-care assignment;
- other unprofessional conduct in relation to the practice of nursing;
- general nurse competency regarding adherence to minimum nursing standards.

As with all allegations received by the Board, the alleged conduct by a nurse will be thoroughly investigated to determine what, if any, violations of the NPA and rules have occurred. If evidence of violations exists, the Board must then determine what level of sanction is appropriate to take on the nurse's license, and what specific stipulation requirements will be applied. Depending upon the case analysis, Board actions may range from the case being closed with no findings or action, all the way to suspension and/or revocation/voluntary surrender of the nurse's license.

Safe Harbor Peer Review:

If a nurse feels he/she is being asked to accept an assignment that would potentially cause the nurse to violate his/her duty to a patient, the nurse may be able to invoke "safe harbor," depending on whether or not the nurse's employer meets requirements that would make it mandatory for the employer to have a peer review plan in place. This is established in the NPA, Chapter 303 *Peer Review*, and in Rule 217.20 *Safe Harbor Peer Review and Whistleblower Protections.* Safe Harbor has two effects related to the nurse's license:

(1) It is a means by which a nurse can request a peer review committee determination of a specific situation in relation to the nurse's duty to a patient; and

(2) It affords the nurse immunity from Board action against the nurse's license if the nurse invokes Safe Harbor in accordance with Rule 217.20. For the nurse to activate this immunity status, the nurse must notify the assigning supervisor at the time the assignment request is made, and the nurse must submit the required information in writing as specified in Rule 217.20(d)(3)(A) or on the Board's Safe Harbor Quick Request Form.

For more information about Safe Harbor, see "related links" at the end of this article.

Links to Related Articles (all of the following are located on the Board's web page):

- Safe Harbor Form http://www.bon.state.tx.us/practice/Safe.htm.
- FAQ on Overtime/Hours of Work http: www.bon.state.tx.us/faq-practice.html#overtime
- FAQ on Peer Review ftp://www.bon.state.tx.us/PeerReview-FAQs.pdf
- FAQ on Staffing Ratios http://www.bon.state.tx.us/practice/faq-practice.html#Staffing
- FAQ on Floating ftp://www.bon.state.tx.us/floating.pdf

This paragraph explains how the BON staff handle allegations of abandonment.

Safe harbor nursing peer review may provide the nurse some options if she or he is uncertain as to whether leaving an assignment may constitute abandonment. See Part VI (Patient Advocacy) of this Guide.

- FAQ on When Does a Nurse's Duty to a Patient Begin and End http://www.bon.state.tx.us/practice/faq-nurseduty.html
- RN Update, July 2002: Overview of TDH Staffing Plans and CNO Requirement Rules

(Adopted 01/2005); (Reviewed - 01/2009)

POSITION STATEMENT 15.29 USE OF SOCIAL MEDIA BY NURSES

With the rapidly growing use of social media sites and applications such as Facebook, Twitter, LinkedIn, YouTube, and blogs, professional obligations to patients, peers, and employers may be unclear. While the Board recognizes that the use of social media can be a valuable tool in healthcare, there are potential serious consequences if used inappropriately. Online postings may harm patients if protected health information is disclosed. These types of postings may reflect negatively on individual nurses, the nursing profession, the public's trust of our profession, as well as jeopardize careers.

Both the National Council of State Boards of Nursing (NCSBN) and the American Nurses Association (ANA) endorse each other's guidelines and principles on the use of social media in order for it to be used appropriately and without harm to patients. The benefits of social media are many, and include:

- Networking and nurturing relationships
- Exchange of knowledge and forum for collegial interchange
- Dissemination and discussion of nursing and health related education, research, best practices
- Educating the public on nursing and health related matters" (ANA, 2012, para. 4).

However, if used indiscriminately, the risks are great, and include:

- Information taking on a life of its own where inaccuracies become fact
- Patient privacy being breached
- The public's trust of nurses being compromised
- Individual nursing careers being undermined" (ANA, 2012, para. 5).

In a recent survey by the NCSBN, many of the responding boards reported that they had received complaints about nurses inappropriately using social media sites. Nurses have been disciplined by boards, fired by employers, and criminally charged for the inappropriate or unprofessional use of social media (NCSBN, 2012).

To ensure the mission to protect and promote the welfare of the people of Texas, the Texas Board of Nursing supports both the guidelines and principles of social media use by the NCSBN and ANA. In keeping with the NCSBN guidelines, it is the Board's position that:

- *Nurses must recognize that they have an ethical & legal obligation to maintain patient privacy and confidentiality at all times.*
- *Nurses are strictly prohibited from transmitting by way of any electronic media any patient-related image. In addition, nurses are restricted from transmitting any information that may be reasonably anticipated to violate patient rights to confidentiality or privacy, or otherwise degrade or embarrass the patient.*
- *Nurses do not identify patients by name or post or publish information that may lead to the identification of a patient. Limiting access to postings through privacy settings is not sufficient to ensure privacy.*
- *Nurses do not refer to patients in a disparaging manner, even if the patient is not identified.*
- *Nurses do not take photos or videos of patients on personal devices, including cell phones. Follow employer policies for taking photographs or video of patients for treatment or other legitimate purposed using employer-provided devices.*
- *Nurses maintain professional boundaries in the use of electronic media. Like in-person relationships, the nurse has the obligation to establish, communicate and enforce professional boundaries with patients in the online environment. Use caution when having online social contact with patients or former patients. Online contact*

This position statement was adopted by the BON in 2012. It reflects guidelines and principles mutually recognized by the American Nurses Association and the National Council of State Boards of Nursing. The guidelines for the nurse to follow are set out in italics.

Specific guidelines nurses should follow.

with patients or former patients blurs the distinction between a professional and personal relationship. The fact that a patient may initiate contact with the nurse does not permit the nurse to engage in a personal relationship with the patient.

- *Nurses consult employer policies or supervisor within the organization for guidance regarding work related postings.*
- *Nurses promptly report any identified breach of confidentiality or privacy.*
- *Nurses must be aware of and comply with employer policies regarding use of employer-owned computers, cameras and other electronic devices and use of personal devices in the work place.*
- *Nurses do not make disparaging remarks about employers or co-workers. Do not make threatening, harassing, profane, obscene, sexually explicit, racially derogatory, homophobic or other offensive comments.*
- *Nurses do not post content or otherwise speak on behalf of the employer unless authorized to do so and follow all applicable policies of the employer (NCSBN, 2012).*
- *Nurses update your privacy settings on a regular basis.*

The use of social media can be of tremendous benefit to nurses and patients alike. However, nurses must be aware of the potential consequences of disclosing patient-related information via social media. Nurses must always maintain professional standards, boundaries, and compliance with state and federal laws as stated in 22 TAC § 217.11(1)(A). All nurses have an obligation to protect their patient's privacy and confidentiality (as required by 22 TAC § 217.11(1)(E)) which extends to all environments, including the social media environment.

References:

- American Nurses Association (ANA). (2012) Social networking principles toolkit. Retrieved on 2/21/12 from http://www.nursingworld.org/FunctionalMenuCategories/AboutANA/Social-Media/Social-Networking-Principles-Toolkit.aspx
- National Council of State Boards of Nursing (NCSBN). (2012). Social media guidelines. Retrieved on 2/21/12 from https://www.ncsbn.org/2930.htm

(Adopted: 04/2012), (Revised: 01/2013)

SUBPART D.
SCOPE OF PRACTICE RELATED POSITION STATEMENTS

The position statements, FAQs, and other documents set out in this Subpart B relate to scope of practice issues for nurses. Defining scope of practice is difficult and at best is a snapshot at a single point in time. Nursing and health care generally are dynamic fields in which scopes of practice change as technology and education change. Specific acts that may constitute the practice of professional or vocational nursing today may have been considered the practice of medicine in the past. Likewise, specific acts that may constitute the practice of medicine today may fall within the practice of nursing in the future. A good example of this phenomenon is that the taking of blood pressure was at one time considered to be outside the scope of nursing. The emergence of advanced practice nursing is another. For a discussion of how nursing "changes" over time, see the court case Sermchief v. Gonzales set out in the Part X (Appendices) f this Guide.

When Position Statements 15.27 (LVN Scope of Practice) and 15.28 (RN Scope of Practice) were adopted by the BON in July 2011, the background materials presented to the Board included the following statement about the historical perspective on their adoption:

> *The role of every board of nursing is to protect the public through the regulation of nursing practice. Over the past several decades, differentiated levels of education, licensure, and practice have evolved into a scope of practice continuum that is fairly uniform across the United States.*
>
> *The scope of practice continuum is explained in laws, and rules and regulations.*

Related NPA and BON Rules Provisions

ANNOTATOR's NOTE: *The BON Position Statements 15.27 and 15.28 on scope of practice need to be read against the background of the following provisions of NPA and BON Rules. The NPA provisions can be found in Part I (NPA) of th is Guide and the BON Rules in Part II (Rules).*

NPA Sec. 301.002(_) Definition of Professional Nursing
NPA Sec. 301.002(_) Definition of Vocational Nursing
BON Rule 217.11, Subsecs. (2), (3) and (4)

Position Statement 15.27. The Licensed Vocational Nurse Scope of Practice

The BON recommends that all nurses utilize the Six-Step Decision-Making Model for Determining Nursing Scope of Practice[1] when deciding if an employer's assignment is safe and legally within the nurse's scope of practice.

The Texas Board of Nursing (BON) is authorized by the Texas Legislature to regulate the nursing profession to ensure that every licensee is competent to practice safely. The Texas Nursing Practice Act (NPA) and the Board's Rules and Regulations define the legal scope of practice for licensed vocational nurses (LVN). The LVN scope of practice is a directed scope of practice and requires appropriate supervision. The LVN, with a focus on patient safety, is required to function within the parameters of the legal scope of practice and in accordance with the federal, state, and local laws, rules, regulations, and policies, procedures and guidelines of the employing health care institution or practice setting. ***The LVN is responsible for providing safe, compassionate and focused nursing care to assigned patients with predictable health care needs.***

The purpose of this position statement is to provide direction and recommendations for nurses

One of the most important rules for every nurse in Texas is TAC §Rule 217.11, Standards of Nursing Practice. These standards provide the framework for the minimum acceptable standards of nursing practice, and also serve in determining a nurse's scope of practice.

The Texas Board of Nursing (BON) has always sought to promote accurate interpretation of the nursing licensure laws with nurses and their employers. In order to facilitate an understanding, various resources have been developed to clarify the LVN and RN scope of practice. For example, in 2004, after the Board adopted TAC Rule §217.11, Standards of Nursing Practice; the Interpretive Guideline for the LVN Scope of Practice under Rule 217.11 was developed to further explain the rule. The interpretive guideline clarifies the differences in the scopes of practice between the LVN and RN and was supported by the Differentiated Entry Level Competencies (DELCs) of Graduates of Texas Nursing Programs, Vocational (VN), Diploma/Associate Degree (DIP/ADN), Baccalaureate Degree (BSN).

In October 2010, after the Board approved the revisions to the DELCs and adopted the Differentiated Essential Competencies (DECs) of Graduates of Texas Nursing Programs Evidenced by Knowledge, Clinical Judgments, and Behaviors; the interpretive guideline became outdated.

In order to continue to provide accurate and up-to-date interpretations to nurses and their employers on scope of practice issues, Board staff developed two draft position statements on the LVN and RN scope of practice. TAC Rule §217.11, Standards of Nursing Practice; the Interpretive Guideline for the LVN Scope of Practice under Rule 217.11 and the DECs are the basis for these position statements.

This Position Statement 15.27 (LVN Scope of Practice) and 15.28 (RN Scope of Practice) were both adopted by the BON in July 2011.

The Six-Step Decision-Making Process is set out in Part X (Appendices) of this Guide.

LVNs have a directed scope of practice and function under appropriate supervision. NPA Sec. 301.353 requires LVN practice under supervision.

and their employers regarding the safe and legal scope of practice for licensed vocational nurses and to promote an understanding of the differences between the LVN and RN levels of licensure. The RN scope of practice is interpreted in Position Statement 15.28.

Every nursing education program in the state of Texas is required to ensure that their graduates exhibit competencies outlined in the Board's Differentiated Essential Competencies (DECs) of Graduates of Texas Nursing Programs.[2] These competencies are included in the program of study so that every graduate has the knowledge, clinical behaviors and judgment necessary for LVN entry into safe, competent and compassionate nursing care. The DECs serve as a guideline for employers to assist LVNs as they transition from the educational environment into nursing practice. As LVNs enter the workplace, the DECs serve as the foundation for the development of the LVN scope of practice.

Completion of on-going, informal continuing nursing education offerings and on-the-job trainings in a LVN's area of practice serves to develop, maintain, and expand the level of competency. Because the LVN scope of practice is based upon the educational preparation in the LVN program of study, there are limits to LVN scope of practice expansion parameters. The Board believes that for a nurse to successfully make a transition from one level of nursing practice to the next requires the completion of a formal program of education.[3]

The LVN Scope of Practice

The LVN is an advocate for the patient and the patient's family and promotes safety by practicing within the NPA and the BON Rules and Regulations. LVN scope of practice does not include acts of medical diagnosis or the prescription of therapeutic or corrective measures.[4] The practice of vocational nursing must be performed under the supervision of a RN, APRN, physician, physician assistant, podiatrist or dentist.[5] Supervision is defined as the active process of directing, guiding, and influencing the outcome of an individual's performance of an activity.[6] The LVN is precluded from practicing in a completely independent manner; however, direct and on-site supervision may not be required in all settings or patient care situations. Determining the proximity of an appropriate clinical supervisor, whether available by phone or physical presence, should be made by the LVN and the LVN's clinical supervisor by evaluating the specific situation, taking into consideration patient conditions and the level of skill, training and competence of the LVN. An appropriate clinical supervisor may need to be physically available to assist the LVN should emergent situations arise.

The setting in which the LVN provides nursing care should have well defined policies, procedures, and guidelines, in which assistance and support are available from an appropriate clinical supervisor. The Board recommends that newly licensed LVNs work in structured settings for a period of 12-18 months, such as nursing homes, hospitals, rehabilitation centers, skilled nursing facilities, clinics or private physician offices.[7] This allows the new nurse sufficient practice experience in more structured settings in order to assimilate knowledge from their education. As competencies are demonstrated, if the LVN transitions to unstructured settings where the clinical supervisor may not be on-site, it is the LVN's responsibility to ensure he or she has access to an appropriate clinical supervisor and that the policies, procedures and guidelines for that particular setting are established to guide the LVN practice.

The LVN uses a systematic problem-solving process in the care of multiple patients with predictable health care needs to provide individualized, goal-directed nursing care. LVNs may contribute to the plan of care by collaborating with interdisciplinary team members, the patient and the patient's family. The essential components of the nursing process are described in a side by side comparison of the different levels of education and licensure (see Table).

Assessment

The LVN assists in determining the physical and mental health status, needs, and preferences of culturally, ethnically, and socially diverse patients and their families based on interpretation of health-related data. The LVN collects data and information, recognizes changes in conditions and reports this to the RN supervisor or another appropriate clinical supervisor to

See Position Statement 15.10 set out below for a more detailed discussion of CNE not being a mechanism for expanding scope of practice.

See definition of "vocational nursing" in NPA Sec. 301.002(5).

See NPA Sec. 301.353 for required LVN supervision.

assist in the identification of problems and formulation of goals, outcomes and patient-centered plans of care that are developed in collaboration with patients, their families, and the interdisciplinary health care team. The LVN participates in the nursing process by appraising the individual patient's status or situation at hand. Also known as a focused assessment, this appraisal may be considered a component of a more comprehensive assessment performed by a RN or another appropriate clinical supervisor. For example, a RN may utilize the data and information collected and reported by the LVN in the formation of the nursing process; however, the RN's comprehensive assessment lays the foundation for the nursing process. The LVN reports the data and information collected either verbally or in writing. Written documentation must be accurate and complete, and according to policies, procedures and guidelines for the employment setting.[8]

Planning

The second step in which the LVN participates and contributes to the nursing process is planning. After the focused assessment, the LVN reports data and other information such as changes in patient conditions to the appropriate clinical supervisor, such as a RN. This information may be considered in planning, problem identification, nursing diagnoses, and formulation of goals, teaching plans and outcomes by the RN supervisor or another appropriate clinical supervisor. A nursing plan of care for patients is developed by the RN and thus the RN has the overall responsibility to coordinate nursing care for patients.

Implementation

Implementing the plan of care is the third step in the nursing process. The LVN is responsible for providing safe, compassionate and focused nursing care to assigned patients with predictable health care needs. The LVN may implement aspects of the plan of care within legal, ethical, and regulatory parameters and in consideration of patient factors. The LVN organizes aspects of patient care based on identified priorities. Delegating tasks to unlicensed assistive personnel (UAPs) is beyond the scope of practice for LVNs; however, LVNs may make appropriate assignments to other LVNs and UAPs according to Rule 217.[11](2).6 The RN is generally responsible and accountable for supervising not only the LVN's practice but the UAP's performance of tasks as well. For example, the RN may have trained, verified competency and delegated the tasks to a UAP and the LVN may then proceed to assign those tasks that need to be accomplished for that day. Teaching and counseling are interwoven throughout the implementation phase of the nursing process and LVNs can participate in implementing established teaching plans for patients and their families with common health problems and well defined health learning needs.

Evaluation

A critical and fourth step in the nursing process is evaluation. The LVN participates in the evaluation process identifying and reporting any alterations in patient responses to therapeutic interventions in comparison to expected outcomes. The LVN may contribute to the evaluation phase by suggesting any modifications to the plan of care that may be necessary and making appropriate referrals to facilitate continuity of care.

Essential Skills Use in the Nursing Process

Communication

Communication is a fundamental component in the nursing process. The LVN must communicate verbally, in writing, or electronically with members of the healthcare team, patients and their families on all aspects of the nursing care provided to patients. Communications must be appropriately documented in the patient record or nursing care plan. Because LVNs are members of the healthcare team, provide nursing care, and contribute to the nursing process, collaboration is a quality that is crucial to the communication process. When patient conditions or situations have changed or exceeded the LVN's level of competency and scope of practice, the

LVNs perform focused assessments. See also Rule 217.11(2).

LVNs do not delegate to unlicensed persons but may make appropriate assignments and provide supervision. The legal difference between "delegation" and "assignment" is that delegation confers legal authority to do something they otherwise cannot legally do. Assignment is directing a person to do something she or he has the legal authority to do.

LVN must be prepared to seek out his or her clinical supervisor and actively cooperate to develop solutions that ensure patient safety.

Clinical Reasoning

Clinical reasoning is another integral component in the nursing process. LVNs must use clinical reasoning and established evidence-based policies, procedures or guidelines as the basis for decision making in nursing practice. LVNs are accountable and responsible for the quality of nursing care provided and must exercise prudent nursing judgment to ensure the standards of nursing practice are met at all times.[9]

Employment Setting

When an employer hires a nurse to perform a job, the nurse must assure that it is safe and legal. For instance, the LVN must have a clinical supervisor who is knowledgeable and aware of his or her role. Caution must be exercised not to overstep the legal parameters of nursing practice when an employer may not understand the limits of the LVN scope of practice and makes an assignment that is not prudent or safe. The LVN must determine before he or she engages in an activity or assignment whether he or she has the education, training, skill, competency and the physical and emotional ability to safely carry out the activity or assignment.[10] The LVN's duty is to always provide safe, compassionate, and focused nursing care to patients.

Making Assignments

The LVN's duty to patient safety when making assignments to others is to take into consideration the education, training, skill, competence and physical and emotional ability of the persons to whom the assignments are made. [11] [12] If the LVN makes assignments to another LVN or UAP, he or she is responsible for reasonable and prudent decisions regarding those assignments. It is not appropriate and is beyond the scope of practice for a LVN to supervise the nursing practice of a RN. However, in certain settings, i.e.: nursing homes, LVNs may expand their scope of practice through experience, skill and continuing education to include supervising the practice of other LVNs, under the oversight of a RN or another appropriate clinical supervisor. The supervising LVN may have to directly observe and evaluate the nursing care provided depending on the LVN's skills and competence, patient conditions and emergent situations. Timely and readily available communication between the supervising LVN and the clinical supervisor is essential to provide safe and effective nursing care.

Summary

The LVN, with a focus on patient safety, is required to function within the parameters of the legal scope of practice and in accordance with the federal, state, and local laws, rules, regulations, and policies, procedures and guidelines of the employing health care institution or practice setting. The LVN functions under his or her own license and assumes accountability and responsibility for quality of care provided to patients and their families according to the standards of nursing practice.[9] The LVN demonstrates responsibility for continued competence in nursing practice, and develops insight through reflection, self-analysis, self-care, and lifelong learning.

The table below offers a brief synopsis of how the scope of practice for nurses differs based on educational preparation and level of licensure. These are minimum competencies, but also set limits on what the LVN or RN can do at his or her given level of licensure, regardless of experience.

---

[1]Texas Board of Nursing (2010). Six-step decision-making model for determining nursing scope of practice

[2]Texas Board of Nursing (2010). Differentiated essential competencies (DECs) of graduates of Texas Nursing Programs.

[3]Texas Board of Nursing (2011). Position statement 15.10 Continuing education: Limitations for expanding scope of practice.

LVNs do not delegate to unlicensed persons but may make appropriate assignments and provide supervision. The legal difference between "delegation" and "assignment" is that delegation confers legal authority to do something they otherwise cannot legally do. Assignment is directing a person to do something she or he has the legal authority to do.

The nurse's ultimate responsibility is to the client/patient. Under the Lunsford case, nurses have a duty directly to patients and that duty cannot be overridden by hospital policies or physicians' orders. The Lunsford case is set out in Part X (Appendices) of this Guide.

[4]Texas Nursing Practice Act, TOC § 301.002(5).
[5]Texas Nursing Practice Act, TOC § 301.353.
[6]Texas Administrative Code, 22 TAC §217.11(2).
[7]Texas Board of Nursing (2011). Rules and guidelines governing the graduate vocational and registered nurse candidates or newly licensed vocational or registered nurse.
[8]Texas Administrative Code, 22 TAC §217.11(1)(D).
[9]Texas Administrative Code, 22 TAC §217.11.
[10]Texas Administrative Code, 22 TAC §217.11(1)(T).
[11]Texas Administrative Code, 22 TAC §217.11(1)(S).
[12]Texas Administrative Code, 22 TAC §217.11(2)(B).

Additional Resources

Idaho Board of Nursing (2010). Position on safety to practice.
Kentucky Board of Nursing. (2005). Components of licensed practical nursing practice (AOS #27 LPN Practice).
National Council of State Boards of Nursing. (2009). Changes in healthcare professions' scope of practice: Legislative considerations.
North Carolina Board of Nursing. (2010). LPN scope of practice: Clarification: Position statement for LPN practice.
North Carolina Board of Nursing. (2010). RN and LPN scope of practice components of nursing comparison chart.
North Carolina Board of Nursing. (2010). RN scope of practice: Clarification: Position statement for RN practice.
Texas Administrative Code, 22 TAC §224.
Texas Administrative Code, 22 TAC §225.

(Adopted 07/2011), (Revised: 01/2013), (Reviewed 01/2012)

TABLE AND FAQ'S

ANNOTATOR'S NOTE: *The table for Position Statement 15.27 (LVN Scope) is the same as the table for Position Statement 15.28 (RN Scope). The Table for both position statements is set out following 15.28. Set out following the table are FAQs the BON has prepared about Position Statements 15.27 and 15.28.*

POSITION STATEMENT 15.28. THE REGISTERED NURSE SCOPE OF PRACTICE

The BON recommends that all nurses utilize the Six-Step Decision-Making Model for Determining Nursing Scope of Practice[1] when deciding if an employer's assignment is safe and legally within the nurse's scope of practice.

The Texas Board of Nursing (BON) is authorized by the Texas Legislature to regulate the nursing profession to ensure that every licensee is competent to practice safely. The Texas Nursing Practice Act (NPA) defines the legal scope of practice for professional registered nurses (RN).[2] The RN takes responsibility and accepts accountability for practicing within the legal scope of practice and is prepared to work in all health care settings, and may engage in independent nursing practice without supervision by another health care provider. The RN, with a focus on patient safety, is required to function within the parameters of the legal scope of practice and in accordance with the federal, state, and local laws; rules and regulations; and policies, procedures and guidelines of the employing health care institution or practice setting. ***The RN is responsible***

This Position Statement 15.28 (RN Scope of Practice) and 15.27 (LVN Scope of Practice) were both adopted by the BON in July 2011.

The Six-Step Decision-Making Process is set out in Part X (Appendices) of this Guide.

for providing safe, compassionate, and comprehensive nursing care to patients and their families with complex healthcare needs.

The purpose of this position statement is to provide direction and recommendations for nurses and their employers regarding the safe and legal scope of practice for RNs and to promote an understanding of the differences in the RN education programs of study and between the RN and LVN levels of licensure. The LVN scope of practice is interpreted in Position Statement 15.27.

Every nursing educational program in the state of Texas is required to ensure that their graduates exhibit competencies outlined in the Board's Differentiated Essential Competencies (DECs) of Graduates of Texas Nursing Programs.[3] These competencies are included in the program of study so that every graduate has the knowledge, clinical behaviors and judgment necessary for RN entry into safe, competent and compassionate nursing care. The DECs serve as a guideline for employers to assist RNs as they transition from the educational environment into nursing practice. As RNs enter the workplace, the DECs serve as the foundation for the development of the RN scope of practice.

Completion of on-going, informal continuing nursing education offerings and on-the-job trainings in a RN's area of practice serves to develop, maintain, and expand competency. Because the RN scope of practice is based upon the educational preparation in the RN program of study, there are limits to the expansion of the scope. The Board believes that for a nurse to successfully make a transition from one level of nursing practice to the next requires the completion of a formal program of education.[4]

The RN Scope of Practice

The professional registered nurse is an advocate for the patient and the patient's family, and promotes safety by practicing within the NPA and the BON Rules and Regulations. The RN provides nursing services that require substantial specialized judgment and skill. The planning and delivery of professional nursing care is based on knowledge and application of the principles of biological, physical and social science as acquired by a completed course of study in an approved school of professional nursing. Unless licensed as an advanced practice registered nurse, the RN scope of practice does not include acts of medical diagnosis or the prescription of therapeutic or corrective measures.[2] RNs utilize the nursing process to establish the plan of care in which nursing services are delivered to patients. The level and impact of the nursing process differs between the RN and LVN as well as between the different levels of RN education (see Table).

Assessment

The comprehensive assessment is the first step, and lays the foundation for the nursing process. The comprehensive assessment is the initial and ongoing, extensive collection, analysis and interpretation of data. Nursing judgment is based on the assessment process. The RN uses clinical reasoning and knowledge, evidence-based outcomes, and research as the basis for decision-making and comprehensive care. Based upon the comprehensive assessment the RN determines the physical and mental health status, needs, and preferences of culturally, ethnically, and socially diverse patients and their families using evidence-based health data and a synthesis of knowledge. Surveillance is an essential step in the comprehensive assessment process. The RN must anticipate and recognize changes in patient conditions and determines when reassessments are needed.

Planning

The second step in the nursing process is planning. The RN synthesizes the data collected during the comprehensive assessment to identify problems, make nursing diagnoses, and to formulate goals, teaching plans and outcomes. A nursing plan of care for patients is developed by the RN, who has the overall responsibility to coordinate nursing care for patients. Teaching plans address health promotion, maintenance, restoration, and prevention of risk factors. The RN utilizes evidence-based practice, published research, and information from patients and the interdisciplinary health care team during the planning process.

Implementation

Implementing the plan of care is the third step in the nursing process. The RN may begin, deliver, assign or delegate certain interventions within the plan of care for patients within legal, ethical, and regulatory parameters and in consideration of health restoration, disease prevention, wellness, and promotion of healthy lifestyles. The RN's duty to patient safety when making assignments to other nurses or when delegating tasks to unlicensed staff is to consider the education, training, skill, competence, and physical and emotional abilities of those to whom the assignments or delegation is made. The RN is responsible for reasonable and prudent decisions regarding assignments and delegation. The RN scope of practice may include the supervision of LVNs. Supervision of LVN staff is defined as the process of directing, guiding, and influencing the outcome of an individual's performance and activity.[5] The RN may have to directly observe and evaluate the nursing care provided depending on the LVN's skills and competence, patient conditions, and emergent situations.

The RN may determine when it is appropriate to delegate tasks to unlicensed personnel and maintains accountability for how the unlicensed personnel perform the tasks. The RN is responsible for supervising the unlicensed personnel when tasks are delegated. The proximity of supervision is dependent upon patient conditions and skill level of the unlicensed personnel. In addition, teaching and counseling are interwoven throughout the implementation phase of the nursing process.

Evaluation and Re-assessment

A critical and fourth step in the nursing process is evaluation. The RN evaluates and reports patient outcomes and responses to therapeutic interventions in comparison to benchmarks from evidence-based practice and research findings, and plans any follow-up care and referrals to appropriate resources that may be needed. The evaluation phase is one of the times when the RN reassesses patient conditions and determines if interventions were effective and if any modifications to the plan of care are necessary.

Essential Skills Used in the Nursing Process

Communication

Communication is an essential and fundamental component used during the nursing process. The RN must communicate verbally, in writing, or electronically with members of the healthcare team, patients and their families in all aspects of the nursing care provided to patients. These communications must be appropriately documented in the patient record or nursing care plan. Because RNs plan, coordinate, initiate and implement a multidisciplinary team's approach to patient care, collaboration is a quality crucial to the communication process. When patient conditions or situations exceed the RN's level of competency, the RN must be prepared to seek out other RNs with greater competency or other health care providers with differing knowledge and skill sets and actively cooperate to ensure patient safety.

Clinical Reasoning

Clinical reasoning is another integral component in the nursing process. RNs use critical thinking skills to problem-solve and make decisions in response to patients, their families and the healthcare environment. RNs are accountable and responsible for the quality of nursing care provided and must exercise prudent and professional nursing judgment to ensure the standards of nursing practice are met at all times.

Employment Setting

When an employer hires a RN to perform a job, the RN must assure that it is safe and legal. Caution must be exercised not to overstep the legal parameters of nursing practice when an employer may not understand the limits of the RN scope of practice and makes an assignment that

The legal difference between "delegation" and "assignment" is that delegation confers legal authority to do something they otherwise cannot legally do. Assignment is directing a person to do something she\he has the legal authority to do. Only RNs may delegate; LVNs may make appropriate assignments.

is not safe. The RN must determine before he or she engages in an activity or assignment whether he or she has the education, training, skill, competency and the physical and emotional ability to safely carry out the activity or assignment.[6] The RN's duty is to always provide safe, compassionate, and comprehensive nursing care to patients.

Summary

The RN, with a focus on patient safety, is required to function within the parameters of the legal scope of practice and in accordance with the federal, state, and local laws; rules and regulations; and policies, procedures and guidelines of the employing health care institution or practice setting. The RN functions under his or her own license and assumes accountability and responsibility for quality of care provided to patients and their families according to the standards of nursing practice[7] The RN demonstrates responsibility for continued competence in nursing practice, and develops insight through reflection, self-analysis, self-care, and lifelong learning.

The table below offers a brief synopsis of how the scope of practice for nurses differs based on educational preparation and level of licensure. These are minimum competencies, but also set limits on what the LVN or RN can do at his or her given level of licensure, regardless of experience.

---

[1] Texas Board of Nursing (2010). Six-step decision-making model for determining nursing scope of practice.

[2] Texas Nursing Practice Act, TOC §301.002(2)

[3] Texas Board of Nursing (2010). Differentiated essential competencies (DECs) of graduates of Texas Nursing Programs

[4] Texas Board of Nursing (2011). Position statement 15.10 Continuing education: Limitations for expanding scope of practice.

[5] Texas Administrative Code, 22 TAC §217.11(2)

[6] Texas Administrative Code, 22 TAC §217.11(1)(T)

[7] Texas Administrative Code, 22 TAC §217.11

Additional Resources

Idaho Board of Nursing (2010). Position on safety to practice.

Kentucky Board of Nursing. (2005). Components of licensed practical nursing practice (AOS #27 LPN Practice).

National Council of State Boards of Nursing. (2009). Changes in healthcare professions' scope of practice: Legislative consideration.

North Carolina Board of Nursing. (2010). LPN scope of practice: Clarification: Position statement for LPN practice.

North Carolina Board of Nursing. (2010). RN and LPN scope of practice components of nursing comparison chart.

North Carolina Board of Nursing. (2010). RN scope of practice: Clarification: Position statement for RN practice.

Texas Administrative Code, 22 TAC §224 (2011).

Texas Administrative Code, 22 TAC §225 (2011).

Texas Board of Nursing (2011). Rules and guidelines governing the graduate vocational and registered nurse candidates or newly licensed vocational or registered nurse.

(Adopted 07/2011), (Revised: 01/2013), (Reviewed 01/2012)

TABLE AND FAQ'S

ANNOTATOR'S NOTE: *The table for Position Statement 15.27 (LVN Scope) and Position Statement 15.28 (RN Scope) is the same and is set out on the next page. Set out following the table are FAQs the BON has prepared about Position Statements 15.27 and 15.28.*

The nurse's ultimate responsibility is to the client/patient. Under the Lunsford case, nurses have a duty directly to patients and that duty cannot be overridden by hospital policies or physicians' orders. The Lunsford case is set out in Part X (Appendices) of this Guide.

TABLE
POSITION STATEMENTS 15.27 & 15.28

ANNOTATOR'S NOTE: *The following table is the same for both Position Statements 15.27 (LVN scope) and 15.28 (RN scope).*

Synopsis Of Differences in Scope Of Practice for Licensed Vocational, Associate, Diploma and Baccalaureate Degree Nurses

Nursing Practice	**LVN Scope of Practice** *Directed/Supervised Role*	**ADN or Diploma RN Scope of Practice** *Independent Role*	**BSN RN Scope of Practice** *Independent Role*
Education	The curriculum for the VN education is in a clinically intensive certificate program of approximately one year in length. The Texas BON rules mandate a minimum of 558 theory and 840 clinical hours in the VN program of study. The VN curriculum includes instruction in five basic areas of nursing care: adults; mothers and newborns; children; elderly; and individuals with mental health problems. Clinical experience in a unit or a facility specifically designed for psychiatric care is optional. Required support courses should provide instruction in biological, physical, social, behavioral, and nursing sciences, including body structure and function, microbiology, pharmacology, nutrition, signs of emotional health, human growth and development, vocational adjustments, and nursing skills.	ADN programs require a minimum of two full years of study, integrating a balance between courses in liberal arts; natural, social, and behavioral sciences; and nursing. Academic associate degrees consist of 60-72 credit hours with approximately half the program requirements in nursing courses. The Texas BON approved curriculum includes requirements for didactic instruction and clinical experiences in four contents areas: medical-surgical, maternal/ child health, pediatrics, and mental health nursing. Diploma programs are hospital based, single purpose schools of nursing that consist of two-three years of general education and support courses.	The BSN program of study integrates approximately 60 hours from liberal arts and natural, social, and behavioral science courses and approximately 60-70 hours of nursing courses. In addition to the ADN/Diploma education requirements, BSN education includes instruction in community health, public health, research, nursing leadership, and nursing management with preparation and skills to practice evidence based nursing.

Synopsis Of Differences in Scope Of Practice for Licensed Vocational, Associate, Diploma and Baccalaureate Degree Nurses			
Nursing Practice	**LVN Scope of Practice** *Directed/Supervised Role*	**ADN or Diploma RN Scope of Practice** *Independent Role*	**BSN RN Scope of Practice** *Independent Role*
Supervision	Supervision is required for the LVN scope of practice. LVNs are not licensed for independent nursing practice. A LVN must ensure that he or she has an appropriate clinical supervisor, i.e. RN, APRN, Physician, PA, Dentist or Podiatrist. The proximity of a clinical supervisor depends on skills and competency of the LVN, patient conditions and practice setting. Direct, on-site supervision may not always be necessary depending on the LVN's skill and competence and should be determined on a case-by-case situation taking into consideration the practice setting laws. However, clinical supervisors must provide timely and readily available supervision and may have to be physically present to assist LVNs should emergent situations occur.	Provides supervision to other RNs, LVNs and UAPs. Supervision of LVN staff is defined as the process of directing, guiding, and influencing the outcome of an individual's performance and activity.	Provides supervision to other RNs, LVNs and UAPs. Supervision of LVN staff is defined as the process of directing, guiding, and influencing the outcome of an individual's performance and activity.

Synopsis Of Differences in Scope Of Practice for Licensed Vocational, Associate, Diploma and Baccalaureate Degree Nurses			
Nursing Practice	**LVN Scope of Practice** ***Directed/Supervised Role***	**ADN or Diploma RN Scope of Practice** ***Independent Role***	**BSN RN Scope of Practice** ***Independent Role***
Setting	Provides focused nursing care to individual patients with predictable health care needs under the direction of an appropriate clinical supervisor. The setting may include areas with well defined policies, procedures and guidelines with assistance and support from appropriate clinical supervisors, i.e. nursing home, hospital, rehabilitation center, skilled nursing facility, clinic, or a private physician office. As competencies are demonstrated, if the LVN transitions to other settings, it is the LVN's responsibility to ensure he or she has an appropriate clinical supervisor and that the policies, procedures and guidelines for that particular setting are available to guide the LVN practice.	Provides independent, direct care to patients and their families who may be experiencing complex health care needs that may be related to multiple conditions. Provides healthcare to patients with predictable and unpredictable outcomes in various settings.	Provides independent, direct care to patients, families, populations, and communities experiencing complex health care needs that may be related to multiple conditions. Provides healthcare to patients with predictable and unpredictable outcomes in various settings.

Synopsis Of Differences in Scope Of Practice for Licensed Vocational, Associate, Diploma and Baccalaureate Degree Nurses

Nursing Practice	LVN Scope of Practice *Directed/Supervised Role*	ADN or Diploma RN Scope of Practice *Independent Role*	BSN RN Scope of Practice *Independent Role*
Assessment	Assists, contributes and participates in the nursing process by performing a focused assessment on individual patients to collect data and gather information. A focused assessment is an appraisal of the situation at hand for an individual patient and may be performed prior to the RN's initial and comprehensive assessment. The LVN reports the assessment information and changes in patient conditions to an appropriate clinical supervisor.	Independently performs an initial or ongoing comprehensive assessment (Extensive data collection). Anticipates changes in patient conditions to include emergent situations. Reports and documents information and changes in patient conditions to a health care practitioner and or a responsible party. Determines the physical and mental health status, needs, and preferences of culturally diverse patients and their families.	Independently performs an initial or ongoing comprehensive assessment (Extensive data collection). Anticipates changes in patient conditions to include emergent situations. Reports and documents information and changes in patient conditions to a health care practitioner and or a responsible party. Determines the physical and mental health status, needs, and preferences of culturally diverse patients, families, populations and communities.

Synopsis Of Differences in Scope Of Practice for Licensed Vocational, Associate, Diploma and Baccalaureate Degree Nurses

Nursing Practice	**LVN Scope of Practice** ***Directed/Supervised Role***	**ADN or Diploma RN Scope of Practice** ***Independent Role***	**BSN RN Scope of Practice** ***Independent Role***
Planning	Uses clinical reasoning based on established evidence-based policies, procedures and guidelines for decision-making. May assign specific daily tasks and supervise nursing care to other LVNs or UAPs.	Uses clinical reasoning based on established evidence-based policies, procedures and guidelines for decision-making. Analyzes assessment data to identify problems, formulate goals and outcomes, and develops nursing plans of care for patients and their families. May assign tasks and activities to other nurses. May delegate tasks to UAPs.	Uses clinical reasoning based on established evidence-based practice outcomes and research for decision-making and comprehensive care. Synthesizes comprehensive data to identify problems, formulate goals and outcomes, and develop nursing plans of care for patients, families, populations, and communities. May assign tasks and activities to other nurses. May delegate tasks to UAPs.

Synopsis Of Differences in Scope Of Practice for Licensed Vocational, Associate, Diploma and Baccalaureate Degree Nurses			
Nursing Practice	**LVN Scope of Practice** ***Directed/Supervised Role***	**ADN or Diploma RN Scope of Practice** ***Independent Role***	**BSN RN Scope of Practice** ***Independent Role***
Implementation	Provides safe, compassionate and focused nursing care to patients with predictable health care needs. Implements aspects of the nursing care plan, including emergency interventions under the direction of the RN or another appropriate clinical supervisor. Contributes to the development and implementation of teaching plans for patients and their families with common health problems and well-defined health needs.	Provides safe, compassionate, comprehensive nursing care to patients, and their families through a broad array of health care services. Implements the plan of care for patients and their families within legal, ethical, and regulatory parameters and in consideration of disease prevention, wellness, and promotion of healthy lifestyles. Develops and implements teaching plans to address health promotion, maintenance, and restoration.	Provides safe, compassionate, comprehensive nursing care to patients, families, populations, and communities through a broad array of health care services. Implements the plan of care for patients, families, populations, and communities within legal, ethical, and regulatory parameters and in consideration of disease prevention, wellness, and promotion of healthy lifestyles. Develops and implements teaching plans to address health promotion, maintenance, restoration, and population risk reduction.

Synopsis Of Differences in Scope Of Practice for Licensed Vocational, Associate, Diploma and Baccalaureate Degree Nurses

Nursing Practice	LVN Scope of Practice *Directed/Supervised Role*	ADN or Diploma RN Scope of Practice *Independent Role*	BSN RN Scope of Practice *Independent Role*
Evaluation	Participates in evaluating effectiveness of nursing interventions. Participates in making referrals to resources to facilitate continuity of care.	Evaluates and reports patient outcomes and responses to therapeutic interventions in comparison to benchmarks from evidence-based practice, and plans follow-up nursing care to include referrals for continuity of care.	Evaluates and reports patient, family, population, and community outcomes and responses to therapeutic interventions in comparison to benchmarks from evidence-based practice and research, and plans follow-up nursing care to include referrals for continuity of care.

Frequently Asked Questions (FAQs) Regarding Position Statements 15.27, the LVN Scope of Practice and 15.28, the RN Scope of Practice

1) I am a LVN and read in Position Statements 15.27 and 15.28 that it is the LVN's responsibility to ensure that he or she has an appropriate Clinical Supervisor. Who can be my clinical supervisor?

Each LVN is required to ensure that he or she has the appropriate supervisor prior to accepting an assignment, a position or employment. The Nursing Practice Act (NPA) Section 301.353 states that "*the practice of vocational nursing must be performed under the supervision of a registered nurse, physician, physician assistant, podiatrist, or dentist.*" Rule 217.11, Standards of Nursing Practice, (2) further goes on to require and explain that "*the licensed vocational nurse practice is a directed scope of nursing practice under the supervision of a registered nurse, advanced practice registered nurse, physician's assistant, physician, podiatrist, or dentist. Supervision is the process of directing, guiding, and influencing the outcome of an individual's performance of an activity.*"

LVNs provide valuable and essential nursing care in different types of health care settings. When LVNs work in settings, such as hospitals, long-term care facilities, rehabilitation centers, or skilled nursing facilities, RNs are mostly likely to serve as the LVN's supervisor. LVNs also work in private physician or dentist offices, where physicians, dentists and podiatrists function as the LVN's supervisor. Because LVNs may practice in these various health care settings, the clinical supervisor is a term used to describe the different licensed healthcare providers that are authorized in the NPA to supervise and direct the LVN's practice, i.e.: registered nurse, advanced practice registered nurse, physician, physician assistant, podiatrist or dentist. These types of clinical supervisors oversee the nursing practice of a LVN by monitoring the health status of patients and then directing the LVN's actions to ensure the delivery of safe and effective nursing care.

2) In Position Statements 15.27 and 15.28, I read that LVNs are responsible for providing safe, compassionate and focused nursing care to assigned patients with predictable health care needs. What does predictable mean in this statement?

The LVN in Texas provides nursing care to patients with health care needs that are predictable in nature, under the direction and supervision of a registered nurse, advanced practice registered nurse, physician, physician assistant, podiatrist or dentist. The term predictable describes health conditions that behave or occur in an expected way. A predictable health condition does not mean that the patient is always stable. Instead, predictable health conditions follow an expected range or pattern that allows the LVN with his or her clinical supervisor to anticipate and appropriately plan for the needs of patients.

For example, it is appropriate for a LVN to care for a patient with a diagnosis of asthma. The disease process for asthma, while sometimes acute in nature, is predictable or well-known, and the symptoms can be anticipated. The LVN assists his or her clinical supervisor in the development of a plan, in which the LVN provides care, prevents possible complications and stabilizes the symptoms of asthma. In addition, when complications arise or events occur that are outside the predicted range, the LVN must be able to recognize this change in condition and notify his or her clinical supervisor.

Helpful Resources:

Texas Board of Nursing (2010). Differentiated essential competencies (DECs) of graduates of Texas Nursing Programs

Texas Board of Nursing (2011). Position statement 15.27, The LVN Scope of Practice

Texas Board of Nursing (2011). Position statement 15.28, The RN Scope of Practice

Texas Occupations Code, Chapter 301.002(5). Definition of Vocational Nursing

Texas Occupations Code, Chapter 301.353. Supervision of Vocational Nurse

22 Tex. Admin. Code §217.11 (1). Standards of Nursing Practice
22 Tex. Admin. Code §217.11 (2). Standards Specific to Vocational Nurses
August 2011

FAQ - LIST OF TASKS A NURSE CAN/CANNOT PERFORM

Where can I find a list of tasks that LVNs and/or RNs can or cannot do in the State of Texas?

The Nursing Practice Act (NPA) and Board Rules are written broadly so that they can apply to nursing practice in any setting. As such, the BON does not provide lists of tasks or step-by-step procedures of how they are to be carried out by the nurse. It is up to the individual nurse, whether LVN or RN, to utilize good professional judgement in accepting any given assignment and/or performing a given procedure. The BON has no jurisdiction over facility policies, nor can we speak to civil liability issues.

One of the primary rule that applies to a nurse's clinical practice is Rule 217.11"Standards of Nursing Practice." This rule, along with the Nursing Practice Act and all Board Rules may be viewed on our web site. The standards that apply to nearly every situation include (1)(B)- "maintaining a safe environment for patients..", and Standard (1)(T) "accepting appropriate assignments"; other standards may apply depending on the situation.

In relation to nurses, the NPA (in section 301.002 "definition of professional nursing") states that professional nursing does not include "medical diagnosis or prescription of therapeutic or corrective measures." (ie: the RN may not engage in activities that require the use of independent medical judgement). Though the NPA has not yet been revised to incorporate LVNs into this definition, engaging in a task or tasks that requires independent medical judgment is also beyond the scope of practice for a LVN.

In addition to reviewing Rule 217.11, you may wish to look at the board's "Six Step Decision Making Model for Determining Nursing Scope of Practice". This is a flow chart of questions to help the nurse walk through the decision-making process. (Look under "Scope of Practice" on the Nursing Practice Information Page.)

One of the questions in the six step decision making model asks if there is precedent for RNs or LVNs engaging in a given practice. You may wish to check nursing literature, as well as contacting the national nursing organization related to the specialty nursing area in question to see if they endorse RN's and/or LVNs engaging in a given practice.

In addition, some acts may be performed as Delegated Medical Acts. The rules related to this are in the Board of Medical Examiner's Rule 193; however, we do have Position Statement 15.11 "Delegated Medical Acts" that you can view by clicking on "Practice Issues" on the web page when you go through the Table of Contents. Your facility's policy and procedure would also have to permit a given practice.

Neither facility policy nor MD order can discharge the nurse's responsibility for assuring patient safety, or for complying with all of the other rules and requirements in the Nursing Practice Act. A nurse may refuse to engage in any activity that the nurse, in good faith, believes may cause him/her to violate one or more provisions of the NPA and board rules (NPA, Section 301.352). Also see the "Safe Harbor" form on our web page under "Forms" and Rule 217.20 for more information.

POSITION STATEMENT 15.10. CONTINUING EDUCATION: LIMITATIONS FOR EXPANDING SCOPE OF PRACTICE

Foundation for Initial Licensure and/or APRN authorization:

The Board''s Advisory Committee on Education states in its *"Differentiated Entry Level Competencies of Graduates of Texas Nursing Programs, Vocational (VN), Diploma/ Associate Degree (Dip/ADN), Baccalaureate (BSN), September 2002"* (http://www.bon.state.tx.us/about/pdfs/del-comp.pdf) that: "The curricula of each of the nursing

While nurses may expand their individual competencies through CNE, nurses expand their legal scope of practice through formal education. This position statement sets out the role of CNE and its limitations as a way to expand scope of practice.

programs differ, resulting in differentiated entry level competencies of graduates....The competencies of each educational level build upon the previous level." On a national level, the National Council of State Boards of Nursing, Inc. (NCSBN) develops and administers two national nurse licensure examinations; the National Council Licensure Examination for Practical Nurses (NCLEX-PN®), and the National Council Licensure Examination for Registered Nurses (NCLEX-RN®). These two examinations are used by all U.S. state and territorial boards of nursing to test entry-level nursing competence of candidates for licensure as Registered Nurses and as Licensed Practical/Vocational Nurses.

Recognition as an advanced practice registered nurse in Texas requires completion of a master's or post-master's advanced practice program as well as national certification in the advanced role and specialty. To gain recognition as an advanced practice registered nurse in Texas, the nurse must first be licensed as a RN in Texas or have a valid unencumbered RN license from a compact state. The nurse must then submit an application to the Board for "authorization" in the advanced practice role and specialty.

Limitations of "Continuing Education"

The nursing shortage is creating ever greater challenges for those who must fill nursing vacancies at all levels --- LVNs, RNs, and Advanced Practice Registered Nurses (APRNs) in various specialties. As efforts to invent new ways to fill this growing void expand, the Board is receiving a growing number of calls to clarify the term "continuing education" in relation to how far a nurse can expand his/her practice with informal continuing education offerings.

The formal education for entry into nursing practice in Texas is differentiated between vocational and professional (registered) nursing. Formalized education for advanced practice also requires completion of a formal program of education in the advanced practice role and specialty at the master's or post-master's level.

The Board believes that for a nurse to successfully make a transition from one level of nursing practice to the next requires the completion of a formal program of education as defined in the applicable board rule. The Board also believes that completion of on-going, informal continuing education offerings, such as workshops or on-line offerings in a specialty area, serve to expand and maintain the competency of the nurse at the current level of licensure/recognition. No amount of informal or on-the-job-training can qualify a LVN to perform the same level of care as the RN. Likewise, the RN cannot engage in aspects of care that require independent medical judgement in a given APRN role and specialty without the formal education, national certification, and proper authorization in that advanced practice nurse role and specialty.

For example, a LVN with 10 years of home care experience cannot perform the comprehensive assessment and initiate the nursing care plan on a patient newly admitted to the LVN's home care agency's service. This is precluded in both BON Rule 217.11 as well as in the home care regulations. Attending a workshop and/or spending time under the supervision of a RN does not qualify the LVN to engage in practice that is designated in rule as being exclusive to the next level of licensure.

Therefore, any nurse, regardless of experience, who engages in nursing practice that would otherwise require a higher level of licensure or a different level of authorization is practicing outside of his/her scope of practice, and may be subject to disciplinary action congruent with the NPA and Rules applicable to LVNs, RNs, and/or RNs with APRN authorization in a given role/specialty.

(Adopted 01/2005); (Reviewed - 01/2009)

Position Statement 15.11. Delegated Medical Acts.

In carrying out orders from physicians, podiatrists, or dentists for the administration of medications or treatments, nurses are usually engaged in the practice of vocational or professional nursing in accordance with the applicable licensure of the individual nurse. In carrying out some physician orders, however, LVNs or RNs may perform acts not usually considered to be within the scope of vocational or professional nursing practice, respectively. Such tasks are delegated and supervised by physicians, podiatrists, or dentists. RNs who lack authorization as advanced practice

When performing functions outside the scope of his or her professional or vocational nursing license, the RN's or LVN's authority to perform the function must be delegated by another licensed practitioner. Usually, this will be a physician. This position statement provides guidance to RNs and LVNs when performing delegated medical acts.

Drawing the line between what constitutes the practice of professional or vocational nursing and the practice of medicine is difficult at best. Nursing and health care generally are dynamic fields in which scopes of practice change as technology and education change. Specific acts that nurses in a specified role and specialty, and LVNs may not engage in "acts of medical diagnosis or prescription of therapeutic or corrective measures" [NPA, Section 301.002(2) and (5)] as these acts require independent medical judgment, which is beyond the scope of practice of the vocational or registered nurse.

In carrying out the delegated medical function, the nurse is expected to comply with the Standards of Nursing Practice just as if performing a nursing procedure. The Board's position is that a LVN or RN may carry out a delegated medical act if the following criteria are met:

1. The nurse has received appropriate education and supervised practice, is competent to perform the procedure safely, and can respond appropriately to complications and/or untoward effects of the procedure (refer to Standards in Rule 217.11(1)C), (1)(T), (1)(G), (1)(M), (1)(N), and (1)(R);
2. The nurse's education and skill assessment are documented in his/her personnel record;
3. The nursing and medical staffs have collaborated in the development of written policies/procedures/practice guidelines for the delegated acts, these are available to nursing staff practicing in the facility, and the guidelines are reviewed annually, if applicable;
4. The procedure has been ordered by an appropriate licensed practitioner; and
5. Appropriate medical and nursing back-up is available.

The Board recognizes that nursing practice is dynamic and that acts which today may be considered delegated medical acts may in the future be considered within the scope of either vocational or professional nursing practice. The Board, therefore, advises nurses that they must comply with the Board's Standards of Nursing Practice and any other applicable regulations when carrying out nursing and/or delegated medical acts.

(Board Action 09/93; Revised 03/94; Revised 01/2001; Revised 01/2003; Revised 01/2004; Revised 01/2005); (Reviewed - 01/2009)

SIX-STEP DECISION MAKING PROCESS FOR DETERMINING NURSING SCOPE OF PRACTICE

The BON has developed a Six-Step Decision Making Process to assist nurses in making good professional judgments about the nursing tasks or procedures they choose to undertake. It is set out in the Appendices to this Guide.

may constitute the practice of professional or vocational nursing today may have been considered the practice of medicine in the past. Likewise, specific acts that may constitute the practice of medicine today may fall within the practice of nursing in the future. A good example of this phenomenon is that the taking of blood pressure was at one time considered to be outside the scope of nursing.

A distinction must also be made between situations requiring physician delegation and situations requiring a physician's order. Physician delegation is required only when the nurse is performing or functioning outside the scope of his or her professional nursing license. There are also acts that may require a physician's order for the RN or LVN to perform, but which the actual performance of constitutes the practice of professional nursing. The administration of prescription medications is a good example of such an act. There must be a physician's order for the RN or LVN to administer a prescription medication but the actual administration of the medication is a professional nursing act. The RN or LVN, in carrying out a physician's order in most situations, will be practicing professional nursing under the authority of her or his nursing license. In such situations, physician delegation is not occurring even though a physician's order is required.

However, in some situations delegation of medical acts will occur, e.g., laser treatment or making medical diagnoses (APRNs). This position statement provides the RN and LVN guidance in such situations. Frequently, such delegation will occur under protocols (for APNs) or standing orders (for other nurses). See also Position Statement 15.5 relating to initiating a physician's standing orders.

Interpretive Guideline for Differentiating Vocational Nurse Scope of Practice Under Rule 217.11 Standards of Nursing Practice

Scope of Practice for Nurses

Vocational Nurse

(1) **Clarification of Practice Parameters**
Directed practice under the supervision of a registered nurse, advanced practice registered nurse, physician assistant, physician, dentist, or podiatrist.* *(Independent practice not permitted)*

**Direct (onsite or on-unit) supervision is not required. The LVN must have a resource person accessible telephonically or by some other similar means. Proximity to the LVN's practice setting and the level of licensure of a supervisor (RN, MD, etc.) must be determined by the LVN and his/her supervisor on a case-by-case basis and in accordance with any other laws that are applicable in the practice setting.*

(2) **Provider of Care:**

(a) Assist in the determination of predictable healthcare needs of clients within structured healthcare settings who are experiencing common, well defined health problems with predictable outcomes.

(b) Utilize a systematic approach to provide individualized, goal-directed nursing care by:

- (i) collecting data and performing focused nursing assessments;
- (ii) participating in the planning of nursing care needs for clients, and in modifying the nursing care plan for assigned clients;
- (iii) implementing appropriate aspects of care within the LVN's scope of practice, including compliance with other laws as are applicable to the LVNs practice setting;
- (iv) implementing the teaching plan for clients with common health problems and well defined learning needs;
- (v) providing direct basic care to assigned multiple clients in structured settings;
- (vi) assist in the evaluation of the client's responses and outcomes to therapeutic interventions; and
- (vii) utilize a problem-solving approach as the basis for decision making in Vocational Nurse practice

(3) **Coordinator of Care:**
Assign specific tasks, activities and functions and maintain appropriate supervision of licensed and unlicensed personnel in structured health settings for clients with predictable health care needs in accordance with designated job descriptions and/or job duties.

(4) **Member of a Profession:**

(a) Assume accountability and responsibility for the quality of nursing care provided to clients.

(b) Act as a client advocate to maintain a safe environment for clients.

(c) Demonstrate behaviors that promote development of positive outcomes in relation to the practice of vocational nursing.

Registered Nurse

(1) **Clarification of Practice Parameters**
Practice set broadly by the NPA, Section 301.002, that precludes RNs from engaging in "acts of medical diagnosis or prescription of therapeutic or corrective measures"; RNs are permitted to engage in independent practice within the scope of their licensure.

(2) **Provider of Care:**

(a) Determine the predictable or unpredictable health status and health needs of clients (individual and family) through interpretation of health data and preventive health practice in collaboration with clients and interdisciplinary health care team members.

(b) Utilize a systematic approach to provide individualized, goal-directed nursing care by:

- (i) performing comprehensive nursing assessments regarding the health status of the client(s);
- (ii) formulating a nursing care plan based on determination of nursing diagnoses;
- (iii) implementing nursing care within the RN's scope of practice, including compliance with other laws are applicable to the RN's practice setting;
- (iv) developing and implementing teaching plans for clients concerning promotion, maintenance and restoration of health;
- (v) providing for the care of multiple clients (individual and family) either through direct care or assignment and/or delegation of care to other members of the health care team;
- (vi) evaluate client's (individual and family) responses and outcomes to therapeutic interventions; and
- (vii) utilize a critical thinking approach to analyze clinical data and current literature as a basis for decision making in nursing practice.

(3) **Coordinator of Care:**
Make assignments to licensed staff (LVNs, RNs) and delegate to unlicensed staff in compliance with current BON rules in both structured and unstructured health settings for clients with predictable as well as unpredictable health needs.

(4) **Member of a Profession:**

(a) Assume accountability and responsibility for the quality of nursing care provided to clients.

(b) Act as a client advocate to maintain a safe environment for clients.

(c) Serve as a healthcare advocate in monitoring and promoting quality of health care and services for client; and

(d) Participate in activities and act as a leader in promoting best practices within professional nursing.

The table above offers a brief synopsis of how the scope of practice for nurses educated and licensed as vocational nurses differs from nurses educated and licensed as registered nurses. These are minimum competencies, but also set limits on what the LVN or RN can do at his/her given level of licensure, regardless of experience. The interpretive guideline may be viewed in its entirety on the BON web page at www.bon.state.tx.us under the "Nursing Practice Information" section.

2 TEXAS Department of Aging and Disability Services

www.TexasQualityMatters.org

www.dads.state.tx.us
DADS Media Services OIPSIE * January 2010 Publication No. 103

Texas Board of Nursing

SIX STEP DECISION-MAKING PROCESS POSTER

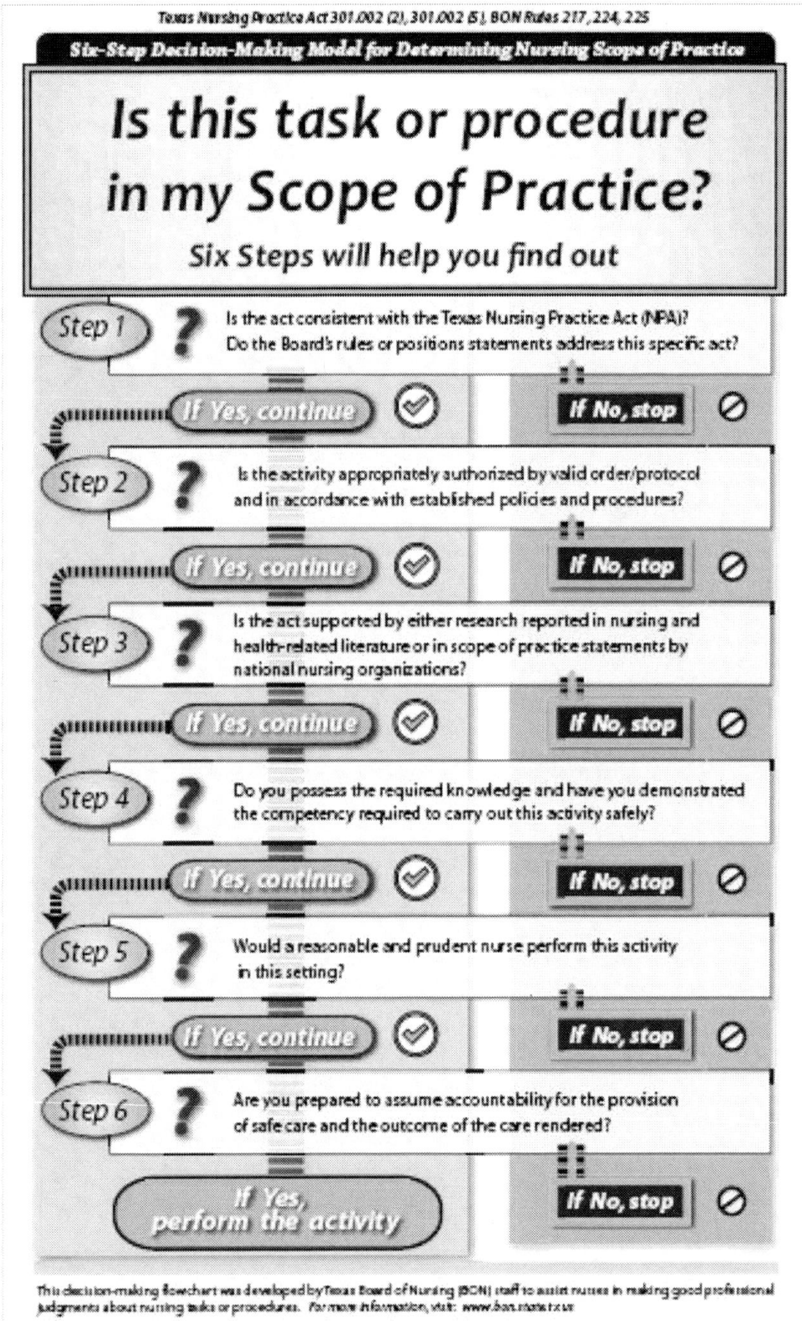

SUBPART E.
OTHER BON PRACTICE-RELATED RESOURCES

***ANNOTATOR'S NOTE**: In addition to the Position Statement and Guidelines, the BON has a number of practice-related materials on its website which can provide valuable guidance to RNs and LVNs in addressing specific practice questions. These materials are largely self-explanatory and can be found on the website at www.bon.state.tx.us. Set out in Part V (Practice-Related Materials) of thsi Guide is a listing of most of the practice related information on the BON's website as of July 2013. A complete outline of the BON website is set out in Part X (Appendices).*

PART IV.

NURSING PEER REVIEW

SUBPART A.
NURSING PEER REVIEW LAW
CHAPTER 303, OCCUPATIONS CODE

Sec. 303.001. DEFINITIONS. In this chapter:

(1) "Board" means the Texas Board of Nursing..

(2) "Nurse" means a registered nurse or a vocational nurse licensed under Chapter 301.

(3) "Nursing" has the meaning assigned by Section 301.002

(4) "Nursing peer review committee" means a committee established under the authority of the governing body of a national, state, or local nursing association, a school of nursing, the nursing staff of a hospital, health science center, nursing home, home health agency, temporary nursing service, or other health care facility, or state agency or political subdivision for the purpose of conducting peer review. The committee includes an employee or agent of the committee, including an assistant, an investigator, an intervenor, an attorney, and any other person who serves the committee in any capacity.

(4-a) "Patient safety committee" means a committee established by an association, school, agency, health care facility, or other organization to address issues relating to patient safety, including:

(A) the entity's medical staff composed of individuals licensed under Subtitle B; or

(B) a medical committee under Subchapter D, Chapter 161, Health and Safety Code.

(5) "Peer review" means the evaluation of nursing services, the qualifications of a nurse, the quality of patient care rendered by a nurse, the merits of a complaint concerning a nurse or nursing care, and a determination or recommendation regarding a complaint. The term includes:

(A) the evaluation of the accuracy of a nursing assessment and observation and the appropriateness and quality of the care rendered by a nurse;

Chapter 303 governs nursing peer review and will be referred to as the "Nursing Peer Review Law" or "NPR Law." It addresses two types of nursing peer review: 1) incident-based nursing peer review, and 2) safe harbor nursing peer review. Incident-based nursing peer review evaluates an incident or a nurse's practice to ascertain the nurse's accountability. Safe harbor nursing peer review is peer review requested by a nurse under NPR Law Sec. 303.005 to determine if, as a nurse, she or he has been requested to engage in conduct that would violate her or his duty to a patient. The BON has adopted rules relating to both incident-based nursing peer review (Rule 217.19) and safe harbor nursing peer review (Rule 217.20).

Since 2007, greater emphasis has been placed on nursing peer review's role in identifying external factors and system inadequacies that may have contributed to a deficiency in care. In fact, the committee's sole function when an employer has made a mandatory report of a nurse to the BON is to identify if external factors contributed to the deficiency in care.

Nursing peer review was first enacted in 1987 together with mandatory reporting as part of legislation popularly referred to as the Professional Nursing Quality Assurance Act. Significant changes have occurred since then.

- *1993: minimum criteria which nursing peer review committees must meet were established; how nursing peer review would apply to the practice of nurses not employed by the facility, e.g., temporary agency nurses, was clarified; and the NPA's mandatory reporting requirements were extended to nursing peer review committee.*
- *1995: incident-based nursing peer review extended to LVNs.*
- *1997: safe harbor nursing peer review was established for RNs (not LVNs). The Hospital Licensing Law was amended to require the Department of State Health Services adopt rules for hospitals to address "compliance with nursing peer review... and the rules of the BON relating to nursing peer review." Health & Safety Code, §241.026.*
- *2003: safe harbor nursing peer review was extended to LVNs.*
- *2007: significant amendments were made to nursing peer review. Greater emphasis was placed on the committee's identification of external factors and system inadequacies that may have contributed to the deficiency in care. The committee will be required to engage in greater sharing of information with other committees within the facility responsible for patient safety and quality of patient care issues.*

A "nursing peer review committee" can operate under the authority of a variety of entities. Almost all operate under the authority of the employing facility. Entities that employ, hire or contract for the services of 10 or more nurses are required to have nursing peer review for certain purposes. See the annotation to NPR Law Sec. 303.0015 for a list of these purposes.

Employees and agents are considered part of the nursing peer review committee. This is important to ensure that the confidentiality and immunity from liability provisions relating to nursing peer review also apply to them.

"Patient safety committee" is defined very broadly to include any committee addressing patient safety issues. Nursing peer review and patient safety committees are mandated to share information. See NPR Law Secs. 303.0075 and 303.011(b).

"Peer review" is broadly defined to include a variety of activities.

(B) a report made to a nursing peer review committee concerning an activity under the committee's review authority;

(C) a report made by a nursing peer review committee to another committee or to the board as permitted or required by law;

(D) implementation of a duty of a nursing peer review committee by a member, an agent, or an employee of the committee; and

(E) the provision of information, advice, and assistance to nurses and other persons relating to:

(i) the rights and obligations of and protections for nurses who raise care concerns or report under Chapter 301 or other state or federal law;

(ii) the rights and obligations of and protections for nurses who request nursing peer review under this chapter;

(iii) nursing practice and patient care concerns; and

(iv) the resolution of workplace and practice questions relating to nursing and patient care.

Sec. 303.0015. REQUIRED ESTABLISHMENT OF NURSING PEER REVIEW COMMITTEE. (a) A person shall establish a nursing peer review committee to conduct nursing peer review under this chapter and Chapter 301:

(1) for vocational nurses, if the person regularly employs, hires, or contracts for the services of 10 or more nurses; and

(2) for professional nurses, if the person regularly employs, hires, or contracts for the services of 10 or more nurses, at least five of whom are registered nurses.

(b) A person required to establish a nursing peer review committee under this section may contract with another entity to conduct the peer review for the person.

Sec. 303.002. GENERAL PROVISIONS REGARDING PEER REVIEW.

(a) *[repealed]*

(b) The board shall enter into a memorandum of understanding with each state agency that licenses, registers, or certifies a facility required by law to have a nursing peer review committee. The memorandum of understanding must:

(1) state the actions the board and agency are to take to encourage compliance with the requirement to have a nursing peer review committee; and

(2) be adopted as a rule of the board and the agency.

(c) A court may not enjoin the activities of a nursing peer review committee under this chapter.

(d) This chapter may not be nullified by a contract.

Paragraph (E) was added in 2011 to ensure immunity from liability and confidentiality protections provided to nursing peer review committees extended to informing and assisting nurses with respect to their patient advocacy rights and obligations. The individuals providing the assistance must be associated with the nursing peer review committee since the protections apply only to the committee and its agents. See Secs. 303,010 (immunity) and 303.006 (confidentiality).

Sec. 303.0015 sets out when an organization must establish a nursing peer review committee. The committee is required to perform certain functions by the following sections of the NPA (Chapter 303) and the Nursing Peer Review Law (Chapter 303).

- *NPA Sec. 301.352 - Review of nurse refusing to engage in a violation of NPA, BON rules or conduct reportable to BON*
- *NPA Secs. 301.402, .407 - Alternate reporting option for individual nurses and others*
- *NPA Sec. 301.405 - Review of incident when nurse reported by employer to identify possible external factors that contributed to nurse's conduct*
- *NPR Law Sec. 303.005 - Safe harbor nursing peer review*

Any employer, facility or other entity that employs or utilizes 10 or more nurses (LVNs and/or RNs) must establish a nursing peer review committee. An exception is provided when four or fewer of the 10 nurses are RNs in which case peer review for RNs is not required. Because of composition and voting requirements imposed by Sec. 303.003 below, it is not practical to conduct nursing peer review of RNs when there are four or fewer. The following scenarios illustrate when nursing peer review is required.

2 LVNs and 7 RNs	*PR not required since not 10 nurses*
8 LVNs and 2 RNs	*PR required for LVNs only since 10 nurses but not 5 RNs*
5 LVNs and 5 RNs	*PR required for both since 10 nurses and 5 are RNs*

There is nothing that prevents an entity from voluntarily providing nursing peer review even when not required. If it does, it will need to comply with this NPR Law and BON Rules 217.19-.20 governing nursing peer review.

An entity may contract with another entity to conduct nursing peer review. See Sec. 303.004 relating to peer review conducted by two entities.

State agencies that license facilities are required to enter into a memorandum of understanding with the BON on how they will encourage facilities they license to comply with nursing peer review requirements. This would be entities employing, hiring or contracting for the services of 10 or more nurses.

Nurses may not be required to contract away their rights relating to peer review under the Nursing PeerRreview Law(Chapter 303); for example, agree in an employment contract to give

(e) The committee shall give the nurse being reviewed at least minimum due process, including notice and opportunity for a hearing.

Sec. 303.003. COMMITTEE MEMBERSHIP. (a) A nursing peer review committee must have nurses as three-fourths of its members.

(b) A nursing peer review committee that conducts a peer review that involves the practice of vocational nursing, to the extent feasible, must include vocational nurses as members and may have only registered nurses and vocational nurses as voting members.

(c) A nursing peer review committee that conducts a peer review that involves the practice of professional nursing must have registered nurses as two-thirds of its members and may have only registered nurses as voting members.

(d) The committee shall include to the extent feasible at least one nurse who has a working familiarity with the area of nursing practice in which the nurse being reviewed practices.

Sec. 303.004. PEER REVIEW BY TWO ENTITIES. (a) A nurse who, as a temporary agency nurse, faculty member, or similar staff member, practices nursing for an educational institution, health care facility, agency, or entity, or a person other than the person who employs or directly compensates the nurse is subject to peer review by both the employer and the other person.

(b) For the purposes of exchanging information, the peer review committee reviewing the nurse's conduct is considered to be established under the authority of both entities.

(c) The two entities may contract as to which entity will conduct peer review of the nurse.

Sec. 303.005. REQUEST FOR PEER REVIEW COMMITTEE DETERMINATION.

up the right to due process.

This standard is designed to ensure that the nurse is given due process including proper notice of what is the wrongful conduct that she or he is alleged to have engaged in and is given a meaningful opportunity to respond to those charges. BON Rule 217.19(a) sets out due process requirements for nursing peer review and includes the right of the nurse to be present at the hearing and to question witnesses and have an attorney at the hearing.

Subsections (a)-(c) set out the composition of the committee based on whether it reviews RNs or LVNs. The committee can include non-nurses as non-voting members.

The qualifier "to the extent feasible" was added to address situations in which the number of LVNs in a facility may be too few to require LVN members on nursing peer review.

Only RNs can vote when RN practice is reviewed.

This was made a non-mandatory standard because of the difficulty that facilities utilizing only a few nurses may have in complying. The phrase "working familiarity with the area of nursing practice" is not further defined, and the BON has not adopted rules defining it.

This section addresses questions about how nursing peer review works when nurses practice in facilities other than the ones employing them. Examples of this are temporary agency nurses and nursing school faculty. This section permits either or both to conduct nursing peer review and to share information.

As a practical matter, the two entities should contract as to which will conduct peer review of the nurse.

NPR Law Sec. 303.005 is popularly referred to as "Safe Harbor Nursing Peer Review." It was enacted in 1997 to expand the protections of NPA Sec. 301.352. Both provisions are designed to provide protection to the nurse who refuses to engage in conduct the nurse believes would be reportable to the BON as a violation of the NPA or BON rules. Nurses can be placed in situations in which they feel they are being forced to choose between a) refusing to carry out an employer's directive, or b) engaging in conduct they believe violates their duty to the patient. Both provisions are intended to address this situation. This right to request nursing peer review was added because the concern had been identified that nurses asked to engage in conduct they believed violated a nurse's duty to a patient were having to choose between a) refusing to engage in the conduct and risking potential disciplinary action by their organization, or b) engaging in the conduct under protest and risking action by the BON – particularly if there were a bad patient outcome. While Sec. 301.352 provides the RN and LVN protection against retaliation, the only way for a nurse to claim those protections was after the retaliation occurred.

Safe Harbor Nursing Peer Review establishes a process by which an RN or LVN, who believes in good faith that she or he is being asked to engage in conduct that violates a nurse's duty to a patient, can 1) request a determination by nursing peer review as to what is the nurse's duty, and 2) engage in the conduct pending nursing peer review's determination without the risk of being disciplined by the BON. "Duty to a patient" is defined in subsection (a).

Neither the organization nor the nurse is protected from accountability to a patient for a bad patient outcome if the nurse engages in the behavior pending nursing peer review's determination.

The BON has adopted Rule 217.20 governing safe harbor nursing peer review. This rule

(a) In this section, "duty to a patient" means conduct required by standards of practice or professional conduct adopted by the board for nurses. The term includes administrative decisions directly affecting a nurse's ability to comply with that duty.

(a-1) For purposes of this section, a nurse or nurse administrator acts in good faith in connection with a request made or an action taken by the nurse or nurse administrator if there is a reasonable factual or legal basis for the request or action.

(b) If a person who is required to establish a nursing peer review committee under Section 303.0015 requests a nurse to engage in conduct that the nurse believes violates a nurse's duty to a patient, the nurse may request, on a form developed or approved by the board, a determination by a nursing peer review committee under this chapter of whether the conduct violates a nurse's duty to a patient.

(c) A nurse who in good faith requests a peer review determination under Subsection (b):

(1) may not be disciplined or discriminated against for making the request;

addresses the nursing peer review process, establishes time lines and gives the nurse certain rights of participation. See Part VI (Patient Advocacy) of this Guide.

For both RNs and LVNs, "duty to patient" is defined by the BON's rules on standards of practice (Rule 217.11) and unprofessional conduct (Rule 217.12). RNs and LVNs should be familiar with these rules.

The reference to administrative decision means that RNs and LVNs who make administrative decisions (e.g., making assignments) that could affect a nurse's duty to patients also have the protections of this section. They can request a nursing peer review determination as to whether requiring a nurse to comply with that administrative decision would make it likely the nurse would be engaging in conduct violating the nurse's duty to patients.

Subsection (a-1) defines what constitutes "good faith" for the purposes of this Section 303.005. The definition parallels language in Department of State Health Services Rule 133.43(b) relating to reporting violation of the department's nurse staffing rules and also the definition of "good faith" for nurse reporting under the NPA. See NPA Sec. 301.4011. A nurse must act in "good faith" to get the protections of safe harbor nursing peer review. See Subsec.(c).

NPR Law Sec. 303.0015 requires anyone that employs or utilizes 10 or more nurses (LVNs and/or RNs) to establish a nursing peer review committee. An exception is provided when four or fewer of the 10 nurses are RNs in which case peer review for RNs is not required.

Under safe harbor, the nursing peer review committee is determining only whether engaging in the requested conduct would violate the nurse's duty to the patient. It is not conducting a review to assign accountability either to the nurse requested to engage in the conduct or the nurse making the request.

BON Rule 217.20 (c)(3) requires the request for safe harbor be a written request. The nurse can use either the Safe Harbor form provided on the Board's website or submit any written request that includes, at a minimum, the following information:

1. *the conduct assigned or requested, including the name and title of the person making the assignment or request;*
2. *a description of the practice setting (e.g., the nurse's responsibilities, resources available, extenuating or contributing circumstances impacting the situation);*
3. *a detailed description of how the conduct would have violated the nurse's duty to a patient or any other provision of the Nursing Practice Act and Board Rules. If possible, reference the specific standard (Rule §217.11) or other section of the Nursing Practice Act and/or Board rules the nurse believes would have been violated;*
4. *any other copies of pertinent documentation available at the time. Additional documents may be submitted to the committee when available at a later time; and*
5. *the nurse's name, title, and relationship to the supervisor making the assignment or request.*

If the nurse does not submit the initial request for Safe Harbor using the form on the BON's website, the facility and nurse shall adhere to the Safe Harbor process as outlined on the BON form. An official copy can be downloaded from its website at www.bon.texas.gov. The BON form incorporates a process that should maximize resolving the disagreement between the RN or LVN making the request and the organization as to what is the nurse's duty in the particular situation. Rule 217.20 and the BON form also establish timetables and processes governing the request. Nurses should be familiar with Rule 217.20 and the BON form so that they can properly request safe harbor nursing peer review if ever needed.

RNs and LVNs who request nursing peer review in good faith are provided several important protections. Note that these protections may be available only after the request is made.

- *The organization cannot discipline a nurse for making a good faith request for nursing peer review.*

(2) may engage in the requested conduct pending the peer review;

(3) is not subject to the reporting requirement under Subchapter I, Chapter 301; and

(4) may not be disciplined by the board for engaging in that conduct while the peer review is pending.

(d) If a nurse requests a peer review determination under Subsection (b) and refuses to engage in the requested conduct pending the peer review, the determination of the peer review committee shall be considered in any decision by the nurse's employer to discipline the nurse for the refusal to engage in the requested conduct, but the determination is not binding if a nurse administrator believes in good faith that the peer review committee has incorrectly determined a nurse's duty. This subsection does not affect the protections provided by Subsection (c)(1) or Section 301.352.

(e) If the conduct for which the peer review is requested under Subsection (b) involves the medical reasonableness of a physician's order, the medical staff or medical director shall be requested to make a determination as to the medical reasonableness of the physician's order, and that determination is determinative of that issue.

(f) A nurse's rights under this section may not be nullified by a contract.

(g) An appropriate licensing agency may take action against a person who violates this section.

(h) A person may not suspend or terminate the employment of, or otherwise discipline or discriminate against, a nurse who in good faith requests a peer review determination under this section or a person who advises a nurse of the nurse's right to request a determination or of the procedures for requesting a determination. A violation of this subsection is subject to Section 301.413.

(i) A person who is required to provide, on request, a nursing peer review committee

- *Pending the nursing peer review committee's determination, the nurse may engage in the conduct.*
- *The nurse is not reportable to the BON for engaging in the conduct and is not subject to discipline by the BON. Once a nursing peer review committee determines the conduct violates the nurse's duty to the patient, the nurse is not protected if she or he continues to engage in the conduct after that determination. See Rule 217.20.*

The nurse must make the request in good faith which is defined by Subsec. (a-1) as having "a reasonable factual or legal basis for the request." Requesting safe harbor nursing peer review may not be used to justify conduct that no reasonable RN or LVN would say is consistent with a nurse's duty to a patient.

This Subsec.. (d) describes the one situation in which a nurse administrator could take action against a nurse even though the nurse requested safe harbor nursing peer review. The situation is limited to when the nurse requests safe harbor nursing peer review but refuses to engage in the conduct pending the nursing peer review committee's determination. In this situation, the nurse can be disciplined for refusing to engage in the conduct but not for making the request. Safe harbor nursing peer review is designed for situations in which reasonable nurses could disagree about what is a nurse's duty to a patient. In such a case, it would normally be reasonable for the nurse to engage in the conduct pending peer review. If the conduct is such a clear violation of a nurse's duty (e.g., request to falsify a patient record) that no reasonable nurse would believe otherwise, the nurse would obviously not engage in the conduct. If the nurse administrator retaliated against the nurse in that situation, the nurse would have protection under Sec. NPA 301.352 for refusing to engage in conduct that violates the NPA or BON rules. The nursing peer review committee also would certainly find that the requested conduct violated the nurse's duty to the patient which would put the nurse administrator at risk if she/he chose to discipline the nurse for refusing to engage in the conduct. The nurse administrator must act in "good faith," meaning there must be a factual or legal basis for the determination. The nurse administrator who requests that a nurse engage in conduct that a nursing peer review committee has determined violates a nurse's duty to a patient would be putting her/his license at some risk unless she/he absolutely is convinced the nursing peer review committee is wrong.

If medical reasonableness is at issue, that issue is to be decided by the medical staff or director. This provision was added at the request of organized medicine because it believed the medical reasonableness of a physician's order should not be determined by a nursing peer review committee.

An RN or LVN cannot be required to contract away her or his rights under this section; for example, sign an employment agreement agreeing not to request nursing peer review.

Violation of this section is a basis for a licensing agency to take action against that organization or person. For example, if a nurse administrator violates this subsection, she/he would be subject to disciplinary action by the BON. If a hospital violates this subsection, it would be subject to action by the Department of State Health Services. NPA Sec. 301.413(b) authorizes a fine up to $25,000.

Retaliation for making a good faith request for safe harbor nursing peer review is prohibited. The nurse's remedies for retaliation are set out in NPA Sec. 301.413. They include filing a lawsuit for damages (minimum of $5,000) and attorney's fees. A complaint can also be filed with the agency that licenses the individual or facility which can impose a fine up to $25,000. The protections are available not only to the nurse requesting safe harbor, but also to any person advising the nurse of her or his rights concerning making the request.

This *Subsec. (i) is designed to ensure nurses are adequately aware of their rights and* determination under Subsection (b) shall adopt and implement a policy to inform nurses of the right to request a nursing peer review committee determination and the procedure for making a request.

Sec. 303.006. CONFIDENTIALITY OF PEER REVIEW PROCEEDINGS. (a) Except as otherwise provided by this chapter, a nursing peer review committee proceeding is confidential and any communication made to a nursing peer review committee is privileged.

(b) A member, agent, or employee of a nursing peer review committee or a participant in a proceeding before the committee may not disclose or be required to disclose a communication made to the committee or a record or proceeding of the committee.

(c) A person who attends a nursing peer review committee proceeding may not disclose or be required to disclose:

(1) information acquired in connection with the proceeding; or

(2) an opinion, recommendation, or evaluation of the committee or a committee member.

(d) A nursing peer review committee member and a person who provides information to the committee may not be questioned about:

(1) the person's testimony before the committee; or

(2) an opinion formed as a result of the committee proceedings.

(e) Except as permitted by this chapter, information that is confidential under this section:

(1) is not subject to subpoena or discovery in any civil matter;

(2) is not admissible as evidence in a judicial or administrative proceeding; and

(3) may not be introduced into evidence in a nursing liability suit arising out of the provision of or a failure to provide nursing services.

(f) If a peer review committee determines that a nurse has not engaged in conduct required to be reported to the nurse's licensing board, a member of the peer review committee whose knowledge of the nurse's conduct was acquired only through the peer review may not report that nurse to the licensing board for that conduct. A committee member is not prohibited from reporting:

(1) the nurse, if the member has knowledge of the nurse's conduct independently of peer review; or

(2) the peer review committee to the licensing board, if the member believes the committee made its determination in bad faith.

Sec. 303.007. DISCLOSURE OF INFORMATION. (a) A nursing peer review committee on request shall disclose written or oral communications made to the committee and the records and proceedings of the committee to:

(1) a licensing authority of any state; or

(2) a law enforcement agency investigating a criminal matter.

(b) A nursing peer review committee may disclose written or oral communications made to the committee and the records and proceedings of the committee to:

(1) a licensing agency of any state;

(2) a law enforcement agency investigating a criminal matter;

(3) the association, school, agency, facility, or other organization under whose authority the committee is established;

(4) another nursing peer review committee;

(5) a peer assistance program approved by the board under Chapter 467, Health and Safety Code;

protections under safe harbor nursing peer review. It imposes a duty on the facility to provide this information.

The nursing peer review proceedings are confidential. It is important that the nursing peer review committee maintain this confidentiality. A nursing peer review committee violating confidentiality risks being found to be operating in bad faith and could risk losing its immunity from liability protections. Care should be taken in how nursing peer review records are maintained to avoid inadvertent disclosure or waiver of confidentiality.

Confidentiality applies to anyone attending the proceedings.

The information is not subject to court subpoena and may not be used in a professional liability lawsuit.

This Subsec. (f) is designed to protect the integrity of the nursing peer review process by preventing an individual member from reporting a nurse to the board because the member disagrees with the committee's decision. This provision does not prevent committee members from reporting the nurse if they have independent knowledge of the nurse's conduct. It also does not prevent individual members from reporting the committee itself or another member if they believe the committee or member acted in bad faith.

It is the committee that is authorized to disclose and not individual members. This subsection requires the nursing peer review committee to respond to requests for information by a licensing and law enforcement authority. NPA Sec. 301.403 mandates reporting by nursing peer review committees to the BON. No request is required.

This Subsec. (b) permits, but does not require, a nursing peer review committee to disclose information to certain entities, i.e., the committee decides whether to disclose or not.

The nursing peer review committee can disclose to the organization under which it functions, e.g., the hospital. However, disclosure should be limited to persons with a need to know.

A nursing peer review committee can disclose information to another nursing peer review committee. However, this does not authorize the nursing peer review committee receiving the information to redisclose that information to its sponsoring organization. For example, the nursing peer review committee receiving the information could not share it with the personnel department.

(6) an appropriate state or federal agency or accrediting organization that accredits a health care facility or school of nursing or surveys a facility for quality of care; or

(7) a person engaged in bona fide research, if all information that identifies a specific individual is deleted.

(c) If a committee discloses information under this section, the committee does not by that action waive the privilege of nondisclosure of committee information and proceedings.

(d) A peer review committee that discloses information under this section and each person who receives the information shall protect, to the extent possible, the identity of each patient.

Sec. 303.0075. SHARING OF INFORMATION. (a) A nursing peer review committee and a patient safety committee established by the same entity may share information.

(b) A record or determination of a patient safety committee, or a communication made to a patient safety committee, is not subject to subpoena or discovery and is not admissible in any civil or administrative proceeding, regardless of whether the information has been provided to a nursing peer review committee. The privileges under this subsection may be waived only through a written waiver signed by the chair, vice chair, or secretary of the patient safety committee. This subsection does not affect the application of Section 303.007 to a nursing peer review committee.

(c) A committee that receives information from another committee shall forward any request to disclose the information to the committee that provided the information.

Sec. 303.008. REBUTTAL STATEMENT. (a) If a nursing peer review committee makes an adverse finding against a nurse, the committee shall provide the nurse with a detailed description of the basis of its finding.

(b) The peer review committee shall give the nurse the opportunity to offer rebuttal information and to submit a rebuttal statement of reasonable length. Any rebuttal statement must be included with any information disclosed by the committee under Section 303.007.

Sec. 303.009. RETALIATORY ACTIONS. (a) A nursing peer review committee, a person participating in peer review, or an organization named as a defendant in a civil action or subjected to other retaliatory action as a result of participation in peer review may file a counterclaim in a pending action or prove a cause of action in a subsequent suit to recover defense costs, including court costs, reasonable attorney's fees, and actual and punitive damages if the suit or retaliatory action is determined to be frivolous, unreasonable, without foundation, or taken in bad faith.

(b) A nursing peer review committee member or a person participating in peer review under this chapter named as a defendant in a civil action or subjected to other retaliatory action as a result of participation in peer review may use information that is otherwise confidential under this chapter to defend the civil action or a civil action that alleges retaliation for the person's participation in peer review.

(c) A person who discloses information under Subsection (b) does not by that action waive the privilege of nondisclosure of all other information privileged under this chapter.

Sec. 303.010. CIVIL LIABILITY. (a) A cause of action does not accrue for an act, statement, determination, or recommendation made, or act reported, without malice, in the course of peer review against:

(1) a member, agent, or employee of a nursing peer review committee; or

(2) a school of nursing, hospital, nursing home, home health agency, health science center, or other health care facility, the nursing staff of such a facility, or a nursing association or other organization.

(b) A person who, without malice, provides records, information, or assistance to a nursing peer review committee:

(1) is not liable in a civil action based on the person's participation or assistance in peer review; and

(2) may not be subjected to retaliatory action as a result of that act.

Patient identities must be protected whenever information is disclosed.

NPR Law Sec. 303.0075 is designed to encourage and facilitate the nursing peer review committee's sharing information with other committees within the facility responsible for patient safety and quality of patient care. Concern about loss of confidentiality frequently inhibits committees from sharing information needed to identify and correct system inadequacies. This section makes clear that the confidentiality attached to the information does not change because it is shared.

If a nursing peer review committee is requested to disclose information received from another committee, it simply refers that request to the other committee.

Whenever the committee makes an adverse finding against the nurse, it has to provide the nurse a detailed description of its finding.

The nursing peer review committee must provide the nurse with an opportunity to file a rebuttal statement to the adverse finding. Once the nurse has filed a rebuttal statement, it must accompany all disclosures of the committee and not just required disclosures.

Committees, members, participants and sponsoring organizations who are sued or otherwise retaliated against for participating in nursing peer review may recover defense costs including attorney fees if the suit is determined to be frivolous, unreasonable, without foundation or filed in bad faith.

Nursing peer review committees, members, and participants may disclose information if sued or otherwise retaliated against as a result of participating in nursing peer review. Such information may be necessary for them to put on an adequate defense.

As long as they act without malice, the nursing peer review committee, members, participants and sponsoring organization are protected from being sued or otherwise retaliated against as a result of participating in nursing peer review.

Persons sharing information with the nursing peer review committee are provided the same protections.

Sec. 303.011. EVALUATION BY COMMITTEE. (a) In evaluating a nurse's conduct, the nursing peer review committee shall review the evidence to determine the extent to which a deficiency in care by the nurse was the result of deficiencies in the nurse's judgment, knowledge, training, or skill rather than other factors beyond the nurse's control. A determination that a deficiency in care is attributable to a nurse must be based on the extent to which the nurse's conduct was the result of a deficiency in the nurse's judgment, knowledge, training, or skill.

(b) The nursing peer review committee shall report a deficiency in care that the committee determines was the result of a factor beyond the nurse's control to a patient safety committee for evaluation. The patient safety committee shall evaluate the influence of the factors on the conduct of the nurse being evaluated and on the practice of other nurses within the entity that established the committee. The committee shall report its findings to the nursing peer review committee.

Sec. 303.012. ERROR CLASSIFICATION SYSTEM. (a) The board may develop a standardized error classification system for use by a nursing peer review committee in evaluating the conduct of a nurse. The board shall make the system available to the committee at no cost.

(b) Information collected as part of an error classification system is a record of the nursing peer review committee and is confidential under Section 303.006.

(c) A nursing peer review committee may report the information collected using the error classification system to the board. The committee may not report to the board under this section information that includes the identity of an individual nurse or patient.

(d) Information the board receives under this section that contains information identifying a specific patient, nurse, or health care facility, the committee, or the sponsoring organization of the committee is confidential and is not subject to disclosure under Chapter 552, Government Code. The board must remove the identifying information from the information before making the remaining information available to the public.

(e) This section does not affect the obligation or authority of a nursing peer review committee to disclose information under Section 303.007.

SUBPART B
SELECTED NPA PROVISIONS RELATING TO NURSING PEER REVIEW

Sec. 301.352. PROTECTION FOR REFUSAL TO ENGAGE IN CERTAIN CONDUCT.

(a) A person may not suspend, terminate, or otherwise discipline, discriminate against, or retaliate against:

(1) a nurse who refuses to engage in an act or omission as provided by Subsection (a-1); or

(2) a person who advises a nurse of the nurse's rights under this section.

(a-1) A nurse may refuse to engage in an act or omission relating to patient care that would constitute grounds for reporting the nurse to the board under Subchapter I, that constitutes a minor incident, or that violates this chapter or a board rule if the nurse notifies the person at the time of the refusal that the reason for refusing is that the act or omission:

Nursing peer review committees must consider external factors in evaluating a nurse's conduct. Under NPA Sec. 301.403, the results of the committee's determination must be included with any required report to the BON. See NPA Sec. 401.403 for what information must be included when a committee reports a nurse to the BON.

This *Subsec. (b) requires that when a nursing peer review committee identifies a deficiency in care was the result of factors beyond the nurse's control, it shall report that information to a patient safety committee for additional investigation and review. Sec. 303.001 defines "patient safety committee" very broadly.*

This section was added in 2011 to facilitate nursing peer review committees' implementing error classification systems and sharing the data collected with the BON serving as the central data depository. The purpose of an error classification system is to collect data about errors in a systematic way so that trends and patterns can be identified and addressed. However, no single nursing peer review committee is likely to have enough data to identify trends and patterns accurately. Since there is a question of whether sharing the information with the board as a state agency would make the data public information,, this section explicitly provides that any identifying information is confidential and not subject to disclosure. The BON has implemented this section through its TERCAP© Pilot (Taxonomy of Error, Root Cause Analysis and Practice Responsibility). Information about the pilot can be found on the BON website under Practice.

The NPA contains several provisions specifically related to nursing peer review.

This provision is designed to provide protection to the RN or LVN who refuses to engage in conduct the nurse believes would be reportable to the BON as a violation of the NPA or BON rules. Nursing peer review's role in this process is set out in Subsec. (b). Sec. 303.005 (Safe Harbor) of the Nursing Peer Review Law is a companion provision that was enacted to give nurses protections before they are retaliated against.

> ***ANNOTATOR'S NOTE:*** *Only the annotations for provisions directly related to nursing peer review are set out. NPA Sec. 301.352, fully annotated, can be found in Part VI (Patient Advocacy) or Part I (NPA) of this Guide.*

(1) constitutes grounds for reporting the nurse to the board; or

(2) is a violation of this chapter or a rule of the board.

(b) An act by a person under Subsection (a) does not constitute a violation of this section if a nursing peer review committee under Chapter 303 determines:

(1) that the act or omission the nurse refused to engage in was not:

(A) conduct reportable to the board under Section 301.403;

(B) a minor incident; or

(C) a violation of this chapter or a board rule; or

(2) that:

(A) the act or omission in which the nurse refused to engage was conduct reportable to the board, a minor incident, or a violation of this chapter or a board rule; and

(B) the person:

(i) rescinds any disciplinary or discriminatory action taken against the nurse;

(ii) compensates the nurse for lost wages;

(iii) restores to the nurse any lost benefits.

(c) A nurse's rights under this section may not be nullified by a contract.

(d) An appropriate licensing agency may take action against a person who violates this section.

(e) *[Repealed]*

(f) A violation of this section is subject to Section 301.413.

Sec. 301.403. DUTY OF PEER REVIEW COMMITTEE TO REPORT. (a) Except as provided by Subsection (b), a nursing peer review committee operating under Chapter 303 that determines that a nurse has engaged in conduct subject to reporting shall file with the board a written, signed report that includes:

(1) the identity of the nurse;

(2) a description of any corrective action taken against the nurse;

(3) a recommendation whether the board should take formal disciplinary action against the nurse and the basis for the recommendation;

(4) a description of the conduct subject to reporting;

(5) the extent to which any deficiency in care provided by the reported nurse was the result of a factor beyond the nurse's control; and

(6) any additional information the board requires.

(b) A report under Subsection (a) is not required if:

(1) the nursing peer review committee determines that the reported conduct was a minor incident that is not required to be reported under board rule; or

(2) the nurse has been reported to the board for the conduct under Section 301.405.

Sec. 301.405(c), (e). DUTY OF PERSON EMPLOYING NURSE TO REPORT.

(c) If a person who makes a report required under Subsection (b) is required under Section 303.0015 to establish a nursing peer review committee, the person shall submit a copy of the report to the nursing peer review committee. The nursing peer review committee shall review the conduct to determine if any deficiency in care by the reported nurse was the result of a factor beyond the nurse's control. A nursing peer review committee that determines that there is reason to believe that the nurse's deficiency in care was the result of a factor beyond the nurse's control shall report the conduct to the patient safety committee at the facility where the reported conduct occurred, or if the facility does not have a patient safety committee, to the chief nursing officer.

(e) The requirement under Subsection (c) that a nursing peer review committee review

The nursing peer review committee's role is addressed in this Subsec. (b) which identifies two situations in which the employer is deemed not to have illegally retaliated.

1. *If the incident is reviewed by a nursing peer review committee and the committee finds that, in its opinion, the nurse's engaging in the conduct she/he refused to do would not in fact have been a violation of the NPA or BON rules, i.e., the nurse was not being asked to engage in reportable conduct or a violation (even a minor violation) of the NPA or BON rules.*
2. *If the peer review committee finds that to have engaged in the conduct would have been a violation of the NPA but the employer makes the nurse whole -- that is, rescinds any disciplinary action taken, pays all back wages and restores any lost benefits.*

The same as with safe harbor peer review, the committee is determining the question of what is the nurse's duty and is not addressing any question of the nurse's accountability. Accordingly, peer review would be conducted under BON Rule 217.20 (safe Harbor Nursing Peer Review).

Nursing peer review committees must report a nurse determined to have engaged in conduct subject to reporting as defined by Sec. 301.401 except when:

- *the conduct constitutes a minor incident not required to be reported by BON rules [See Rule 217.16 (Reporting of Minor Incidents)]; or*
- *the nurse has already been reported to the BON by the facility or employer under Sec. 301.405.*

When reporting a nurse to the BON, the committee's report must include the information required by Subsections (a)(1)-(6). The determination of external factors described in Subsec. (a)(5) is required to be made by the nursing peer review committee under Section 303.011 of the Nursing Peer Review Law. Requiring the committee report to include the information listed in (2)-(6) is designed to assist the BON in deciding how to handle the report and what action to take against the RN or LVN as a result of the report.

An individual nurse's reporting an incident to peer review satisfies that nurse's duty to report to the BON under Sec. 301.402. See Sec. 301.402(e). Individual committee members are restricted in what they may report to the BON independently of the committee. See Sec. 303.006(f) of the Nursing Peer Review Law.

NPR Law Sec. 303.0015 requires persons that employ or utilize 10 or more nurses (LVNs and/or RNs) to establish a nursing peer review committee. An exception is provided when four or fewer of the 10 nurses are RNs in which case peer review for RNs is not required. The role of nursing peer review in mandatory employer reporting is not to review the incident to determine the nurse's accountability, but rather to review the incident to determine the role system deficiencies and external factors played. If external factors played a role, then other nurses may be placed in a similar situation in which the lack of adequate systems makes the error more likely to occur. The committee need not make a definitive determination of the role of external factors but rather the standard is if there "is reason to believe" the factors contributed to the error. The nursing peer review committee then refers the issue to another committee (or CNO) with more expertise in conducting error investigation, review and analysis. That committee (or CNO) is also more likely to be able to initiate the process for addressing external factors.

Review by the nursing peer review committee is advisory only and does not limit what the nurse and the incident does not subject a person's administrative decision to discipline a nurse to the peer review process.

Sec. 301.410. REPORT REGARDING IMPAIRMENT BY CHEMICAL DEPENDENCY, MENTAL ILLNESS, OR DIMINISHED MENTAL CAPACITY. (a) A person who is required to report a nurse under this subchapter because the nurse is impaired or suspected of being impaired by chemical dependency or mental illness may report to a peer assistance program approved by the board under Chapter 467, Health and Safety Code, instead of reporting to the board or requesting review by a nursing peer review committee.

(b) A person who is required to report a nurse under this subchapter because the nurse is impaired or suspected of being impaired by chemical dependency or diminished mental capacity must report to the board if the person believes that an impaired nurse committed a practice violation.

Sec. 301.413. RETALIATORY ACTION

> ***ANNOTATOR'S NOTE:*** *Sec. 301.413 is not being set out here but can be found in both Part I (NPA) and Part VI (Patient Advocacy) of this Guide.*

SUBPART C
BON RULES RELATING TO NURSING PEER REVIEW

Rule 217.19 INCIDENT-BASED NURSING PEER REVIEW
Rule 217.20 SAFE HARBOR NURSING PEER REVIEW
Rule 217.16 REPORTING OF MINOR INCIDENTS, SUBSECS. (g), (d), (e)

NURSING PEER REVIEW -- RULES 217.19 AND 217.20

ANNOTATOR'S NOTE: *Headings have been added to some subsections to facilitate reading.*

RULE 217.19 INCIDENT-BASED NURSING PEER REVIEW AND WHISTLEBLOWER PROTECTIONS.

(a) Definitions.
(b) Purpose.
(c) Applicability of Incident-Based Peer Review.
(d) Minimum Due Process.
(e) Use of Informal Work Group In Incident Based Peer Review.
(f) Exclusions to Minimum Due Process Requirements.
(g) Incident-Based Peer Review of a Nurse's Impaired Practice/Lack of Fitness.
(h) Confidentiality of Proceedings.
(i) Committee Responsibility to Evaluate and Report.
(j) Nurse's Duty to Report.
(k) State Agency Duty to Report.
(l) Integrity of Incident-Based Peer Review Process.
(m) Reporting Conduct of other Practitioners or Entities: Whistleblower Protections.

administrative/personnel action the employer may take against the nurse. The employer is not prohibited from taking administrative/personnel action prior to peer review.

If it is believed the reported nurse's conduct results from chemical dependency or mental illness and no practice violation is involved, the nurse may be reported to a board-approved peer assistance program instead of to the BON. The Texas Peer Assistance Program for Nurses is the only program approved by the BON. Its phone number is 1-800-288-5528. See Rule 217.13. If a practice violation is involved, Subsec. (b) requires reporting the nurse directly to the BON.

If a practice violation is involved, the nurse must be reported to the Board. The Board may refer the nurse to peer assistance. See the annotations to NPA Secs. 301.410, .4105, .4106 in Part I (NPA).

Sec. 301.413 sets out the remedies for violation from retaliation for requesting safe harbor nursing peer review under Sec. 303.005. They include filing a lawsuit for damages or a complaint with the appropriate licensing agency. See Part I (NPA) of this Guide for the text and annotations for the section.

BON Rule 217.19 governs incident-based nursing peer review and Rule 217.20 governs safe harbor nursing peer review. The BON website includes additional information about nursing peer review. www.bon.texas.gov. Select "Nursing Practice" and then "Peer Review."

When the BON published proposed revisions to this rule, the preamble stated:

> *In response to the first Institute of Medicine (IOM) report, "To Err is Human," the concept of having a peer review committee examine external factors contributing to a nursing error was incorporated into §217.19(a)(7) in 2001. As national patient safety efforts continue to focus on external system factors, SB 993 amended §301.305(c) to require that a peer review committee examine any required report of a nurse to the Board by a nurse's employer or practice setting when a nurse is terminated, suspended for seven or more days, or received other substantive disciplinary action. The intent is to prevent external factors that negatively impact patient safety from going unchecked and unchanged – the issues and surrounding circumstances do not go away because the nurse was terminated, suspended, made a "do not return," etc. New language in §301.305(c) further mandates that the peer review committee report to a facility's patient safety committee if it is determined that external factors did impact or contribute to the nurse's error.*
>
> * * * * *
>
> *The Board is aware that holding a peer review is a time-consuming process and may be a hardship on a facility or agency trying to staff direct patient care*

(a) Definitions.

(1) Assignment--Designated responsibility for the provision or supervision of nursing care for a defined period of time in a defined work setting. This includes but is not limited to the specified functions, duties, practitioner orders, supervisory directives, and amount of work designated as the individual nurse's responsibility. Changes in the nurse's licensure responsibilities may occur at any time during the work period.

(2) Bad Faith--Knowingly or recklessly taking action not supported by a reasonable factual or legal basis. The term includes misrepresenting the facts surrounding the events under review, acting out of malice or personal animosity towards the nurse, acting from a conflict of interest, or knowingly or recklessly denying a nurse due process.

(3) Chief Nursing Officer (CNO)--The registered nurse, by any title, who is administratively responsible for the nursing services at a facility, association, school, agency, or any other setting that utilizes the services of nurses.

(4) Conduct Subject to Reporting - defined by Texas Occupations Code §301.401 of the Nursing Practice Act as conduct by a nurse that:

(A) violates the Nursing Practice Act (NPA) or a Board rule and contributed to the death or serious injury of a patient;

(B) causes a person to suspect that the nurse's practice is impaired by chemical dependency or drug or alcohol abuse;

(C) constitutes abuse, exploitation, fraud, or a violation of professional boundaries; or

(D) indicates that the nurse lacks knowledge, skill, judgment, or conscientiousness to such an extent that the nurse's continued practice of nursing could reasonably be expected to pose a risk of harm to a patient or another person, regardless of whether the conduct consists of a single incident or a pattern of behavior.

(5) Duty to a patient--A nurse's duty is to always advocate for patient safety, including any nursing action necessary to comply with the standards of nursing practice (§217.11 of this title) and to avoid engaging in unprofessional conduct (§217.12 of this title). This includes administrative decisions directly affecting a nurse's ability to comply with that duty.

(6) Good Faith--Taking action supported by a reasonable factual or legal basis. Good faith precludes misrepresenting the facts surrounding the events under review, acting out of malice or personal animosity, acting from a conflict of interest, or knowingly or recklessly denying a nurse due process.

(7) Incident-Based Peer Review--Incident-based peer review focuses on determining if a nurse's actions, be it a single event or multiple events (such as in reviewing up to five (5) minor incidents by the same nurse within a year's period of time) should be reported to the Board, or if the nurse's conduct does not require reporting because the conduct constitutes a minor incident that can be remediated. The review includes whether external factors beyond the nurse's control may have contributed to any deficiency in care by the nurse, and to report such findings to a patient safety committee as applicable.

(8) Malice--Acting with a specific intent to do substantial injury or harm to another.

needs at the same time pulling nurses off to participate in peer review. It is hoped that, by permitting the use of a smaller workgroup of the peer review committee, the peer review process can be effective, easier than in the past, less intimidating, less time-consuming, and can promote safer patient care.

Texas Register (2/15/08)

Rule 217.20 also has a definition of "assignment" but the phrase "changes in the nurse's licensure liability" in the last sentence reads "changes in the nurse's assignment." The latter makes more sense and not using the same terminology here was probably an oversight.

Bad faith includes a mental element of "knowingly or recklessly" engaging in the conduct. See also the definitions of "good faith" and "malice." In 2011, use of the terms "without malice" and "bad faith" in the NPA were replaced with the term "good faith." "Good faith" is defined in NPA Sec. 301.4011 and does not include a lack of malice. This definition may need to be updated to reflect the Sec. 301.4011 definition.

Who is the CNO is not determined by what title is used. The CNO is responsible for assuring compliance with these rules. See Section (l)(2).

This definition is directly from NPA §301.401. See annotations to the Sec. 301.401 in Part I (NPA) of this Guide.

The BON's standards of practice (Rule 217.11) and unprofessional conduct (Rule 217.12) rules provide more detailed guidance on what a nurse's duty is.

In 2011, the terms "without malice" and "bad faith" were replaced in the NPA with the term "good faith." "Good faith" is defined in NPA Sec. 301.4011 and does not include a lack of malice. This definition may need to be updated to reflect the Sec. 301.4011 definition.

Malice involves a more specific intent to do harm than does bad faith. In 2011, the terms "without malice" and "bad faith" were replaced in the NPA with the term "good faith." "Good faith" is defined in NPA Sec. 301.4011 and does not include a lack of malice. This definition may need to be updated to reflect the Sec. 301.4011 definition.

(9) Minor incident--Conduct by a nurse that does not indicate that the nurse's continued practice poses a risk of harm to a patient or another person as described in §217.16 of this title.

(10) Nurse Administrator--Chief Nursing Officer (CNO) or the CNO's designee.

(11) Nursing Peer Review Law (NPR Law)--Chapter 303 of the Texas Occupations Code (TOC). Nurses involved in nursing peer review must comply with the NPR Law.

(12) Nursing Practice Act (NPA)--Chapter 301 of the Texas Occupations Code (TOC). Nurses must comply with the NPA.

(13) Patient Safety Committee--Any committee established by an association, school, agency, health care facility, or other organization to address issues relating to patient safety including:

(A) the entity's medical staff composed of individuals licensed under Subtitle B (Medical Practice Act, Texas Occupations Code §151.001, et seq.);

(B) a medical committee under Subchapter D, Chapter 161 of the Health and Safety Code (§§161.031 - 161.033); or

(C) a multi-disciplinary committee, including nursing representation, or any committee established by the same entity to promote best practices and patient safety.

(14) Peer Review-Defined by TOC §303.001(5) (NPR Law) as the evaluation of nursing services, the qualifications of a nurse, the quality of patient care rendered by a nurse, the merits of a complaint concerning a nurse or nursing care, and a determination or recommendation regarding a complaint. The term also includes the provision of information, advice, and assistance to nurses and other persons relating to the rights and obligations of and protections for nurses who raise care concerns, report under Chapter 301, request peer review, and the resolution of workplace and practice questions relating to nursing and patient care. The peer review process is one of fact finding, analysis and study of events by nurses in a climate of collegial problem solving focused on obtaining all relevant information about an event. Peer review conducted by any entity must comply with NPR.Law and with applicable Board rules related to incident-based or safe harbor peer review..

(15) Safe Harbor--A process that protects a nurse from employer retaliation, suspension, termination, discipline, discrimination, and licensure sanction when a nurse makes a good faith request for peer review of an assignment or conduct the nurse is requested to perform and that the nurse believes could result in a violation of the NPA or Board rules. Safe Harbor must be invoked prior to engaging in the conduct or assignment for which peer review is requested, and may be invoked at anytime during the work period when the initial assignment changes.

(16) Texas Occupations Code (TOC)--One of the topical subdivisions or "codes" into which the Texas Statutes or laws are organized. The Texas Occupations Code contains the statutes governing occupations and professions including the health professions. Both the NPA and NPR Law are located within these statutes. The TOC can be changed only by the Texas Legislature.

(17) Whistleblower Protections--Protections available to a nurse that prohibit retaliatory action by an employer or other entity because the nurse:

(A) made a good faith request for Safe Harbor Nursing Peer Review under TOC §303.005(c) (NPR Law) and 22 TAC §217.20 of this title;

(B) refused to engage in an act or omission relating to patient care that would constitute a violation of the NPA or Board rules as permitted by TOC §301.352 (NPA) (Protection for Refusal to Engage in Certain Conduct). A nurse invoking Safe Harbor under § 217.20 of this title must comply with §217.20(g) of this title if the nurse refuses to engage in the conduct or assignment; or

(C) made a lawful report of unsafe practitioners, or unsafe patient care practices or conditions, in accordance with TOC §301.4025 (NPA) (report of unsafe practices of non-nurse entities) and subsection (j)(2) of this section.

(b) Purpose. The purpose of this rule is to:

(1) define minimum due process to which a nurse is entitled under incident-based peer review,

This definition of "minor incident" is taken from NPA §301.401. See th e annotations to Sec. 301.401 in Part I (NPA) of this Guide.

A "patient safety committee" is any committee within the facility that addresses patient care concerns. This definition tracks the definition in NPR Law §303.001. See the annotations to that section in Subpart A above.

Ideally, nursing would like to see nursing peer review function as a collegial problem-solving process. There is significant anecdotal evidence that this ideal is frequently not realized. The greater emphasis (beginning in 2008) on peer review's role in identifying external factors and system deficiencies may result in peer review coming closer to this ideal in the future. The focus of the BON's minor incident reporting on remediation may also promote a more collegial process.

Due process requirements are set out in Subsection (d).

(2) provide guidance to facilities, agencies, schools, or anyone who utilizes the services of nurses in the development and application of incident-based peer review plans,

(3) assure that nurses have knowledge of the plan, and

(4) provide guidance to the incident-based peer review committee in its fact finding process.

(c) Applicability of Incident-Based Peer Review. TOC §303.0015 (NPR Law) requires a person who regularly employs, hires or contracts for the services of ten (10) or more nurses (for peer review of an RN, at least 5 of the 10 must be RNs) to conduct nursing peer review for purposes of TOC §301.401(1) and §301.402(e) (NPA) (relating to alternate reporting by nurses to nursing peer review when a nurse engages in conduct subject to reporting), §301.403 (relating to nursing peer review committee reporting), §301.405(c) (relating to nursing peer review of external factors as part of employer reporting), and §301.407(b) (relating to alternate reporting by state agencies to peer review).

(d) Minimum Due Process.

(1) ***[Due Process Required]*** A licensed nurse subject to incident-based peer review is entitled to minimum due process under TOC §303.002(e) (NPR Law). Any person or entity that conducts incident-based peer review must comply with the due process requirements of this section even if the person or entity does not utilize the number of nurses described by subsection (c) of this section.

(2) ***[Required Policy]*** A facility conducting incident-based peer review shall have written policies and procedures that, at a minimum, address:

(A) the level of participation of nurse or nurse's representative at an incident-based peer review hearing beyond that required by paragraph (3)(F) of this subsection;

(B) confidentiality and safeguards to prevent impermissible disclosures including written agreement by all parties to abide by TOC §§303.006 and 303.007, 303.0075 (NPR Law) and subsection (h) of this section;

(C) handling of cases involving nurses who are impaired or suspected of being impaired by chemical dependency, drug or alcohol abuse, substance abuse/misuse, "intemperate use," mental illness, or diminished mental capacity in accordance with the TOC §301.410, and subsection (g) of this section;

(D) reporting of nurses to the Board by incident-based peer review committee in accordance with the TOC §301.403, and subsection (i) of this section; and

(E) effective date of changes to the policies which in no event shall apply to incident-based peer review proceedings initiated before the change was adopted unless agreed to

NPR Law §303.0015 requires facilities to establish a Nursing Peer Review Committee to conduct nursing peer review under either the NPA or the NPR Law:

- *for LVNs if utilize 10 or more nurses*
- *for RNs if utilize 10 or more nurses and 5 of those 10 are RNs*

Four NPA provisions require incident-based nursing peer review which could result in the nurse being reported to the BON and must be conducted in accordance with this Rule 217.19 :

- *NPA §301.402 (Alternate reporting to Nursing Peer Review Committee by individual nurse)*
- *NPA §301.403 (Nursing Peer Review Committee reporting to BON)*
- *§301.405 (Nursing peer review of external factors after employer/facility has reported nurse to BON)*
- *NPA §301.407 (Alternate reporting to Nursing Peer Review Committee by a state agency)*

Two sections of NPA and NPR Law also require nursing peer review but review conducted under these sections would be conducted in accordance with Rule 217.20 (relating to Safe Harbor Nursing Peer Review) since the committee is not determining a nurse's accountability.

- *NPR Law §303.005 (Safe Harbor Nursing Peer Review)*
- *NPR Law §301.352 (Nursing peer review of a nurse's claim that she/he was retaliated against because she/he refused to violate the NPA or a BON rule. This review is after the alleged retaliation has occurred and is not the same as Safe Harbor Nursing Peer Review.)*

Nursing peer review conducted as part of reporting of a minor incident under BON Rule 217.16 may be seen as another type of nursing peer review. That review could result in the nurse being reported to the BON. Consequently, except when Rule 217.16 specifically provides for another process to be followed, it would be conducted in accordance with this Rule 217.19.

NPR Law Sec. 303.002(d) requires the nurse be provided "minimum due process including notice and opportunity for hearing." Failure to provide could result in loss of immunity from liability protections provided by the NPR Law. If an entity not required to have nursing peer review voluntarily provides a type of nursing peer review governed by this rule, the entity must provide the due process required by this Subsec. (d). See Subdivision. (d)(3) for the details of the due process required.

These are the minimum policies and procedures that facilities must adopt. A facility can adopt policies and procedures that exceed these minimum requirements.

Subsection (3)(F) gives a nurse extensive rights of participation in proceedings but Subsec. (5)(B) gives the nurse's attorney or nurse peer only the right to confer with the nurse. Facility policies can extend greater rights of participation to the nurse's attorney or nurse peer.

If a practice violation is not involved, the NPA Sec. 301.410 permits a nurse to be reported to a BON-approved peer assistance program in lieu of being reported to the BON or being peer reviewed. See Subsec. (g) for how nursing peer review must proceed if the committee suspects the nurse's practice may be impaired.

in writing by the nurse being reviewed.

(3) ***[Due Process Requirements]*** In order to meet the minimum due process required by TOC ch. 303 (NPR Law), the nursing peer review committee must:

(A) comply with the membership and voting requirements as set forth in TOC §303.003 (NPR Law);

(B) exclude from the committee, including attendance at the peer review hearing, any person or persons with administrative authority for personnel decisions directly relating to the nurse. This requirement does not exclude a person who is administratively responsible over the nurse being reviewed from appearing before the committee to speak as a fact witness;

(C) provide written notice to the nurse in person or by certified mail at the last known address the nurse has on file with the facility that:

(i) the nurse's practice is being evaluated;

(ii) the incident-based peer review committee will meet on a specified date not sooner than 21 calendar days and not more than 45 calendar days from date of notice, unless:

(I) the incident-based peer review committee determines an extended time period (extending the 45 days by no more than an additional 45 days) is necessary in order to consult with a patient safety committee; or

(II) otherwise agreed upon by the nurse and incident-based peer review committee; and

(iii) includes the information required by subparagraph (D) of this paragraph.

(D) Include in the notice required by subparagraph (C) of this paragraph:

(i) a description of the event(s) to be evaluated in sufficient detail to inform the nurse of the incident, circumstances and conduct (error or omission), including date(s), time(s), location(s), and individual(s) involved. The patient/client shall be identified by initials or number to the extent possible to protect confidentiality but the nurse shall be provided the name of the patient/client;

(ii) the name, address, telephone number of contact person to receive the nurse's response; and

(iii) a copy of this rule (§217.19 of this title) and a copy of the facility's incident-based peer review plan, policies and procedures.

(E) provide the nurse the opportunity to review, in person or by attorney, the documents concerning the event under review, at least 15 calendar days prior to appearing before the committee;

(F) provide the nurse the opportunity to:

(i) submit a written statement regarding the event under review;

(ii) call witnesses, question witnesses, and be present when testimony or evidence is being presented;

(iii) be provided copies of the witness list and written testimony or evidence at least 48 hours in advance of proceeding;

(iv) make an opening statement to the committee;

(v) ask questions of the committee and respond to questions of the committee; and

(vi) make a closing statement to the committee after all evidence is presented;

(G) complete its review no more than fourteen (14) calendar days after the

Paragraph (3) sets out what due process must be provided to a nurse under Incident-based Nursing Peer Review. Because the committee is determining the nurse's accountability, the due process requirements are significant.

The nursing peer review committee is required to have a certain percentage of RNs and LVNs. If feasible, at least one nurse should be from the same area of practice as the nurse being reviewed. Only nurses can vote and only RNs when an RN is reviewed. See Annotations to NPR Law §303.003.

Having individuals on a committee who have direct administrative authority over, or make personnel decisions about, the nurse being reviewed undermines the integrity of the nursing peer review process.

Written notice to the nurse being reviewed is required.

These timelines are designed to provide for timely resolution and also to give the nurse time to prepare. Review of external factors can extend the total time peer review takes up to an additional 45 days.

The nurse needs to be given sufficient detail to know what is being alleged she or he did wrong in order to prepare an adequate response.

The nurse needs to have working knowledge with these documents since they provide important rights.

The nurse or the nurse's attorney has the right to review documents.

This Paragraph (3)(F) sets out important rights for the nurse. These rights apply only to the nurse and not to the attorney or nurse peer who may accompany the nurse to the hearing under paragraph (5)(B) below.

The nurse has the right to be present at the hearing and question witnesses. Under Paragraph (5)(B) below, the nurse has the right to have an attorney or nurse peer accompany her or him to the hearing. However, the attorney or nurse peer does not have a right to question witnesses unless either permitted by the facility's policies or under parity of participation described in Paragraph (5)(D).

incident-based peer review hearing, or in compliance with subparagraph (C)(ii) of this paragraph relating to consultation with a patient safety committee;

(H) provide written notice to the nurse in person or by certified mail at the last known address the nurse has on file with the facility of the findings of the committee within ten (10) calendar days of when the committee's review has been completed; and

(I) permit the nurse to file a written rebuttal statement within ten (10) calendar days of the notice of the committee's findings and make the statement a permanent part of the incident-based peer review record to be included whenever the committee's findings are disclosed;

(4) ***[Committee Decision Cannot Be Overruled]*** An incident-based peer review committee's determination to report a nurse to the Board cannot be overruled, changed, or dismissed.

(5) ***Nurse's Right To Representation.***

(A) A nurse shall have a right of representation as set out in this paragraph. These rights are minimum requirements and a facility may allow the nurse more representation. The incident-based peer review process is not a legal proceeding; therefore, rules governing legal proceedings and admissibility of evidence do not apply and the presence of attorneys is not required.

(B) The nurse has the right to be accompanied to the hearing by a nurse peer or an attorney. Representatives attending the incident-based peer review hearing must comply with the facility's incident-based peer review policies and procedures regarding participation beyond conferring with the nurse.

(C) If either the facility or nurse will have an attorney or representative present at the incident-based peer review hearing in any capacity, the facility or nurse must notify the other at least seven (7) calendar days before the hearing that they will have an attorney or representative attending the hearing and in what capacity.

(D) Notwithstanding any other provisions of these rules, if an attorney representing the facility or incident-based peer review committee is present at the incident-based peer review hearing in any capacity, including serving as a member of the incident-based peer review committee, the nurse is entitled to "parity of participation of counsel." "Parity of participation of counsel" means that the nurse's attorney is able to participate to the same extent and level as the facility's attorney, e.g., if the facility's attorney can question witnesses, the nurse's attorney must have the same right.

(6) ***[Nurse's Right Not To Participate]*** A nurse whose practice is being evaluated may properly choose not to participate in the proceeding after the nurse has been notified under paragraph (3)(C) of this subsection. If a nurse elects not to participate in incident-based peer review, the nurse waives any right to procedural due process under TOC §303.002 (NPR Law) and this subsection.

(e) Use of Informal Work Group In Incident Based Peer Review. A facility may choose to initiate an informal review process utilizing a workgroup of the nursing incident-based peer review committee provided there are written policies for the informal workgroup that require:

(1) ***[Nurse's Consent Required]*** the nurse be informed of how the informal work group

Subparagraph (C)(ii) above provides for up to an additional 45 days for the entire peer review process if an adequate review of external factors requires more time.

The nurse has a right to file a rebuttal statement and if she/he does, the statement must be included whenever the Nursing Peer Review Committee findings are disclosed.

The determination of a Nursing Peer Review Committee cannot be overruled by the CNO or facility. In certain situations, e.g., a personnel decision, the CNO or facility may not be bound and may even take action inconsistent with the committee's determination. However, that does not change what the committee's findings and determination were.

Although not a legal proceeding, the nurse has a right of representation. The extent to which the attorney or peer can participate beyond attending is addressed by Subdivisions (B) and (D). A nurse's right to consult with or utilize an attorney outside of the hearing is not limited. See also Subsec. (3).

The nurse has a right to be accompanied to the peer review hearing by an attorney or nurse peer. The attorney or nurse peer's participation at the hearing is limited to conferring with the nurse unless facility policies or Subdivision (D) permit greater participation. A good analogy is a witness at a congressional hearing. The witness can confer with the attorney but the attorney does not respond directly to questions.

Each party has to notify the other that it will have an attorney at the hearing. This gives them the opportunity to decide it they wish to have their own attorney present.

If the facility permits its attorney to participate beyond conferring, then the nurse's attorney may also participate at the same level.

A nurse can elect not to participate in nursing peer review. However, the committee would still conduct its review and possibly report the nurse to the BON.

Use of an informal workgroup has been an option since 2008. Use of an informal workgroup requires fewer resources and has less stringent requirements than regular peer review, so it may be advantageous for a facility to use. An informal workgroup will probably have 2-3 members since it is likely the facility will want more than 1 member and having more than 3 is not likely to save resources. The workgroup is likely to make decisions by consensus, so there is probably no need to have an odd number of members.

The facility must have written policies governing informal workgroups.

Because an informal workgroup has less due process, the nurse has to consent to its use.

will function, and consent, in writing, to the use of an informal work group. A nurse does not waive any right to incident-based peer review by accepting or rejecting the use of an informal work group;

(2) ***[Impaired Practice]*** if the informal work group suspects that the nurse's practice is impaired by chemical dependency or diminished mental capacity, the chair person must be notified to determine if peer review should be terminated and the nurse reported to the Board or to a Board-approved peer assistance program as required by subsection (g) of this section;

(3) ***[Membership]*** the informal work group comply with the membership and voting requirements of subsection (d)(3)(A) and (B) of this section;

(4) ***[Right to Meeting]*** the nurse be provided the opportunity to meet with the informal work group;

(5) ***[Right to Reject Decision]*** the nurse have the right to reject any decision of the informal work group and to then have his/her conduct reviewed by the peer review committee, in which event members of the informal work group shall not participate in that determination; and

(6) ***[Ratification of Decision]*** ratification by the committee chair person of any decision made by the informal work group. If the chair person disagrees with a determination of the informal work group to remediate a nurse for one or more minor incidents, the chair person shall convene the full peer review committee to make a determination regarding the conduct in question; and

(7) ***[Notification of CNO]*** the chair person communicate any decision of the informal work group to the CNO or nurse administrator.

(f) Exclusions to Minimum Due Process Requirements. The minimum due process requirements set out in subsection (d) of this section do not apply to:

(1) ***[Employer Mandated Reporting]*** peer review conducted solely in compliance with TOC §301.405(c) (NPA) relating to review of external factors, after a report of a nurse to the Board has already occurred under TOC §301.405(b) (relating to mandatory report by employer, facility or agency); or

(2) ***[Peer Review Identifies Impaired Practice]*** reviews governed by subsection (g) of this section involving nurses whose practice is suspected of being impaired due to chemical dependency, drug or alcohol abuse, substance abuse/misuse, "intemperate use," mental illness, or diminished mental capacity;

(3) ***[Individual Reporting Suspects Impaired Practice]*** when a person required to report a nurse believes that a nurse's practice is impaired or suspected of being impaired and has also resulted in a violation under TOC §301.410(b), that requires a direct report to the Board.

(g) Incident-Based Peer Review of a Nurse's Impaired Practice/Lack of Fitness.

(1) ***[Suspension of Peer Review]*** When a nurse's practice is impaired or suspected of being impaired due to chemical dependency, drug or alcohol abuse, substance abuse/misuse, "intemperate use," mental illness, or diminished mental capacity, peer review of the nurse shall be suspended. The nurse shall be reported to the Board or to a Board-approved peer assistance program in accordance with TOC §301.410 (related to reporting of impairment):

(A) if there is no reasonable factual basis for determining that a practice violation is involved, the nurse shall be reported to:

As with the full committee, a nurse with suspected impaired practice must be reported to the BON.

The composition of the informal workgroup must meet the same criteria as the full committee, i.e., at least 75% nurses, 66% RNs if RN being reviewed, only RNs vote on RNs, no one involved in personnel decision, etc.

The nurse must be provided an opportunity to meet with the workgroup.

The nurse does not have to accept the workgroup's decision and can always ask to be reviewed by the full committee. If the incident goes to the full committee, members of the informal workgroup cannot sit on the full committee since doing so is likely to be prejudicial to the nurse.

If the workgroup's decision is not ratified by the chair of the full Nursing Peer Review Committee, the full committee must review the nurse. Having the chair ratify the review is designed to promote consistency.

A decision of the workgroup must be conveyed to the CNO.

Because failure to provide due process may subject a facility to liability, it is important that there be as little ambiguity as possible about when due process must be provided to the nurse. This subsection identifies situations in which a facility is not required to provide due process.

When an employer/facility has made a mandatory report to the BON, it is required to conduct peer review to evaluate the role of external factors. Since the nurse is already before the BON and the committee is not reviewing the nurse, due process is not applicable.

Subsection (g) below requires that if impaired practice is suspected that the peer review process must be suspended and the nurse reported to the BON or a board-approved peer assistance program.. If due process requirements were not suspended, the nurse could claim she/he is still entitled to a hearing.

If the person reporting the nurse to nursing peer review suspects impaired practice, that person should report the nurse directly to the BON. Consequently, there is no due process requirement on the committee such as notifying the nurse that has been reported to peer review. However, if the committee accepts the report, then Subsection (2) would apply and the nurse would be entitled to due process up to the time the committee suspended its review and reported the nurse to the BON.

Whenever a nurse is suspected of impaired practice and a practice violation is involved, the nurse must be reported to the BON. This subsection sets out how a nursing peer review committee is to handle cases when impaired practice is suspected. See NPA Sec. 301.410.

(i) the Board; or

(ii) a Board-approved peer assistance program, that shall handle reporting the nurse in accordance with §217.13 of this title; or

(B) if there is a reasonable factual basis for a determination that a practice violation is involved, the nurse shall be reported to the Board.

(2) ***[External Factors Review]*** Following suspension of peer review of the nurse, the committee shall proceed to evaluate external factors to determine if:

(A) any factors beyond the nurse's control contributed to a practice violation; and

(B) any deficiency in external factors enabled the nurse to engage in unprofessional or illegal conduct.

(3) ***[External Factors Reporting]*** If the committee determines under paragraph (2) of this subsection that external factors do exist for either paragraph (2)(A) or (2)(B) of this subsection, the committee shall report its findings to a patient safety committee or to the CNO or nurse administrator if there is no patient safety committee.

(4) ***[Due Process Not Violated]*** A facility, organization, contractor, or other entity does not violate a nurse's right to due process under subsection (d) of this section by suspending the committee's review of the nurse and reporting the nurse to the Board in accordance with paragraph (2) of this subsection.

(5) ***[Self Reporting]*** Paragraph (1) of this subsection does not preclude a nurse from self-reporting to a peer assistance program or appropriate treatment facility.

(h) Confidentiality of Proceedings.

(1) ***[Confidentiality Required]*** Confidentiality of information presented to and/or considered by the incident-based peer review committee shall be maintained and the information not disclosed except as provided by TOC §§303.006, 303.007, and 303.0075 (NPR Law). Disclosure/discussion by a nurse with the nurse's attorney is proper because the attorney is bound to the same confidentiality requirements as the nurse.

(2) ***[Permissible Sharing of Information]*** In accordance with TOC §303.0075, a nursing incident-based peer review committee, including an entity contracted to conduct peer review under TOC §303.0015(b), and any patient safety committee established by the same entity, may share information.

(A) A record or determination of a patient safety committee, or a communication made to a patient safety committee, is not subject to subpoena or discovery and is not admissible in any civil or administrative proceeding, regardless of whether the information has been provided to a nursing peer review committee.

(B) The privileges under this subsection may be waived only through a written waiver signed by the chair, vice chair, or secretary of the patient safety committee.

(C) This section does not affect the application of TOC §303.007 (NPR Law) (relating to disclosures by peer review committee) to a nursing peer review committee.

(D) A committee that receives information from another committee shall forward any request to disclose the information to the committee that provided the information.

(3) ***[Required Policy]*** A CNO or Nurse Administrator shall assure that policies are in place relating to sharing of information and documents between an Incident-Based Nursing Peer Review committee and a patient safety committee(s) that at a minimum, address:

(A) separation of confidential Incident-Based Nursing Peer Review information from the nurse's human resource file;

Because of the difficulty and uncertainty in determining if a practice violation is involved, all third-party reports to the Texas Peer Assistance Program for Nurses (TPAPN) are reviewed jointly by the staff of the BON and TPAPN to determine if the nurse is appropriate for TPAPN.

If review of the nurse is suspended and the nurse is reported to the BON or peer assistance, the committee must still evaluate the role of external factors. For example, it might determine that better processes were needed to identify nurses with potential impaired practice.

A nurse's due process rights are not violated if peer review is suspended and the nurse is reported as required by this subsection.

Since 2008, TPAPN's policy has been that any nurse who self-reports to TPAPN and fails to successfully complete the program is referred to the BON. Previously, the policy had been to refer the nurse only if the nurse's practice posed an immediate danger to patients.

Nursing peer review is confidential to protect the nurse, committee and facility.

Committees within a facility may be reluctant to share information because of concern that such sharing may result in a loss of confidentiality. The NPR Law permits and encourages sharing of information between the Nursing Peer Review Committee and other patient safety committees at the facility without loss of confidentiality.

NPR Law Sec. 303.007 governs disclosure of information by the committee and any request for information produced by the Nursing Peer Review Committee itself would be governed by that section. That section requires disclosure to the BON and similar entities. A request for information provided the committee by a patient safety committee is governed by Subdivision (D) below.

Any request for disclosure of information received from a patient safety committee must be referred to that committee. Disclosure would be governed by the laws applying to that committee.

The CNO must assure there are policies in place to protect confidentiality when the Nursing Peer Review Committee shares information with a patient safety committee and those policies must address the items listed.

(B) methods in which shared communications and documents are labeled and maintained as to which committee originated the documents or communications;

(C) the confidential and separate nature of incident-based peer review and patient safety committee proceedings including shared information and documents; and

(D) the treatment of nurses who violate the policies including when a violation may result in a nurse being reported to the Board or a nursing peer review committee.

(i) Committee Responsibility to Evaluate and Report.

(1) ***[External Factors]*** In evaluating a nurse's conduct, the incident-based peer review committee shall review the evidence to determine the extent to which any deficiency in care by the nurse was the result of deficiencies in the nurse's judgment, knowledge, training, or skill rather than other factors beyond the nurse's control. A determination that a deficiency in care is attributable to a nurse must be based on the extent to which the nurse's conduct was the result of a deficiency in the nurse's judgment, knowledge, training, or skill.

(2) ***[Minor Incidents]*** An incident-based peer review committee shall consider whether a nurse's conduct constitutes one or more minor incidents under §217.16 (Minor Incidents) of this title. In accordance with that section, the committee may determine that the nurse:

(A) can be remediated to correct the deficiencies identified in the nurse's judgment, knowledge, training, or skill; or

(B) should be reported to the Board for either a pattern of practice that fails to meet minimum standards, or for one or more events that the incident-based peer review committee determines cannot be categorized as a minor incident(s).

(3) ***[When Report Not Required]*** An incident-based nursing peer review committee is not required to submit a report to the Board if:

(A) the committee determines that the reported conduct was a minor incident that is not required to be reported in accordance with provisions of §217.16 (Minor Incident) of this title; or

(B) the nurse has already been reported to the Board under TOC §301.405(b) (NPA) (employer reporting requirements).

(4) ***[Content of Report]*** If the committee determines it is required to report a nurse to the Board, the committee shall submit to the Board a written, signed report that includes:

(A) the identity of the nurse;

(B) a description of the conduct subject to reporting;

(C) a description of any corrective action taken against the nurse;

(D) a recommendation as to whether the Board should take formal disciplinary action against the nurse, and the basis for the recommendation;

(E) the extent to which any deficiency in care provided by the reported nurse was the result of a factor beyond the nurse's control; and

(F) any additional information the Board requires.

(5) ***[Reporting External Factors]*** If an incident-based peer review committee determines that a deficiency in care by the nurse was the result of a factor(s) beyond the nurse's control, in compliance with TOC §303.011(b) (NPR Law) (related to required peer review committee report when external factors contributed to a nurse's deficiency in care), the committee must submit a report to the applicable patient safety committee, or to the CNO or nurse administrator if there is no patient safety committee. A patient safety committee must report its findings back to the incident-based peer review committee.

(6) ***[Timeline]*** An incident-based peer review committee is not required to withhold its determination of the nurse being incident-based peer reviewed, pending feedback from a patient safety committee, unless the committee believes that a determination from a patient safety committee is necessary in order for the incident-based peer review committee to determine if the nurse's conduct is reportable.

(A) If an incident-based peer review committee finds that factors outside the nurse's control contributed to a deficiency in care, in addition to reporting to a patient safety committee,

Nursing peer review is required to allocate fault accountability between the nurse's conduct and system deficiencies. The nurse is to be held accountable only for her or his own conduct and not for system deficiencies.

The committee should address minor incidents in accordance with Rule 217.16 which in most circumstances will not require reporting to the BON if remediation will correct any deficiencies identified in the nurse's practice.

The committee is not required to report to the BON if:

- *it determines the incident is a minor incident not required to be reported under Rule 217.16.*
- *the nurse has been reported by the employer/facility as a mandated report under §301.405.*

Any committee report to the BON must contain the information listed.

If a Nursing Peer Review Committee determines any deficiencies in care were the result of external factors, it must report its findings to an appropriate patient safety committee within the facility. If there is no patient safety committee, then it must report to the CNO. Since NPR Law §303.001 defines "patient safety committee" very broadly, most facilities will likely have a patient safety committee.
The patient safety committee must report back to the Nursing Peer Review Committee.

This subsection (6) sets out the timelines a nursing peer review committee must comply with.

the incident-based peer review committee may also make recommendations for the nurse, up to and including reporting to the Board.

(B) An incident-based peer review committee may extend the time line for completing the incident-based peer review process (extending the 45 days by no more than an additional 45 days) if the committee members believe they need input from a patient safety committee. The incident-based peer review committee must complete its review of the nurse within this 90-day time frame.

(7) ***[Committee Decision Cannot Be Overruled]*** An incident-based peer review committee's determination to report a nurse to the Board cannot be overruled, changed, or dismissed.

(j) Nurse's Duty to Report.

(1) ***[Report to Peer Review Satisfies Duty]*** A report made by a nurse to a nursing incident-based peer review committee will satisfy the nurse's duty to report to the Board under TOC §301.402 (mandatory report by a nurse) provided that the following conditions are met:

(A) The reporting nurse shall be notified of the incident-based peer review committee's actions or findings and shall be subject to TOC §303.006 (confidentiality of peer review proceedings); and

(B) The nurse has no reason to believe the incident-based peer review committee made its determination in bad faith.

(2) ***[Retaliation Prohibited]*** A nurse may not be suspended, terminated, or otherwise disciplined, retaliated, or discriminated against for filing a report in good faith under this section and TOC §301.402(f) (retaliation for a report made in good faith prohibited) or advising a nurse of the nurse's rights and obligations under this section and §301.402(f). A violation of this subsection or TOC §301.402(f) is subject to TOC §301.413 that provides a nurse the right to file a civil suit to recover damages. The nurse may also file a complaint with the regulatory agency that licenses or regulates the nurse's practice setting. The BON does not have regulatory authority over practice settings or civil liability.

(k) State Agency Duty to Report. A state agency that has reason to believe that a nurse has engaged in conduct subject to reporting shall report the nurse in writing to:

(1) the Board; or

(2) the applicable nursing peer review committee in lieu of reporting to Board.

(l) Integrity of Incident-Based Peer Review Process.

(1) ***[Good Faith Required]*** Incident-Based Peer Review must be conducted in good faith. A nurse who knowingly participates in incident-based peer review in bad faith is subject to disciplinary action by the Board.

(2) ***[CNO Responsible]*** The CNO or nurse administrator of a facility, association, school, agency, or of any other setting that utilizes the services of nurses is responsible for knowing the requirements of this rule and for taking reasonable steps to assure that incident-based peer review is implemented and conducted in compliance with the NPA, NPR Law, and this section.

(3) ***[Committee Decision Cannot Be Overruled]*** A determination by an incident-based peer review committee, a CNO, nurse administrator, or an individual nurse to report a nurse to the Board cannot be overruled, dismissed, changed, or reversed. An incident-based peer review committee, CNO, and individual nurse each have a separate responsibility to protect the public by

The timeline can be extended for up to 45 days if the committee believes it needs input from a patient safety committee on external factors.

The determination of a Nursing Peer Review Committee cannot be overruled by the CNO or facility. In certain situations, e.g., a personnel decision, the CNO or facility may not be bound and may even take action inconsistent with the committee's determination. However, that does not change what the committee's findings and determination were.

NPA §301.402 gives individual nurses an explicit option to report to a nursing peer review committee in lieu of to the BON. A nurse's reporting to a nursing peer review committee will satisfy the nurse's duty to report. If the nurse subsequently decides to make a report to the BON, she or he may do so.

The nursing peer review committee must notify the reporting nurse of findings, so that the nurse can decide if she or he still wants to report to the BON. Reporting to nursing peer review does not prevent a nurse from reporting to the BON. Section 303.006 sets out the confidentiality requirements of nursing peer review and the reporting nurse must also maintain the confidentiality required under that section.

The nurse's reporting duty is not satisfied if she or he believes the committee acted in bad faith and the nurse must make a report to the BON.

A nurse cannot be retaliated against for making a protected report. If retaliation in fact occurs, the nurse has certain remedies including filing a complaint with the appropriate state agency or filing a civil lawsuit for damages. The nurse's remedies are governed by NPA §301.413. Legislation (SB 192) in 2011 replaced the terminology "not in bad faith" and "without malice" in the NPA with "good faith." This Rule may need to be amended to reflect this change.

A state agency may report a nurse to a nursing peer review committee in lieu of reporting the nurse to the BON.

Nursing peer review must be conducted in good faith.

As the administrator responsible for nursing services, the CNO is responsible for taking reasonable steps to implement nursing peer review.

The determination of a Nursing Peer Review Committee cannot be overruled by the CNO or facility. In certain situations, e.g., a personnel decision, the CNO or facility may not be bound and may even take action inconsistent with the committee's determination. However, that does not change what the committee's findings and determination were. NPR Law §303.006(f) prohibits reporting a nurse to the Board as set forth in TOC §301.402, §301.405, 22 TAC §217.11(1)(K) of this title, and this section.

(m) Reporting Conduct of other Practitioners or Entities: Whistleblower Protections.

(1) ***[Clarifying Qualifier]*** This section does not expand the authority of any incident-based peer review committee or the Board to make determinations outside the practice of nursing.

(2) ***[Reporting of Practitioners and Facilities]*** In a written, signed report to the appropriate licensing Board or accrediting body, and in accordance with TOC §301.4025 (report of unsafe practices of non-nurse entities), a nurse may report a licensed health care practitioner, agency, or facility that the nurse has reasonable cause to believe has exposed a patient to substantial risk of harm as a result of failing to provide patient care that conforms to:

(A) minimum standards of acceptable and prevailing professional practice, for a report made regarding a practitioner; or

(B) statutory, regulatory, or accreditation standards, for a report made regarding an agency or facility.

(3) ***[Reporting a Patient Care Concern]*** A nurse may report to the nurse's employer or another entity at which the nurse is authorized to practice any situation that the nurse has reasonable cause to believe exposes a patient to substantial risk of harm as a result of a failure to provide patient care that conforms to minimum standards of acceptable and prevailing professional practice or to statutory, regulatory, or accreditation standards. For purposes of this subsection, an employer or entity includes an employee or agent of the employer or entity.

(4) ***[Retaliation Prohibited]*** A person may not suspend or terminate the employment of, or otherwise discipline, retaliate, or discriminate against, a person who reports, in good faith, under this subsection or who advises a nurse of the nurse's rights and obligations under this subsection. A violation of this subsection is subject to TOC §301.413 (NPA) that provides a nurse the right to file a civil suit to recover damages. The nurse may also file a complaint with the regulatory agency that licenses or regulates the nurse's practice setting. The BON does not have regulatory authority over practice settings or civil liability.

RULE §217.20. SAFE HARBOR NURSING PEER REVIEW

> ***ANNOTATOR'S NOTE**: The content of Rule 217.20 is set out in Part VI (Patient Advocacy) of this Guide.*

RULE 217.16. REPORTING OF MINOR INCIDENTS, SUBSECS. (g) and (d)-(e).

(g) Nursing Peer Review Committee.

(1) If a report is made to the peer review committee, the committee must investigate and conduct incident-based nursing peer review in compliance with Nursing Peer Review Law in Texas Occupations Code §303 and §217.19 of this title.

(2) Review of a nurse's conduct or practice may be accomplished by either an informal work group of the nursing peer review committee as provided under §217.19(e) of this title or the full nursing peer review committee prior to a report being made to the board.

(3) A nursing peer review committee receiving a report involving a minor incident or incidents must review the incident(s) and other conduct of the nurse during the previous 12 months to determine if the nurse's continuing to practice poses a risk of harm to patients or other persons and whether remediation would be reasonably expected to adequately mitigate such risk if it exists. The committee must consider the special considerations set out in subsection (c) of this section.

(4) The nursing peer review committee need not report the nurse to the Board if the peer review committee determines that either:

(A) the nurse's continuing to practice does not pose a risk of harm to patients or *a member of the nursing peer review committee from reporting the nurse to the BON unless the member has knowledge of the incident acquired independently of being on the committee.*

This Subsection (m)(1) reaffirms that the BON and nursing peer review committee have jurisdiction only over nurses and nursing.

This Subsection (2) tracks NPA §301.4025(a).

This Subsection (3) tracks NPA §301.4025(b).

A nurse cannot be retaliated against for making a protected report. If retaliation in fact occurs, the nurse has certain remedies including filing a complaint with the appropriate state agency or filing a civil lawsuit for damages. The nurse's remedy of filing a civil lawsuit is governed by NPA §301.413.

Since safe harbor nursing peer review relates to patient advocacy by nurses, Rule 217.20 is set out in the patient advocacy section of this Guide.

The three subsections set out relate to the role of nursing peer review in the reporting of minor incidents, primarily defined in Subsec. (g). The entire Rule is set out in Part VII (Reporting) of this Guide.

The nursing peer review committee may use an informal work group.

In reviewing a minor incident, a nursing peer review committee must look at the nurse's practice over the past 12 months to determine any patterns of behavior.

See Subsec. (c) below for these considerations.

The committee has considerable discretion in determining if a nurse needs to be reported to the BON.

other persons; or

(B) remediation could reasonably be expected to adequately mitigate any such risk and the nurse successfully completes the remediation.

(5) If a nurse terminates employment while undergoing remediation activities as directed by a peer review committee under paragraph (3) of this subsection, the peer review committee may either:

(A) report the nurse to the BON;

(B) report to the peer review committee of the new employer, if known, with the nurses written consent;

(C) re-evaluate the nurse's current conduct to determine if the nurse did complete sufficient remediation and is deemed safe to practice.

(c) Factors to be Considered in Evaluating if Conduct Must Be Reported to the Board.

(1) A nurse involved in a minor incident need not be reported to the Board unless the conduct indicates the nurse:

(A) ignored a substantial risk that exposed a patient or other person to significant physical, emotional or financial harm or the potential for such harm;

(B) lacked a conscientious approach to or accountability for his/her practice;

(C) lacked the knowledge and competencies to make appropriate clinical judgments and such knowledge and competencies cannot be easily remediated; or

(D) indicates the nurse has engaged in a pattern of multiple minor incidents that demonstrate the nurse's continued practice would pose a risk of harm to patients or others.

(2) Evaluation of Multiple Incidents.

(A) Evaluation of Conduct. In evaluating whether multiple incidents constitute grounds for reporting it is the responsibility of the nurse manager or supervisor or peer review committee to determine if the minor incidents indicate a pattern of practice that demonstrates the nurse's continued practice poses a risk and should be reported.

(B) Evaluation of Multiple Incidents. In practice settings with nursing peer review, the nurse must be reported to peer review if a nurse commits five minor incidents within a 12-month period. In practice settings with no nursing peer review, the nurse who commits five minor incidents within a 12 month period must be reported to the Board.

(C) Nurse Manager and Nurse Supervisor Responsibilities. Regardless of the time frame or number of minor incidents, if a nurse manager or supervisor believes the minor incidents indicate a pattern of practice that poses a risk of harm that cannot be remediated, the nurse should be reported to the Board or Peer Review Committee.

(3) Other factors that may be considered in determining whether a minor incident should be reported to the Board are:

(A) the significance of the nurse's conduct in the particular practice setting; and

(B) the presence of contributing or mitigating circumstances, including systems issues or factors beyond the nurse's control, in relation to the nurse's conduct.

(d) Conduct Required to be Reported.

(1) A nurse must be reported to the board or to a nursing peer review committee for the following conduct:

(A) An error that contributed to a patient's death or serious harm.

(B) Criminal Conduct defined in Texas Occupations Code §301.4535.

(C) A serious violation of the board's Unprofessional Conduct rule §217.12 of this title (relating to Unprofessional Conduct) involving intentional or unethical conduct including but not limited to fraud, theft, patient abuse or patient exploitation.

(D) A practice-related violation involving impairment or suspected impairment by reason of chemical dependency, intemperate use, misuse or abuse of drugs or alcohol, mental illness, or diminished mental capacity required to be reported in accordance with §301.410(b) of

If a nurse leaves employment before completing remediation, the nursing peer review committee has options other than reporting the nurse to the BON.

Subsections (c) and (d) are being set out since they are needed to fully understand the role of nursing peer review described in Subsec. (g). Nursing peer review will use these considerations in determining what is appropriate action, if any, to take against the nurse.

Facilities with nursing peer review have more options in addressing nurses who commit multiple minor incidents because they can report the nurse to peer review rather than the BON.

If system errors are the primary cause, the presumption is that a nurse does not need to be reported to the BON.

This Subsec. (D) sets out when the nursing peer review committee must report a nurse to the BON.

"Contributed to" is an undefined term but is probably something less than "caused." Subdivision (2) requires the committee to maintain documentation when a "death or serious harm" is involved and the nurse is not reported to the BON.

the Nursing Practice Act and §217.19(g) of this title (relating to Incident Based Nursing Peer Review and Whistle Blower Protections).

(2) If a nursing peer review committee determines that a nurse engaged in the conduct listed in subsection (c)(1)(A) - (D) of this section the committee must report the nurse to the board. For errors involving the death or serious injury of a patient, if a nursing peer review committee makes a determination that a nurse has not engaged in conduct subject to reporting to the board, the committee must maintain documentation of the rationale for their belief that the nurse's conduct failed to meet each of the factors in paragraph (1)(A) - (D) of this subsection.

SUBPART D
HOSPITAL LICENSING LAWS AND RULES RELATING TO NURSING PEER REVIEW

HOSPITAL LICENSING LAW
DSHS HOSPITAL LICENSING RULES – NURSING

1. HOSPITAL LICENSING LAW (EXCERPTS) (HEALTH & SAFETY CODE, CHAPTER 241)

SEC. 241.026(a), (b). MINIMUM STANDARDS.

(a) The board shall adopt and enforce rules to further the purposes of this chapter. The rules at a minimum shall address:

[1-5 omitted]

6. Compliance with nursing peer review under Subchapter I, Chapter 301 and Chapter 303, Occupations Code, and the rules of the Texas Board of Nursing relating to peer review.

(b) In adopting rules, the board shall consider the conditions of participation for certification under Title XVIII of the Social Security Act (42 U.S.C. Section 1395 et seq.) and the standards of the Joint Commission on Accreditation of Healthcare Organizations and will attempt to achieve consistency with those conditions and standards.

2. DEPARTMENT OF STATE HEALTH SERVICES RULE (25 TAC 133.41)

SEC. 133.41 HOSPITAL FUNCTIONS AND SERVICES.

(o) NURSING SERVICES - Subsecs. (2)(G)(ii)(VII) and (6)

(2)(G) The hospital shall adopt, implement and enforce a written official nurse services staffing plan.

(ii) The plan shall:

(VII) incorporate a process that facilitates the timely and effective identification of concerns about the adequacy of the staffing plan by the nurse staffing committee established pursuant to subparagraph (F) of this paragraph. This process shall include:

(-a-) a prohibition on retaliation for reporting concerns;

(-b-) - (-f-) [*Omitted*]

(-g-) use of the nurse safe harbor peer review process pursuant to Occupations Code, §303.005;

(6) Reporting and peer review of a vocational or registered nurse. A hospital shall adopt, implement, and enforce a policy to ensure that the hospital complies with the Occupations Code §§301.401 - 301.403, 301.405 and Chapter 303 (relating to Grounds for Reporting Nurse, Duty of Nurse to Report, Duty of Peer Review Committee to Report, Duty of Person Employing

Nursing peer review committee has a duty to report the nurse to the BON under the circumstances described in Subdivision (1) above.

The hospital licensing law and Department of State Health Services (DSHS) rules require hospitals to implement nursing peer review.

DSHS has adopted Rule 133.41(o)(5) requiring hospitals to comply. See below.

Each hospital must have a written staffing plan.

One of the components of the plan must be a process for reporting of concerns about staffing that is non-retaliatory and incorporates safe harbor nursing peer review.

This section requires hospitals to implement policies to assure compliance with other laws and regulations relating to nursing including mandatory reporting, peer review and minor incidents.

Nurse to Report, and Nursing Peer Review respectively), and with the rules adopted by the Texas Board of Nursing in 22 TAC §217.16 (relating to Minor Incidents), §217.19 (relating to Incident-Based Nursing Peer Review and Whistleblower Protections), and §217.20 (relating to Safe Harbor Peer Review for Nurses Whistleblower Protections).

PART V.

NURSING PRACTICE RELATED MATERIALS

ANNOTATOR'S NOTE: *This Part V is designed to pull together into a single location the various NPA provisions and BON rules, position statements, guidelines, FAQs and policies which most directly address nursing practice issues for nurses. This pulling together is accomplished through listing the provisions under the following headings:*

Nursing Practice Act Provisions
BON Rules
BON Position Statements
BON Interpretive Guidelines and Policies
BON Newsletter - Board of Nursing Bulletin
Information on BON Website
Scope of Practice Materials

A number of the documents are set out in other parts of this Guide. The rest can be found on the BON's website.

NURSING PRACTICE RELATED MATERIALS

NURSING PRACTICE ACT
BON RULES
BON POSITION STATEMENTS
BON INTERPRETIVE GUIDELINES
BON NEWSLETTER
BON WEBSITE - PRACTICE-RELATED INFORMATION
SCOPE OF PRACTICE MATERIALS

ANNOTATOR'S NOTE: *The BON adds new practice-related information on an ongoing basis to its website, and nurses interested in a specific topic should check the website.*

1. NURSING PRACTICE ACT PROVISIONS - *PART I OF THIS GUIDE*

Sec. 301.002. Definitions of "Professional Nursing" and "Vocational Nursing"
Sec. 301.151. BON's Rule-making Authority
Sec. 301.351. Titles and Nametag
Sec, 301.353. Supervision of the Vocational Nurse
Sec. 301.401-.402. Nurses' Duty to Report to BON
Sec. 301.452. Grounds for Disciplinary Action by BON

2. BON RULES - *PART II OF THIS GUIDE*

Rule 217.11 Standards of Nursing Practice
- Sec. (1) Standards Applicable to All Nurses
- Sec. (2) Standards Specific to LVNs
  (directed scope of practice, nursing process for LVNs, assignments to unlicensed persons by LVNs, LVN scope of practice)
- Sec. (3) Standards Specific to RNs
  (Nursing process for RNs, delegation to unlicensed persons)
- Sec. (4) Standards Specific to APRNs

Rule 217.12 Unprofessional Conduct
Rule 224 Delegation in Acute Setting or for Acute Conditions
Rule 225 Delegation in Independent Living Environments for Stable Conditions
Rule 217.10 Titles and Nametags
Rule 217.18 Assisting at Surgery
Rule 217.14 RNs Performing Radiologic Procedures
Rule 221 Advanced Practice Registered Nurses
Rule 222 Prescriptive Authority for APRNs

3. BON POSITION STATEMENTS - *PART III OF THIS GUIDE*

15.1. Nurses Carrying Out Orders From Physician Assistants
15.2. The Role of the Licensed Vocational Nurse in the Pronouncement of Death
15.3. LVNs Engaging in Intravenous Therapy, Venipuncture, or PICC Lines
15.4. Educational Mobility
15.5. Nurses with Responsibility for Initiating Physician Standing Orders
15.6. Board Rules Associated with Alleged Patient "Abandonment"
15.7. The Role of LVNs & RNs in Management and/or Administering Medications via the Epidural or Intrathecal Catheter Routes

15.8. Roles of the Nurse in Moderate Sedation
15.9. Performance of Laser Therapy by RNs or LVNs
15.10. Continuing Education: Limitations for Expanding Scope of Practice
15.11. Delegated Medical Acts
15.12. Use of American Psychiatric Association Diagnoses by LVNs, RNs or APRNs
15.13. The Role of LVNs and RNs as School Nurses
15.14. Duty of a Nurse in Any Practice Setting
15.15. Board's Jurisdiction Over a Nurse's Practice in Any Role and Use of the Nursing Title
15.16. Development of Nursing Education Programs
15.17. Board of Nursing/Board of Pharmacy, Joint Position Statement, Medication Error
15.18. Nurses Carrying Out Orders from Advanced Practice Registered Nurses
15.19. Nurses Carrying Out Orders from Pharmacists for Drug Therapy Management
15.20. Registered Nurses in the Management of an Unwitnessed Arrest in a Resident in a Long-term Care Facility
15.21. *[Deleted 1/2005]*
15.22. APRNs Providing Medical Aspect of Care for Themselves or Others with Whom There Is a Close Personal Relationship
15.23. The RN's Use of Complementary Modalities
15.24. Nurses Engaging in Reinsertion of Permanently Placed Feeding Tubes
15.25. Administration of Medications & Treatments by LVNs
15.26. Simulation in Prelicensure Nursing Education
15.27. The Licensed Vocational Nurse Scope of Practice
15.28. The Registered Nurse Scope of Practice
15.29. Use of Social Media by Nurses

4. BON GUIDELINES AND POLICIES - *PART III OF THIS GUIDE*

1. Rules and Guidelines Governing the Graduate Vocational And Registered Nurse Candidates Or Newly Licensed Vocational Or Registered Nurse
2. Guidelines for Transitioning of the Experienced Nurse Back into Clinical Practice Or into a New Practice Setting
3. APRN - Guidelines for Determining APRN Scope of Practice
4. APRN - CNS Diagnosis and Management Course Guidelines

5. BON NEWSLETTER

The BON publishes a quarterly newsletter - the TEXAS BOARD OF NURSING BULLETIN. It is a valuable source of the latest information about the regulation of nursing in Texas. It regularly has a Q&A section on practice.

6. INFORMATION ON BON WEBSITE - *The BON has a number of practice-related materials on its website that can provide valuable guidance to RNs and LVNs in addressing specific practice questions. These materials are largely self-explanatory and can be found on the website at www.bon.texas.gov. Set out below is a listing of most of the practice related information on the BON's website as of July 2013. Materials on the following four BON website sections are included:*

A. Nursing Practice
B. Advanced Practice

C. Employer
D. Disciplinary Action

***ANNOTATOR'S NOTE**: The BON adds new practice-related information on an ongoing basis to its website, and nurses interested in a specific topic should check the website.*

A. NURSING PRACTICE SECTION

Nursing Practice Information
Nurse Licensure Compact (NLC) Fact Sheet
Frequently Asked Questions
Nursing Peer Review/Incident-Based and Safe Harbor
Delegation Resource Packet
Scope of Practice
Guidelines & Interpretive Guidelines
Advanced Practice Information
Position Statements
APRN Scope of Practice
H1N1 Influenza, Seasonal Influenza, and Pneumococcal Vaccinations
TERCAP Pilot Project

1. NURSING PRACTICE INFORMATION SUBSECTION

Abandonment
- Position Statement 15.6 - Rules Associated With Alleged Patient "Abandonment"

Advanced Practice Nursing
- APRN General Page
- Position Statement 15.18 - RNs Carrying out Orders from Advanced Practice Registered Nurses

Alternative & Complimentary Therapies
- Position Statement 15.23 - Use of Complementary Modalities by the LVN or RN
- Position Statement 15.9 - Performance of Laser Therapy by RNs or LVNs

Board Position Statements

Copying a Nursing License

Continuing Competency
- Continuing Competency
- Forensic Evidence Requirement

Delegation
- Rule 224 - Delegation of Nursing Tasks by Registered Professional Nurses to Unlicensed Personnel for Clients with Acute Conditions or in Acute Care Environments
- Rule 225 - RN Delegation to Unlicensed Personnel and Tasks Not Requiring Delegation in Independent Living Environments for Clients with Stable and Predictable Conditions
- Delegation Resource Packet
- Paramedics/EMTs in the Emergency Department (ED)

Drug Use by Nurses
- Nurse Admitted as Patient Under the Influence (also see Substance Abuse)

Documentation
- Co-signature on Documentation relating to Graduate Nurses & Graduate Vocational Nurses
- Co-signature on LVN Actions/Documentation

Employment Issues
- Proposed Nursing Work Hours Position Statement

Floating
Overtime, Hours of Work
Staffing Ratios

First Assisting
Nursing Practice Act, Sections 301.354
Rule 217.18 - Registered Nurse First Assistants

Guidelines
Rules and Guidelines Governing the Graduate Vocational and Registered Nurse Candidates or Newly Licensed Vocational or Registered Nurse
Guidelines for Transitioning of the Experienced Nurse either back into clinical practice or into a new practice setting
Interpretive Guideline for LVN Scope of Practice Under Rule 217.11

Moderate (Conscious) Sedation
Position Statement 15.8 - The Role of the Nurse in Moderate Sedation

Laws Impacting Nursing (Other than the Nursing Practice Act and the Board's Rules and Regulations)
EMTALA (Emergency Medical Treatment and Active Labor Act)
FAQs - Nurse's Role with the Emergency Medical Treatment & Labor Act

Licensure Issues
Graduate Vocational Nurse and/or Graduate Nurse
Rule 217.3 - Temporary Authorization to Practice/Temporary Permit
Rules & Guidelines Governing the Graduate Registered Nurse and the Newly Licensed Registered Nurse
Rule 220 - Nurse Licensure Compact

Nursing Process
Rule 217.11 - Standards of Nursing Practice

Peer Review
Rule 217.16 - Minor Incidents
Rule 217.19 - Incident-based Peer Review and Whistleblower Protections
Rule 217.20 - Safe Harbor Peer Review and Whistleblower Protections
Safe Harbor Information and Forms
Peer Review Frequently Asked Questions
Nursing Peer Review Statutes and Rules Reference Table

Poison Control Information

Position Statements
Complete set of the Board's Position Statements relating to Practice

Practice Setting/Specialty Area Specific
Surgery (See First Assisting)
Community Based Services
Home Health - GNs, GVNs, and Newly Licensed Nurses Practicing in Home Health Settings
MOU – 2001: Defines circumstances under which the provision of health-related tasks or services by a home and community support services agency (HCSSA) does not constitute the practice of professional nursing.
MOU – 2011: Outlines the requirements that will apply to a state-wide pilot program implemented by DADS, and how the program relates to when telephone on-call services may be provided by a Licensed Vocational Nurse (LVN)
School Nursing
School Nurse Quick Card Review
School Nurse With Unlicensed Diabetes Care Assistants (UDCAs)
Position Statement 15.13 Role of the LVNs & RNs As School Nurses

Pronouncement of Death

by Registered Nurse (with/without Life Support)
Texas Statute re: Pronouncement of Death
Position Statement 15.20 - Nurses in the Management of an Unwitnessed Arrest in a Resident in a Long Term Care Facility

Safe Harbor *(See Peer Review)*

Scope of Practice

Position Statement 15.27 The Licensed Vocational Nurse Scope of Practice
Position Statement 15.28 The Registered Nurse Scope of Practice
FAQ - List of Tasks a Nurse Can/Cannot Perform
Rule 217.11 - Standards of Nursing Practice
LVN's Performing Triage/Telephonic Nursing/Being On-Call
LVN's Performing Initial Assessments
LVN's and Nursing Care Plans
LVN's "Supervision of Practice"
Six-Step Decision-Making Model for Determining Nursing Scope of Practice (Document)
Six-Step Decision-Making Model for Determining Nursing Scope of Practice (Poster)
Scope of Practice Poster
Additional information on APRN Scope of Practice
Position Statement 15.14 - Duty of a Nurse in any Practice Setting
When Does a Nurse's Duty to a Patient Begin?

Substance Abuse

Eligibility and Disciplinary Sanctions for Nurses with Substance Abuse, Misuse, Substance Dependency, or other Substance Use Disorder
Information Regarding Substance Abuse and Misuse of Certain Prescription Drugs: Health Professionals resources on the appropriate use of pain medication as well as the misuse and diversion of addictive medication

Unprofessional Conduct

Rule 217.12 - Unprofessional Conduct
Disciplinary Sanction Policies

Volunteer Retired Nurse

Volunteer Retired Nurse - FAQs

2. Frequently Asked Questions Subsection

BON Rules and Regulation Relating to Telenursing and Telehealth
Copying Nursing License
Co-signature on Documentation relating to Graduate Nurses &Graduate Vocational Nurses
Co-signature on LVN Actions/Documentation
Delegation and the Advanced Practice Registered Nurse
Delegation of CPAP and BiPAP Procedures
Differentiating the Role of the BON from the Role of Nursing (Professional) Associations
Forensic Evidence Collection
"Floating" to other Clinical Nursing Units
GNs, GVNs, and Newly Licensed Nurses Practicing in Home Health Settings
H1N1 Influenza, Seasonal Influenza, and Pneumococcal Vaccinations
List of Tasks a Nurse Can/Cannot Perform
LVN's Performing Triage/Telephonic Nursing/Being On-Call
LVN's Performing Initial Assessments
LVN's and Nursing Care Plans
LVN's "Supervision of Practice"
Mandatory Overtime/Consecutive Shifts
Nurse Admitted As Patient Under the Influence

Nurses Performing Radiologic Procedures
Nurse's Role with the Emergency Medical Treatment & Labor Act
Nursing Peer Review
Off Label Administration of Ketamine for Pain Management by a Nurse
Practice of Nursing
Practice Recommendations for Newly Licensed Nurses
Paramedics/EMTs in the Emergency Department (ED)
Role of the School Nurse With Unlicensed Diabetes Care Assistants
FAQ - Regarding Position Statements 15.27, The LVN Scope of Practice and 15.28, The RN Scope of Practice
Staffing Ratios
Training of Military Personnel in Civilian Hospitals
Volunteer Retired Nurse Authorization
When Does a Nurse's Duty to a Patient Begin and End

B. ADVANCED PRACTICE SECTION

Advanced Practice Credentials

FAQ - Doctoral Degrees in Nursing and Using the Title "Dr."

Advanced Practice Nurse - Scope of Practice

Guidelines for determining Scope of Practice with FAQs related to Scope of Practice

Advanced Practice Applications

Check Status of Application for Initial Licensure (Endorsement, Examination or Advanced Practice Registered Nurse)
BON to Discontinue Issuance of Paper Letters for APRN Interim Approval and Prescriptive Authority
Definitions Page for Online APRN Application Status Checks
Online - Advanced Practice Nurse Application (with option for Prescriptive Authority)
Paper - Advanced Practice Nurse Application (with option for Prescriptive Authority)
Specific Information for Completing the Advanced Practice Nurse Application
Advanced Practice Application FAQs
Registration for Outpatient Anesthesia Providers
APN Refresher Course/Extended Orientation Information

Prescriptive Authority

Application for Prescriptive Authority
Obtaining a DEA Number
What needs to be on a prescription?

Renewals

Online Renewal: http://www.texas.gov/NASApp/bnexam/BNExamManager
BON downloadable renewal forms

Regulation of Advanced Practice Registered Nurses

Consensus Model for APRN Regulation

Advanced Practice Nursing Education

CNS Diagnosis and Management Course Guidelines
Doctor of Nursing Practice Degree

National Certification

Recognized National Certification Examinations
Acute Care Pediatric Nurse Practitioner Examination
APRN Certification Exam Review Criteria
APRN Certification Exam Review Policy

BON Rules Relating to Advanced Practice Nursing

Rule 221 - Advanced Practice Nurses
Rule 222 - Advanced Practice Nurses with Prescriptive Authority

Rule 219 - Advanced Practice Nursing Education Programs
Rule 217.11 - Standards of Nursing Practice
Rule 217.12 - Unprofessional Conduct
Rule 216 - Continuing Education

Current BON Position Statements Relating to Advanced Practice Nursing Issues

15.6 Board Rules Associated With Alleged Patient "Abandonment"
15.8 The Role of the Nurse in Moderate Sedation
15.9 Performance of Laser Therapy by RNs or LVNs
15.10 Continuing Education: Limitations for Expanding Scope of Practice
15.12 Use of DSM-IV Diagnoses
15.14 Duty of a Nurse in Any Practice Setting
15.17 Texas Board of Nursing/Board of Pharmacy, Joint Position Statement, Medication Error
15.18 RNs Carrying Out Orders from Advanced Practice Nurses
15.22 APNs Providing Medical Aspects of Care for Themselves or Others With Whom There is a Close Personal Relationship
15.23 The RNs Use of Complementary Modalities

Information on the Nurse Licensure Compact

General Information (BON Site)
General Information (NCSBN Site): https://www.ncsbn.org/156.htm.
Participating states: https

C. EMPLOYER SECTION

Nursys E-notification Service *[Disciplinary and Licensure Alerts]*

Bulletins

Quarterly Newsletters

Compact

NLCA Legal Memorandum to Employers
Nurse Licensure Compact (NLC) Fact Sheet - Overview of What Nurse Employers Need to Know regarding the licensure compact
Nurse Licensure Compact - Rules, Law and FAQs
Nurse Licensure Compact - Video Overview

Contact Information

Contact the Board

Discipline

Disciplinary Action and Imposter Alerts
How to File a Complaint

Employment Issues

NLCA Legal Memorandum to Employers
Floating to Unfamiliar Practice Settings
Mandatory Overtime/Consecutive Shifts
Re-entering the Workforce or Transitioning to a New Setting
Staffing Ratios

Frequently Asked Questions

Disciplinary - FAQ's
Education - FAQ's
Licensing - FAQ's
Nursing Refresher Courses, Extensive Orientations and Nursing Programs of Study - FAQ's
Practice - FAQ's
Students/Prospective Students - FAQ's

Licensing Information

NCSBN Licensure Quick Confirm a license

Verify a License
Newly Licensed Recommendations
Nursing Peer Review
Peer Review - FAQ's
Nursing Peer Review/Incident-Based and Safe Harbor
Nursing Practice and Advanced Practice Information
Nursing Statistics
Scope of Practice
APRN Scope of Practice
General Scope of Nursing Practice
TERCAP Pilot Project

D. Disciplinary Action Section

The following FAQs, policies and guidelines are found under the Disciplinary Action section of the BON website but are included because they contain information relevant to nursing practice.

Frequently Asked Questions About Enforcement
Investigatory and Disciplinary Process
Guidelines for Physical and Psychological Evaluations
Disciplinary Sanctions for Sexual Misconduct
Disciplinary Sanctions for Fraud, Theft and Deception
Eligibility and Disciplinary Sanctions for Nurses with Substance Abuse, Misuse, Substance Dependency, or other Substance Use Disorder
Disciplinary Sanctions for Lying and Falsification
Disciplinary Guidelines for Criminal Conduct

7. SCOPE OF PRACTICE MATERIALS

Materials specifically related to scope of practice are set out in Subpart D of Part III of this Guide and can also be found on the BON website under Nursing Practice.

PART VI.

PATIENT ADVOCACY PROTECTIONS

ANNOTATOR'S NOTE: *This Part VI is designed to pull together into a single location the various laws and regulations that provide protections for nurses against retaliation for advocating for their patients.*

SUBPART A.
SAFE HARBOR NURSING PEER REVIEW LAW

1. SAFE HARBOR NURSING PEER REVIEW LAW, SEC. 303.005, OCCUPATIONS CODE

Sec. 303.005. Request for Nursing Peer Review Committee Determination.

(a) In this section, "duty to a patient" means conduct required by standards of practice or professional conduct adopted by the board for nurses. The term includes administrative decisions directly affecting a nurse's ability to comply with that duty.

(a-1) For purposes of this section, a nurse or nurse administrator acts in good faith in connection with a request made or an action taken by the nurse or nurse administrator if there is a reasonable factual or legal basis for the request or action.

(b) If a person who is required to establish a nursing peer review committee under Section 303.0015 requests a nurse to engage in conduct that the nurse believes violates a nurse's duty to a patient, the nurse may request, on a form developed or approved by the board, a determination by a nursing peer review committee under this chapter of whether the conduct violates a nurse's duty to a patient.

Safe harbor nursing peer review provides perhaps the greatest patient advocacy protection for nurses since it provides prospective protection before the nurse engages in the conduct.

Sec. 303.005 of the Nursing Peer Review Law (NPR Law) is popularly referred to as "Safe Harbor Nursing Peer Review." It was enacted in 1997 to expand the protections of NPA Sec. 301.352. Both provisions are designed to provide protection to the nurse who refuses to engage in conduct the nurse believes would be a violation of the nurse's duty to a patient, i.e., violate the NPA or BON rules. Nurses can be placed in situations in which they feel they are being forced to choose between a) refusing to carry out an employer's directive, or b) engaging in conduct they believe violates their duty to the patient. Both provisions are intended to address this situation. This right to request nursing peer review was added because the concern had been identified that nurses asked to engage in conduct they believed violated a nurse's duty to a patient were having to choose between a) refusing to engage in the conduct and risking potential disciplinary action by their organization, or b) engaging in the conduct under protest and risking action by the BON – particularly if there were a bad patient outcome. While Sec. 301.352 provides the RN and LVN protection against retaliation, the only way for a nurse to claim those protections was after the retaliation occurred

This NPR Law Sec. 303.005 establishes a process by which an RN or LVN, who believes in good faith that she or he is being asked to engage in conduct that violates a nurse's duty to a patient, can 1) request a determination by nursing peer review as to what is the nurse's duty, and 2) engage in the conduct pending nursing peer review's determination without the risk of being disciplined by the BON. "Duty to a patient" is defined in subsection (a). Neither the organization nor the nurse is protected from accountability to a patient for a bad patient outcome if the nurse engages in the behavior pending nursing peer review's determination.

The BON has adopted Rule 217.20 governing safe harbor nursing peer review. This rule addresses the nursing peer review process, establishes time lines and gives the nurse certain rights of participation.

For both RNs and LVNs, "duty to patient" is defined by the BON's rules on standards of practice (Rule 217.11) and unprofessional conduct (Rule 217.12). RNs and LVNs should be familiar with these rules.

The reference to administrative decision means that RNs and LVNs who make administrative decisions (e.g., making assignments) that could affect a nurse's duty to patients also have the protections of this section. They can request a nursing peer review determination as to whether requiring a nurse to comply with that administrative decision would make it likely the nurse would be engaging in conduct violating the nurse's duty to patients.

Subsec. (a-1) defines what constitutes "good faith" for the purposes of this Section 303.005. The definition parallels language in Department of State Health Services Rule 133.43(b) relating to reporting violation of the department's nurse staffing rules and also the definition of "good faith" for nurse reporting under the NPA. See NPA Sec. 301.4011. A nurse must act in "good faith" to get the protections of safe harbor nursing peer review. See Subsec.(c).

NPR Law Sec. 303.0015 requires anyone that employs or utilizes 10 or more nurses (LVNs and/or RNs) to establish a nursing peer review committee. An exception is provided when four or fewer of the 10 nurses are RNs in which case peer review for RNs is not required. See Sec. 303.0015.

The nursing peer review committee determines only whether engaging in the requested

(c) A nurse who in good faith requests a peer review determination under Subsection (b):

(1) may not be disciplined or discriminated against for making the request;

(2) may engage in the requested conduct pending the peer review;

(3) is not subject to the reporting requirement under Subchapter I, Chapter 301; and

(4) may not be disciplined by the board for engaging in that conduct while the peer review is pending.

(d) If a nurse requests a peer review determination under Subsection (b) and refuses to engage in the requested conduct pending the peer review, the determination of the peer review committee shall be considered in any decision by the nurse's employer to discipline the nurse for the refusal to engage in the requested conduct, but the determination is not binding if a nurse administrator believes in good faith that the peer review committee has incorrectly determined a nurse's duty. This subsection does not affect the protections provided by Subsection (c)(1) or Section 301.352.

conduct would violate the nurse's duty to the patient. Its purpose is not to assign accountability to either the nurse or the nurse making the request.

BON Rule 217.20 (c)(3) requires the request for safe harbor be a written request. The nurse can either use the safe harbor form provided on the board's website or submit any written request that includes, at a minimum, the following information:

1. *the conduct assigned or requested, including the name and title of the person making the assignment or request;*
2. *a description of the practice setting (e.g., the nurse's responsibilities, resources available, extenuating or contributing circumstances impacting the situation);*
3. *a detailed description of how the conduct would have violated the nurse's duty to a patient or any other provision of the Nursing Practice Act and board rules. If possible, reference the specific standard (Rule §217.11) or other section of the Nursing Practice Act and/or board rules the nurse believes would have been violated;*
4. *any other copies of pertinent documentation available at the time. Additional documents may be submitted to the committee when available at a later time; and*
5. *the nurse's name, title, and relationship to the supervisor making the assignment or request.*

If the nurse does not submit the initial request for safe harbor using the form on the BON's website, the facility and nurse still msut adhere to the safe harbor process as outlined on the BON form. An official copy can be downloaded from its website at www.bon.texas.gov. The BON form incorporates a process that should maximize resolving the disagreement between the RN or LVN making the request and the organization as to what is the nurse's duty in the particular situation. Rule 217.20 and the BON form also establish timetables and processes governing the request. Nurses should be familiar with Rule 217.20 and the BON form so that they can properly request safe harbor nursing peer review if ever needed.

RNs and LVNs who request safe harbor nursing peer review in good faith are provided several important protections. Note that these protections may be available only after the request is made.

- *The organization cannot discipline a nurse for making a good faith request for nursing peer review.*
- *Pending the nursing peer review committee's determination, the nurse may engage in the conduct.*
- *The nurse is not reportable to the BON for engaging in the conduct and is not subject to discipline by the BON. Once a nursing peer review committee determines the conduct violates the nurse's duty to the patient, the nurse is not protected if she or he continues to engage in the conduct after that determination. See Rule 217.20.*

The nurse must make the request in good faith which is defined by Subsec. (a-1) as having "a reasonable factual or legal basis for the request." Requesting safe harbor nursing peer review may not be used to justify conduct that no reasonable RN or LVN would say is consistent with a nurse's duty to a patient.

This Subsec. (d) describes the one situation in which a nurse administrator could take action against a nurse even though the nurse requested safe harbor nursing peer review. The situation occurs when the nurse requests safe harbor nursing peer review but refuses to engage in the conduct pending the nursing peer review committee's determination. In this situation, the nurse can be disciplined for refusing to engage in the conduct but not for making the request. Safe harbor nursing peer review is designed for situations in which reasonable nurses could disagree about what is a nurse's duty to a patient. In such a case, it would normally be reasonable for the nurse to engage in the conduct pending peer review. If the conduct is such a clear violation of a nurse's duty (e.g., request to falsify a patient record) that no reasonable nurse would believe otherwise, the nurse would obviously not engage in the conduct. If the nurse administrator retaliated against the nurse in that situation, the nurse would have protection under Sec. NPA 301.352 for refusing to engage in conduct that violates the NPA or BON rules. The nursing peer

(e) If the conduct for which the peer review is requested under Subsection (b) involves the medical reasonableness of a physician's order, the medical staff or medical director shall be requested to make a determination as to the medical reasonableness of the physician's order, and that determination is determinative of that issue.

(f) A nurse's rights under this section may not be nullified by a contract.

(g) An appropriate licensing agency may take action against a person who violates this section.

(h) A person may not suspend or terminate the employment of, or otherwise discipline or discriminate against, a nurse who in good faith requests a peer review determination under this section or a person who advises a nurse of the nurse's right to request a determination or of the procedures for requesting a determination. A violation of this subsection is subject to Section 301.413.

(i) A person who is required to provide, on request, a nursing peer review committee determination under Subsection (b) shall adopt and implement a policy to inform nurses of the right to request a nursing peer review committee determination and the procedure for making a request.

2. BON Safe Harbor Nursing Peer Review Rule

Annotator's Note: *Headings have been added to some sections of rule to facilitate reading.*

§217.20. Safe Harbor Nursing Peer Review and Whistleblower Protections

(a) Definitions.
(b) Purpose.
(c) Applicability of Safe Harbor Nursing Peer Review.
(d) Invoking Safe Harbor.
(e) Safe Harbor Protections.
(f) Exclusions to Safe Harbor Protections.
(g) Nurse's Right To Refuse To Engage In Certain Conduct Pending Nursing Safe Harbor Peer Review Determination.
(h) Minimum Due Process.
(i) Safe Harbor Timelines.
(j) General Provisions.
(k) Use of Informal Work Group In Safe Harbor Nursing Peer Review.

review committee also would certainly find that the requested conduct violated the nurse's duty to the patient which would put the nurse administrator at risk if she/he chose to discipline the nurse for refusing to engage in the conduct. The nurse administrator must act in "good faith," meaning there must be a factual or legal basis for the determination. The nurse administrator who requests that a nurse engage in conduct that a nursing peer review committee has determined violates a nurse's duty to a patient would be putting her/his license at some risk unless she/he absolutely is convinced the nursing peer review committee is wrong.

If medical reasonableness is at issue, that issue is to be decided by the medical staff or director. This requirement was included to address concern by organized medicine that it was not appropriate for a nursing peer review committee to be determining the medical reasonableness of a physician's order.

An RN or LVN cannot be required to contract away her or his rights to request safe harbor nursing peer review; for example, sign an employment agreement agreeing not to request nursing peer review.

The reference is to Sec. 303.005 (Safe Harbor Nursing Peer Review). A violation of this Sec. 303.005 is a basis for a licensing agency to take action against that organization or person. For example, if a nurse administrator violates this subsection, she/he would be subject to disciplinary action by the BON. If a hospital violates this subsection, it would be subject to action by the Department of State Health Services. NPA Sec. 301.413(b) authorizes a fine up to $25,000.

Retaliation for making a good faith request for safe harbor nursing peer review is prohibited. The nurse's remedies for retaliation are set out in NPA Sec. 301.413. They include filing a lawsuit for damages (minimum of $5,000) and attorney's fees. A complaint can also be filed with the agency that licenses the individual or facility which can impose a fine up to $25,000. The protections are available not only to the nurse requesting safe harbor, but also to any person advising the nurse of her or his rights concerning making the request. See Subpart D. below.

This Subsec. (i) is designed to ensure nurses are adequately aware of their rights and protections under safe harbor nursing peer review. It imposes a duty on the facility to provide this information.

In implementing amendments to the Nursing Peer Review Law made by the 2007 Legislature, the BON completely rewrote this Rule 217.20 relating to safe harbor nursing peer review (Rules 217.19 and 217.20).

The most significant changes to Rule 217.20 as part of a 2008 rewrite were:

1. *adding a definitions section [217.20(a)]*
2. *simplifying the process for requesting Safe Harbor Nursing Peer Review [217.20(d)]*
3. *providing additional guidance to a nurse in deciding whether to engage in the requested conduct or assignment while awaiting the determination by nursing peer review*
4. *setting out the entire process for invoking safe harbor and for handling the request (previously much of process had been only in the BON form) [217.20(d),(g),(h), (i), (j)]*
5. *authorizing the use of informal workgroups [217.20(f)]*

The BON website at www.bon.texas.gov includes information about safe harbor nursing peer review. Select "Nursing Practice" and then "Peer Review." Additional information is also set out in Part X (Appendices) of this Guide.

(l) Reporting Conduct of other Practitioners or Entities; Whistleblower Protections.

(a) Definitions.

(1) Assignment--Designated responsibility for the provision or supervision of nursing care for a defined period of time in a defined work setting. This includes but is not limited to the specified functions, duties, practitioner orders, supervisory directives, and amount of work designated as the individual nurse's responsibility. Changes in the nurse's assignment may occur at any time during the work period.

(2) Bad Faith--Knowingly or recklessly taking action not supported by a reasonable factual or legal basis. The term includes misrepresenting the facts surrounding the events under review, acting out of malice or personal animosity towards the nurse, acting from a conflict of interest, or knowingly or recklessly denying a nurse due process.

(3) Chief Nursing Officer (CNO)--The registered nurse, by any title, who is administratively responsible for the nursing services at a facility, association, school, agency, or any other setting that utilizes the services of nurses.

(4) Conduct Subject to Reporting - defined by Texas Occupations Code §301.401 of the Nursing Practice Act as conduct by a nurse that:

(A) violates the Nursing Practice Act (NPA) or a Board rule and contributed to the death or serious injury of a patient;

(B) causes a person to suspect that the nurse's practice is impaired by chemical dependency or drug or alcohol abuse;

(C) constitutes abuse, exploitation, fraud, or a violation of professional boundaries; or

(D) indicates that the nurse lacks knowledge, skill, judgment, or conscientiousness to such an extent that the nurse's continued practice of nursing could reasonably be expected to pose a risk of harm to a patient or another person, regardless of whether the conduct consists of a single incident or a pattern of behavior.

(5) Duty to a patient--A nurse's duty is to always advocate for patient safety, including any nursing action necessary to comply with the standards of nursing practice (§217.11 of this title) and to avoid engaging in unprofessional conduct (§217.12 of this title). This includes administrative decisions directly affecting a nurse's ability to comply with that duty.

(6) Good Faith--Taking action supported by a reasonable factual or legal basis. Good faith precludes misrepresenting the facts surrounding the events under review, acting out of malice or personal animosity, acting from a conflict of interest, or knowingly or recklessly denying a nurse due process.

(7) Incident-Based Peer Review--Incident-based peer review focuses on determining if a nurse's actions, be it a single event or multiple events (such as in reviewing up to five (5) minor incidents by the same nurse within a year's period of time) should be reported to the Board, or if the nurse's conduct does not require reporting because the conduct constitutes a minor incident that can be remediated. The review includes whether external factors beyond the nurse's control may have contributed to any deficiency in care by the nurse, and to report such findings to a patient safety committee as applicable.

(8) Malice--Acting with a specific intent to do substantial injury or harm to another.

(9) Minor incident--Conduct by a nurse that does not indicate that the nurse's continued practice poses a risk of harm to a patient or another person as described in §217.16 (Minor Incident) of this title.

(10) Nurse Administrator--Chief Nursing Officer (CNO) or the CNO's designee.

(11) Nursing Peer Review Law (NPR law)--Chapter 303 of the Texas Occupations Code

Changes during the assignment can be so significant that it becomes equivalent to a new assignment. See Subsec. (d)(1)(B).

Bad faith includes a mental element of "knowingly or recklessly" engaging in the conduct. See also the definitions of "good faith" and "malice." In 2011, the terms "without malice " and "bad faith" throughout the NPA were replaced with the term "good faith." "Good faith" as defined in NPR Law 303.005 and NPA Sec. 301.4011 does not include a lack of malice. This definition may need to be updated to reflect the statutory definition of good faith.

Who is the CNO is not determined by what title is used. The CNO is responsible for assuring compliance with these rules. See Section (l)(2).

This definition is directly from NPA §301.401. See annotations to this definition in Part I (NPA) of this Guide.

The BON's standards of practice (Rule 217.11) and unprofessional conduct (Rule 217.12) rules provide more detailed guidance on what a nurse's duty is.

This definition tracks Sec. 303.005(a-1). In 2011, the terms "without malice " and "bad faith" throughout the NPA were replaced with the term "good faith." "Good faith" as defined in NPR Law 303.005 and NPA Sec. 301.4011 does not include a lack of malice. This definition may need to be updated to reflect the statutory definition of good faith.

Malice involves a more specific intent to do harm than does bad faith. In 2011, the terms "without malice" and "bad faith" were replaced in the NPA with the term "good faith." "

Definition is taken from NPA §301.401.

(TOC). Nurses involved in nursing peer review must comply with the NPR Law.

(12) Nursing Practice Act (NPA)--Chapter 301 of the Texas Occupations Code (TOC). Nurses must comply with the NPA.

(13) Patient Safety Committee--Any committee established by an association, school, agency, health care facility, or other organization to address issues relating to patient safety including:

(A) the entity's medical staff composed of individuals licensed under Subtitle B (Medical Practice Act, Texas Occupations Code §151.001, et seq);

(B) a medical committee under Subchapter D, Chapter 161 of the Health and Safety Code (§§161.031 - 161.033); or

(C) a multi-disciplinary committee, including nursing representation, or any committee established by the same entity to promote best practices and patient safety.

(14) Peer Review – Defined by TOC §303.001(5) (NPR Law) as the evaluation of nursing services, the qualifications of a nurse, the quality of patient care rendered by a nurse, the merits of a complaint concerning a nurse or nursing care, and a determination or recommendation regarding a complaint. The term also includes the provision of information, advice, and assistance to nurses and other persons relating to the rights and obligations of and protections for nurses who raise care concerns, report under Chapter 301, request peer review, and the resolution of workplace and practice questions relating to nursing and patient care. The peer review process is one of fact finding, analysis and study of events by nurses in a climate of collegial problem solving focused on obtaining all relevant information about an event. Peer review conducted by any entity must comply with NPR Law and with applicable Board rules related to incident-based or safe harbor peer review.

(15) Safe Harbor--A process that protects a nurse from employer retaliation, suspension, termination, discipline, discrimination, and licensure sanction when a nurse makes a good faith request for peer review of an assignment or conduct the nurse is requested to perform and that the nurse believes could result in a violation of the NPA or Board rules. Safe Harbor must be invoked prior to engaging in the conduct or assignment for which peer review is requested, and may be invoked at anytime during the work period when the initial assignment changes.

(16) Texas Occupations Code (TOC)--One of the topical subdivisions or "codes" into which the Texas Statutes or laws are organized. The Texas Occupations Code contains the statutes governing occupations and professions including the health professions. Both the NPA and NPR Law are located within these statutes. The TOC can be changed only by the Texas Legislature.

(17) Whistleblower Protections--Protections available to a nurse that prohibit retaliatory action by an employer or other entity because the nurse:

(A) made a good faith request for Safe Harbor Nursing Peer Review under Texas Occupations Code §303.005(c) and 22 TAC §217.20 of this title; or

(B) refused to engage in an act or omission relating to patient care that would constitute a violation of the NPA or Board rules as permitted by TOC §301.352 (NPA) (Protection for Refusal to Engage in Certain Conduct). A nurse invoking Safe Harbor under §217.20 of this title must comply with §217.20(g) of this title if the nurse refuses to engage in the conduct or assignment; or

(C) made a lawful report of unsafe practitioners, or unsafe patient care practices or conditions, in accordance with TOC §301.4025 (report of unsafe practices of non-nurse entities) and subsection (j)(2) of this section.

(b) Purpose. The purpose of this rule is to:

(1) define the process for invoking Safe Harbor;

(2) define minimum due process to which a nurse is entitled under safe harbor peer review;

(3) provide guidance to facilities, agencies, employers of nurses, or anyone who utilizes the services of nurses in the development and application of peer review plans;

(4) assure that nurses have knowledge of the plan as well as their right to invoke Safe

A patient safety committee is any committee within the facility that addresses patient care concerns. This definition tracks the definition in NPR Law §303.001.

Ideally, nursing would like to see nursing peer review function as a collegial problem-solving process. There is significant anecdotal evidence that this ideal is frequently not realized. The greater emphasis of SB 993, enacted in 2007, on peer review's role in identifying external factors and system deficiencies may result in peer review coming closer to this ideal in the future. The focus of the BON's minor incident reporting on remediation may also promote a more collegial process.

Harbor; and

(5) provide guidance to the peer review committee in making its determination of the nurse's duty to the patient.

(c) Applicability of Safe Harbor Nursing Peer Review.

(1) ***[Required Peer Review]*** Texas Occupations Code §303.0015 (NPR Law) requires a person who regularly employs, hires or contracts for the services of ten (10) or more nurses (for peer review of an RN, at least 5 of the 10 must be RNs) to permit a nurse to request Safe Harbor Peer Review when the nurse is requested or assigned to engage in conduct that the nurse believes is in violation of his/her duty to a patient.

(2) ***[Voluntary Peer Review]*** Any person or entity that conducts Safe Harbor Nursing Peer Review is required to comply with the requirements of this rule.

(d) Invoking Safe Harbor.

(1) ***[When Must Request]*** Safe Harbor must be invoked prior to engaging in the conduct or assignment and at any of the following times:

(A) when the conduct is requested or assignment made;

(B) when changes occur in the request or assignment that so modify the level of nursing care or supervision required compared to what was originally requested or assigned that a nurse believes in good faith that patient harm may result; or

(C) when the nurse refuses to engage in the requested conduct or assignment.

(2) ***[Making Request]*** The nurse must notify the supervisor requesting the conduct or assignment in writing that the nurse is invoking Safe Harbor. The content of this notification must meet the requirements for a Quick Request Form described in paragraph (3) of this subsection. A detailed written account of the Safe Harbor request that meets the minimum requirements for

NPR Law §303.0015 requires facilities to establish a Nursing Peer Review Committee to conduct nursing peer review under either the NPA or the NPR Law:

- *for LVNs if utilize 10 or more nurses*
- *for RNs if utilize 10 or more nurses and 5 of those 10 are RNs*

NPR Law Sec. 303.005 (safe harbor nursing peer review) is the only provision specifically requiring an organization have the type of nursing peer review which must be conducted in accordance with this Rule 217.20. However, it is likely that Rule 217.20 also applies to nursing peer review conducted under NPA §301.352. Nursing peer review under §301.352 evaluates a nurse's claim that she/he was retaliated against because she/he refused to violate NPA or a BON rule. This review is after the alleged retaliation has occurred so it is not safe harbor nursing peer review. However, the committee is determining whether the requested conduct violates the NPA or BON rules, which is similar to what the committee does in conducting safe harbor nursing peer review.

The following sections of NPA also require nursing peer review but review conducted under these sections would be conducted in accordance with Rule 217.19 (relating to incident-based nursing peer review).

- *§301.402 (Alternate reporting to Nursing Peer Review by individual nurse)*
- *§301.403 (Nursing Peer Review Committee reporting to BON)*
- *§301.405 (Nursing peer review of external factors after employer/facility has reported nurse to BON)*
- *§301.407 (Alternate reporting to Nursing Peer Review by a state agency)*

A final type of nursing peer review is peer review conducted as part of reporting of a minor incident under BON Rule 217.16. Since that review could result in the nurse being reported to the BON, it should be conducted in accordance with this Rule 217.19 except when Rule 217.16 specifically provides for a different process.

If a facility, which is not required to provide Safe Harbor Nursing Peer Review, elects to provide safe harbor nursing peer review, it must abide by the requirements of this rule.

Because the nurse is protected from disciplinary action by the BON and from retaliation by the employer, the request has to be made before the nurse engages in the conduct. Safe harbor cannot be requested after the fact. The times when safe harbor must be requested are:

1. When the conduct is requested or the assignment made

2. When changes in the assignment or requested conduct are so significant that a de facto "new" assignment occurs and is one the nurse believes violates her or his duty to the patient.

3. If the nurse decides not to engage in the conduct awaiting the nursing peer review committee's determination, the request must be made when the nurse refuses to engage in the conduct or assignment.

A request must be made in writing giving the information required in the Quick Request Form described in Paragraph (3) or the information required by the Comprehensive Written Form described in Paragraph (4). If only the information required by the Quick Request Form is provided when initially requesting safe harbor, the additional information required by the

the Comprehensive Written Request described in paragraph (4) of this subsection must be completed before leaving the work setting at the end of the work period.

(3) ***Quick Request Form.***

(A) A nurse wishing to invoke Safe Harbor must make an initial request in writing that at a minimum includes the following:

(i) the nurse(s) name making the safe harbor request and his/her signature(s);

(ii) the date and time of the request;

(iii) the location of where the conduct or assignment is to be completed;

(iv) the name of the person requesting the conduct or making the assignment; and

(v) a brief explanation of why safe harbor is being requested.

(B) The BON Safe Harbor Quick Request Form may be used to invoke the initial request for Safe Harbor, but use of the form is not required. The initial written request may be in any written format provided the above minimum information is provided.

(4) ***Comprehensive Written Request for Safe Harbor Peer Review.***

(A) A nurse who invokes Safe Harbor must supplement the initial written request under paragraph (3)(A) of this subsection by submitting a comprehensive request in writing before leaving the work setting at the end of the work period. This comprehensive written request must include a minimum of the following information:

(i) the conduct assigned or requested, including the name and title of the person making the assignment or request;

(ii) a description of the practice setting, e.g., the nurse's responsibilities, resources available, extenuating or contributing circumstances impacting the situation;

(iii) a detailed description of how the requested conduct or assignment would have violated the nurse's duty to a patient or any other provision of the NPA and Board Rules. If possible, reference the specific standard (§217.11 of this title) or other section of the NPA and/or Board rules the nurse believes would have been violated. If a nurse refuses to engage in the requested conduct or assignment, the nurse must document the existence of a rationale listed under subsection (g) of this section.

(iv) If applicable, the rationale for the nurse's not engaging in the requested conduct or assignment awaiting the nursing peer review committee's determination as to the nurse's duty. The rationale should refer to one of the justifications described in subsection (g)(2) of this section for not engaging in the conduct or assignment awaiting a peer review determination.

(v) any other copies of pertinent documentation available at the time. Additional documents may be submitted to the committee when available at a later time; and

(vi) the nurse's name, title, and relationship to the supervisor making the assignment or request.

(B) The BON Comprehensive Request for Safe Harbor Form may be used when submitting the detailed request for Safe Harbor, but use of the form is not required. The comprehensive written request may be in any written format provided the above minimum information is included.

(5) ***[Maintaining Records]*** The nurse invoking Safe Harbor is responsible for keeping a copy of the request for Safe Harbor.

(6) ***[Medical Reasonableness]*** A nurse may invoke Safe Harbor to question the medical reasonableness of a physician's order in accordance with TOC §303.005(e) (NPR Law). In this situation, the medical staff or medical director shall determine whether the order was reasonable.

Comprehensive Written Request must be provided at the end of the work period.

The Quick Request Form requires a minimum amount of information and is designed to permit the nurse to make the request with a minimal amount of disruption in providing care. The elements required are listed.

The BON developed a Quick Request Form, but it is not required that the nurse use that form as long as the required information is provided. If the request for safe harbor is made by providing only the information required by this Paragraph (3), the nurse must provide the additional information required by Paragraph (4) at the end of the work period. See Subdivision (2) above.

A complete request for safe harbor must include the information required by this Paragraph (4). If not provided at the time of the original request, it must be provided by the end of the work period. See Subdivision (2) above.

The information provided must be the items listed.

The BON has developed a Comprehensive Request Form but it is not required that the nurse use that form as long as the required information is provided. See Subdivision (2) above.

The nurse is responsible for keeping records of the request. It is important that she or he do so since if a report is made to the BON, the nurse will need to be able to prove that she/he had requested safe harbor.

If a question of medical reasonableness of a physician's order is at issue, then the medical staff or medical director must be involved.

(e) Safe Harbor Protections.

(1) ***[Prerequisites for Protections]*** To activate protections outlined in TOC §303.005(c) and paragraph (2) of this subsection, the nurse shall:

(A) invoke Safe Harbor in good faith;

(B) notify the supervisor in writing that he/she intends to invoke Safe Harbor in accordance with subsection (d) of this section. This must be done prior to engaging in the conduct or assignment for which safe harbor is requested and at any of the following times:

(i) when the conduct is requested or assignment made;

(ii) when changes occur in the request or assignment that so modify the level of nursing care or supervision required compared to what was originally requested or assigned that a nurse believes in good faith that patient harm may result; or

(iii) when the nurse refuses to engage in the requested conduct or assignment.

(2) ***[Protections Provided]*** TOC §303.005(c) and (h) (NPR Law) and §301.352 provide the following protections:

(A) A nurse may not be suspended, terminated, or otherwise disciplined, retaliated, or discriminated against for requesting Safe Harbor in good faith.

(B) A nurse or other person may not be suspended, terminated, or otherwise disciplined, retaliated, or discriminated against for advising a nurse in good faith of the nurse's right to request a determination, or of the procedures for requesting a determination.

(C) A nurse is not subject to being reported to the Board and may not be disciplined by the Board for engaging in the conduct awaiting the determination of the peer review committee as permitted by subsection (g) of this section. A nurse's protections from disciplinary action by the Board for engaging in the conduct or assignment awaiting peer review determination remain in place for 48 hours after the nurse is advised of the peer review committee's determination. This time limitation does not affect the nurse's protections from retaliation by the facility, agency, entity or employer under TOC §303.005(h) (NPR Law) for requesting Safe Harbor.

(3) ***[Remedies Available]*** If retaliation occurs, TOC §301.413 (NPA) provides a nurse the right to file civil suit to recover damages. The nurse may also file a complaint with the appropriate regulatory agency that licenses or regulates the nurse's practice setting. The BON does not have regulatory authority over practice settings or civil liability.

(4) ***[Patient's Right to Sue]*** Safe Harbor protections do not apply to any civil action for patient injury that may result from the nurse's practice.

(f) Exclusions to Safe Harbor Protections.

(1) A nurse's protections from disciplinary action by the Board under subsection (e)(2) of this section do not apply to:

(A) the nurse who invokes Safe Harbor in bad faith;

(B) conduct the nurse engages in prior to the request for Safe Harbor; or

(C) conduct unrelated to the reason for which the nurse requested Safe Harbor.

(2) If the peer review committee determines that a nurse has engaged in conduct subject to reporting that is not related to the request for Safe Harbor, the committee must comply with the requirements of §217.19 (Incident-Based Nursing Peer Review) of this title.

(g) Nurse's Right To Refuse To Engage In Certain Conduct Pending Nursing Safe

Safe harbor provides the nurse significant protections, and in order to be entitled to those protections, the nurse must:

1. *make the request in good faith. "Good faith" is defined in Subsection (a).*
2. *make the request in writing as required by Subsection (d)*
3. *make the request at one of the permitted times under Subsection (d)(1)*

The nurse making the request may not be retaliated against for making the request by the employer or facility.

A colleague, who advises a nurse of her/his right to request and how to request safe harbor, may not be retaliated against by the employer or facility.

The BON may not take action against the nurse's license for engaging in the conduct or assignment awaiting the nursing peer review committee's determination as to the nurse's duty.

If a nurse is retaliated against, the nurse can file a complaint with the BON against any nurse involved in the retaliation and with the appropriate licensing agency against the entity involved. The nurse may also file a lawsuit against either or both for damages resulting from the retaliation. NPA §301.413 provides details about timelines, presumptions and damages that might be recovered.

Since a patient is an innocent third party with respect to the request for safe harbor, a request for safe harbor does not abrogate a patient's right to seek recovery for any patient injury proximately caused by the nurse's engaging in the requested conduct or assignment. The existence of this possibility is why it is to the benefit of both the nurse and the facility for nursing peer review to complete its review as soon as possible.

The protections provided by safe harbor are <u>not</u> available:

1. *if the nurse made the request in bad faith;*
2. *for any conduct engaged in prior to requesting safe harbor; or*
3. *for conduct unrelated to the conduct for which safe harbor was requested. For example, if a nurse requested safe harbor because she/he felt unqualified for the assignment, falsifying a patient record would not be protected conduct.*

If the peer review committee believes the nurse engaged in conduct subject to reporting that was unrelated to the request for safe harbor, the committee's review of that conduct must be conducted as incident-based nursing peer review under Rule 217.19.

One of the more difficult questions to address in safe harbor nursing peer review is whether

Harbor Peer Review Determination.

(1) ***[Decision Not to Engage in Conduct]*** A nurse invoking safe harbor may engage in the requested conduct or assignment while awaiting peer review determination unless the conduct or assignment is one in which:

(A) the nurse lacks the basic knowledge, skills, and abilities that would be necessary to render the care or engage in the conduct requested or assigned at a minimally competent level such that engaging in the requested conduct or assignment would expose one or more patients to an unjustifiable risk of harm; or

(B) the requested conduct or assignment would constitute unprofessional conduct and/or criminal conduct such as fraud, theft, patient abuse, exploitation, or falsification.

(2) ***[Process if Do Not Engage in Conduct]*** If a nurse refuses to engage in the conduct or assignment because it is beyond the nurse's scope as described under paragraph (1)(A) of this subsection:

(A) the nurse and supervisor must collaborate in an attempt to identify an acceptable assignment that is within the nurse's scope and enhances the delivery of safe patient care; and

(B) the results of this collaborative effort must be documented in writing and maintained in peer review records by the chair of the peer review committee.

(h) Minimum Due Process.

(1) ***[Policy Required]*** A person or entity required by TOC §303.005(i) to provide nursing peer review shall adopt and implement a policy to inform nurses of their right to request a nursing peer review committee determination (Safe Harbor Nursing Peer Review) and the procedure for making a request.

(2) ***[Minimum Requirements]*** In order to meet the minimum due process required by TOC chapter 303, the nursing peer review committee shall:

(A) comply with the membership and voting requirements as set forth in TOC §303.003;

(B) exclude from the committee membership, any persons or person with administrative authority for personnel decisions directly affecting the nurse;

(C) limit attendance at the Safe Harbor Nursing Peer Review hearing by a CNO, nurse administrator, or other individual with administrative authority over the nurse, including the individual who requested the conduct or made the assignment, to appearing before the safe harbor peer review committee to speak as a fact witness; and

(D) Permit the nurse requesting safe harbor to:

(i) appear before the committee;

the nurse should engage in the conduct or assignment awaiting the peer review committee's determination of the nurse's duty to the patient. Safe harbor is designed to address the situation when both the nurse and nurse supervisor are acting in good faith and have a reasonable disagreement over what is the nurse's duty to the patient in a particular situation.

Normally, in such a situation it is in the best interest of the patient for the nurse to engage in the conduct or assignment while awaiting the committee's determination. However, there can be situations when it is not. This Subsection (g) attempts to provide the nurse some guidance in making her/his decision. There are potential consequences to the nurse if she or he decides not to engage in the requested conduct or assignment awaiting nursing peer review since the CNO may be able to take personnel action against the nurse for not engaging in the conduct or assignment. See Subsec. (J)(4) below.

In practice, making this determination is likely to be difficult.

This determination is much easier to make. For example, the nurse should refuse to falsify a record.

Because of the potential harm to patients of the nurse not engaging in the requested conduct or assignment while awaiting the peer review's determination, this Paragraph (2) sets out a process that must be followed before the nurse does so.

This gives a nurse specific due process rights. However, they are not as extensive as for incident-based nursing peer review. In safe harbor nursing peer review, the committee is not evaluating the nurse for purposes of accountability. Rather, it is determining whether the nurse's engaging in the requested conduct would violate the nurse's duty to a patient.

A policy must be adopted and implemented to inform nurses of their right to request safe harbor nursing peer review and how to make a request.

A nursing peer review committee is required to have a certain percentage of RNs and LVNs. If feasible, at least one nurse should be from the same area of practice as the nurse being reviewed. Only nurses can vote and only RNs when an RN is reviewed. See Annotations to NPR Law §303.003.

Having individuals on a committee who have direct administrative authority over, or make personnel decisions about, the nurse being reviewed undermines the integrity of the nursing peer review process.

Certain administrators are limited in when they can be present at the meeting. This is intended to ensure a fair process.

The nurse has a right to be present at the meeting, to ask questions, and to explain why she/he believes that she/he has been asked to engage in conduct that violates a nurse's duty to the patient.

(ii) ask questions and respond to questions of the committee; and

(iii) make a verbal and/or written statement to explain why he or she believes the requested conduct or assignment would have violated a nurse's duty to a patient.

(i) Safe Harbor Timelines.

(1) ***[Completion of Review]*** The Safe Harbor Nursing Peer Review committee shall complete its review and notify the CNO or nurse administrator within 14 calendar days of when the nurse requested Safe Harbor.

(2) ***[Notification of Nurse]*** Within 48 hours of receiving the committee's determination, the CNO or nurse administrator shall review these findings and notify the nurse requesting safe harbor of both the committee's determination and whether the administrator believes in good faith that the committee's findings are correct or incorrect.

(3) ***[Expiration of Protections from BON Action]*** The nurse's protection from disciplinary action by the Board for engaging in the conduct or assignment awaiting peer review determination expires 48 hours after the nurse is advised of the peer review committee's determination. The expiration of this protection does not affect the nurse's protections from retaliation by the facility, agency, entity or employer under TOC §303.005(h) for requesting Safe Harbor.

(j) General Provisions.

(1) ***[CNO Responsible]*** The Chief Nursing Officer (CNO) or nurse administrator of a facility, association, school, agency, or of any other setting that utilizes the services of nurses is responsible for knowing the requirements of this Rule and for taking reasonable steps to assure that peer review is implemented and conducted in compliance with the NPA and the NPR law.

(2) ***[Good Faith Required]*** Safe Harbor Nursing Peer Review must be conducted in good faith. A nurse who knowingly participates in nursing peer review in bad faith is subject to disciplinary action by the Board.

(3) ***[Confidentiality]*** The peer review committee and participants shall comply with the confidentiality requirement of TOC §303.006 and §303.007 relating to confidentiality and limited disclosure of peer review information.

(4) ***[Personnel Action]*** If a nurse requests a Safe Harbor Peer Review determination under TOC §303.005(b) and refuses to engage in the requested conduct or assignment pending the safe harbor peer review, the determinations of the committee are not binding if the CNO or nurse administrator believes in good faith that the committee has incorrectly determined a nurse's duty.

(A) In accordance with TOC §303.005(d), the determination of the safe harbor peer review committee shall be considered in any decision by the nurse's employer to discipline the nurse for the refusal to engage in the requested conduct.

(B) If the CNO or nurse administrator in good faith disagrees with the committee's determination, the rationale for disagreeing must be recorded and retained with the peer review records.

(C) If the CNO or nurse administrator believes the peer review was conducted in bad faith, she/he has a duty to report the nurses involved under TOC §301.402 (NPA) and 22 TAC §217.11(1)(K) of this title.

(D) This section does not affect the protections under TOC §303.005(c)(1) and §301.352 relating to a nurse's protection from disciplinary action or discrimination for making a request for Safe Harbor Peer Review.

(k) Use of Informal Work Group In Safe Harbor Nursing Peer Review. A facility may choose to initiate an informal review process utilizing a workgroup of the nursing peer review committee provided that the final determination of the nurse's duty complies with the time lines set out in this rule and there are written policies for the informal workgroup that require:

There is a very short timeline (not more than 14 days) for the nursing peer review committee to make its determination as to the nurse's duty to the patient. It is to both the nurse's benefit and facility's benefit to resolve the issue as quickly as possible, because if patient injury occurs during the period the committee is making its determination, the patient has a right to sue for that injury.

The CNO is responsible for implementing safe harbor nursing peer review.

All participants must act in good faith.

Confidentiality must be maintained.

The taking of disciplinary action against the nurse requesting safe harbor raises some difficult questions. The nurse cannot be retaliated against for making the request. However, what if the nurse believes it is a situation in which she/he should not engage in the conduct or assignment while awaiting peer review's determination and in fact refuses to do so? In such a case, the CNO or nurse administrator is not prohibited from taking personnel action against the nurse for that refusal (i.e., for the nurse's not engaging in the conduct but not for making the request). However, it appears that the CNO or administrator would do so at considerable risk if the peer review committee's determination was that the requested conduct in fact violated the nurse's duty to the patient. See Paragraph (4)(D).

NPR Law §303.005(c)(1) provides protection against retaliation for making the request. NPA §301.352 provides a remedy if a nurse is retaliated against for refusing to engage in conduct that violates the NPA or a BON rule.

Use of an informal workgroup requires fewer resources and has less stringent requirements than regular peer review, so it may be advantageous for a facility to use. An informal workgroup will probably have 2-3 members since the facility likely will want more than 1 member on the workgroup and having more than 3 is unlikely to save resources. The workgroup is likely to work off a consensus so probably no need to have an odd number of members. The facility must have

(1) ***[Nurse's Consent Required]*** the nurse to:

(A) be informed how the informal workgroup will function and that the nurse does not waive any right to peer review by accepting or rejecting the use of an informal workgroup; and

(B) consent, in writing, to the use of an informal workgroup;

(2) ***[Membership]*** the informal workgroup to comply with the membership and voting requirements of subsection (h) of this section;

(3) ***[Right to Meeting]*** the nurse to be provided the opportunity to meet with the informal workgroup;

(4) ***[Right to Reject Decision]*** the nurse to have the right to reject any decision of the informal workgroup and have the entire committee determine if the requested conduct or assignment violates the nurse's duty to the patient(s), in which event members of the informal workgroup shall not participate in that determination;

(5) ***[Ratification of Decision]*** ratification by the safe harbor peer review committee chair person of any decision made by the informal workgroup. If the chair person disagrees with a determination of the informal workgroup, the chair person shall convene the full peer review committee to review the conduct in question; and

(6) ***[Notification of CNO]*** the peer review chair person communicate any decision of the informal work group to the CNO or nurse administrator.

(l) Reporting Conduct of other Practitioners or Entities; Whistleblower Protections.

(1) ***[Clarifying Qualifier]*** This subsection does not expand the authority of any safe harbor peer review committee or the Board to make determinations outside the practice of nursing.

(2) ***[Reporting Practitioners and Facilities]*** In a written, signed report to the appropriate licensing Board or accrediting body, and in accordance with TOC §301.4025, a nurse may report a licensed health care practitioner, agency, or facility that the nurse has reasonable cause to believe has exposed a patient to substantial risk of harm as a result of failing to provide patient care that conforms to:

(A) minimum standards of acceptable and prevailing professional practice, for a report made regarding a practitioner; or

(B) statutory, regulatory, or accreditation standards, for a report made regarding an agency or facility.

(3) ***[Reporting Patient Care Concerns]*** A nurse may report to the nurse's employer or another entity at which the nurse is authorized to practice any situation that the nurse has reasonable cause to believe exposes a patient to substantial risk of harm as a result of a failure to provide patient care that conforms to minimum standards of acceptable and prevailing professional practice or to statutory, regulatory, or accreditation standards. For purposes of this subsection, an employer or entity includes an employee or agent of the employer or entity.

(4) ***[Retaliation Prohibited]*** A person may not suspend or terminate the employment of, or otherwise discipline, retaliate, or discriminate against, a person who reports, in good faith, under this section or advises a nurse of the nurse's rights and obligations under this section. A violation of this subsection is subject to TOC §301.413 that provides a nurse the right to file civil suit to recover damages. The nurse may also file a complaint with the regulatory agency that licenses or regulates the nurse's practice setting. The BON does not have regulatory authority over practice settings or civil liability.

3. Forms and Resource Materials for Safe Harbor Nursing Peer Review

Annotator's Note: *More detailed information about requesting safe harbor* *written policies governing informal workgroups.*

Because the informal workgroup process has less due process, the nurse has to consent to its use.

The composition of the informal workgroup must meet the same criteria as the full committee, i.e., at least 75% nurses, 66% RNs if an RN is being reviewed, only RNs vote on RNs, no one involved in personnel decision, etc.

The nurse must be provided an opportunity to meet with the workgroup.

The nurse does not have to accept the workgroup's decision and can always ask to be reviewed by the full committee. If the request goes to the full committee, members of the informal workgroup cannot sit on the full committee since doing so is likely to be prejudicial to the nurse.

If the workgroup's decision is not ratified by the chair of the full Nursing Peer Review Committee, the full committee must review the nurse. Having the chair ratify will help assure consistency.

The same as with a decision by the full committee, a decision of the workgroup must be conveyed to the CNO.

This Subsec. (l)(1) reaffirms that the BON and nursing peer review have jurisdiction only over nurses and nursing.

This Subsec. (l)(2) tracks NPA §301.4025(a).

This Subsec. (l)(3) tracks NPA §301.4025(b).

A nurse cannot be retaliated against for making a protected report. If retaliation in fact occurs, the nurse has certain remedies including filing a complaint with the appropriate state agency or filing a civil lawsuit for damages. The nurse's remedy of filing a lawsuit is governed by NPA §301.413. See Subpart D below.

These materials set out are more "how-to" materials and include:

nursing peer review and the process for reviewing a request are set out in the Appendices to this Guide.

SUBPART B
REPORTING PROTECTIONS

1. NURSING PRACTICE ACT
2. HOSPITAL SETTING
3. LONG-TERM CARE SETTING
4. HOME AND COMMUNITY SERVICES SETTING
5. PUBLICLY-EMPLOYED NURSES

1. NURSING PRACTICE ACT PROVISIONS

Sec. 301.4011. GOOD FAITH REPORT BY NURSE. In this subchapter, a report is considered to be made in good faith if:

(1) the person reporting believed that the report was required or authorized; and

(2) there was a reasonable factual or legal basis for that belief.

Sec. 301.402. MANDATORY REPORT BY NURSE. Subsecs. (f) , (g)

(f) A person may not suspend or terminate the employment of, or otherwise discipline, discriminate against, or retaliate against, a person who:

(1) reports in good faith under this section; or

(2) advises a nurse of the nurse's rights and obligations under this section.

(g) A violation of Subsection (f) is subject to Section 301.413.

Sec. 301.4025. OPTIONAL REPORT BY NURSE. Subsecs. (c), (d)

(c) A person may not suspend or terminate the employment of, or otherwise discipline, discriminate against, or retaliate against, a person who:

(1) reports in good faith under this section; or

(2) advises a nurse of the nurse's right to report under this section.

(d) A violation of Subsection (c) is subject to Section 301.413.

Sec. 301.412. REPORTING IMMUNITY. A person who in good faith makes a report required or authorized under this subchapter, or a person who advises a nurse of the nurse's right or obligation to report under this subchapter:

(1) is immune from civil and criminal liability that, in the absence of the immunity, might result from making the report or giving the advice; and

(2) may not be subjected to other retaliatory action as a result of making the report or giving the advice.

Flowchart of Safe Harbor Nursing Peer Review Process
Practical Guide to Nurse's Rights Under Safe Harbor Nursing Peer Review
Forms for Requesting Safe Harbor Nursing Peer Review

A number of provisions in the Nursing Practice Act and other laws provide nurses protections against retaliation and discrimination because they report patient care concerns.

This definition of "good faith" was added in 2011 and is the standard consistently used throughout the NPA and Nursing Peer Review Law to identify protected patient advocacy activities. It combines a subjective standard of the person's belief with an objective standard that the belief be reasonable. The definition is based on the definition the Texas Supreme Court established for whistleblower cases in Wichita Co. v. Hart, 917 S.W.2d 779 (Tex. 1996).

ANNOTATOR'S NOTE: *NPA Sec. 301.402 addresses mandatory reporting by nurses of other nurses. See Part s I (NPA) and VI (Reporting) of this Guide for the full text of Sec. 301.402.*
Subsection. (f) explicitly prohibits discrimination or retaliation against a nurse for reporting as authorized by this Sec. 301.402.
A person who advises a nurse on her or his right to report is also protected from retaliation.

Sec. 301.413 gives the nurse, who is illegally retaliated against, two remedies – filing a lawsuit for damages and filing a complaint with the appropriate licensing agency. If the nurse prevails in the lawsuit the minimum recovery is $5,000 in damages plus attorney fees. If the licensing agency finds retaliation, it can impose a fine of up to $25,000. See Subpart D below.

ANNOTATOR'S NOTE: *NPA Sec. 301.4025 addresses optional reporting by nurses of 1) practitioners (non-nurses) and facilities and 2) pateint care concerns within a facility. See Part s I (NPA) and VI (Reporting) of this Guide for the full text of Sec. 301.402.*
Subsection (c) explicitly prohibits discrimination or retaliation against a nurse for reporting as authorized by this Sec. 301.4025.
A person who advises a nurse on her or his right to report is also protected from retaliation.

Sec. 301.413 gives the nurse illegally retaliated against two remedies – filing a lawsuit for damages and filing a complaint with the appropriate licensing agency. If the nurse prevails in the lawsuit the minimum recovery is $5,000 in damages plus attorney fees. If the licensing agency finds retaliation, it can impose a fine of up to $25,000. See Subpart D. below.

Persons reporting in good faith are protected from both civil and criminal liability and also from retaliation for making the report. Practitioners are often justifiably concerned that if they report another practitioner, they are going to be sued for professional slander or some other reason. This section is designed to prevent such concerns from having a chilling effect on good faith reporting. "Authorized" reports include reports of other practitioners and facilities under Sec. 301.4025.
Persons who advise a nurse about the nurse's right or duty to report and protections available when reporting are also protected.

SEC. 301.413. RETALIATORY ACTION. SUBSECS. (b), (b-1)

ANNOTATOR'S NOTE: Because it governs the remedies available for various types of illegal retaliation, Sec. 301.413 is set out in full in Subpart D. Only Subsections (b) and ((b-1) are set out here.

(b) A person may not suspend, terminate, or otherwise discipline, discriminate against, or retaliate against a person who:

(1) reports in good faith under this subchapter;

(2) requests, in good faith, a nursing peer review committee determination under Section 303.005;

(3) refuses to engage in conduct as authorized by Section 301.352; or

(4) advises a nurse of the nurse's right to:

(A) report under this subchapter;

(B) request a nursing peer review committee determination under Section 303.005; or

(C) refuse to engage in conduct as authorized by Section 301.352.

2. HOSPITAL SETTING

HEALTH & SAFETY CODE, SEC. 257.003(a)(4), (5), NURSE STAFFING .

(a) The governing body of a hospital shall adopt, implement, and enforce a written nurse staffing policy to ensure that an adequate number and skill mix of nurses are available to meet the level of patient care needed. The policy must include a process for:

(4) encouraging nurses to provide input to the committee [nurse staffing committee] relating to nurse staffing concerns;

(5) protecting from retaliation nurses who provide input to the committee; and

HEALTH & SAFETY CODE, SEC. 161.134. RETALIATION AGAINST EMPLOYEES PROHIBITED. (a) A hospital, mental health facility, or treatment facility may not suspend or terminate the employment of or discipline or otherwise discriminate against an employee for reporting to the employee's supervisor, an administrator of the facility, a state regulatory agency, or a law enforcement agency a violation of law, including a violation of this chapter, a rule adopted under this chapter, or a rule adopted by the Texas Board of Mental Health and Mental Retardation, the Texas Board of Health, or the Texas Commission on Alcohol and Drug Abuse.

(b) A hospital, mental health facility, or treatment facility that violates Subsection (a) is liable to the person discriminated against. A person who has been discriminated against in violation of Subsection (a) may sue for injunctive relief, damages, or both.

(c) A plaintiff who prevails in a suit under this section may recover actual damages, including damages for mental anguish even if an injury other than mental anguish is not shown.

(d) In addition to an award under Subsection (c), a plaintiff who prevails in a suit under this section may recover exemplary damages and reasonable attorney fees.

(e) In addition to amounts recovered under Subsections (c) and (d), a plaintiff is entitled to, if applicable:

(1) reinstatement in the plaintiff's former position;

(2) compensation for lost wages; and

(3) reinstatement of lost fringe benefits or seniority rights.

This Subsec. (b) provides specific protections for nurses engaged in protected patient advocacy activities from being terminated or retaliated against. The reference to "subchapter" is the reporting provisions of the NPA (Secs. 301.401-.419) which include mandatory and optional reporting. In its 1998 opinion Clark v. Texas Home Health, Inc., the Texas Supreme Court upheld a liberal interpretation of this section as providing "a cause of action for retaliatory acts against persons reporting under [Subchapter Sec. 301.401-.419]." The opinion is set out in Part X (Appendices) to this Guide.

Persons who advise a nurse about the nurse's right or duty to report and protections available when reporting are also protected under this section.

In addition to the protections for nurses provided by the Nursing Practice Act, the laws and regulations governing the hospital setting provide additional protections to nurses reporting patient care concerns in those settings.

The hospital governing body's policies must include a process for protecting nurses from retaliation for providing input to the committee.

The protections provided by this section are very similar to those provided by NPA Sec. 301.413 for nurses generally and Health & Safety Code 242.133 relating to long-term care facilities.

(f) A plaintiff suing under this section has the burden of proof, except that it is a rebuttable presumption that the plaintiff's employment was suspended or terminated, or that the employee was disciplined or discriminated against, for making a report related to a violation if the suspension, termination, discipline, or discrimination occurs before the 60th day after the date on which the plaintiff made a report in good faith.

(g) A suit under this section may be brought in the district court of the county in which:

(1) the plaintiff was employed by the defendant; or

(2) the defendant conducts business.

(h) A person who alleges a violation of Subsection (a) must sue under this section before the 180th day after the date the alleged violation occurred or was discovered by the employee through the use of reasonable diligence.

(i) This section does not abrogate any other right to sue or interfere with any other cause of action.

(j) Each hospital, mental health facility, and treatment facility shall prominently and conspicuously post for display in a public area of the facility that is readily available to patients, residents, employees, and visitors a statement that employees and staff are protected from discrimination or retaliation for reporting a violation of law. The statement must be in English and in a second language.

HEALTH & SAFETY CODE, SEC. 241.026(a)(6). MINIMUM STANDARDS.

(a) The board shall adopt and enforce rules to further the purposes of this chapter. The rules at a minimum shall address:

(6) compliance with nursing peer review under Subchapter I, Chapter 301 and Chapter 303, Occupations Code, and the rules of the Texas Board of Nursing relating to peer review.

DSHS RULE §133.43. DISCRIMINATION OR RETALIATION STANDARDS.

(a) Posting requirements for reporting a violation of law. In accordance with Health and Safety Code (HSC), §161.134(j) and §161.135(h), each hospital shall prominently and conspicuously post for display in a public area of the hospital that is readily visible to patients, residents, employees, and visitors a statement that nonemployees, employees and staff are protected from discrimination or retaliation for reporting a violation of law. The statement shall be in English and in a second language appropriate to the demographic makeup of the community served.

(b) Discrimination relating to employee reporting a violation of law. In accordance with HSC, §161.134(a), and §133.41(o)(2)(I)(i)(III) of this title (relating to Hospital Functions and Services), a hospital may not suspend or terminate the employment of, discipline, or otherwise discriminate against an employee for reporting in good faith to the employee's supervisor, an administrator of the hospital, a state or federal regulatory agency, a national accrediting organization or a law enforcement agency a violation of law, including a violation of the Act or this chapter. For purposes of this subsection, a report is not made in good faith if there is not a reasonable factual or legal basis for making the report.

(c) Retaliation relating to nonemployee reporting a violation of law. In accordance with HSC, §161.135(a), a hospital may not retaliate against a person who is not an employee for reporting a violation of law, including a violation of the Act or this chapter.

DSHS RULE §133.41(o) HOSPITAL NURSING SERVICES - Subsecs. (2)(G)(ii)(VII) and (6)

(2)(G) The hospital shall adopt, implement and enforce a written official nurse services staffing plan.

(ii) The plan shall:

(VII) incorporate a process that facilitates the timely and effective identification of concerns about the adequacy of the staffing plan by the nurse staffing committee established

The Department of State Health Services has adopted Rule 133.41(o)(5) requiring hospitals to comply with the NPA, NPR Law and BON rules. See below.

At the same time it adopted the hospital nurse staffing rules, the Department of State Health Services strengthened its rule providing protection to nurses reporting concerns.

ANNOTATOR'S NOTE. The reference to 133.41(o)(2)(I)(i)(III) is an outdated reference to an earlier version of the nurse staffing rules. The correct reference is 133.41(o)(2)(G)(ii)(VII).

Each hospital must have a written staffing plan.

One of the components of the plan must be a process for reporting of concerns about staffing that is non-retaliatory and incorporates safe harbor nursing peer review.

pursuant to subparagraph (F) of this paragraph. This process shall include:

(-a-) a prohibition on retaliation for reporting concerns;

(-b-) a requirement that nurses report concerns timely through appropriate channels within the hospital;

(-c-) orientation of nurses on how to report concerns and to whom;

(-d-) encouraging nurses to provide input to the committee relating to nurse staffing concerns;

(-e-) review, assessment, and response by the committee to staffing concerns expressed to the committee;

(-f-) a process for providing feedback during the committee meeting on how concerns are addressed by the advisory committee established under subparagraph (F) of this paragraph; and

(-g-) use of the nurse safe harbor peer review process pursuant to Occupations Code, §303.005;

(6) Reporting and peer review of a vocational or registered nurse. A hospital shall adopt, implement, and enforce a policy to ensure that the hospital complies with the Occupations Code §§301.401 - 301.403, 301.405 and Chapter 303 (relating to Grounds for Reporting Nurse, Duty of Nurse to Report, Duty of Peer Review Committee to Report, Duty of Person Employing Nurse to Report, and Nursing Peer Review respectively), and with the rules adopted by the Texas Board of Nursing in 22 TAC §217.16 (relating to Minor Incidents), §217.19 (relating to Incident-Based Nursing Peer Review and Whistleblower Protections), and §217.20 (relating to Safe Harbor Peer Review for Nurses and Whistleblower Protections).

DSHS RULE 133.45(e). MISCELLANEOUS POLICIES AND PROTOCOLS.

(e) Harassment and abuse. A hospital shall adopt, implement and enforce a written policy for identifying and addressing instances of alleged verbal or physical abuse or harassment of hospital employees or contracted personnel by other hospital employees or contracted personnel or by a health care provider who has clinical privileges at the hospital.

3. LONG-TERM CARE SETTING

HEALTH & SAFETY CODE, SEC. 242.133. RETALIATION AGAINST EMPLOYEES PROHIBITED. (a) In this section, "employee" means a person who is an employee of an institution or any other person who provides services for an institution for compensation, including a contract laborer for the institution.

(b) An employee has a cause of action against an institution, or the owner or another employee of the institution, that suspends or terminates the employment of the person or otherwise disciplines or discriminates or retaliates against the employee for reporting to the employee's supervisor, an administrator of the institution, a state regulatory agency, or a law enforcement agency a violation of law, including a violation of this chapter or a rule adopted under this chapter, or for initiating or cooperating in any investigation or proceeding of a governmental entity relating to care, services, or conditions at the institution.

(c) The petitioner may recover:

(1) the greater of $1,000 or actual damages, including damages for mental anguish even if an injury other than mental anguish is not shown and damages for lost wages if the petitioner's employment was suspended or terminated;

(2) exemplary damages;

(3) court costs; and (4) reasonable attorney's fees.

(d) In addition to the amounts that may be recovered under Subsection (c), a person

This section requires hospitals to implement policies to assure compliance with other laws and regulations relating to nursing including mandatory reporting, peer review and minor incidents.

At the same time it adopted the hospital nurse staffing rules, the Department of State Health Services adopted this rule requiring hospitals to have written policies for preventing verbal and physical abuse and harassment.

In addition to the protections for nurses provided by the Nursing Practice Act, the laws and regulations governing the long-term care setting provide additional protections to nurses reporting patient care concerns in those settings.

The protections provided by this section are very similar to those provided by NPA Sec. 301.413 for nurses generally and Health & Safety Code 161.134 relating to hospitals.

whose employment is suspended or terminated is entitled to appropriate injunctive relief, including, if applicable:

(1) reinstatement in the person's former position; and

(2) reinstatement of lost fringe benefits or seniority rights.

(e) The petitioner, not later than the 90th day after the date on which the person's employment is suspended or terminated, must bring suit or notify the Texas Workforce Commission of the petitioner's intent to sue under this section. A petitioner who notifies the Texas Workforce Commission under this subsection must bring suit not later than the 90th day after the date of the delivery of the notice to the commission. On receipt of the notice, the commission shall notify the institution of the petitioner's intent to bring suit under this section.

(f) The petitioner has the burden of proof, except that there is a rebuttable presumption that the person's employment was suspended or terminated for reporting abuse or neglect if the person is suspended or terminated within 60 days after the date on which the person reported in good faith.

(g) A suit under this section may be brought in the district court of the county in which:

(1) the plaintiff resides;

(2) the plaintiff was employed by the defendant; or

(3) the defendant conducts business.

(h) Each institution shall require each employee of the institution, as a condition of employment with the institution, to sign a statement that the employee understands the employee's rights under this section. The statement must be part of the statement required under Section 242.122. If an institution does not require an employee to read and sign the statement, the periods under Subsection (e) do not apply, and the petitioner must bring suit not later than the second anniversary of the date on which the person's employment is suspended or terminated.

4. HOME AND COMMUNITY SERVICES SETTING

HEALTH & SAFETY CODE SEC. 142.0093. RETALIATION PROHIBITED. (a) A person licensed under this chapter may not retaliate against another person for filing a complaint, presenting a grievance, or providing in good faith information relating to home health, hospice, or personal assistance services provided by the license holder.

(b) This section does not prohibit a license holder from terminating an employee for a reason other than retaliation.

5. PUBLIC EMPLOYMENT SETTING

GOVERNMENT CODE CH. 554. TEXAS PUBLIC EMPLOYEES WHISTLEBLOWER LAW

***ANNOTATOR'S NOTE**: Only selective provisions are being set out.*

Sec. 554.001. DEFINITIONS.

[omitted]

Sec. 554.002. RETALIATION PROHIBITED FOR REPORTING VIOLATION OF LAW. (a) A state or local governmental entity may not suspend or terminate the employment of, or take other adverse personnel action against, a public employee who in good faith reports a violation of law by the employing governmental entity or another public employee to an appropriate law enforcement authority.

In addition to the protections for nurses provided by the Nursing Practice Act, the laws and regulations governing the home health settings provide additional protections to nurses reporting patient care concerns in those settings.

Publicly-employed nurses are nurses employed in a practice setting operated by a state or local governmental entity such as the stat or a, county, city, hospital district, or school district. These settings include public hospitals, state prisons, county jails, public schools and public health clinics. The Texas Employee's Whistleblower Law provides protections for publicly-employed nurses and other public employees.

Section 554.002	*Identifies the type of reporting protected from retaliation*
Sections 554.003-.0010	*Sets out remedies available when retaliation occurs*

This Sec. 554.002 identifies the type of reporting conduct protected from retaliation. Good faith reporting to an "appropriate law enforcement authority" is protected. "Good faith" has been defined by the Texas Supreme Court in Wichita Co. v. Hart, 917 S.W.2d 779 (Tex. 1996) similar to NPA Sec. 301.4011 as requiring 1) the person reporting believe the report was required or authorized and 2) there being a reasonable factual or legal basis for that belief. "Appropriate

(b) In this section, a report is made to an appropriate law enforcement authority if the authority is a part of a state or local governmental entity or of the federal government that the employee in good faith believes is authorized to:

(1) regulate under or enforce the law alleged to be violated in the report; or

(2) investigate or prosecute a violation of criminal law

Sec. 554.003. RELIEF AVAILABLE TO PUBLIC EMPLOYEE. (a) A public employee whose employment is suspended or terminated or who is subjected to an adverse personnel action in violation of Section 554.002 is entitled to sue for:

(1) injunctive relief;

(2) actual damages;

(3) court costs; and

(4) reasonable attorney fees.

(b) In addition to relief under Subsection (a), a public employee whose employment is suspended or terminated in violation of this chapter is entitled to:

(1) reinstatement to the employee's former position or an equivalent position;

(2) compensation for wages lost during the period of suspension or termination; and

(3) reinstatement of fringe benefits and seniority rights lost because of the suspension or termination.

(c) In a suit under this chapter against an employing state or local governmental entity, a public employee may not recover compensatory damages for future pecuniary losses, emotional pain, suffering, inconvenience, mental anguish, loss of enjoyment of life, and other nonpecuniary losses in an amount that exceeds:

(1) $50,000, if the employing state or local governmental entity has fewer than 101 employees in each of 20 or more calendar weeks in the calendar year in which the suit is filed or in the preceding year;

(2) $100,000, if the employing state or local governmental entity has more than 100 and fewer than 201 employees in each of 20 or more calendar weeks in the calendar year in which the suit is filed or in the preceding year;

(3) $200,000, if the employing state or local governmental entity has more than 200 and fewer than 501 employees in each of 20 or more calendar weeks in the calendar year in which the suit is filed or in the preceding year; and

(4) $250,000, if the employing state or local governmental entity has more than 500 employees in each of 20 or more calendar weeks in the calendar year in which the suit is filed or in the preceding year.

(d) If more than one subdivision of Subsection (c) applies to an employing state or local governmental entity, the amount of monetary damages that may be recovered from the entity in a suit brought under this chapter is governed by the applicable provision that provides the highest damage award.

Sec. 554.0035. WAIVER OF IMMUNITY. A public employee who alleges a violation of this chapter may sue the employing state or local governmental entity for the relief provided by this chapter. Sovereign immunity is waived and abolished to the extent of liability for the relief allowed under this chapter for a violation of this chapter.

Sec. 554.004. BURDEN OF PROOF; PRESUMPTION; AFFIRMATIVE DEFENSE.

(a) A public employee who sues under this chapter has the burden of proof, except that if the suspension or termination of, or adverse personnel action against, a public employee occurs not later than the 90th day after the date on which the employee reports a violation of law, the suspension, termination, or adverse personnel action is presumed, subject to rebuttal, to be because the employee made the report.

(b) It is an affirmative defense to a suit under this chapter that the employing state or local governmental entity would have taken the action against the employee that forms the basis of the *law enforcement" is defined in Subsec. (b) and includes a regulatory agency responsible for the regulation or enforcement of the law alleged to be violated. For example, the Texas Medical Board would be the "appropriate law enforcement authority" for reporting a physician and the Department of State Health Services for reporting a hospital.*

The relief is similar to what is available in the NPA except that exemplary damages cannot be recovered. The amount of monetary damages is limited based on number of employees the governmental entity has. See Subsec. (c)

The amount of monetary damages is limited based on number of employees the governmental entity has.

This section is an example of the language needed to explicitly waive sovereign immunity.

This presumption is similar to rebuttal presumption in the Nursing Practice Act except it is only 60 days in the NPA.

suit based solely on information, observation, or evidence that is not related to the fact that the employee made a report protected under this chapter of a violation of law.

Sec. 554.005. LIMITATION PERIOD. Except as provided by Section 554.006, a public employee who seeks relief under this chapter must sue not later than the 90th day after the date on which the alleged violation of this chapter:

(1) occurred; or

(2) was discovered by the employee through reasonable diligence.

Sec. 554.006. USE OF GRIEVANCE OR APPEAL PROCEDURES. (a) A public employee must initiate action under the grievance or appeal procedures of the employing state or local governmental entity relating to suspension or termination of employment or adverse personnel action before suing under this chapter.

(b) The employee must invoke the applicable grievance or appeal procedures not later than the 90th day after the date on which the alleged violation of this chapter:

(1) occurred; or

(2) was discovered by the employee through reasonable diligence.

(c) Time used by the employee in acting under the grievance or appeal procedures is excluded, except as provided by Subsection (d), from the period established by Section 554.005.

(d) If a final decision is not rendered before the 61st day after the date procedures are initiated under Subsection (a), the employee may elect to:

(1) exhaust the applicable procedures under Subsection (a), in which event the employee must sue not later than the 30th day after the date those procedures are exhausted to obtain relief under this chapter; or

(2) terminate procedures under Subsection (a), in which event the employee must sue within the time remaining under Section 554.005 to obtain relief under this chapter.

Sec. 554.007. WHERE SUIT BROUGHT.

[omitted]

Sec. 554.008. CIVIL PENALTY. (a) A supervisor who in violation of this chapter suspends or terminates the employment of a public employee or takes an adverse personnel action against the employee is liable for a civil penalty not to exceed $15,000.

(b) The attorney general or appropriate prosecuting attorney may sue to collect a civil penalty under this section.

(c) A civil penalty collected under this section shall be deposited in the state treasury.

(d) A civil penalty assessed under this section shall be paid by the supervisor and may not be paid by the employing governmental entity.

(e) The personal liability of a supervisor or other individual under this chapter is limited to the civil penalty that may be assessed under this section.

Sec. 554.009. NOTICE TO EMPLOYEES. (a) A state or local governmental entity shall inform its employees of their rights under this chapter by posting a sign in a prominent location in the workplace.

(b) The attorney general shall prescribe the design and content of the sign required by this section.

Sec. 554.010. AUDIT OF STATE GOVERNMENTAL ENTITY AFTER SUIT.

[omitted]

The time within which to file a lawsuit is 90 days which is shorter than most other whistleblower laws. This 90 days can be extended if grievance procedures are initiated. But the grievance has to be initiated within 90 days.

An individual must exhaust any grievance process within the agency.

The individual supervisor may be sued but the penalty is limited to $15,000.

Governmental entities are required to give employees notice of their rights under this law.

SUBPART C
REFUSAL TO ENGAGE IN REPORTABLE CONDUCT

NPA SEC. 301.352. PROTECTION FOR REFUSAL TO ENGAGE IN CERTAIN CONDUCT.

(a) A person may not suspend, terminate, or otherwise discipline, discriminate against, or retaliate against:

(1) a nurse who refuses to engage in an act or omission as provided by Subsection (a-1); or

(2) a person who advises a nurse of the nurse's rights under this section.

(a-1) A nurse may refuse to engage in an act or omission relating to patient care that would constitute grounds for reporting the nurse to the board under Subchapter I, that constitutes a minor incident, or that violates this chapter or a board rule if the nurse notifies the person at the time of the refusal that the reason for refusing is that the act or omission:

(1) constitutes grounds for reporting the nurse to the board; or

(2) is a violation of this chapter or a rule of the board.

(b) An act by a person under Subsection (a) does not constitute a violation of this section if a nursing peer review committee under Chapter 303 determines:

(1) that the act or omission the nurse refused to engage in was not:

(A) conduct reportable to the board under Section 301.403;

(B) a minor incident; or

(C) a violation of this chapter or a board rule; or

(2) that:

(A) the act or omission in which the nurse refused to engage was conduct reportable to the board, a minor incident, or a violation of this chapter or a board rule; and

(B) the person:

(i) rescinds any disciplinary or discriminatory action taken against the nurse;

(ii) compensates the nurse for lost wages;

(iii) restores to the nurse any lost benefits.

(c) A nurse's rights under this section may not be nullified by a contract.

(d) An appropriate licensing agency may take action against a person who violates this section.

(e) *[Repealed]*

(f) A violation of this section is subject to Section 301.413.

This provision is designed to provide protection to the RN or LVN who refuses to engage in conduct the nurse believes would be reportable to the BON as a violation of the NPA or BON rules. Nurses can be placed in situations in which they feel they are faced with having to choose between a) refusing to carry out an employer's directive, or b) engaging in conduct the nurse believes violates the NPA or BON rules. NPR Law Sec. 303.005 is a companion provision permitting RNs and LVNs to request nursing peer review if they believe they are requested to engage in conduct that violates their duty to a patient.

Discriminating or retaliating against a nurse for refusing to engage in conduct that would violate a BON rule or subject the nurse to being reported to the BON is prohibited.

When refusing to engage in the conduct, the RN or LVN must state that the reason for the refusal is that the nurse believes it violates the NPA or BON rules. The most important BON rules are those defining standards of practice and unprofessional conduct. The references to "minor incidents" and "violations of this chapter [NPA] or BON rules" are included to ensure protection for the nurse even if the conduct involved is a minor incident not reportable to the BON under Rule 217.16.

Subsection (b) sets out two situations in which the employer is deemed <u>not</u> to have violated this section.

1. *If the incident is reviewed by a nursing peer review committee and the committee finds that, in its opinion, the nurse's engaging in the conduct she/he refused to do would not in fact have been a violation of the NPA or BON rules, i.e., the nurse was not being asked to engage in reportable conduct or a violation (even a minor violation) of the NPA or BON rules.*
2. *If the peer review committee finds that to have engaged in the conduct would have been a violation of the NPA but the employer makes the nurse whole -- that is, rescinds any disciplinary action taken, pays all back wages and restores any lost benefits.*

Nurses may not be required to contract away their rights, for example, agree in an employment contract to give up their right under this Sec. 301.352.

Violation of this section is a basis for a licensing agency to take action against that organization or person. For example, if a nurse administrator violates this section, she/he would be subject to disciplinary action by the BON. If a hospital violates this section, it would be subject to action by the Department of State Health Services. See also Sec. 301.413(b-1).

Sec. 301.413 sets out the remedies available to a nurse who is discriminated or retaliated against in violation of this Sec. 301.352. Those remedies include filing a complaint with the appropriate licensing agency or filing a lawsuit for damages (minimum of $5,000) and attorney's fees.

SUBPART D.
NURSES' REMEDIES FOR RETALIATION UNDER NPA

1. Remedies Under NPA and NPR Law

Sec. 301.413. RETALIATORY ACTION.

(a) A person may file a counter claim in a pending action or prove a cause of action in a subsequent suit to recover defense costs, including reasonable attorney's fees and actual and punitive damages, if:

(1) the person is named as a defendant in a civil action or subjected to other retaliatory action as a result of:

(A) filing a report required or authorized, or reasonably believed to be required or authorized, under this subchapter as a result of refusing to engage in conduct as authorized by Section 301.352;

(B) requesting in good faith a nursing peer review committee determination under Section 303.005; or

(C) providing advice to a person regarding:

(i) filing a report required or authorized, or reasonably believed to be required or authorized, under this subchapter as a result of refusing to engage in conduct as authorized by Section 301.352; or

(ii) requesting in good faith a nursing peer review committee determination under Section 303.005; and

(2) the suit or retaliatory action is determined to be frivolous, unreasonable, or taken in bad faith.

(b) A person may not suspend, terminate, or otherwise discipline, discriminate against, or retaliate against a person who:

(1) reports in good faith under this subchapter;

(2) requests, in good faith, a nursing peer review committee determination under Section 303.005;

(3) refuses to engage in conduct as authorized by Section 301.352; or

(4) advises a nurse of the nurse's right to:

(A) report under this subchapter;

(B) request a nursing peer review committee determination under Section 303.005; or

Section 301.413 sets out the remedies available to nurses who have been retaliated or discriminated against because they engaged in protected patient advocacy activities or because they advised another nurse of these patient advocacy protections. The activities protected are:

1. *Refusing to engage in conduct subject to reporting or that would violate NPA or BON rule (NPA Sec. 301.352)*
2. *Reporting a nurse (NPA Sec. 301.402), a practitioner (other than a nurse) or a facility (NPA Sec. 301.4025(a)) or raising of patient care concern within a facility (Sec. 301.4025(b))*
3. *Requesting safe harbor nursing peer review (NPR Law Sec. 303.005)*
4. *Advising a nurse on protections (1)-(3)*

It was amended in 2007 by SB 993 to make explicit that the remedies of this section applied to all of the reports listed above. A cross-reference was also added to each of the sections listed tying them to the remedies set out in this Sec. 301.413.

This Subsec. (a) provides general legal recourse to any person sued or otherwise retaliated against for engaging in protected patient advocacy activities.

It appears that there should be an "or" between "subchapter" and "as a result" but this it the way the statute reads. See history of change to this Subsec. (a) in SBs 993 (2007), 476 (2009), 192 (2011) and also wording of Subsecs. (b), (c).

Persons who advise a nurse about the nurse's right or duty to report and protections available when reporting are also protected under this section.

It appears that there should be an "or" between "subchapter" and "as a result" but this it the way the statute reads. See history of changes to this Subsec. (a) in SBs 993 (2007), 476 (2009), 192 (2011) and also wording of Subsecs. (b), (c).

This Subsec. (b) provides specific protections for persons reporting, in good faith, from being terminated or retaliated against at their job. It covers not only mandatory reporting, but also any reporting authorized by this section, e.g., reporting other providers under Sec. 301.402. In a 1998 opinion, <u>Clark v. Texas Home Health, Inc.</u>, the Texas Supreme Court upheld a liberal interpretation of this section as providing "a cause of action for retaliatory acts against persons reporting under this [Sec. 301.401-.419]." The opinion is set out in the Appendices to this Guide.

Persons who advise a nurse about the nurse's right or duty to report and protections available when reporting are also protected under this section.

(C) refuse to engage in conduct as authorized by Section 301.352.

(b-1) A person suspected of violating Subsection (b) may be reported to the appropriate licensing agency and, notwithstanding any other provision, that agency may impose an administrative penalty not to exceed $25,000 against the person if the agency finds a violation of Subsection (b). An administrative penalty imposed under this subsection is in addition to other penalties the agency is authorized to impose and is subject to the procedural requirements applicable to the appropriate licensing agency.

(c) A person who reports under this subchapter, refuses to engage in conduct as authorized by Section 301.352, or requests a nursing peer review committee determination under Section 303.005, or a person who advises a nurse of the nurse's right to report under this subchapter, refuse to engage in conduct as authorized by Section 301.352, or request a nursing peer review committee determination under Section 303.005, has a cause of action against a person who violates Subsection (b), and may recover:

(1) the greater of:

(A) actual damages, including damages for mental anguish even if no other injury is shown; or

(B) $5,000;

(2) exemplary damages;

(3) court costs; and

(4) reasonable attorney's fees.

(d) In addition to the amount recovered under Subsection (c), a person whose employment is suspended or terminated in violation of this section is entitled to:

(1) reinstatement in the employee's former position or severance pay in an amount equal to three months of the employee's most recent salary; and

(2) compensation for wages lost during the period of suspension or termination.

(e) A person who brings an action under this section has the burden of proof. It is a rebuttable presumption that the person was suspended, terminated, or otherwise disciplined, discriminated against, or retaliated against for reporting under this subchapter, for refusing to engage in conduct as authorized by Section 301.352, for requesting a peer review committee determination under Section 303.005, or for providing advice to a person regarding reporting under this subchapter, refusing to engage in conduct as authorized by Section 301.352, or requesting a peer review committee determination under Section 303.005 if:

(1) the person was suspended, terminated, or otherwise disciplined, discriminated against, or retaliated against within 60 days after the date the report, refusal, or request was made or the advice was given; and

(2) the board or a court determines that:

(A) the report that is the subject of the cause of action was:

(i) authorized or required under Section 301.402, 301.4025, 301.403, 301.405, 301.406, 301.407, 301.408, 301.409, or 301.410; and

(ii) made in good faith;

(B) the request for a peer review committee determination that is the subject of the cause of action was:

(i) authorized under Section 303.005; and

(ii) made in good faith;

(C) the refusal to engage in conduct was authorized by Section 301.352; or

(D) the advice that is the subject of the cause of action was given in good faith.

(f) An action under this section may be brought in a district court of the county in which:

(1) the plaintiff resides;

(2) the plaintiff was employed by the defendant; or

(3) the defendant conducts business.

Licensed practitioners or facilities that retaliate may be reported to their licensing board which may impose a fine of up to $25,000. The agency could also take action against the practitioner's or facility's license.

The person reporting may recover not only actual damages including mental anguish, but also exemplary damages and attorney's fees. The minimum recovery for actual damages is set at $5,000.

Proving that a person's motive was retaliation can be difficult. This section addresses this difficulty by creating a rebuttal presumption that any adverse action taken within 60 days of the protected conduct was taken in retaliation. A rebuttal presumption is one that creates a presumption that can be overcome by opposing evidence. The person alleged to have retaliated against the nurse would have to present such opposing evidence. Once she/he does, then the burden of proof returns to the nurse to prove the retaliation. The rebuttal presumption prevents the defendant from simply denying the retaliation without putting on any evidence of the reason for the alleged retaliatory conduct. Once the defendant puts in evidence, that evidence can be evaluated, challenged and refuted.

(g) Subject to Subsection (h), a nurse employed by a hospital operated by or on behalf of a state or local governmental entity who alleges a violation of Subsection (b) may sue the state or local governmental entity for relief under this section, and the sovereign immunity of the state or local governmental entity from suit and from liability is waived for the limited purpose of allowing the nurse to maintain a lawsuit in state court to obtain that relief. Relief under this section is in addition to any other remedies a nurse may have under state or federal law as a public employee. In this subsection:

(1) "Local governmental entity," "public employee," and "state governmental entity" have the meanings assigned by Section 554.001, Government Code.

(2) "Hospital" has the meaning assigned by Section 241.003, Health and Safety Code, and includes a mental hospital licensed under Chapter 577, Health and Safety Code.

(h) Relief may be granted in a lawsuit brought under Subsection (g) for an alleged violation of Subsection (b)(1) based on a report made by a nurse under Section 301.4025(b) only if the nurse:

(1) made the report:

(A) in writing, which may be provided electronically; or

(B) verbally, if authorized by the nurse's employer or another entity at which the nurse is authorized to practice;

(2) made the report to:

(A) the nurse's supervisor;

(B) a committee authorized under state or federal law to receive reports under Section 301.4025(b); or

(C) an individual or committee authorized by the nurse's employer or another entity at which the nurse is authorized to practice; and

(3) made the report not later than:

(A) the fifth day after the date the nurse became aware of the situation if the situation involves a single incident; or

(B) the fifth day after the date the nurse became aware of the most recent occurrence of the situation if the situation involves multiple incidents or a pattern of behavior.

(i) For purposes of Subsection (h), "supervisor" means an individual who has authority over the responsibilities of the nurse making the report or an individual who is in the nurse's chain of command.

(j) The following provisions of Chapter 554, Government Code, apply to a lawsuit under Subsection (g):

(1) the type of relief and the amount of damages available to a public employee under Section 554.003;

(2) the time during which a public employee must seek relief under Section 554.005; and

(3) the requirement that a public employee use the grievance or appeal procedures of the state or local governmental entity before suing for relief under Section 554.006.

(k) A lawsuit under Subsection (g) against a state governmental entity shall be brought in a district court in Travis County or a county in which all or part of the acts or omissions giving rise to the cause of action occurred.

(l) A lawsuit under Subsection (g) against a local governmental entity shall be brought in a district court in a county in which all or part of the entity is located.

2. Remedies Under Other Laws

ANNOTATOR'S NOTE*. The remedies available under laws are set out in Subpart B above and include the laws covering the hospital, long-term care, home health, and public employment settings.*

Subsections (g)-(l) were added in 2013 (HB 581) to provide public hospital employed nurses a right to file a lawsuit to recover damages resulting from retaliation for engaging in patient advocacy activities protected under Subsection (b). Without this type of explicit waiver of sovereign immunity, public hospital employed nurses would have to seek recovery under the Public Employee Whistleblower Law (Government Code, Chap. 554). That law covers only external reporting and not all of the activities listed under Subsection (b). This Subsection applies only to public hospital employed nurses and not to nurses employed by other public entities such as a jail or county health department. The Public Employee Whistleblower Law is set out in Part VI (Advocacy Protections) of this Guide.

Subsections (h) and (i) were added by the Legislature to address concern that a county or other entity operating a public hospital might be sued for retaliation without ever being aware that the nurse made a protected report of unsafe care. A report under Sec. 301.4025(b) is an optional report in a facility about unsafe care.

A supervisor is anyone in the nurse's chain of command. Supervisor was defined this way so nurse could raise concerns to administration if felt an immediate supervisor was not adequately addressing a concern.

The type of relief that a public hospital employed nurse can recover is subject to the limitations set out in the Public Employee Whistleblower Law. It sets a limit on the amount of damages based on the size of the governmental entity and also does not permit punitive damages. The Public Employee Whistleblower Law is set out in Part VI (Advocacy Protections) of this Guide.

Subsections (k) and (l) determine where a lawusit by a public hospitla employed nurse must be filed.

Most of the remedies are not as detailed as those set out in NPA Sec. 301.413 nor are the protected patient advocacy activities as broadly defined. If more than one law applies (e.g., Sec. 301.413 and hospital licensing law), the nurse has the benefit of both and would seek the most

3. Remedies for Publicly-Employed Nurses

ANNOTATOR'S NOTE. *The law providing remedies specifically to publicly-employed nurses is the Texas Whistleblower Law set out in Subpart B above.*

SUBPART E.
PROTECTIONS FROM NEGATIVE JOB REFERENCE

Labor Code Sec. 103.003(b). AUTHORIZED DISCLOSURES RELATING TO NURSES.

(b) An employer may not disclose information about a licensed nurse or licensed vocational nurse that relates to conduct that is protected under Section 301.352 or 303.005, Occupations Code. The employer must provide an affected nurse an opportunity to submit a statement of reasonable length to the employer to establish the application of Section 301.352 or 303.005, Occupations Code.

favorable remedy available.

Special considerations apply to publicly employed nurses because of the doctrine of sovereign immunity. Publicly-employed nurses are nurses employed in a practice setting operated by a sate or local governmental entity such as the state, county, city hospital district or school district. These settings include public hospitals, state prisons, county jails, public schools and public health clinics. The Texas Employee's Whistleblower Law provides protections for publicly-employed nurses and other public employees.

A governmental entity cannot be sued unless it gives its permission to be sued. This is referred to as sovereign immunity, i.e., as the "sovereign" they are immune from being sued without their consent. When a governmental entity consents to being sued, it is said to have "waived sovereign immunity." Texas law requires there be an explicit waiver of sovereign immunity. The government consents by the legislature passing a law giving its permission for specific types of situations. The Texas Public Whistleblower Law is an example of a waiver of sovereign immunity.

Prior to 2013, NPA Sec. 301.413 did not include a waiver of sovereign immunity. In 2013, legislation (HB 581) was passed amending Sec. 301.413 to add explicitly waiving sovereign immunity for nurses employed by a hospital operated by or on behalf of a state or local governmental entity. This would include a hospital operated by the state, a hospital district or a county. Nurses employed by these public hospitals have the right to file a law suit for illegal retaliation both under the Sec. 301.413 of the NPA and also the Public Employees Whistleblower Law. Sec. 301.413 does limit some of remedies (e.g., type and amount) to those available under the Public Employee Whistleblower Law. See Sec. 301.413(g)-(l) above.

The remedy for retaliation available to publicly-employed nurses in other settings will continue to be only those available under the Public Employee Whistleblower Law (PEWL). One of the most significant differences is the PEWL applies only to external reports made to law enforcement or a regulatory agency and not to internal reports or to requests for safe harbor nursing peer review. Any retaliation would still be illegal but the nurse is likely not to have the right to file a lawsuit for monetary harm caused by the retaliation.

The Texas Labor Code gives employers significant protections from liability when sharing information about prospective employees. To protect nurses who advocate for their patients from getting a "bad job reference," this provision was included. Sections 301.352 and 303.005 relate to protections for nurses refusing to engage in reportable conduct and safe harbor nursing peer review.

SUBPART F.
SUMMARY OF PATIENT ADVOCACY AND WHISTLEBLOWER PROTECTIONS FOR NURSES IN TEXAS

Patients are best served when nurses can be patient advocates without fear of retaliation. Texas has significant patient advocacy protections for nurses that have resulted from legislative initiatives over the past 20 years.

Protections from Retaliation: In 1987 protections were provided for nurses, who reported a licensed health care practitioner or facility to their licensing agency. This was followed by additional protections in 1995 (protections for refusal to engage in reportable conduct), 1997 (safe harbor nursing peer review), 1999 (protections from retaliation with negative job reference), 2002 (protections included in hospital staffing rules for raising staffing concerns), 2003 (protection when reporting patient care concerns within a facility) and 2007 (clarifying and enhancing protections).

Remedies if Retaliation Occurs: Sec. 301.413 of the Nursing Practice Act sets out the remedies available to nurses who are retaliated against. It authorizes a civil lawsuit for damages (minimum recovery of $5000), attorney's fees, and exemplary damages. It also creates a presumption that any disciplinary action taken against a nurse within 60 days of the nurse's reporting the conduct or raising the patient care concern was taken in retaliation against the nurse. The facility then has the burden of proving otherwise. A nurse also can report the facility or any individual health care practitioner involved in the retaliation to the appropriate licensing agency.

Other Laws Not Limited to Nurses: In addition to laws like the Nursing Practice Act which provide specific protections to nurses, there are other laws protecting all employees, including nurses, in certain settings. These include the laws set out earlier relating to hospitals, long-term care, home health and public employees.

Table Showing Protections and Remedies: The table on the opposite page summarizes the protections provided to Texas nurses when advocating on behalf of their patients and the remedies available if they are retaliated against for engaging in protected advocacy.

Texas Law or Agency Rules	Conduct Covered
Safe Harbor Nursing Peer Review NPR Law §303.005	1. Nurse believes she/he is being requested to engage in conduct that would violate nurse's duty to patient as defined by BON standards of practice and unprofessional conduct rules 2. Nurse advised another nurse about rights under safe harbor nursing peer review
Refusal to Engage in Conduct that Would Violate NPA/BON Rule NPA §301.352	Nurse refusing to engage in conduct that would violate NPA or BON rule or make nurse subject to reporting to BON
Reporting a Patient Care Concern NPA §301.4025	Nurse reporting concern within facility about patient(s) being exposed to substantial risk of harm due to failure of facility or practitioner to conform to minimum professional standards or regulatory/accreditation standards
Reporting Staffing Concerns in Hospitals H&S Code §257.003 DSHS Rules §133.41(o)(2)(G)(ii)(VII) and §133.43	Nurse reporting of staffing concerns in hospital to nurse staffing advisory committee
Reporting a Practitioner or Facility/Agency NPA §301.4025	Nurse reporting a facility or practitioner for exposing a patient to substantial risk of harm due to failure to conform to minimum professional standards or regulatory/ accreditation standards
Mandatory Reporting of Nurse NPA 301.402 (Note: This is in addition to permitted reporting under §301.4025)	Nurse reporting a nurse to BON or to NPR in lieu of reporting to BON who engages in conduct subject to mandatory reporting
Other Laws Not Specific to Nurses H&S Code §§161.134 (hospitals), 242.133 (long-term care), 142.0093 (home health), Govt Code 554.003 (public employment)	Conduct covered varies with each law.

PART VII.

MANDATORY, OPTIONAL, AND ALTERNATE REPORTING

ANNOTATOR'S NOTE: *This Part VII is designed to pull together into a single location the key provisions of the NPA and BON rule governing mandatory reporting. Only the more important provisions are included in this Part VII. Additional NPA provisions relating to mandatory reporting can be found in Part I (NPA) of this Guide Secs. 301.401-.419.*

OVERVIEW

ANNOTATOR'S NOTE: *Only the more important provisions relating to mandatory reporting are included in this Part VII. All NPA provisions relating to mandatory reporting can be found in Part 1 (NPA) of this Guide Secs. 301.401-.419.*

SUBPART A.
CONDUCT THAT MUST BE REPORTED

NPA SEC. 301.401. DEFINITIONS. In this subchapter:

(1) "Conduct subject to reporting" means conduct by a nurse that:

(A) violates this chapter or a board rule and contributed to the death or serious injury of a patient;

(B) causes a person to suspect that the nurse's practice is impaired by chemical dependency or drug or alcohol abuse;

(C) constitutes abuse, exploitation, fraud, or a violation of professional boundaries; or

(D) indicates that the nurse lacks knowledge, skill, judgment, or conscientiousness to such an extent that the nurse's continued practice of nursing could reasonably be expected to pose a risk of harm to a patient or another person, regardless of whether the conduct consists of a single incident or a pattern of behavior.

Mandatory reporting of nurses by nurses was first enacted in 1987 as part of legislation commonly referred to as the Professional Nursing Quality Assurance Act and has been significantly amended since then. The legislation (2003) creating a single licensing act for RNs and LVNs extended reporting requirements to LVNs. Legislation (SB 993) passed in 2007 shifted the perspective reflected in the regulation and reporting of nursing. The pre-2007 perspective was that errors are primarily caused by "bad" individuals, and when an error occurs the job of the regulatory system is to identify and punish the individual who made the error. The post-2007 perspective is to view errors as primarily the result of system inadequacies that either made the error likely to occur or failed to provide the safeguards needed to prevent the error from occurring. Implementing this new perspective involved modifying the NPA mandatory reporting provisions to emphasize that the nurses who should be reported to the BON are those whose continued practice poses a risk of harm to patients and not competent, safe nurses who made a single mistake. For a graphic depiction of the reporting process reflected in SB 993 see the flowchart in Part X (The Appendices) of this Guide.

The NPA sections relating to reporting can be grouped as follows:

- *Sec. 301.401 defines "conduct subject to reporting."*
- *Secs. 301.402-.4025 identify the reporting responsibilities of nurses including voluntary reporting of other providers and facilities.*
- *Secs. 301.403-.409 identify the responsibilities of other persons/entities to report nurses to the BON.*
- *Secs. 301.410-.4106 address reporting of nurses whose practice is impaired by chemical dependency, mental illness, or diminished mental capacity and how the board handles the reports.*
- *Secs. 301.411-.413 address issues of immunity from liability and retaliation protections related to reporting.*
- *Secs. 301.414-.418 address how the BON is to handle reports received, notifying the reported nurse, investigation of report, etc.*
- *Sec. 301.419 addresses reporting of minor incidents and other general issues relating to reporting.*

This definition of "conduct subject to reporting" is used in subsequent sections defining specific reporting requirements for nurses, employers and others. The definition identifies three specific types of conduct subject to reporting and a fourth broader type simply identified as conduct indicating an inability to practice safely. The three specific types of conduct are:

1. *death or serious injury related conduct*
2. *suspected chemical dependency*
3. *bad character conduct such as fraud, abuse, etc.*

The fourth broadly identified conduct is:

4. *conduct, whether a one time incident or pattern of behavior, that indicates nurse's continued practice would pose risk to patients*

The intent of the definition is to make the focus of reporting be the nurse who lacks the competence or conscientiousness to practice safely rather than the competent nurse who made a single error or who was placed in a situation in which the lack of adequate systems made the error more likely to happen.

In some cases, near misses and close calls may be "conduct subject to reporting." The role of the licensing/regulatory system whenever possible is to identify the incompetent or unsafe practitioner before harm is done. Exposing a patient to risk of harm and not just actual harm can

(2) "Minor incident" means conduct by a nurse that does not indicate that the nurse's continued practice poses a risk of harm to a patient or another person. This term is synonymous with "minor error" or "minor violation of this chapter or board rule."

(3)-(4) *[omitted definitions of "nursing education program" and "nursing student"]*

NPA SEC. 301.4011. GOOD FAITH REPORT BY NURSE. In this subchapter, a report is considered to be made in good faith if:

(1) the person reporting believed that the report was required or authorized; and

(2) there was a reasonable factual or legal basis for that belief.

SUBPART B.
WHO MUST REPORT NURSES

1. INDIVIDUAL NURSES

NPA SEC. 301.402. MANDATORY REPORT BY NURSE.

(a) *[Repealed]*

(b) A nurse shall report to the board in the manner prescribed under Subsection (d) if the nurse has reasonable cause to suspect that:

(1) another nurse has engaged in conduct subject to reporting; or

(2) the ability of a nursing student to perform the services of the nursing profession would be, or would reasonably be expected to be, impaired by chemical dependency.

(c) *[Repealed]*

be the basis for the BON to discipline an RN or LVN. See Rule 217.12(4). An example of reportable conduct that does not involve actual harm would be a nurse who through recklessness is about to administer a medication by the wrong route (with almost certain harm to patient) but another nurse catches the mistake before the medication is administered. Being on duty under the influence is another example.

A minor incident is one that does not indicate a nurse's continuing to practice poses a risk of harm to patients. Sometimes, in a non-typical situation, a minor nursing error can unexpectedly result in significant patient harm, e.g., a non-typical reaction to a medication. Even though the error is minor, it seems counter-intuitive to describe the situation as a "minor" incident. However, the fact that patient harm, even significant harm, resulted from a nurse's error does not automatically mean it is not a minor incident or violation. This definition permits describing such cases as a "minor violation" or "minor error" instead of "minor incident."

This definition of "good faith" was added in 2011 and is the standard consistently used throughout the NPA and Nursing Peer Review Law to identify protected patient advocacy activities. It combines a subjective standard of the person's belief with an objective standard that the belief be reasonable. The definition is based on the definition the Texas Supreme Court established for whistleblower cases in Wichita Co. v. Hart, 917 S.W.2d 779 (Tex. 1996). It does not get into the nurse's motives in making the report.

Persons required to report nurses are:
- *Individual Nurses*
- *Nursing Peer Review Committees*
- *Employers*
- *State Agencies*
- *Nursing Education Programs*
- *Professional associations, insurers and prosecutors*

This section addresses the reporting responsibilities of individual RNs and LVNs.

Also see BON Rule 217.(11)(1)(K) [Standards of Practice] and Rule 217.12(11)(D) [Unprofessional Conduct] regarding nurses's duty to report.

Nurses must report other nurses reasonably suspected of having engaged in conduct subject to reporting as defined by Sec. 301.401 above. Subsec. (e) below permits alternate reporting to:
- *a nursing peer review committee*
- *a nursing educational program in which the student is enrolled*

Reporting a nurse to a supervisor or employer does not satisfy a nurse's reporting obligation under this subsection. See Sec. 301.410 for specific provisions relating to nurses suspected of chemical dependency or mental illness.

A nursing student is required to be reported only if there is reason to suspect the student's problem with chemical dependency would negatively affect practice after she/he is licensed. The nurse reporting has to predict behaviors after the student is licensed. The requirement to report students with a suspected chemical dependency problem applies not only to faculty members, but also to other nurses, e.g., nurses who interface with the student in clinicals may discover a student has a dependency problem. Under Subsec. (d), an individual nurse can satisfy his/her reporting duty by reporting to the educational program, which may have a duty under Sec. 301.404 to report to the BON.

(d) A report by a nurse under Subsection (b) must:

(1) be written and signed; and

(2) include the identity of the nurse or student and any additional information required by the board.

(e) Instead of reporting to the board under Subsection (b), a nurse may make a report required under:

(1) Subsection (b)(1) to a nursing peer review committee under Chapter 303; or

(2) Subsection (b)(2) to the nursing educational program in which the student is enrolled.

(f) A person may not suspend or terminate the employment of, or otherwise discipline, discriminate against, or retaliate against, a person who:

(1) reports in good faith under this section; or

(2) advises a nurse of the nurse's rights and obligations under this section.

(g) A violation of Subsection (f) is subject to Section 301.413.

2. NURSING PEER REVIEW COMMITTEES

NPA SEC. 301.403. DUTY OF PEER REVIEW COMMITTEE TO REPORT. (a) Except as provided by Subsection (b), a nursing peer review committee operating under Chapter 303 that determines that a nurse has engaged in conduct subject to reporting shall file with the board a written, signed report that includes:

(1) the identity of the nurse;

(2) a description of any corrective action taken against the nurse;

(3) a recommendation whether the board should take formal disciplinary action against the nurse and the basis for the recommendation;

(4) a description of the conduct subject to reporting;

(5) the extent to which any deficiency in care provided by the reported nurse was the result of a factor beyond the nurse's control; and

(6) any additional information the board requires.

(b) A report under Subsection (a) is not required if:

(1) the nursing peer review committee determines that the reported conduct was a minor incident that is not required to be reported under board rule; or

(2) the nurse has been reported to the board for the conduct under Section 301.405.

3. EMPLOYERS

NPA SEC. 301.405. DUTY OF PERSON EMPLOYING NURSE TO REPORT. (a) This section applies only to a person who employs, hires, or contracts for the services of a nurse, including:

(1) a health care facility, including a hospital, health science center, nursing home, or home health agency;

(2) a state agency;

(3) a political subdivision;

(4) a school of nursing; and

A report must be in writing and signed. That is the nurse may not report anonymously. However, the nurse's identity is confidential with very limited exceptions. See NPA Sec. 301.417.

The individual nurse can satisfy his/her duty with respect to reporting:

- *a nurse by reporting to a nursing peer review committee,*
- *a nursing student by reporting to the educational program. The educational program may have a duty to report to the BON under Sec. 301.404. The program will likely be in a better position to make the determination about the student's chemical dependency than an individual faculty member is.*

See BON Rule 217.19(j) below for alternate reporting to nursing peer review.

This Subsec. (f) explicitly prohibits discrimination or retaliation against a nurse for reporting a nurse under this Sec. 301.402.

A person who advises a nurse on her or his right to report is also protected from retaliation.

Sec. 301.413 gives the nurse, who is illegally retaliated against, two remedies – filing a lawsuit for damages and filing a complaint with the appropriate licensing agency. If the nurse prevails in the lawsuit the minimum recovery is $5,000 in damages plus attorney fees. If the licensing agency finds retaliation, it can impose a fine of up to $25,000.

Nursing peer review committees must report a nurse determined by the committee to have engaged in conduct subject to reporting as defined by Sec. 301.401 <u>except</u> when:

- *the conduct constitutes a minor incident not required to be reported by BON rules [See Rule 217.16 (Reporting of Minor Incidents)]; or*
- *the nurse has already been reported to the BON by the facility or employer under Sec. 301.405.*

When reporting a nurse to the BON, the committee's report must include the information required by Subsections (a)(1)-(6). The determination of external factors described in Subsec. (a)(5) is required to be made by the nursing peer review committee under Section 303.011 of the Nursing Peer Review Law. Requiring the committee report to include the information listed in (2)-(6) is designed to assist the BON in deciding how to handle the report and what action to take against the RN or LVN as a result of the report.

The operations of nursing peer review committees are governed by Chapter 303 of the Occupations Code relating to nursing peer review. See Part IV (Nursing Peer Review) of this Guide. An individual nurse's reporting an incident to peer review satisfies that nurse's duty to report to the BON under Sec. 301.402. See Sec. 301.402(e). Individual nursing peer review committee members are restricted in what they may report to the BON independently of the committee. See Sec. 303.006(f) of the Nursing Peer Review Law.

Employer is defined very broadly to include any person or entity who employs, hires or contracts for a nurse's services. The relationship does not have to be that of employer-employee.

(5) a temporary nursing service.

(b) A person that terminates, suspends for more than seven days, or takes other substantive disciplinary action, as defined by the board, against a nurse, or a substantially equivalent action against a nurse who is a staffing agency nurse, because the nurse engaged in conduct subject to reporting shall report in writing to the board:

(1) the identity of the nurse;

(2) the conduct subject to reporting that resulted in the termination, suspension, or other substantive disciplinary action or substantially equivalent action; and

(3) any additional information the board requires.

(c) If a person who makes a report required under Subsection (b) is required under Section 303.0015 to establish a nursing peer review committee, the person shall submit a copy of the report to the nursing peer review committee. The nursing peer review committee shall review the conduct to determine if any deficiency in care by the reported nurse was the result of a factor beyond the nurse's control. A nursing peer review committee that determines that there is reason to believe that the nurse's deficiency in care was the result of a factor beyond the nurse's control shall report the conduct to the patient safety committee at the facility where the reported conduct occurred, or if the facility does not have a patient safety committee, to the chief nursing officer.

(d) *[Repealed]*

(e) The requirement under Subsection (c) that a nursing peer review committee review the nurse and the incident does not subject a person's administrative decision to discipline a nurse to the peer review process.

(f) - (h) *[Repealed]*

4. STATE AGENCIES

NPA SEC. 301.407. DUTY OF STATE AGENCY TO REPORT. (a) This section applies only to a state agency that:

(1) licenses, registers, or certifies:

(A) a hospital;

(B) a nursing home;

(C) a health science center;

(D) a home health agency; or

(E) another health care facility or agency; or

(2) surveys a facility or agency listed in Subdivision (1) regarding the quality of nursing care provided by the facility or agency.

(b) Unless expressly prohibited by state or federal law, a state agency that has reason to believe that a nurse has engaged in conduct subject to reporting shall report the nurse in writing to the board or to a nursing peer review committee under Chapter 303.

The taking of substantive disciplinary action against a nurse because of practice-related conduct (technically, "conduct subject to reporting") is what triggers the duty of employers to report. There is no duty on an employer to report a nurse unless it takes such disciplinary action. It seems reasonable to assume an employer would not take substantive disciplinary action against a nurse for practice-related conduct unless that conduct in fact constituted "conduct subject to reporting" as defined by Sec. 301.401. This duty to report applies to all employers regardless of size.

The taking of disciplinary action against a nurse for administrative/personnel reasons, e.g., being consistently late in turning in time sheets, is not reportable. In some cases, administrative or personnel-related and practice-related conduct can overlap. For example, being late to work could endanger a patient if there is no coverage. However, normally it should be fairly clear as to which conduct forms the basis for the disciplinary action.

A temporary agency nurse must be reported to the BON if the employer takes action against the temporary agency nurse substantially equivalent to action that would require reporting an employed nurse. An example might be instructing the agency not to send the nurse to the facility in the future.

Sec. 303.0015 requires persons, who employ or utilize 10 or more nurses (LVNs and/or RNs), to establish a nursing peer review committee. An exception is provided when four or fewer of the 10 nurses are RNs in which case peer review for RNs is not required. The review required by a nursing peer review committee under this section is not review of the nurse, but rather of the incident, for the purpose of determining the potential role of external factors. Since the nurse has been reported to the BON by the employer, the nurse's conduct will be evaluated by Board. If external factors played a role, then other nurses may be placed in a similar situation in which the lack of adequate systems makes the error more likely to occur. The committee need not make a definitive determination of the role of external factors but rather the standard is if there "is reason to believe" the factors contributed to the deficiency in care. The nursing peer review committee then refers the issue to another committee (or CNO) with more expertise in conducting error investigation review and analysis. That committee (or CNO) is also more likely to be able to initiate the process for addressing external factors.

Review by the nursing peer review committee is advisory only and does not limit what administrative/personnel action the employer may take against the nurse. The employer is not prohibited from taking administrative/personnel action prior to peer review.

Various state agencies license or survey health care facilities, e.g., the Department of State Health Services (DSHS) surveys hospitals and the Department of Aging and Disability Services (DADS) surveys nursing homes. In the course of licensing or surveying a facility, the agency may review nursing care. This section imposes a duty on the agency to report a nurse, if it becomes aware that the nurse has engaged in conduct subject to reporting.

The agency may report the nurse to nursing peer review and doing so satisfies its duty under this subsection.

5. NURSING EDUCATION PROGRAMS

NPA SEC. 301.404. DUTY OF NURSING EDUCATIONAL PROGRAM TO REPORT. A nursing educational program that has reasonable cause to suspect that the ability of a nursing student to perform the services of the nursing profession would be, or would reasonably be expected to be, impaired by chemical dependency shall file with the board a written, signed report that includes the identity of the student and any additional information the board requires.

NPA SEC. 301.406. DUTY F CERTAIN PROFESSIONAL ASSOCIATIONS TO REPORT.
NPA SEC. 301.408. DUTY OF LIABILITY INSURERS TO REPORT.
NPA SEC. 301.409. DUTY OF PROSECUTING ATTORNEY TO REPORT.

> ***ANNOTATOR'S NOTES.*** *These NPA sections are not being set out because they don't result in significant reporting of nurses. They can be found in Part I (NPA) of this Guide.*

SUBPART C.
ALTERNATE REPORTING OF NURSES

1. TO PEER ASSISTANCE PROGRAMS

NPA SEC. 301.410. REPORT REGARDING IMPAIRMENT BY CHEMICAL DEPENDENCY, MENTAL ILLNESS, OR DIMINISHED MENTAL CAPACITY.

(a) A person who is required to report a nurse under this subchapter because the nurse is impaired or suspected of being impaired by chemical dependency or mental illness may report to a peer assistance program approved by the board under Chapter 467, Health and Safety Code, instead of reporting to the board or requesting review by a nursing peer review committee.

(b) A person who is required to report a nurse under this subchapter because the nurse is impaired or suspected of being impaired by chemical dependency or diminished mental capacity must report to the board if the person believes that an impaired nurse committed a practice violation.

SEC. 301.4105. BOARD RESPONSIBILITY FOLLOWING REPORT. The board shall determine whether a nurse violated this chapter or a rule adopted under this chapter for any case reported to the board in which the nurse's ability to perform the practice of nursing was impaired or suspected of being impaired by chemical dependency or diminished mental capacity and in which the nurse is suspected of committing a practice violation. The board, in deciding whether to take disciplinary action against the nurse for a violation of this chapter or board rules, shall balance the need to protect the public and the need to ensure the impaired nurse seeks treatment.

2. TO NURSING PEER REVIEW COMMITTEES

NURSING PRACTICE ACT SECS. 301.402(e), 301.407(b)

NPA SEC. 301.402(e) INDIVIDUAL NURSE REPORTS

(e) Instead of reporting to the board under Subsection (b), a nurse may make a report

Educational programs must report only if there is reason to suspect the student's problem with chemical dependency would negatively affect practice after she/he is licensed. The program reporting has to predict behaviors after the student is licensed. Individual nurses have a similar duty to report under Sec. 301.402(b)(2) but that duty can be satisfied by reporting the student to the educational program. See Sec. 301.402(e). An educational program reporting nurse faculty members would be governed by Sec. 301.405 (employer reporting).

Professional associations, insurers and prosecuting attorneys have a duty to report certain nurses. Because multiple nurses and other practitioners can be named in a lawsuit and then dismissed, reports by insurers can produce groundless reporting. NPA Sec. 301.416(c) gives the Board considerable discretion in investigating reports by insurers.

This Subpart identifies those situations in which a nurse can be reported to an entity other than the BON. Normally, it is to the nurse's benefit to be reported to one of these alternate entities.

If it is believed the reported nurse's conduct results from chemical dependency or mental illness and no practice violation is involved, the nurse may be reported to a board-approved peer assistance program instead of to the BON. The Texas Peer Assistance Program for Nurses (TPAPN) is the only program approved by the BON.

If a practice violation is involved, then Subsec. (b) requires reporting directly to the BON. The Board and TPAPN have implemented a screening process to determine if such cases are appropriate for the Board to refer to TPAPN.

This section needs to be read in conjunction with Sec. 301.410(b) above. This section describes how the BON should handle reports involving suspected impairment and a practice violation.

The BON does not have to take disciplinary action against a nurse just because a practice violation is involved. It may still be appropriate to refer the nurse to TPAPN without any additional disciplinary action subject to the nurse successfully completing TPAPN.

In addition to being an entity to which nurses can report nurses in lieu of reporting them directly to the BON, the nursing peer review committee also plays an important role in addressing how minor incidents are handled and reported. See Subpart I below.

The individual nurse can satisfy his/her reporting duty with respect to:

required under:

(1) Subsection (b)(1) to a nursing peer review committee under Chapter 303; or

(2) Subsection (b)(2) to the nursing educational program in which the student is enrolled.

NPA SEC. 301.407(b) STATE AGENCY REPORTS

(b) Unless expressly prohibited by state or federal law, a state agency that has reason to believe that a nurse has engaged in conduct subject to reporting shall report the nurse in writing to the board or to a nursing peer review committee under Chapter 303.

BON RULE 217.19(j). ALTERNATE REPORTING TO NURSING PEER REVIEW.

(j) NURSE'S DUTY TO REPORT.

(1) A report made by a nurse to a nursing incident-based peer review committee will satisfy the nurse's duty to report to the Board under TOC §301.402 (mandatory report by a nurse) provided that the following conditions are met:

(A) The reporting nurse shall be notified of the incident-based peer review committee's actions or findings and shall be subject to TOC §303.006 (confidentiality of peer review proceedings); and

(B) The nurse has no reason to believe the incident-based peer review committee made its determination in bad faith.

BON RULE 217.16. MINOR INCIDENT REPORTING, SUBSECS. (c) AND (h)

SUBSEC. (c)(2)

(A) Evaluation of Conduct. In evaluating whether multiple incidents constitute grounds for reporting it is the responsibility of the nurse manager or supervisor or peer review committee to determine if the minor incidents indicate a pattern of practice that demonstrates the nurse's continued practice poses a risk and should be reported.

(B) Evaluation of Multiple Incidents. In practice settings with nursing peer review, the nurse must be reported to peer review if a nurse commits five minor incidents within a 12-month period. In practice settings with no nursing peer review, the nurse who commits five minor incidents within a 12 month period must be reported to the Board.

(C) Nurse Manager and Nurse Supervisor Responsibilities. Regardless of the time frame or number of minor incidents, if a nurse manager or supervisor believes the minor incidents indicate a pattern of practice that poses a risk of harm that cannot be remediated, the nurse should be reported to the Board or Peer Review Committee.

SUBSEC. (h) A Right to Report. Nurses and other persons are encouraged not to report minor incidents to the Board unless required to do so by this rule, but nothing in this rule is intended to prevent reporting of a potential violation directly to the Board or to a nursing peer review committee.

3. NURSING PEER REVIEW COMMITTEE REPORTING TO BON.

SEC. 301.403. DUTY OF PEER REVIEW COMMITTEE TO REPORT.

- *a nurse by reporting to a nursing peer review committee,*
- *a nursing student by reporting to the educational program. The educational program may have a duty to report to the BON under Sec. 301.404. The program will likely be in a better position to make the determination about the student's chemical dependency than an individual faculty member is.*

A state agency required to report a nurse has the option of reporting the nurse to nursing peer review in lieu of reporting her or him to the Board.

NPA §301.402 gives individual nurses an explicit option to report to a nursing peer review committee in lieu of to the BON. A nurse's reporting to a nursing peer review committee will satisfy the nurse's duty to report. Reporting to a nursing peer review committee does not prevent a nurse from reporting to the BON.

The nursing peer review committee must notify the reporting nurse of findings, so that the nurse can decide if she or he still wants to report to the BON. Reporting to nursing peer review does not prevent a nurse from reporting to the BON. Section 303.006 sets out the confidentiality requirements of nursing peer review and the nurse reporting must also maintain the confidentiality required under that section.

The nurse's reporting duty is not satisfied if she or he believes the committee acted in bad faith.

In addition to being an entity to which nurses can report nurses in lieu of reporting them directly to the BON, the nursing peer review committee also plays an important role in addressing how minor incidents are handled and reported..

Although a nurse can always be reported to the BON, the BON encourages persons not to do so unless reporting is required under this rule.

Nursing peer review committees must report a nurse determined by the committee to have engaged in conduct subject to reporting as defined by Sec. 301.401 except when:

- *the conduct constitutes a minor incident not required to be reported by BON rules [See*

(b) A report under Subsection (a) is not required if:

(1) the nursing peer review committee determines that the reported conduct was a minor incident that is not required to be reported under board rule; or

(2) the nurse has been reported to the board for the conduct under Section 301.405.

SUBPART D.
OPTIONAL REPORTING

1. WHO MAY NURSES VOLUNTARILY REPORT

SEC. 301.4025. OPTIONAL REPORT BY NURSE.

(a) In a written, signed report to the appropriate licensing board or accrediting body, a nurse may report a licensed health care practitioner, agency, or facility that the nurse has reasonable cause to believe has exposed a patient to substantial risk of harm as a result of failing to provide patient care that conforms to:

(1) minimum standards of acceptable and prevailing professional practice, for a report made regarding a practitioner; or

(2) statutory, regulatory, or accreditation standards, for a report made regarding an agency or facility.

(b) A nurse may report to the nurse's employer or another entity at which the nurse is authorized to practice any situation that the nurse has reasonable cause to believe exposes a patient to substantial risk of harm as a result of a failure to provide patient care that conforms to minimum standards of acceptable and prevailing professional practice or to statutory, regulatory, or accreditation standards. For purposes of this subsection, an employer or entity includes an employee or agent of the employer or entity.

(c) A person may not suspend or terminate the employment of, or otherwise discipline, discriminate against, or retaliate against, a person who:

(1) reports in good faith under this section; or

(2) advises a nurse of the nurse's right to report under this section.

(d) A violation of Subsection (c) is subject to Section 301.413.

2. WHO MAY REPORT NURSES TO THE BON

SEC. 301.159. BOARD DUTIES REGARDING COMPLAINTS. (a) The board by rule shall:

(1) adopt a form to standardize information concerning complaints made to the board; and

(2) prescribe information to be provided to a person when the person files a complaint with the board.

(b) The board shall provide reasonable assistance to a person who wishes to file a complaint with the board.

SEC. 301.201. PUBLIC INTEREST INFORMATION. (a) The board shall prepare information of public interest describing the functions of the board and the procedures by which complaints are filed with and resolved by the board.

Rule 217.16 (Reporting of Minor Incidents)]; or

- *the nurse has already been reported to the BON by the facility or employer under Sec. 301.405 (Employer Reporting).*

The right of a nurse to report facilities and practitioners other than nurses may become a duty under certain circumstances. See the Appendices to this Guide for a discussion of this issue.

The standard for reporting is "exposed a patient to substantial risk of harm as a result of failing to provide patient care that conforms to the:"

1. *(for practitioners) "minimum standards of acceptable and prevailing professional practice"*
2. *(for facilities) "statutory, regulatory, or accreditation standards"*

Subsection (b) provides nurses protections when reporting within a facility. The best way to address a quality of care concern is frequently to report that concern to the facility. However, the nurse could end up being labeled a "troublemaker" and retaliated against in some way. Subsection (c) below provides nurses protections from retaliation or discrimination for reporting under this Subsec. (b). If an unsafe situation reported involves a nurse's conduct, reporting the situation under this section would not satisfy a nurse's duty to report another nurse under Sec. 301.402 unless the report was to the nursing peer review committee.

Subsec. (c) explicitly prohibits discrimination or retaliation against a nurse for reporting as authorized by this Sec. 301.4025.

A person who advises a nurse on her or his right to report is also protected from retaliation.

Sec. 301.413 gives the nurse, who is illegally retaliated against, two remedies – filing a lawsuit for damages and filing a complaint with the appropriate licensing agency. If the nurse prevails in the lawsuit the minimum recovery is $5,000 in damages plus attorney fees. If the licensing agency finds retaliation, it can impose a fine of up to $25,000.

The BON is required to facilitate the filing of complaints and to assist persons in filing complaints. See also Secs. 301.201 and .202 requiring the BON to provide information of public interest including procedures for filing complaints.

The BON is required to facilitate the filing of complaints and assisting persons in filing complaints. The Health Professions Council maintains a 1-800 line for all health professional licensing boards. See also Sec. 301.159 and 301.202. The BON website has detailed information

(b) The board shall make the information available to the public and appropriate state agencies.

SEC. 301.202. COMPLAINTS. (a) The board by rule shall establish methods by which consumers and service recipients are notified of the name, mailing address, and telephone number of the board for the purpose of directing complaints to the board. The board may provide for that notice:

(1) on each registration form, application, or written contract for services of a person regulated by the board;

(2) on a sign prominently displayed in the place of business of each person regulated by the board; or

(3) in a bill for service provided by a person regulated by the board.

(b) *[repealed]*

(c) The board shall list with its regular telephone number any toll-free telephone number established under other state law that may be called to present a complaint about a health professional.

SEC. 301.457. COMPLAINT AND INVESTIGATION.

(a) The board or any person may initiate a proceeding under this subchapter by filing with the board a complaint against a nurse. The complaint must be in writing and signed by the complainant.

3. OPTIONAL REPORTING OF MINOR INCIDENTS

BON RULE 217.16(h). REPORTING OF MINOR INCIDENTS.

(h) A Right to Report. Nurses and other persons are encouraged not to report minor incidents to the Board unless required to do so by this rule, but nothing in this rule is intended to prevent reporting of a potential violation directly to the Board or to a nursing peer review committee.

SUBPART E.
DUPLICATIVE REPORTING; GROUNDLESS REPORTS

NPA SEC. 301.419. GENERAL PROVISIONS REGARDING DUTY TO REPORT; MINOR INCIDENTS, SUBSECS. (b), (c).

(b) The board shall adopt rules governing reporting required under this subchapter to minimize:

(1) unnecessary duplicative reporting; and

(2) the reporting of a minor incident.

(c) If the board determines that a report submitted under this subchapter is without merit, the board shall expunge the report from the nurse's file.

and forms for filing a complaint.

The BON provides the public with information about how to file complaints against nurses for unsafe or inappropriate care. Also, it may require nurses to provide notice to patients. See also Secs. 301.159 and 301.201.

The Legislature has enacted legislation requiring such a toll-free number. The Health Professions Council maintains a 1-800 line for all health professional licensing boards.

Most complaints will be reports mandated under the mandatory reporting provisions of Subchapter I. However, complaints can come from other sources such as patients, their family, other practitioners, or the BON itself can initiate a complaint. Complaints must be in writing and signed.

Although a nurse can always be reported to the BON, the BON encourages persons not to report a minor incident unless reporting is required under this rule.

Subsec. (b) directs the BON to adopt rules to minimize the reporting of minor incidents. Sec. 301.416(b) gives the BON discretion not to take action if it receives a report involving a minor incident. The BON has adopted Rule 217.16 implementing this section, which elaborates on when a minor incident need not be reported. See Subpart I (Minor Incidents) below.

SUBPART F.
PROTECTIONS FOR NURSE BEING REPORTED

NPA SEC. 301.414. NOTICE AND REVIEW OF REPORT. (a) The board shall notify each nurse who is reported to the board under Section 301.402, 301.403, 301.405, 301.406, 301.407, 301.408, or 301.409 of the filing of the report unless the notification would jeopardize an active investigation.

(b) The nurse or the nurse's authorized representative is entitled on request to review any report submitted to the board under a section specified under Subsection (a) unless doing so would jeopardize an active investigation. The board may not reveal the identity of the person making or signing the report.

NPA SEC. 301.415. REBUTTAL STATEMENT. (a) A nurse who is entitled to receive notice under Section 301.414 or the authorized representative of the nurse may file with the board a statement of reasonable length containing the nurse's rebuttal of any information in the report to the board.

(b) The statement made under Subsection (a) must accompany the part of the report being rebutted.

(c) In investigating the report, the board shall:

(1) review the statement made under Subsection (a); and

(2) evaluate each reason asserted by the nurse to justify the nurse's conduct.

NPA SEC. 301.416(b), (c). INVESTIGATION

(b) If the board determines that the reported conduct does not indicate that the continued practice of nursing by the nurse poses a risk of harm to a client or other person, the board, with the written consent of the nurse and the person making the report, may elect not to proceed with an investigation or to file formal charges. The board shall:

(1) maintain a record of the report; and

(2) investigate the report if it receives two or more reports involving separate incidents regarding the nurse in any five-year period.

(c) The board is not required to investigate a report filed by an insurer under Section 301.408, but shall:

(1) maintain a record of the report; and

(2) investigate the report if it receives two or more reports involving separate incidents regarding the nurse in any five-year period.

NPA SEC. 301.419(c). EXPUNGING OF GROUNDLESS REPORTS

(c) If the board determines that a report submitted under this subchapter is without merit, the board shall expunge the report from the nurse's file.

SUBPART G.
PROTECTIONS FOR NURSE MAKING REPORT

NPA Sec. 301.417. CONFIDENTIALITY REQUIREMENTS; DISCLOSURE OF INFORMATION.

(a) A report required or authorized under this subchapter and the identity of the person making the report are confidential and may not be disclosed except as provided by this section and Section 301.414.

Secs. 301.414 and .415 identify the rights of the reported nurse. This section is designed to provide the nurse some protections from groundless reports. The reported nurse's rights include:

- *being notified that a report has been filed;*
- *reviewing the report but not the identity of the person making the report; and*
- *filing a rebuttal statement that must accompany the report itself.*

See also Sec. 301.419(c) below relating to the expunging of groundless reports.

A reported nurse has the right to file a rebuttal statement with the BON. See also Secs. 301.414 [notice of being reported] and 301.419(c) [expunging of groundless reports].

The rebuttal statement must be included with any disclosure of the report.

While not providing direct protections to the nurse, this Section does provide indirect protection against over reporting to BON by permitting BON not to file formal charges on minor incident reports. All parties have to agree to the BON's not acting on the report. In some cases (e.g., the nurse believes the report is groundless), the reported nurse may want the BON to investigate the incident so it can be cleared from the nurse's record. Section 301.419 requires the BON to adopt rules to minimize reporting of minor incidents. See BON Rule §217.16 and NPA Sec. 301.401(b).

The BON does not have to act on reports by insurance carriers. This is designed to address the problem of lawsuits being filed a considerable time after the incident or that of all nurses involved with a patient being initially named as defendants and then later being dropped from the lawsuit.

Mandatory reporting has the potential for causing harm to RNs and LVNs wrongly reported. This section is designed to provide protection from groundless reports by having the report expunged from the nurse's file.

Unless nurses and other persons reporting are protected from retaliation and lawsuit, they may be hesitant to report. The NPA provides important protections to encourage reporting.

The identity of the person making the report is confidential. The identity is known to the Board but it cannot disclose it. Sec. 301.414 requires disclosure to the nurse being reported that a report has been filed but also prohibits disclosure of identity of person making the report.

(b) The board may disclose the information to the same extent that the board may disclose information relating to a complaint under Section 301.466

(c) *[Repealed]*

(d) In addition to the other authorizations of this section, the information may be disclosed in:

(1) a civil action in which a reporting person is named as a defendant as a result of making the report; or

(2) the prosecution of a cause of action based on a claim that the reporting person was subject to retaliatory action as a result of making the report.

NPA Sec. 301.412. Reporting Immunity. A person who in good faith makes a report required or authorized under this subchapter, or a person who advises a nurse of the nurse's right or obligation to report under this subchapter:

(1) is immune from civil and criminal liability that, in the absence of the immunity, might result from making the report or giving the advice; and

(2) may not be subjected to other retaliatory action as a result of making the report or giving the advice.

NPA Sec. 301.413. Retaliatory Action.

(a) A person may file a counter claim in a pending action or prove a cause of action in a subsequent suit to recover defense costs, including reasonable attorney's fees and actual and punitive damages, if:

(1) the person is named as a defendant in a civil action or subjected to other retaliatory action as a result of:

(A) filing a report required or authorized, or reasonably believed to be required or authorized, under this subchapter as a result of refusing to engage in conduct as authorized by Section 301.352;

(B) requesting in good faith a nursing peer review committee determination under Section 303.005; or

(C) providing advice to a person regarding:

(i) filing a report required or authorized, or reasonably believed to be required or authorized, under this subchapter as a result of refusing to engage in conduct as authorized by Section 301.352; or

(ii) requesting in good faith a nursing peer review committee determination under Section 303.005; and

(2) the suit or retaliatory action is determined to be frivolous, unreasonable, or taken in bad faith.

(b) A person may not suspend, terminate, or otherwise discipline, discriminate against, or retaliate against a person who:

(1) reports in good faith under this subchapter;

(2) requests, in good faith, a nursing peer review committee determination under

Sec. 301.466 governs disclosure of complaints. Complaints are confidential until formal charges are filed. To whom it can be disclosed before that time is limited, e.g,, it may be disclosed to a nursing board in another state.

Persons reporting in good faith are protected from both civil and criminal liability and also from retaliation for making the report. Practitioners are often justifiably concerned that if they report another practitioner, they are going to be sued for professional slander or some other reason. This section is designed to prevent such concerns from having a chilling effect on good faith reporting. "Authorized" reports include reports of other practitioners and facilities under Sec. 301.4025.

Persons who advise a nurse about the nurse's right or duty to report and protections available when reporting are also protected.

This Sec. 301.413 sets out the remedies available to nurses who have been retaliated or discriminated against because they engaged in protected patient advocacy activities or because they advised another nurse of these patient advocacy protections. The activities protected are:

1. *Refusing to engage in conduct subject to reporting or that would violate NPA or BON rule (NPA Sec. 301.352)*
2. *Reporting a nurse (NPA Sec. 301.402), a practitioner (other than a nurse) or a facility (NPA Sec. 301.4025(a)) or raising of patient care concern within a facility (Sec. 301.4025(b))*
3. *Requesting safe harbor nursing peer review (NPR Law Sec. 303.005)*
4. *Advising a nurse on protections (1)-(3)*

See Subsection (b) below and Part VI (Patient Advocacy Protections).

This Subsec. (a) provides general legal recourse to any person sued or otherwise retaliated against for engaging in protected patient advocacy activities.

It appears that there should be an "or" between "subchapter" and "as a result" but this it the way the statute reads. See history of change to this Subsec. (a) in SBs 993 (2007), 476 (2009), 192 (2011) and also wording of Subsecs. (b), (c).

Persons who advise a nurse about the nurse's right or duty to report and protections available when reporting are also protected under this section.

It appears that there should be an "or" between "subchapter" and "as a result" but this it the way the statute reads. See history of changes to this Subsec. (a) in SBs 993 (2007), 476 (2009), 192 (2011) and also wording of Subsecs. (b), (c).

This Subsec. (b) provides specific protections for persons reporting, in good faith, from being terminated or retaliated against at their job. It covers not only mandatory reporting, but also any reporting authorized by this section, e.g., reporting other providers under Sec. 301.402. In a 1998 opinion, Clark v. Texas Home Health, Inc., the Texas Supreme Court upheld a liberal

Section 303.005;

(3) refuses to engage in conduct as authorized by Section 301.352; or

(4) advises a nurse of the nurse's right to:

(A) report under this subchapter;

(B) request a nursing peer review committee determination under Section 303.005; or

(C) refuse to engage in conduct as authorized by Section 301.352.

(b-1) A person suspected of violating Subsection (b) may be reported to the appropriate licensing agency and, notwithstanding any other provision, that agency may impose an administrative penalty not to exceed $25,000 against the person if the agency finds a violation of Subsection (b). An administrative penalty imposed under this subsection is in addition to other penalties the agency is authorized to impose and is subject to the procedural requirements applicable to the appropriate licensing agency.

(c) A person who reports under this subchapter, refuses to engage in conduct as authorized by Section 301.352, or requests a nursing peer review committee determination under Section 303.005, or a person who advises a nurse of the nurse's right to report under this subchapter, refuse to engage in conduct as authorized by Section 301.352, or request a nursing peer review committee determination under Section 303.005, has a cause of action against a person who violates Subsection (b), and may recover:

(1) the greater of:

(A) actual damages, including damages for mental anguish even if no other injury is shown; or

(B) $5,000;

(2) exemplary damages;

(3) court costs; and

(4) reasonable attorney's fees.

(d) In addition to the amount recovered under Subsection (c), a person whose employment is suspended or terminated in violation of this section is entitled to:

(1) reinstatement in the employee's former position or severance pay in an amount equal to three months of the employee's most recent salary; and

(2) compensation for wages lost during the period of suspension or termination.

(e) A person who brings an action under this section has the burden of proof. It is a rebuttable presumption that the person was suspended, terminated, or otherwise disciplined, discriminated against, or retaliated against for reporting under this subchapter, for refusing to engage in conduct as authorized by Section 301.352, for requesting a peer review committee determination under Section 303.005, or for providing advice to a person regarding reporting under this subchapter, refusing to engage in conduct as authorized by Section 301.352, or requesting a peer review committee determination under Section 303.005 if:

(1) the person was suspended, terminated, or otherwise disciplined, discriminated against, or retaliated against within 60 days after the date the report, refusal, or request was made or the advice was given; and

(2) the board or a court determines that:

(A) the report that is the subject of the cause of action was:

(i) authorized or required under Section 301.402, 301.4025, 301.403, 301.405, 301.406, 301.407, 301.408, 301.409, or 301.410; and

(ii) made in good faith;

(B) the request for a peer review committee determination that is the subject of the cause of action was:

(i) authorized under Section 303.005; and

(ii) made in good faith;

(C) the refusal to engage in conduct was authorized by Section 301.352; or *interpretation of this section as providing "a cause of action for retaliatory acts against persons reporting under this [Sec. 301.401-.419]." The opinion is set out in the Appendices to this Guide.*

Persons who advise a nurse about the nurse's right or duty to report and protections available when reporting are also protected under this section.

Licensed practitioners or facilities that retaliate may be reported to their licensing board, which may impose a fine of up to $25,000. The agency could also take action against the practitioner's or facility's license.

The person reporting may recover not only actual damages including mental anguish, but also exemplary damages and attorney's fees. The minimum recovery for actual damages is set at $5,000.

Proving that a person's motive was retaliation can be difficult. This section addresses this difficulty by creating a rebuttal presumption that any adverse action taken within 60 days of the protected conduct was taken in retaliation. A rebuttal presumption is one that creates a presumption that can be overcome by opposing evidence. The person alleged to have retaliated against the nurse would have to present such opposing evidence. Once he/she does, then the burden of proof returns to the nurse to prove the retaliation. The rebuttal presumption prevents the defendant from simply denying the retaliation without putting on any evidence of the reason for the alleged retaliatory conduct. Once the defendant puts in evidence, that evidence can be evaluated, challenged and refuted.

(D) the advice that is the subject of the cause of action was given in good faith.

(f) An action under this section may be brought in a district court of the county in which:

(1) the plaintiff resides;

(2) the plaintiff was employed by the defendant; or

(3) the defendant conducts business.

(g) Subject to Subsection (h), a nurse employed by a hospital operated by or on behalf of a state or local governmental entity who alleges a violation of Subsection (b) may sue the state or local governmental entity for relief under this section, and the sovereign immunity of the state or local governmental entity from suit and from liability is waived for the limited purpose of allowing the nurse to maintain a lawsuit in state court to obtain that relief. Relief under this section is in addition to any other remedies a nurse may have under state or federal law as a public employee. In this subsection:

(1) "Local governmental entity," "public employee," and "state governmental entity" have the meanings assigned by Section 554.001, Government Code.

(2) "Hospital" has the meaning assigned by Section 241.003, Health and Safety Code, and includes a mental hospital licensed under Chapter 577, Health and Safety Code.

(h) Relief may be granted in a lawsuit brought under Subsection (g) for an alleged violation of Subsection (b)(1) based on a report made by a nurse under Section 301.4025(b) only if the nurse:

(1) made the report:

(A) in writing, which may be provided electronically; or

(B) verbally, if authorized by the nurse's employer or another entity at which the nurse is authorized to practice;

(2) made the report to:

(A) the nurse's supervisor;

(B) a committee authorized under state or federal law to receive reports under Section 301.4025(b); or

(C) an individual or committee authorized by the nurse's employer or another entity at which the nurse is authorized to practice; and

(3) made the report not later than:

(A) the fifth day after the date the nurse became aware of the situation if the situation involves a single incident; or

(B) the fifth day after the date the nurse became aware of the most recent occurrence of the situation if the situation involves multiple incidents or a pattern of behavior.

(i) For purposes of Subsection (h), "supervisor" means an individual who has authority over the responsibilities of the nurse making the report or an individual who is in the nurse's chain of command.

(j) The following provisions of Chapter 554, Government Code, apply to a lawsuit under Subsection (g):

(1) the type of relief and the amount of damages available to a public employee under Section 554.003;

(2) the time during which a public employee must seek relief under Section 554.005; and

(3) the requirement that a public employee use the grievance or appeal procedures of the state or local governmental entity before suing for relief under Section 554.006.

(k) A lawsuit under Subsection (g) against a state governmental entity shall be brought in a district court in Travis County or a county in which all or part of the acts or omissions giving rise to the cause of action occurred.

(l) A lawsuit under Subsection (g) against a local governmental entity shall be brought in a district court in a county in which all or part of the entity is located.

Subsections (g)-(l) were added in 2013 (HB 581) to provide public hospital employed nurses a right to file a lawsuit to recover damages resulting from retaliation for engaging in patient advocacy activities protected under Subsection (b). Without this type of explicit waiver of sovereign immunity, public hospital employed nurses would have to seek recovery under the Public Employee Whistleblower Law (Government Code, Chap. 554). That law covers only external reporting and not all of the activities listed under Subsection (b). This Subsection applies only to public hospital employed nurses and not to nurses employed by other public entities such as a jail or county health department. The Public Employee Whistleblower Law is set out in Part VI (Advocacy Protections) of this Guide.

Subsections (h) and (i) were added by the Legislature to address concern that a county or other entity operating a public hospital might be sued for retaliation without ever being aware that the nurse made a protected report of unsafe care. A report under Sec. 301.4025(b) is an optional report in a facility about unsafe care.

A supervisor is anyone in the nurse's chain of command. Supervisor was defined this way so nurse could raise concerns to administration if felt an immediate supervisor was not adequately addressing a concern.

The type of relief that a public hospital employed nurse can recover is subject to the limitations set out in the Public Employee Whistleblower Law. It sets a limit on the amount of damages based on the size of the governmental entity and also does not permit punitive damages. The Public Employee Whistleblower Law is set out in Part VI (Advocacy Protections) of this Guide.

Subsections (k) and (l) determine where a lawusit by a public hospitla employed nurse must be filed.

BON RULES 217.19(j)(2) and 217.20(e)

Rule 217.19. Incident-Based Nursing Peer Review and Whistleblower Protections

(j) Nurse's Duty to Report.

(1) A report made by a nurse to a nursing incident-based peer review committee will satisfy the nurse's duty to report to the Board under TOC §301.402 (mandatory report by a nurse) provided that the following conditions are met:

(A) The reporting nurse shall be notified of the incident-based peer review committee's actions or findings and shall be subject to TOC §303.006 (confidentiality of peer review proceedings); and

(B) The nurse has no reason to believe the incident-based peer review committee made its determination in bad faith.

(2) A nurse may not be suspended, terminated, or otherwise disciplined, retaliated, or discriminated against for filing a report in good faith under this section and TOC §301.402(f) (retaliation for a report made in good faith prohibited) or advising a nurse of the nurse's rights and obligations under this section and §301.402(f). A violation of this subsection or TOC §301.402(f) is subject to TOC §301.413 that provides a nurse the right to file a civil suit to recover damages. The nurse may also file a complaint with the regulatory agency that licenses or regulates the nurse's practice setting. The BON does not have regulatory authority over practice settings or civil liability

Rule §217.20. Safe Harbor Peer Review for Nurses and Whistleblower Protections

(e) Safe Harbor Protections.

(1) To activate protections outlined in TOC §303.005(c) and paragraph (2) of this subsection, the nurse shall:

(A) invoke Safe Harbor in good faith;

(B) notify the supervisor in writing that he/she intends to invoke Safe Harbor in accordance with subsection (d) of this section. This must be done prior to engaging in the conduct or assignment for which safe harbor is requested and at any of the following times:

(i) when the conduct is requested or assignment made;

(ii) when changes occur in the request or assignment that so modify the level of nursing care or supervision required compared to what was originally requested or assigned that a nurse believes in good faith that patient harm may result; or

(iii) when the nurse refuses to engage in the requested conduct or assignment.

(2) TOC §303.005(c) and (h) (NPR Law) and §301.352 provide the following protections:

(A) A nurse may not be suspended, terminated, or otherwise disciplined, retaliated, or discriminated against for requesting Safe Harbor in good faith.

(B) A nurse or other person may not be suspended, terminated, or otherwise disciplined, retaliated, or discriminated against for advising a nurse in good faith of the nurse's right to request a determination, or of the procedures for requesting a determination.

(C) A nurse is not subject to being reported to the Board and may not be disciplined by the Board for engaging in the conduct awaiting the determination of the peer review committee as permitted by subsection (g) of this section. A nurse's protections from disciplinary action by the Board for engaging in the conduct or assignment awaiting peer review determination remain in place for 48 hours after the nurse is advised of the peer review committee's determination. This time limitation does not affect the nurse's protections from retaliation by the facility, agency, entity or employer under TOC §303.005(h) (NPR Law) for requesting Safe Harbor.

BON Rules 217.19 and 217.20 address both nursing peer review and whistleblower protections. The subsections addressing protections for reporting are being set out. They largely track the language of the NPA Sec.301.413 and NPR Law Sec. 303.005.

The BON has regulatory authority only over the nurse; not the agency licensing the facility.

Even though the nurse's protection (for continuing to engage in the conduct) from the BON taking action against the nurse's license expires 48 hours after the peer review committee's determination, the nurse's protection from retaliation for making the request does not expire.

(3) If retaliation occurs, TOC §301.413 (NPA) provides a nurse the right to file civil suit to recover damages. The nurse may also file a complaint with the appropriate regulatory agency that licenses or regulates the nurse's practice setting. The BON does not have regulatory authority over practice settings or civil liability.

(4) Safe Harbor protections do not apply to any civil action for patient injury that may result from the nurse's practice.

SUBPART H.
PROMOTING COMPLIANCE

NPA SEC. 301.419(d). GENERAL PROVISIONS REGARDING DUTY TO REPORT; MINOR INCIDENTS.

(d) The board shall inform, in the manner the board determines appropriate, nurses, facilities, agencies, and other persons of their duty to report under this subchapter.

DSHS RULE 133.41 HOSPITAL FUNCTIONS AND SERVICES.

(o)(6) NURSING SERVICES

(6) Reporting and Peer Review of a Vocational or Registered Nurse. A hospital shall adopt, implement, and enforce a policy to ensure that the hospital complies with the Occupations Code §§301.401 - 301.403, 301.405 and Chapter 303 (relating to Grounds for Reporting Nurse, Duty of Nurse to Report, Duty of Peer Review Committee to Report, Duty of Person Employing Nurse to Report, and Nursing Peer Review respectively), and with the rules adopted by the Texas Board of Nursing in 22 TAC §217.16 (relating to Minor Incidents), §217.19 (relating to Incident-Based Nursing Peer Review and Whistleblower Protections), and §217.20 (relating to Safe Harbor Peer Review for Nurses and Whistleblower Protections).

SUBPART I.
MINOR INCIDENT REPORTING

BON RULE 217.16. REPORTING OF MINOR INCIDENTS.

The BON does not have regulatory authorty over lawsuits.

The protections provided a nurse requesting safe harbor do not include preventing a patient who may be injured from filing lawsuit for that injury.

The reference to "subchapter" is to NPA Secs. 301.401-.419.

This section requires hospitals to implement policies to assure compliance with other laws and regulations relating to nursing including mandatory reporting, peer review and minor incidents.

This Rule implements NPA Sec. 301.419 which authorizes the BON to adopt rules to minimize the reporting of minor incidents. Under NPA Sec. 301.403, nursing peer review committees do not have to report nurses whose conduct is not reportable under this rule.

A flowchart is set out in Part X (Appendices) showing how minor incidents should be handled under this rule.

The rule re-enforces the paradigm that minor incidents are best addressed at the facility level and the BON's focus should be on those nurses whose continuing practice poses a risk of harm to patients. When making changes to the rule in 2006, the BON included the following statement in the preamble published in the TEXAS REGISTER:

> *It is not uncommon for the Board to encounter a list of on-going practice-related errors preceding a serious incident that serves as the "last straw," resulting in a nurse being reported to the Board. Rarely has the nurse in such a scenario been "remediated" by the facility or nurse manager for the previous collection of practice-related errors. Had the nurse's practice been reviewed by a facility's peer review committee at an earlier stage in the process, perhaps corrective actions could have been initiated at the facility/employer level prior to more serious practice errors occurring. Timely and pre-emptive actions would serve to protect the public, and may spare the nurse being reported to the*

217.16. Reporting of Minor Incidents.

(a) Purpose. The Board believes protection of the public is not enhanced by the reporting of every minor incident that may be a violation of the Texas Nursing Practice Act or a board rule. This is particularly true when there are mechanisms in place in the nurse's practice setting to identify nursing errors, detect patterns of practice, and take corrective action to remediate deficits in a nurse's judgment, knowledge, training, or skill. This rule is intended to provide guidance to nurses, nursing peer review committees and others in determining whether a nurse has engaged in conduct that indicates the nurse's continued practice would pose a risk of harm to patients or others and should be reported to the board.

(b) Definition. A "minor incident" as defined under Nursing Practice Act §301.401(2) means conduct by a nurse that may be a violation of the Nursing Practice Act or a Board rule but does not indicate the Nurse's continued practice poses a risk of harm to a patient or another person.

(c) Factors to be Considered in Evaluating if Conduct Must Be Reported to the Board.

(1) A nurse involved in a minor incident need not be reported to the Board unless the conduct indicates the nurse:

(A) ignored a substantial risk that exposed a patient or other person to significant physical, emotional or financial harm or the potential for such harm;

(B) lacked a conscientious approach to or accountability for his/her practice;

(C) lacked the knowledge and competencies to make appropriate clinical judgments and such knowledge and competencies cannot be easily remediated; or

(D) indicates the nurse has engaged in a pattern of multiple minor incidents that demonstrate the nurse's continued practice would pose a risk of harm to patients or others.

(2) Evaluation of Multiple Incidents.

(A) Evaluation of Conduct. In evaluating whether multiple incidents constitute grounds for reporting it is the responsibility of the nurse manager or supervisor or peer review committee to determine if the minor incidents indicate a pattern of practice that demonstrates the nurse's continued practice poses a risk and should be reported.

(B) Evaluation of Multiple Incidents. In practice settings with nursing peer review, the nurse must be reported to peer review if a nurse commits five minor incidents within a 12-month period. In practice settings with no nursing peer review, the nurse who commits five minor incidents within a 12 month period must be reported to the Board.

(C) Nurse Manager and Nurse Supervisor Responsibilities. Regardless of the time frame or number of minor incidents, if a nurse manager or supervisor believes the minor incidents indicate a pattern of practice that poses a risk of harm that cannot be remediated, the nurse should be reported to the Board or Peer Review Committee.

(3) Other factors that may be considered in determining whether a minor incident should be reported to the Board are:

(A) the significance of the nurse's conduct in the particular practice setting; and

(B) the presence of contributing or mitigating circumstances, including systems issues or factors beyond the nurse's control, in relation to the nurse's conduct.

(d) Conduct Required to be Reported.

(1) A nurse must be reported to the board or to a nursing peer review committee for the following conduct:

(A) An error that contributed to a patient's death or serious harm.

(B) Criminal Conduct defined in Texas Occupations Code §301.4535.

Board unnecessarily.

The BON recognizes that not all incidents are appropriate for being reported to the BON.

Purpose of rules to is provide guidance in determining whether a nurse has engaged in conduct that indicates the nurse's continued practice would pose a risk of harm to patients or others and should be reported to the board.

The NPA definition of "minor incident" focuses on whether a nurse's continuing to practice nursing poses a risk of harm to patients.

Subsection (c) identifies factors to be considered in determining if an incident is a minor incident that need not be reported to the BON.

A nurse needs to be reported only if one of the factors (A)-(D) is present. See Subsecs. (d) and (e) for conduct that must be reported.

Multiple incidents require special consideration, because they may indicate a pattern of behavior that would, in turn, indicate the nurse's continuing to practice poses a risk of harm to patients.

Facilities with nursing peer review have more options in addressing multiple incidents at the facility level. Five incidents within a 12-month period must be reported to the nursing peer review committee or the BON.

Even if there are not five incidents a nurse must be reported if the incidents indicate a pattern of practice that may pose a risk of harm to patients or others.

Factors that may be considered in determining if a minor incident should be reported to the board.

Role of system issues is a consideration.

Certain incidents must be reported to the BON or nursing peer review committee.

(C) A serious violation of the board's Unprofessional Conduct rule §217.12 of this title (relating to Unprofessional Conduct) involving intentional or unethical conduct including but not limited to fraud, theft, patient abuse or patient exploitation.

(D) A practice-related violation involving impairment or suspected impairment by reason of chemical dependency, intemperate use, misuse or abuse of drugs or alcohol, mental illness, or diminished mental capacity required to be reported in accordance with §301.410(b) of the Nursing Practice Act and §217.19(g) of this title (relating to Incident Based Nursing Peer Review and Whistle Blower Protections).

(2) If a nursing peer review committee determines that a nurse engaged in the conduct listed in subsection (c)(1)(A) - (D) of this section the committee must report the nurse to the board. For errors involving the death or serious injury of a patient, if a nursing peer review committee makes a determination that a nurse has not engaged in conduct subject to reporting to the board, the committee must maintain documentation of the rationale for their belief that the nurse's conduct failed to meet each of the factors in paragraph (1)(A) - (D) of this subsection.

(e) Conduct Normally Not Required to Be Reported to the Board.

(1) An incident should be evaluated to determine if:

(A) the incident is primarily the result of factors beyond the nurse's control and addressing those factors is more likely to prevent the incident from reoccurring; or

(B) the incident was a medication error caused primarily by factors beyond the nurse's control rather than failure of the nurse to exercise proper clinical judgment. Board Position Statement 15.17 Texas Board of Nursing/Board of Pharmacy Joint Position Statement/Medication Error provides guidelines for evaluating medication errors found at http://www.bon.state.tx.us/practice/position.html#15.17.

(2) If either of the conditions listed in paragraph (1) of this subsection are present, a presumption should exist that the nurse's conduct does not indicate the nurse's continued practice poses a risk of harm to a patient or another person and does not need to be reported to the board. medication errors.

(f) Documentation of Minor Incidents. A minor incident should be documented as follows:

(1) A report must be prepared and maintained for a minimum of 12 months that contains a complete description of the incident, patient record number, witnesses, nurse involved and the action taken to correct or remedy the problem.

(2) If a medication error is attributable or assigned to the nurse as a minor incident, the record of that incident should indicate why the error is being attributed or assigned to the nurse.

(g) Nursing Peer Review Committee.

(1) If a report is made to the peer review committee, the committee must investigate and conduct incident-based nursing peer review in compliance with Nursing Peer Review Law in Texas Occupations Code §303 and §217.19 of this title.

(2) Review of a nurse's conduct or practice may be accomplished by either an informal work group of the nursing peer review committee as provided under §217.19(e) of this title or the full nursing peer review committee prior to a report being made to the board.

(3) A nursing peer review committee receiving a report involving a minor incident or incidents must review the incident(s) and other conduct of the nurse during the previous 12 months to determine if the nurse's continuing to practice poses a risk of harm to patients or other persons and whether remediation would be reasonably expected to adequately mitigate such risk if it exists. The committee must consider the special considerations set out in subsection (c) of this section.

A nursing peer review committee must report to the board for conduct identified in this Subdivision (2).

Subsection (e) describes when an incident does not need to be reported.

The role of factors beyond a nurse's control should be evaluated.

Medication errors should be carefully evaluated.

If system errors are the primary cause, then the presumption is that the nurse's continuing to practice does not pose a risk of harm to patients.

Minor incidents must be documented.

Subsection (g) addresses how nursing peer review is to handle minor incident reports it receives. Minor incidents can always be reported to a nursing peer review committee in lieu of reporting to the BON. Rule 217.19 (incident-based nursing peer review) applies because the committee's review could end up in the nurse's being reported to the board.

The nursing peer review committee may use an informal process. This is likely to permit more efficient use of resources in handling minor incidents reported to the peer review committee.

In reviewing a minor incident, the nursing peer review committee must look at the nurse's conduct over the previous 12 months.

(4) The nursing peer review committee need not report the nurse to the Board if the peer review committee determines that either:

(A) the nurse's continuing to practice does not pose a risk of harm to patients or other persons; or

(B) remediation could reasonably be expected to adequately mitigate any such risk and the nurse successfully completes the remediation.

(5) If a nurse terminates employment while undergoing remediation activities as directed by a peer review committee under paragraph (3) of this subsection, the peer review committee may either:

(A) report the nurse to the BON;

(B) report to the peer review committee of the new employer, if known, with the nurses written consent;

(C) re-evaluate the nurse's current conduct to determine if the nurse did complete sufficient remediation and is deemed safe to practice.

(h) A Right to Report. Nurses and other persons are encouraged not to report minor incidents to the Board unless required to do so by this rule, but nothing in this rule is intended to prevent reporting of a potential violation directly to the Board or to a nursing peer review committee.

(i) Mis-classifying to Avoid Reporting. Intentionally mis-classifying an incident to avoid reporting may result in violation of the mandatory reporting statute.

(j) Chief Nursing Officer or Nurse Administrator Responsibility. The Chief Nursing Officer, Nurse Administrator or registered nurse by any title who is responsible for nursing services shall be responsible for taking reasonable steps to assure that minor incidents are handled in compliance with this rule and any other applicable law.

(k) Nurses Reported to the Board. If a nurse is reported to the board, the board shall review the nurse's conduct to determine if it indicates the nurse's continued practice poses a risk of harm to a patient or another person. If it does not the board may elect not to proceed with filing formal charges.

The nursing peer review committee has considerable discretion in how it handles minor incidents and whether the nurse needs to be reported to the BON. The likelihood of successful remediation is a consideration.

As indicated in other provisions of this rule, the possibility of successful remediation is an important consideration.

This Subdivision. (5) addresses the options available to a nursing peer review committee when a nurse leaves employment before remediation is completed.

Although a nurse can always be reported to the BON, the BON encourages persons not to do so unless reporting is required under this rule.

Nurses may not use this rule as a way to avoid mandatory reporting to the BON.

The CNO is responsible for implementing this rule.

If a nurse is reported to the BON, the board should evaluate the nurse's conduct to determine if it is a minor incident.

PART VIII.

NURSE LICENSURE COMPACTS

SUBPART A.
RN/LVN LICENSURE COMPACT

1. COMPACT – CHAPTER 304 OCCUPATIONS CODE

Sec. 304.001. NURSE LICENSURE COMPACT. The Nurse Licensure Compact is enacted and entered into with all other jurisdictions that legally join in the compact, which is as follows:

NURSE LICENSURE COMPACT

ARTICLE 1. FINDINGS AND DECLARATION OF PURPOSE

[Omitted]

ARTICLE 2. DEFINITIONS. In this compact:

* * * * *

(e) "Home state" means the party state that is the nurse's primary state of residence.

The Nurse Licensure Compact is an interstate compact designed to facilitate the practice of nursing (electronically and physically) across state lines. An interstate compact is a contract between states. One of the more familiar interstate compacts is the driver's license compact that permits drivers to drive in multiple states under a single driver's license. The Nurse Licensure Compact operates in a similar manner. Nurses licensed in one state are able to practice in another state without a separate license. Like a contract, the Nurse Licensure Compact applies only to states that elect to adopt it – referred to as "party states." The Nurse Licensure Compact is frequently described as "state based, nationally recognized, locally enforced." The nurse's license is adopted at the state level, it is recognized nationally, and each state enforces its own practice laws and standards. Under the compact, the state of licensure is the nurse's state of primary residence.

The Compact consists of the 11 articles set out below. The articles marked with a "✔" are the more important and are the only ones included in this Guide. The other articles can be found on the BON website or at www.statutes.legis.state.tx.us/. *Select Occupations Code and then Chapter 304.*

Article. 1	*Findings and Declarations*
✔*Article. 2*	*Definitions*
✔*Article. 3*	*General Provisions and Jurisdiction*
✔*Article. 4*	*Application for Licensure*
✔*Article. 5*	*Adverse Actions*
✔*Article. 6.*	*Additional Authorities of Party States BONs*
✔*Article. 7*	*Coordinated Licensure Information System*
Article. 8	*Compact Administration*
Article. 9	*Immunity*
Article. 10	*Effective Date, Withdrawing and Amending*
Article. 11	*Construction*

Since the Compact is a contract, each state must adopt substantially the same (ideally identical) language without any substantial differences. The Compact language was developed by the National Council of State Boards of Nursing after several years of studying the best way to regulate interstate practice.

States can adopt, and most states have adopted, additional provisions relating to the Compact to address particular needs of their state. The only requirement is that these additional provisions cannot be inconsistent with the Compact or its intent. Texas enacted several such provisions.

As of July 2013, 24 states had adopted the Compact and several had legislation pending. Missouri was the most recent (2010) state to adopt the compact.

The BON has adopted Rule 220 implementing the Compact.

The BON website at www.bon.texas.gov has considerable information on multistate licensure including a video, fact sheets, FAQs and information for employers. Select "Verification & Licensing" and then "Multistate Regulation." The BON website also links to the National Council of State Boards of Nursing which has additional information.

ANNOTATOR'S NOTE: *Only key definitions are set out.*

The home state is the state of licensure. "Primary state of residence" will need to be defined

(f) "Home state action" means any administrative, civil, equitable, or criminal action permitted by the home state's laws that are imposed on a nurse by the home state's licensing board or other authority, including actions against an individual's license such as revocation, suspension, probation, or any other action that affects a nurse's authorization to practice.

* * * * *

(h) "Multistate licensing privilege" means current, official authority from a remote state permitting the practice of nursing as a registered nurse, licensed practical nurse, or licensed vocational nurse in the party state. All party states have the authority, in accordance with existing state due process laws, to take actions against the nurse's privilege, including revocation, suspension, probation, or any other action that affects a nurse's authorization to practice.

* * * * *

(j) "Party state" means any state that has enacted this compact.

(k) "Remote state" means a party state, other than the home state, in which:

(1) a patient is located at the time nursing care is provided; or

(2) in the case of the practice of nursing not involving a patient, the recipient of nursing practice is located.

(l) "Remote state action" means:

(1) an administrative, civil, equitable, or criminal action permitted by a remote state's laws that are imposed on a nurse by the remote state's licensing board or other authority, including an action against an individual's multistate licensing privilege to practice in the remote state; and

(2) a cease and desist order and other injunctive or equitable orders issued by remote states or the licensing boards of remote states.

* * * * *

(n) "State practice laws" means a party state's laws and regulations that govern the practice of nursing, define the scope of nursing practice, and create the methods and grounds for imposing discipline. The term does not include the initial qualifications for licensing or requirements necessary to obtain and retain a license, except for qualifications or requirements of the home state.

ARTICLE 3. GENERAL PROVISIONS AND JURISDICTION. (a) A license to practice registered nursing issued by a home state to a resident in that state will be recognized by each party state as authorizing a multistate licensing privilege to practice as a registered nurse in the party state. A license to practice licensed practical nursing or licensed vocational nursing issued by a home state to a resident in that state will be recognized by each party state as authorizing a multistate licensing privilege to practice as a licensed practical nurse or vocational nurse in the party state. To obtain or retain a license, an applicant must meet the home state's qualifications for a license and license renewal as well as all other applicable state laws.

(b) A party state may, in accordance with state due process laws, limit or revoke the multistate licensing privilege of any nurse to practice in the party state and may take any other necessary actions under the party state's applicable laws to protect the health and safety of the party state's citizens. If a party state takes this action, the party state shall promptly notify the administrator of the coordinated licensure information system. The administrator of the coordinated licensure information system shall promptly notify the home state of any such actions by remote states.

(c) A nurse practicing in a party state must comply with the state practice laws of the state in which the patient is located at the time care is provided. The practice of nursing includes patient care and all nursing practice defined by the party state's practice laws. The practice of nursing will *by rule.*

Only the home state will be able to take action against the nurse's license. It is the only state that issues the nurse a license.

Under Article 3(a), being licensed in a party state automatically gives the nurse the privilege to practice in other party states without any additional licensure or registration requirements. This privilege is referred to as a "multistate licensure privilege." Any party state can take action against a nurse's multistate licensure privilege to practice in that state.

Only states adopting the Compact are party states.

"Remote state" is a non-home party state where the nurse practices. Note that practice occurs where the patient or recipient of nursing practice is located and not where the nurse is located.

Remote states will take action against the nurse's multistate licensure privilege and not against the nurse's license.

"State practice laws" are all laws of a party state governing nursing practice except for laws relating to licensure qualifications. Practice laws include laws defining scope of practice and regulating the disciplining of nurses.

This is a key article in the Compact because it addresses how the nurse's practice will be regulated and establishes what laws will govern the nurse's practice.

Each party state agrees to recognize the license issued by a party state as authorizing the nurse to practice in their state. This establishes the concept of a single multistate license. The phrase "to practice as a (registered/vocational) nurse" is the language used in nursing practice acts to identify who must have a nursing license. This terminology should confer on the nurse holding a multistate licensure privilege the authority to practice in the party state to the same extent as licensees and to use the title "RN" or "LVN."

The nurse must meet the licensure standards/requirements of the home state, i.e., primary state of residence.

Any party state will have the authority to take action against the nurse's privilege to practice in that state, i.e., against the nurse's multistate licensure privilege. Only the home state may take action against the nurse's license.

The sharing of information among party states occurs through the Coordinated Licensure Information System. This is addressed in more detail in Article 7.

Nurses will have to comply with the laws of the party state in which they practice, i.e., where the patient or recipient of nursing practice is located.

The nurse's scope of practice is defined by the laws of the party state where the nurse subject a nurse to the jurisdiction of the nurse licensing board, the courts, and the laws of the party state.

(d) This compact does not affect additional requirements imposed by states for advanced practice registered nursing. However, a multistate licensing privilege to practice registered nursing granted by a party state shall be recognized by another party state as a license to practice registered nursing if the state's law requires the license as a precondition for qualifying for advanced practice registered nurse authorization.

(e) Individuals not residing in a party state may apply for a nurse license under the laws of a party state. However, the license granted to these individuals will not be recognized as granting the privilege to practice nursing in any other party state unless explicitly agreed to by that party state.

ARTICLE 4. APPLICATION FOR LICENSE IN A PARTY STATE. (a) Once an application for a license is submitted, the licensing board in a party state shall ascertain, through the coordinated licensure information system, whether:

(1) the applicant has held or is the holder of a license issued by another state;

(2) a restriction exists on the multistate licensing privilege; and

(3) any other adverse action by any state has been taken against the license.

(b) A nurse in a party state shall hold a license that is issued by the home state in only one party state at a time.

(c) A nurse who intends to change the nurse's primary state of residence may apply for a license in the new home state in advance of the change. However, a new license will not be issued by a party state until a nurse provides satisfactory evidence to the new home state's licensing board of a change in the nurse's primary state of residence.

(d) When a nurse changes the nurse's primary state of residence by moving from:

(1) a party state to another party state and obtains a license from the new home state, the license from the former home state is no longer valid;

(2) a non-party state to a party state and obtains a license from the new home state, the individual state license issued by the non-party state is not affected and remains in full force if provided by the laws of the non-party state; and

(3) a party state to a non-party state, the license issued by the prior home state converts to a state license valid only in the former home state and does not entitle the nurse to the multistate licensing privilege to practice in other party states.

ARTICLE 5. ADVERSE ACTIONS. (a) The licensing board of a remote state shall promptly report to the administrator of the coordinated licensure information system a remote state action and the factual and legal basis for the action, if known. The licensing board of a remote state shall promptly report any significant current investigative information yet to result in a remote state action. The administrator of the coordinated licensure information system shall promptly notify the home state of these reports.

(b) The licensing board of a party state shall have the authority to complete a pending *practices, i.e., where the patient or recipient of nursing practice is located, and not by the state where the nurse is located or licensed.*

The nurse's practicing in a party state will establish the BONs' and courts' jurisdiction over the nurse, i.e., their authority to discipline the nurse.

The Compact does not include advanced practice registered nursing. The current lack of uniform standards among states for recognition of APRNs makes it impractical for states to agree to mutually recognize each other's recognition of APRNs. However, if recognition as an APRN requires licensure as an RN, the license issued by the home state satisfies that requirement. NCSBN has developed a separate compact for APRNs.

Because not all states will adopt the Compact at the same time, party states will continue to license nurses who practice in their states but do not reside in a party state. Only licenses issued by a home state, i.e., primary state of residence, include the privilege to practice in other party states. For example, a nurse licensed by Texas can practice in Arkansas (a party state) without getting an Arkansas license but can practice in Louisiana (a nonparty state) only if she/he gets a Louisiana license.

This article governs how the licensing process will work.

Before the home state issues a nurse a license it must verify, through the Coordinated Licensure Information System, the status of any license issued by another state.

A nurse can hold a license only from one party state which must be the home state, i.e., primary state of residence.

A nurse who changes her/his primary state of residence from one party state to another must obtain a new license from the new party state that is now the nurse's primary state of residence.

This Section (d) sets out the various licensing requirements if a nurse changes residence between party states or between a party and nonparty state. Since not all states will adopt the Compact at the same time, nurses may be practicing in both party and nonparty states. Nurses will need to be aware of whether the state(s) in which they reside and practice have adopted the Compact and to be sure they are properly licensed.

If a nurse moves from a party to a nonparty state, the nurse's multistate license is lost and the nurse will have to obtain a license from every state in which the nurse practices. For example, if a nurse residing and licensed in Texas practices in Texas (party state), Arkansas (party state) and Louisiana (nonparty state) moves from Texas to Louisiana, the nurse's Texas license will convert to a regular license and the nurse will need to get both a Louisiana and an Arkansas license.

This article addresses "adverse actions." Article 2(a) defines "adverse action" as disciplinary action against the nurse and the nurse's license or multistate licensure privilege by the home or remote state.

Any adverse action must be reported to the Coordinated Licensure Information System.

The Coordinated Licensure Information System will notify the home state so it can take appropriate action against the nurse's license.

This Section (b) addresses what happens if a nurse changes home states during a pending investigation of a nurse who changes the nurse's primary state of residence during the course of the investigation and to take appropriate action. The licensing board shall promptly report the conclusions of the investigations to the administrator of the coordinated licensure information system. The administrator of the coordinated licensure information system shall promptly notify the new home state of any action.

(c) A remote state may take adverse action affecting the multistate licensing privilege to practice in that party state. However, only the home state has the power to impose adverse action against the license issued by the home state.

(d) For purposes of imposing adverse action, the licensing board of the home state shall give the same priority and effect to reported conduct received from a remote state as it would to conduct occurring in the home state. In so doing, the licensing board shall apply its state laws to determine appropriate action.

(e) The home state may take adverse action based on the factual findings of the remote state only if each state follows its own procedures for imposing the adverse action.

(f) This compact does not affect a party state's decision that participation in an alternative program may be used instead of licensing action and that the participation shall remain non-public if required by the party state's laws. Party states must require a nurse who enters an alternative program to agree not to practice in any other party state during the term of the alternative program without prior authorization from the other party state.

ARTICLE 6. ADDITIONAL AUTHORITIES OF PARTY STATE NURSE LICENSING BOARDS

[Omitted]

ARTICLE 7. COORDINATED LICENSURE INFORMATION SYSTEM. (a) All party states shall participate in a cooperative effort to create a coordinated database of all licensed registered nurses, licensed practical nurses, and licensed vocational nurses. This system will include information on the licensing and disciplinary history of each nurse, as contributed by party states, to assist in the coordination of nurse licensing and enforcement efforts.

(b) Notwithstanding any other provision of law, all party states' licensing boards shall promptly report to the coordinated licensure information system adverse actions, actions against multistate licensing privileges, any current significant investigative information yet to result in adverse action, and denials of applications and the reasons for the denials.

(c) Current significant investigative information shall be transmitted only to party state licensing boards through the coordinated licensure information system.

(d) Notwithstanding any other provision of law, all party states' licensing boards that contribute information to the coordinated licensure information system may designate information that may not be shared with non-party states or disclosed to other entities or individuals without the express permission of the contributing state.

(e) Any personally identifiable information obtained by a party state's licensing board from the coordinated licensure information system may not be shared with non-party states or disclosed to other entities or individuals except to the extent permitted by the laws of the party state contributing the information.

investigation.

The remote state, i.e., state of practice, can take action against the nurse's multistate licensure privilege but not the nurse's license. Only the home state can take action against the nurse's license since it is the state that issues the license. If the home state revokes or suspends a nurse's license, the nurse's multistate licensure privilege to practice in other party states will also be automatically revoked or suspended. Under Articles 2(h), 3(b) and 6(c), any party state can take action against the nurse's multistate licensure privilege to practice in its state.

If the home state receives a report of a nurse's conduct in another party state, its investigation of that conduct must be given the same priority as if the conduct had occurred in its own state. Since only the home state can take action against the nurse's license, it is important that the home state gives investigations of conduct that occur in other party states the same priority it would if the conduct occurred in its state. The home state applies its own laws in taking action against that nurse.

A home state can take action on the factual finding of the remote state and doesn't have to conduct a new investigation of the same facts.

This section addresses alternative/alternate programs such as peer assistance for nurses experiencing problems with chemical dependency or mental illness.

Nurses in alternate programs must notify a party state before practicing in that state.

This article addresses the information collection system. This system is referred to in the Compact as the "Coordinated Licensure Information System" but is also known as "NurSys."

Party states are required to report information to the Coordinated Licensure Information System.

"Current significant investigative information" is defined in Article 2(d) as not including minor infractions.

Only party states will have access to current significant investigative information. All states will have access to information about final actions.

Information does not lose its character as public or non-public information just because it is shared with the Coordinated Licensure Information System. The contributing state will need to designate the information that cannot be shared with anyone but party states.

Personally identifiable information obtained by a party state cannot be redislosed except as permitted by the contributing state's laws. This is true even if the information would be public information under the laws of the party state receiving the information.

(f) Information contributed to the coordinated licensure information system that is subsequently required to be expunged by the laws of the party state contributing that information shall be expunged from the coordinated licensure information system.

(g) Each compact administrator shall act jointly and in consultation with the administrator of the coordinated licensure information system to formulate necessary and proper procedures for the identification, collection, and exchange of information under this compact.

ARTICLE. 8. COMPACT ADMINISTRATION

[Omitted]

ARTICLE. 9. IMMUNITY

[Omitted]

ARTICLE. 10. EFFECTIVE DATE, WITHDRAWING AND AMENDING

[Omitted]

ARTICLE. 11. CONSTRUCTION

[Omitted]

SUBPART B
APRN COMPACT

1. COMPACT – CHAPTER 305, OCCUPATIONS CODE

***ANNOTATOR'S NOTE**: The RN/LVN Compact set out in Subpart A does not apply to advanced practice nursing. In 2007 as part of Sunset review of the Board of Nursing, the Advanced Practice Registered Nurse Licensure Compact (APRN Licensure Compact) was enacted as a separate compact as Chapter 305 of the Occupations Code. Its implementation was contingent on the BON adopting rule by December 31, 2011. That did not occur because the National Council of State Boards of Nursing was reviewing the APRN Compact for possible modification The anticipated date that states will be able to implement the APRN Compact is January 2016. Texas would have to pass new legislation adopting the revised APRN compact language.*

The Coordinated Licensure Information System must expunge any information that the contributing state must expunge.

The compact administrators have authority to adopt rules as to how the Coordinated Licensure Information System will operate. The compact administrators consist of the heads of the licensing boards of each party state.

Information about the APRN Compact can be found on website of the National Council of State Boards of Nursing.

PART IX.

SELECTED OTHER LAWS AND RULES RELATING TO NURSING PRACTICE

SUBPART A.
HOSPITAL NURSE STAFFING

1. HOSPITAL SAFE STAFFING LAW, Health & Safety Code, Chapter 257

Sec. 257.001. DEFINITIONS. In this chapter:

(1) "Committee" means a nurse staffing committee required by this chapter.

(2) "Department" means the Department of State Health Services.

(3) "Hospital" means:

(A) a general hospital or special hospital, as those terms are defined by Section 241.003, including a hospital maintained or operated by this state; or

(B) a mental hospital licensed under Chapter 577.

(4) "Patient care unit" means a unit or area of a hospital in which registered nurses provide patient care.

ANNOTATIONS

In addition to the NPA and BON rules, nurses must comply with a variety of other laws and regulations that govern their practice. These vary among practice settings. The BON Standards of Nursing Practice (Rule 217.11) require that nurses know and conform to all the state and federal laws and regulations affecting their area of practice. This Part sets out a few such laws and rules.

> ***ANNOTATOR'S NOTE:*** *Only Subparts A-C include line-by-line annotations. The remaining laws and regulations are set out in newspaper column format with Annotator's Notes at the beginning of the Subpart or individual provision.*

As part of addressing the nursing shortage in the late 1990's, Texas Nurses Association (TNA) and Texas Hospital Association (THA) agreed to address nurse staffing as a significant practice environment issue for nurses. In 2002, TNA and THA jointly petitioned the Department of State Health Services (DSHS) (then the Department of Health) to strengthen its rule governing nurse staffing in hospitals. In 2009, the Hospital Safe Staffing Law was passed which built on these rules and reflected an agreement reached by TNA and THA. In addition to addressing nurse staffing, the Hospital Safe Staffing Law also addressed mandatory overtime. The legislation added Chapter 257 (Nurse Staffing) and Chapter 258 (Mandatory Overtime) to the Health & Safety Code.

The Hospital Safe Staffing Law takes what is commonly referred to as a "mandated staffing plan" approach to assuring adequate staffing. An alternate approach is referred to as a "mandated ratio" approach. The "mandated staffing plan" approach mandates that hospitals have a staffing plan that meets certain criteria and that it establish a nurse staffing committee. The nurse staffing committee must have significant input into development of a staffing plan, which takes into account the unique characteristics of that individual hospital. In contrast, the "mandated ratio" approach mandates in statute a nurse-patient ratio (normally different ratios for different units) for all hospitals without regard to their size, location, patient population, or the experience and education of the nursing staff.

This Subpart A sets out Ch. 257 relating to nurse staffing and Subpart B sets out Ch. 258 relating to mandatory overtime.

Definitions

Any reference to "department" in this law is to the Department of State Health Services.

This definition is designed to ensure the staffing law applies to all types of hospitals - for-profit and nonprofit; private and public; special and general; and non-psychiatric and psychiatric.

"Patient care unit" is defined because staffing levels must be set specific to each patient care unit. See Subsecs 257.003(a)(2), (b)(2).

Sec. 257.002. LEGISLATIVE FINDINGS. (a) The legislature finds that:

(1) research supports a conclusion that adequate nurse staffing is directly related to positive patient outcomes and nurse satisfaction with the practice environment;

(2) nurse satisfaction with the practice environment is in large measure determined by providing an adequate level of nurse staffing based on research findings and patient intensity;

(3) nurse satisfaction and patient safety can be adversely affected when nurses work excessive hours; and

(4) hospitals and nurses share a mutual interest in patient safety initiatives that create a healthy environment for nurses and appropriate care for patients.

(b) In order to protect patients, support greater retention of registered nurses, and promote adequate nurse staffing, the legislature intends to establish a mechanism whereby nurses and hospital management shall participate in a joint process regarding decisions about nurse staffing.

Sec. 257.003. NURSE STAFFING POLICY AND PLAN.

(a) The governing body of a hospital shall adopt, implement, and enforce a written nurse staffing policy to ensure that an adequate number and skill mix of nurses are available to meet the level of patient care needed. The policy must include a process for:

(1) requiring the hospital to give significant consideration to the nurse staffing plan recommended by the hospital's nurse staffing committee and to that committee's evaluation of any existing plan;

(2) adopting, implementing, and enforcing an official nurse services staffing plan that is based on the needs of each patient care unit and shift and on evidence relating to patient care needs;

(3) using the official nurse services staffing plan as a component in setting the nurse staffing budget;

(4) encouraging nurses to provide input to the committee relating to nurse staffing concerns;

(5) protecting from retaliation nurses who provide input to the committee; and

(6) ensuring compliance with rules adopted by the executive commissioner of the Health and Human Services Commission relating to nurse staffing.

(b) The official nurse services staffing plan adopted under Subsection (a) must:

(1) reflect current standards established by private accreditation organizations, governmental entities, national nursing professional associations, and other health professional organizations;

(2) set minimum staffing levels for patient care units that are:

(A) based on multiple nurse and patient considerations; and

(B) determined by the nursing assessment and in accordance with evidence-based

Legislative Findings

Legislative findings are helpful in understanding the Legislature's intent in passing the Hospital Safe Staffing Law.

Finding (3) relates to the mandatory overtime section of the law.

Subsection (b) recognizes that staffing decisions should be a collaborative effort between nurses and management.

Hospital Governing Body Involvement.

One of the purposes of the nurse staffing law is to ensure involvement of the hospital board in setting policies relating to nurse staffing. The policy adopted by the governing body must:

1. Provide that both the staffing plan recommended by the nurse staffing committee and the committee's evaluation of the current staffing plan be given significant consideration.

2. Provide that the staffing plan be unit and shift based.

3. Provide for the staffing plan to be a component in setting the budget.

4. Encourage input to committee from nurses and.

5. Protect nurses from retaliation

6. Ensure compliance with the nurse staffing rules of the Department of State Health Services. The intent of the staffing law is that hospital boards adopt policies that wrap around and enhance the nurse staffing rules. The reference is to executive commissioner of Health and Human Services adopting the rules because the commissioner technically adopts the rule.

Official Staffing Plan

In a strict sense, the law provides for two nurse staffing plans:

1. *The staffing plan developed and recommended by the nurse staffing committee;*
2. *The "official nurse services staffing plan" which is the staffing plan finally adopted by the hospital.*

The relationship between the two is that in adopting the final plan the hospital is required to give "significant consideration" to the plan recommended by the committee and also to the committee's evaluation of the existing plan. See Sec. 257.003(a)(1).

The official plan must:

1. Reflect recognized staffing standards.

2. Set minimum staffing levels for each unit based on the considerations listed.

safe nursing standards;

(3) include a method for adjusting the staffing plan for each patient care unit to provide staffing flexibility to meet patient needs; and

(4) include a contingency plan when patient care needs unexpectedly exceed direct patient care staff resources.

(c) The hospital shall:

(1) use the official nurse services staffing plan:

(A) as a component in setting the nurse staffing budget; and

(B) to guide the hospital in assigning nurses hospital-wide; and

(2) make readily available to nurses on each patient care unit at the beginning of each shift the official nurse services staffing plan levels and current staffing levels for that unit and that shift.

Sec. 257.004. NURSE STAFFING COMMITTEE.

(a) A hospital shall establish a nurse staffing committee as a standing committee of the hospital.

(b) The committee shall be composed of members who are representative of the types of nursing services provided in the hospital.

(c) The chief nursing officer of the hospital is a voting member of the committee.

(d) At least 60 percent of the members of the committee must be registered nurses who:

(1) provide direct patient care during at least 50 percent of their work time; and

(2) are selected by their peers who provide direct patient care during at least 50 percent of their work time.

(e) The committee shall meet at least quarterly.

(f) Participation on the committee by a hospital employee as a committee member is part of the employee's work time, and the hospital shall compensate that member for that time accordingly. The hospital shall relieve a committee member of other work duties during committee meetings.

(g) The committee shall:

(1) develop and recommend to the hospital's governing body a nurse staffing plan that meets the requirements of Section 257.003;

(2) review, assess, and respond to staffing concerns expressed to the committee;

(3) identify the nurse-sensitive outcome measures the committee will use to evaluate the effectiveness of the official nurse services staffing plan;

(4) evaluate, at least semiannually, the effectiveness of the official nurse services staffing plan and variations between the plan and the actual staffing; and

(5) submit to the hospital's governing body, at least semiannually, a report on nurse staffing and patient care outcomes, including the committee's evaluation of the effectiveness of the official nurse services staffing plan and aggregate variations between the staffing plan and actual staffing.

(h) In evaluating the effectiveness of the official nurse services staffing plan, the

3. Include a way to adjust the plan.

4. Include a contingency plan for unexpected staffing needs.

Hospital Responsibilities

1. *Must use the official plan as a component in setting staffing budget and in assigning nurses. A hospital cannot set a budget and simply direct that staffing conform to the budget.*
2. *Must make information available to nurses about plan staffing levels and actual staffing levels.*

Committee Status

The committee must be a standing committee of the hospital. The committee has certain reporting responsibilities to the governing body. See Sec. 257.004(g)(5).

Committee Composition and Operations

The committee should be representative of types of nursing services provided in the hospital and composed of at least the CNO and 60% direct care RNs. The nurse staffing rules also require a representative from infection control, quality assurance, or risk management.

The 60% direct care RNs must be "selected" by their direct care RN peers. While a direct election is not required, the nurses ultimately selected must be direct care RNs who are selected by direct care RNs.

The intent of Subsec. (f) is to be sure committee members can devote their attention to the committee.

Committee Responsibilities

The committee shall:

1. Develop and recommend a plan using the same considerations that the hospital must use in developing the official plan.

2. Receive and respond to staffing concerns.

3 - 5. Be the entity within the hospital responsible for evaluating the staffing plan by:

- *Identifying the nurse sensitive-outcome measures that will be used in evaluating the official plan.*
- *Evaluating the effectiveness of the official nurse services staffing plan.*
- *Reporting the committee's evaluation to the governing body.*

The committee must consider certain factors in its evaluation of the official nurse services committee shall consider patient needs, nursing-sensitive quality indicators, nurse satisfaction measures collected by the hospital, and evidence-based nurse staffing standards.

Sec. 257.005. REPORTING OF STAFFING INFORMATION TO DEPARTMENT.

(a) A hospital shall annually report to the department on:

(1) whether the hospital's governing body has adopted a nurse staffing policy as required by Section 257.003;

(2) whether the hospital has established a nurse staffing committee as required by Section 257.004 that meets the membership requirements of that section;

(3) whether the nurse staffing committee has evaluated the hospital's official nurse services staffing plan as required by Section 257.004 and has reported the results of the evaluation to the hospital's governing body as provided by that section; and

(4) the nurse-sensitive outcome measures the committee adopted for use in evaluating the hospital's official nurse services staffing plan.

(b) Information reported under Subsection (a) is public information.

(c) To the extent possible, the department shall collect the data required under Subsection (a) as part of a survey required by the department under other law.

2. NURSE STAFFING RULE - ALL HOSPITALS OTHER THAN PSYCHIATRIC, Texas Department of State Health Services Rule 133.41(o), (25 Tx Admin Code 133.41)

> ***ANNOTATOR'S NOTE**: Section headings have been added to facilitate reading. The headings added are in brackets and are not part of the actual rules.*

staffing plan.

The hospital must report annually certain information about fulfilling its responsibilities related to developing and implementing a staffing plan. The "department" is the Department of Health and Human Services.

The information reported is public information.

Nurse staffing is addressed in two sections of the hospital licensing rules. The first is in Rule 133.41(f) relating to responsibilities of the hospital governing board. One of the key features of the Hospital Safe Staffing Law was to give the hospital governing board specific responsibilities with respect to nurse staffing and to make the nurse staffing committee a standing committee of the governing board that reports directly to the board. The second place nurse staffing is addressed is in Rule 133.41(o) relating to nursing services. This section closely tracks the language of the law itself while retaining provisions in the staffing rules originally adopted in 2002 relating to issues not addressed in the staffing law, e.g. the provisions relating to orientation and assignments.

The nurse staffing rule is lengthy and fairly complex so understanding its general structure and organization can facilitate reading and understanding. The following is an outline of the rule.

Outline of Staffing Rule

(f) Governing body
- *(8) Nurse staffing*

(o) Nursing services
- ***(1) Organization***
  - *(A) CNO qualifications*
  - *(B) CNO qualification exemption for rural hospitals*
  - *(C) CNO responsibilities*
  - *(D) CNO reports to CEO*
  - *(E) CNO role*
- ***(2) Staffing and Delivery of Care***
  - *(A) Licensure verification of nurses*
  - *(B) Adequate personnel*
  - *(C) RN availability*
  - *(D) RN assessment*
  - *(E) Nursing care plan*
  - *(F) Staffing Committee*
    - *(i) Composition*
    - *(ii) Serving on committee is compensated time*
    - *(iii) Frequency of meetings*
    - *(iv) Responsibilities*

§133.41. Hospital Functions and Services.

(f) Governing body.

(8) Nurse Staffing. The governing body shall adopt, implement and enforce a written nurse staffing policy to ensure that an adequate number and skill mix of nurses are available to meet the level of patient care needed. The governing body policy shall require that hospital administration adopt, implement and enforce a nurse staffing plan and policies that:

(A) require significant consideration be given to the nurse staffing plan recommended by the hospital's nurse staffing committee and the committee's evaluation of any existing plan;

(B) are based on the needs of each patient care unit and shift and on evidence relating to patient care needs;

(C) ensure that all nursing assignments consider client safety, and are commensurate with the nurse's educational preparation, experience, knowledge, and physical and emotional ability;

(D) require use of the official nurse services staffing plan as a component in setting the nurse staffing budget;

(E) encourage nurses to provide input to the nurse staffing committee relating to nurse staffing concerns;

(F) protect from retaliation nurses who provide input to the nurse staffing committee; and

(G) comply with subsection (o) of this section.

(o) Nursing services. The hospital shall have an organized nursing service that provides 24-hour nursing services as needed.

(1) Organization. The hospital shall have a well-organized service with a plan of administrative authority and delineation of responsibilities for patient care.

(G) Staffing Plan
- *(i) General requirements*
- *(ii) Components*
  - *(I) Staffing levels*
  - *(II) Adjustments by shift*
  - *(III) Contingency plan*
  - *(IV) Staffing Standards*
  - *(V) Staffing effectiveness evaluation*
  - *(VI) Nurses input*
  - *(VII) Orientation & assignments*
  - *(VIII) Staffing budget*
- *(iii) Posting of plan*
- *(iv) Semi-annual plan evaluation*
- *(v) Retention of plan*

(H) Use of nonemployed nurses

(I) Reporting to DSHS

(3) Mandatory Overtime
- *(A) Definitions*
- *(B) Prohibited overtime*
- *(C) Voluntary overtime not prohibited*
- *(D) On-call time*
- *(E) Exceptions*
- *(F) Process when exception applies*
- *(G) Retaliation prohibited*

The nurse staffing law gives the hospital governing board specific responsibilities with respect to nurse staffing and makes the nurse staffing committee a standing committee of the governing board that reports directly to the board. Subdivision (8) reflects this responsibility of the hospital governing board relating to nurse staffing. Details of what must be included in the plan are addressed in Subsection (o) set out below.

This requirement reflects that nurses have a duty, established by the BON, not to make or accept specific assignments for which they are not "fit for duty" even if the staffing plan or overtime rules would generally permit accepting the assignment.

Subsection (o) is the section of the hospital licensing rules which addresses nursing services in hospitals and is set out below.

This Subsec.133.41(o) of the hospital licensing rules addresses nursing services. This Subsection is the primary provision implementing the nurse staffing law including mandatory overtime.

Subdivision (1) relates to the organization of nursing services in the hospital.

(A) [CNO Education & Qualifications] Nursing services shall be under the administrative authority of a chief nursing officer (CNO) who shall be an RN and comply with one of the following:

(i) possess a master's degree in nursing;

(ii) possess a master's degree in health care administration or business administration;

(iii) possess a master's degree in a health-related field obtained through a curriculum that included courses in administration and management; or

(iv) be progressing under a written plan to obtain the nursing administration qualifications associated with a master's degree in nursing. The plan shall:

(I) describe efforts to obtain the knowledge associated with graduate education and to increase administrative and management skills and experience;

(II) include courses related to leadership, administration, management, performance improvement and theoretical approaches to delivering nursing care; and

(III) provide a time-line for accomplishing skills.

(B) [CNO Education Exemption for Rural Hospitals] The CNO in hospitals with 100 or fewer licensed beds and located in counties with a population of less than 50,000, or in hospitals that have been certified by the Centers for Medicare and Medicaid Services as critical access hospitals in accordance with the Code of Federal Regulations, Title 42, Volume 3, Part 485, Subpart F, §485.606(b), shall be exempted from the requirements in subparagraph (A)(i) - (iv) of this paragraph.

(C) [CNO Responsibilities] The CNO shall be responsible for the operation of the services, including determining the types and numbers of nursing personnel and staff necessary to provide nursing care for all areas of the hospital.

(D) [CNO Reports to CEO] The CNO shall report directly to the individual who has authority to represent the hospital and who is responsible for the operation of the hospital according to the policies and procedures of the hospital's governing board.

(E) [CNO Role] The CNO shall participate with leadership from the governing body, medical staff, and clinical areas, in planning, promoting and conducting performance improvement activities.

(2) Staffing and delivery of care.

(A) [Licensure verification] The nursing services shall adopt, implement and enforce a procedure to verify that hospital nursing personnel for whom licensure is required have valid and current licensure.

(B) [Adequate Personnel] There shall be adequate numbers of RNs, licensed vocational nurses (LVNs), and other personnel to provide nursing care to all patients as needed.

(C) [RN Availability] There shall be supervisory and staff personnel for each department or nursing unit to provide, when needed, the immediate availability of an RN to provide care for any patient.

(D) [RN Assessment] An RN shall be on duty in each building of a licensed hospital that contains at least one nursing unit where patients are present. The RN shall supervise and evaluate the nursing care for each patient and assign the nursing care to other nursing personnel in accordance with the patient's needs and the specialized qualifications and competence of the nursing staff available.

(E) [Nursing Care Plan] The nursing staff shall develop and keep current a nursing plan of care for each patient which addresses the patient's needs.

(F) [Staffing Committee] The hospital shall establish a nurse staffing committee as a standing committee of the hospital. The committee shall be established in accordance with Health and Safety Code (HSC), §§161.031 - 161.033, to be responsible for soliciting and receiving input

Nursing services must be under a CNO. See also Paragraph (C) about the CNO's responsibilities.

The CNO must be master's prepared or progressing toward a master's degree pursuant to a written plan.

CNOs at small, rural hospitals are exempted from the master's requirement.

The CNO must be responsible for nursing services including determining the number and types of nurses needed.

The CNO must report directly to the CEO or whomever is responsible for operation of the hospital according to policies of the hospital governing board.

Subdivision (2) relates to both the general requirements for nursing care and staffing. It addresses establishment of the staffing committee and development of the staffing plan.

Paragraphs (A) - (E) of Subdivision (2) set out the general requirements relating to nursing care and nursing services.

What constitutes an adequate number will be addressed in the staffing plan. See Paragraph (G) below relating to staffing plans.

RNs must be immediately available.

An RN must supervise and evaluate the nursing care for each patient.

There must be a nursing care plan for each patient.

This Paragraph (F) addresses the nurse staffing committee including composition and responsibilities. The committee is a standing committee of the hospital governing body and reports directly to it. The Health & Safety Code sections referred to address hospital committees from nurses on the development, ongoing monitoring, and evaluation of the staffing plan. As provided by HSC, §161.032, the hospital's records and review relating to evaluation of these outcomes and indicators are confidential and not subject to disclosure under Government Code, Chapter 552 and not subject to disclosure, discovery, subpoena or other means of legal compulsion for their release. As used in this subsection, "committee" or "staffing committee" means a nurse staffing committee established under this subparagraph.

(i) [composition] The committee shall be composed of:

(I) at least 60% registered nurses who are involved in direct patient care at least 50% of their work time and selected by their peers who provide direct care during at least 50% of their work time;

(II) at least one representative from either infection control, quality assessment and performance improvement or risk management;

(III) members who are representative of the types of nursing services provided at the hospital; and

(IV) the chief nursing officer of the hospital who is a voting member.

(ii) [compensated time] Participation on the committee by a hospital employee as a committee member shall be part of the employee's work time and the hospital shall compensate that member for that time accordingly. The hospital shall relieve the committee member of other work duties during committee meetings.

(iii) [meetings] The committee shall meet at least quarterly.

(iv) [responsibilities] The responsibilities of the committee shall be to:

(I) develop and recommend to the hospital's governing body a nurse staffing plan that meets the requirements of subparagraph (G) of this paragraph;

(II) review, assess and respond to staffing concerns expressed to the committee;

(III) identify the nurse-sensitive outcome measures the committee will use to evaluate the effectiveness of the official nurse services staffing plan;

(IV) evaluate, at least semiannually, the effectiveness of the official nurse services staffing plan and variations between the plan and the actual staffing; and

(V) submit to the hospital's governing body, at least semiannually, a report on nurse staffing and patient care outcomes, including the committee's evaluation of the effectiveness of the official nurse services staffing plan and aggregate variations between the staffing plan and actual staffing.

(G) [Staffing Plan] The hospital shall adopt, implement and enforce a written official nurse services staffing plan. As used in this subsection, "patient care unit" means a unit or area of a hospital in which registered nurses provide patient care.

(i) [general requirements] The official nurse services staffing plan and policies shall:

(I) require significant consideration to be given to the nurse staffing plan recommended by the hospital's nurse staffing committee and the committee's evaluation of any *and confidentiality and immunity from liability for members.*

The committee must consist of at least 60% direct care RNs who are selected by their direct-care RN peers. The actual selection process is not prescribed but the process has to be one that would permit input by all direct-care RNs. Processes that would do this include direct election or appointment by a nursing congress if the congress itself was selected only by direct care RNs. How the other 40% are selected would be determined by the hospital and could be either direct care RNs or non-direct care RNs.

The nurse staffing committee is not required to have a member from each area in which nursing care is provided, but must be representative of types of nursing services provided, e.g. one nurse may represent perioperative nursing rather than a nurse for each area of pre-operative care, surgery, post-anesthesia care, and post-operative care. However, the committee as a whole must be representative of all types of nursing care provided.

The CNO must be on the committee.

To ensure full participation, nurses serving on the committee must be compensated and relieved of other duties during committee meetings.

The committee has several significant responsibilities:

1. *Recommending a staffing plan: the committee shall develop a plan for recommendation to the hospital governing board*
2. *Receiving input from nurses: the committee must establish a process for receiving, evaluating, and responding to staffing concerns expressed to the committee*
3. *Identifying the nurse-sensitive outcome measures that will be used to evaluate staffing effectiveness*
4. *Evaluating effectiveness of the staffing plan and variances between planned and actual staffing: the committee will consider whether planned staffing was achieved and the overall effect of variances*
5. *Reporting its evaluation of staffing to the hospital governing board: as hospital boards are increasingly involved and accountable for patient safety, their awareness of nurse staffing as a significant factor in patient safety is critical.*

Hospitals must have and enforce an official written nurse staffing plan that includes all areas or units in which registered nurses provide care; this includes all inpatient, outpatient, ambulatory, and procedural areas in which registered nurses care for patients.

This section sets out the requirements staffing plans must meet. The hospital governing body must ensure the policies meet these requirements. See Subsection (f)(8) above relating to the governing body's responsibilities.

While the nurse staffing committee does not develop the official nurse staffing plan, the official plan must give "significant consideration" to the committee's recommended plan. The hospital's existing plan;

(II) be based on the needs of each patient care unit and shift and on evidence relating to patient care needs;

(III) require use of the official nurse services staffing plan as a component in setting the nurse staffing budget;

(IV) encourage nurses to provide input to the nurse staffing committee relating to nurse staffing concerns;

(V) protect from retaliation nurses who provide input to the nurse staffing committee; and

(VI) comply with subsection (o) of this section.

(ii) [components] The plan shall:

(I) [setting staffing levels] set minimum staffing levels for patient care units that are:

(-a-) based on multiple nurse and patient considerations including:

(-1-) patient characteristics and number of patients for whom care is being provided, including number of admissions, discharges and transfers on a unit;

(-2-) intensity of patient care being provided and variability of patient care across a nursing unit;

(-3-) scope of services provided;

(-4-) context within which care is provided, including architecture and geography of the environment, and the availability of technology; and

(-5-) nursing staff characteristics, including staff consistency and tenure, preparation and experience, and the number and competencies of clinical and non-clinical support staff the nurse must collaborate with or supervise.

(-b-) determined by the nursing assessment and in accordance with evidence-based safe nursing standards; and

(-c-) recalculated at least annually, or as necessary;

(II) [adjustments] include a method for adjusting the staffing plan shift to shift for each patient care unit based on factors, such as, the intensity of patient care to provide staffing flexibility to meet patient needs;

(III) [contingency plan] include a contingency plan when patient care needs unexpectedly exceed direct patient care staff resources;

(IV) [on-call time] include how on-call time will be used;

governing board policies must address how this will occur. See Subsection (f)(8) above relating to the governing body's responsibilities. The committee develops its recommended staffing plan based on these same considerations. See Paragraph (F)(iv)(I) above.

The nurse staffing plan should drive the nurse staffing budget rather than the budget driving staffing decisions.

Policies need to identify how concerns about staffing will be solicited from direct care nurses and communicated to the nurse staffing committee.

Nurses who express their concerns about staffing are protected from retaliation.

Ths reference in Subsec. (o) is a self-reference to this rule.

Paragraph (ii) sets out the components that the official staffing plan must address.

Safe staffing is complex and involves a multitude of factors which may be unique to each hospital and each hospital unit. The plan must stipulate minimum staffing levels considering the unique characteristics of patients, staff, and hospital unit.

The hospital must have a method for adjusting staffing based on patient needs. Rather than dictating an acuity system that each hospital must use to determine changes in patient conditions requiring staffing adjustments, the law allows the hospital to select a method for adjusting the staffing plan.

There must be a contingency plan for meeting greater than expected patient care needs.

While on-call has traditionally been utilized in emergency services in order to ensure the availability of responders (such as surgical personnel) in the event of an emergency, hospitals also use on-call to ensure appropriate staffing in non-emergency situations such as census fluctuations or unanticipated changes in staff availability (e.g. call-ins) in all patient care areas. The statute prohibits the use of on-call as a substitute for mandatory overtime, but provides little guidance regarding what specific on-call practices would be prohibited mandatory overtime. The use of on-call varies greatly across hospitals and even within hospital departments. By requiring the staffing plan to describe how on-call time will be used, DSHS has empowered hospital nurse staffing committees to consider the staffing needs of individual departments and determine how on-call time may be appropriately used to ensure safe staffing while avoiding prohibited mandatory overtime. This rule ensures the input of direct care nurses in determining the use of on-call time.

(V) [standards] reflect current standards established by private accreditation organizations, governmental entities, national nursing professional associations, and other health professional organizations and should be developed based upon a review of the codes of ethics developed by the nursing profession through national nursing organizations;

(VI) [evaluation] include a mechanism for evaluating the effectiveness of the official nurse services staffing plan based on patient needs, nursing sensitive quality indicators, nurse satisfaction measures collected by the hospital and evidence based nurse staffing standards. At least one from each of the following three types of outcomes shall be correlated to the adequacy of staffing:

(-a-) nurse-sensitive patient outcomes selected by the nurse staffing committee, such as, patient falls, adverse drug events, injuries to patients, skin breakdown, pneumonia, infection rates, upper gastrointestinal bleeding, shock, cardiac arrest, length of stay, or patient readmissions;

(-b-) operational outcomes, such as, work-related injury or illness, vacancy and turnover rates, nursing care hours per patient day, on-call use, or overtime rates; and

(-c-) substantiated patient complaints related to staffing levels;

(VII) [nurse input] incorporate a process that facilitates the timely and effective identification of concerns about the adequacy of the staffing plan by the nurse staffing committee established pursuant to subparagraph (F) of this paragraph. This process shall include:

(-a-) a prohibition on retaliation for reporting concerns;

(-b-) a requirement that nurses report concerns timely through appropriate channels within the hospital;

(-c-) orientation of nurses on how to report concerns and to whom;

(-d-) encouraging nurses to provide input to the committee relating to nurse staffing concerns;

(-e-) review, assessment, and response by the committee to staffing concerns expressed to the committee;

(-f-) a process for providing feedback during the committee meeting on how concerns are addressed by the committee established under subparagraph (F) of this paragraph; and

(-g-) use of the nurse safe harbor peer review process pursuant to Occupations Code, §303.005;

(VIII) [orientation/assignment] include policies and procedures that require:

(-a-) orientation of nurses and other personnel who provide nursing care to all patient care units to which they are assigned on either a temporary or permanent basis;

(-b-) that the orientation of nurses and other personnel and the competency to perform nursing services is documented in accordance with hospital policy;

(-c-) that nursing assignments be congruent with documented competency; and

(IX) [staffing budget] be used by the hospital as a component in setting the nurse staffing budget and guiding the hospital in assigning nurses hospital wide.

(iii) [posting of plan] The hospital shall make readily available to nurses on each patient care unit at the beginning of each shift the official nurse services staffing plan levels and current staffing levels for that unit and that shift.

(iv) [plan evaluation] There shall be a semiannual evaluation by the staffing committee of the effectiveness of the official nurse services staffing plan and variations between

Several specialty nursing organizations have developed evidence-based standards or guidelines for nurse staffing. The staffing plan must reflect current standards. If the plan does not adopt current standards, the rationale for the variance should be well documented.

The plan must include a mechanism for evaluating its effectiveness using the outcome measures indicated. The nurse staffing committee is responsible for this evaluation and reporting the results to the hospital governing body. See Paragraph(F)(iv) above and Paragraph (iv) below. Most hospitals will not have a large enough number of patients to reach any statistical significance when comparing staffing to patient outcome indicators. Yet, hospitals should strive to identify patterns and relationships between staffing and other indicators that will enable them to continually improve on performance measurements.

The plan must have a process for obtaining input from nurses and providing feedback on how concerns are addressed. This may be accomplished by having the direct care nurses on the staffing committee solicit feedback from their representative patient care areas and report back to the committee. Another option may be to survey direct care nurses about their staffing concerns and have the nurse staffing committee evaluate the survey results. The staffing committee must inform direct care nurses about how their concerns are being addressed.

Nurses must be oriented on the process for reporting their staffing concerns as well as the process for invoking safe harbor. The process for informing nurses of these processes should be described in policy.

Each individual's orientation and competencies must be documented.

Assignments must be made in accordance with the documented competencies.

The staffing plan must be used in setting the staffing budget. The budget cannot first be set and the staffing plan developed to meet the budget. The plan has to be developed first for it to be used as a component in setting the budget.

The plan must be made readily available to nurses at the beginning of each shift.

The plan must be evaluated by the staffing committee at least semiannually. The evaluation must comply with the requirements of this paragraph (iv).

the staffing plan and actual staffing. The evaluation shall consider the outcomes and nursing-sensitive indicators as set out in clause (ii)(VI) of this subparagraph, patient needs, nurse satisfaction measures collected by the hospital, and evidence based nurse staffing standards. This evaluation shall be documented in the minutes of the committee established under subparagraph (F) of this paragraph and presented to the hospital's governing body. Hospitals may determine whether this evaluation is done on a unit or facility level basis. To assist the committee with the semiannual evaluation, the hospital shall report to the committee the variations between the staffing plan and actual staffing. This report of variations shall be confidential and not subject to disclosure under Government Code, Chapter 552 and not subject to disclosure, discovery, subpoena or other means of legal compulsion for their release.

(v) [retention plan] The staffing plan shall be retained for a period of two years.

(H) [Nonemployees] Nonemployee licensed nurses who are working in the hospital shall adhere to the policies and procedures of the hospital. The CNO shall provide for the adequate orientation, supervision, and evaluation of the clinical activities of nonemployee nursing personnel which occur within the responsibility of the nursing services.

(I) [Reporting to DSHS] The hospital shall annually report to the department on:

(i) whether the hospital's governing body has adopted a nurse staffing policy;

(ii) whether the hospital has established a nurse staffing committee that meets the membership requirements of subparagraph (F) of this paragraph;

(iii) whether the nurse staffing committee has evaluated the hospital's official nurse services staffing plan and has reported the results of the evaluation to the hospital's governing body; and

(iv) the nurse-sensitive outcome measures the committee adopted for use in evaluating the hospital's official nurse services staffing plan.

(3) Mandatory Overtime.

ANNOTATOR'S NOTE: *The sections of the rule relating to mandatory overtime are set out in Subpart B (Mandatory Overtime).*

3. NURSE STAFFING RULES - PSYCHIATRIC HOSPITALS
Tex Department of State Health Services Rules 411.473, .493, .496, (25 Tx Admin Code 411)

Rule 411.473. Nursing Services
Rule 411.493. Quality Assessment & Performance Improvement Program
Rule 411.496. Advisory Committee for Nurse Staffing

SUBPART B.
HOSPITAL MANDATORY OVERTIME PROHIBITION

1. MANDATORY OVERTIME LAW
HEALTH & SAFETY CODE, CH.258. MANDATORY OVERTIME FOR NURSES PROHIBITED

Sec. 258.001. DEFINITIONS
Sec. 258.002. MANDATORY OVERTIME
Sec. 258.003. PROHIBITION OF MANDATORY OVERTIME
Sec. 258.004. EXCEPTIONS

Non-employed nurses must be adequately oriented and supervised.

The nurse staffing law specifically requires that this information be reported to Department of State Health Services (DSHS). The data is collected on the DSHS's annual hospital survey.

ANNOTATOR'S NOTE: *These rules are not being set out since they are not that significantly different from Rule 133.41(o) relating to non-psychiatric hospitals.*

This mandatory overtime law was enacted in 2009 as part of the Hospital Safe Staffing Law. See the annotations to Subpart A above.

Sec. 258.005. RETALIATION PROHIBITED

Sec. 258.001. DEFINITIONS. In this chapter:

(1) "Hospital" means:

(A) a general hospital or special hospital, as those terms are defined by Section 241.003, including a hospital maintained or operated by this state; or

(B) a mental hospital licensed under Chapter 577.

(2) "Nurse" means a registered nurse or vocational nurse licensed under Chapter 301, Occupations Code.

(3) "On-call time" means time spent by a nurse who is not working but who is compensated for availability.

Sec. 258.002. MANDATORY OVERTIME. For purposes of this chapter, "mandatory overtime" means a requirement that a nurse work hours or days that are in addition to the hours or days scheduled, regardless of the length of a scheduled shift or the number of scheduled shifts each week. In determining whether work is mandatory overtime, prescheduled on-call time or time immediately before or after a scheduled shift necessary to document or communicate patient status to ensure patient safety is not included.

Sec. 258.003. PROHIBITION OF MANDATORY OVERTIME.

(a) A hospital may not require a nurse to work mandatory overtime, and a nurse may refuse to work mandatory overtime.

(b) This section does not prohibit a nurse from volunteering to work overtime.

(c) A hospital may not use on-call time as a substitute for mandatory overtime.

Sec. 258.004. EXCEPTIONS. (a) Section 258.003 does not apply if:

(1) a health care disaster, such as a natural or other type of disaster that increases the need for health care personnel, unexpectedly affects the county in which the nurse is employed or affects a contiguous county;

(2) a federal, state, or county declaration of emergency is in effect in the county in which the nurse is employed or is in effect in a contiguous county;

(3) there is an emergency or unforeseen event of a kind that:

(A) does not regularly occur;

(B) increases the need for health care personnel at the hospital to provide safe patient care; and

(C) could not prudently be anticipated by the hospital; or

(4) the nurse is actively engaged in an ongoing medical or surgical procedure and the continued presence of the nurse through the completion of the procedure is necessary to ensure the health and safety of the patient.

(b) If a hospital determines that an exception exists under Subsection (a)(3), the hospital shall, to the extent possible, make a good faith effort to meet the staffing need through voluntary overtime, including calling per diems and agency nurses, assigning floats, or requesting an additional day of work from off-duty employees.

"Mandatory overtime," itself, is defined in Sec. 258.002 and not in this section.

On-call is used in defining what constitutes mandatory overtime. See Sec. 258.002.

"Mandatory overtime" is defined in terms of hours scheduled to work and not an absolute number. For example, for a nurse scheduled to work 4 hours, overtime would be 5 hours; for a nurse scheduled to work 12 hours, overtime would be 13 hours.

Pre-scheduled on-call time, as defined in Sec. 258.001(3), is not counted in determining overtime but see Sec. 258.003(c), which prohibits use of on-call as a substitute for mandatory overtime.

A hospital is generally prohibited from using mandatory overtime but certain exceptions do apply. See Sec. 258.004. This prohibition on mandatory overtime applies only to hospitals and does not include nursing homes or home health agencies.

Nurses are <u>not</u> prohibited from working voluntary overtime.

On-call cannot be used as a substitute for mandatory overtime. For example, if nurses are consistently put on-call and consistently called in for actual work, there would be a question if on-call was being used as a substitute for mandatory overtime.

This section sets out four situations in which a hospital could mandate a nurse work overtime. Subsection (b) requires that before a nurse can be required to work overtime on the basis of one of these exceptions, the hospital must make an attempt to find another nurse to work.

1. Heath care disaster that affects either the county in which nurse is employed or a contiguous county.

2. A federal, state or county declared emergency either in the county in which the nurse is employed or a contiguous county.

3. An emergency that meets criteria (A)-(C).

4. Ongoing medical or surgical procedure.

Even if an exception applies, before a nurse can be required to work overtime, the hospital must make an attempt to find another nurse to work.

Sec. 258.005. RETALIATION PROHIBITED. A hospital may not suspend, terminate, or otherwise discipline or discriminate against a nurse who refuses to work mandatory overtime.

2. MANDATORY OVERTIME RULE - DEPARTMENT OF STATE HEALTH SERVICES RULE 133.41(o)(3); (25 TAC 133.41)

(o) Nursing Services.

(3) Mandatory Overtime.

The hospital shall adopt, implement and enforce policies on use of mandatory overtime.

(A) [Definitions] As used in this subsection:

(i) "on-call time" means time spent by a nurse who is not working but who is compensated for availability; and

(ii) "mandatory overtime" means a requirement that a nurse work hours or days that are in addition to the hours or days scheduled, regardless of the length of a scheduled shift or the number of scheduled shifts each week. Mandatory overtime does not include prescheduled on-call time or time immediately before or after a scheduled shift necessary to document or communicate patient status to ensure patient safety.

(B) [Prohibited Overtime] A hospital may not require a nurse to work mandatory overtime, and a nurse may refuse to work mandatory overtime.

(C) [Voluntary Overtime] This section does not prohibit a nurse from volunteering to work overtime.

(D) [On-call time] A hospital may not use on-call time as a substitute for mandatory overtime.

(E) [Exceptions] The prohibitions on mandatory overtime do not apply if:

(i) a health care disaster, such as a natural or other type of disaster that increases the need for health care personnel, unexpectedly affects the county in which the nurse is employed or affects a contiguous county;

(ii) a federal, state, or county declaration of emergency is in effect in the county in which the nurse is employed or is in effect in a contiguous county;

(iii) there is an emergency or unforeseen event of a kind that:

(I) does not regularly occur;

(II) increases the need for health care personnel at the hospital to provide safe patient care; and

Retaliation for refusing to work mandatory overtime is prohibited. A parallel amendment was made to NPA adding Sec. 301.356 stating that a refusal to work mandatory overtime is not patient abandonment.

Subdivision 133.41(o)(3) relates to mandatory overtime and implements the mandatory overtime provisions of the nurse staffing law. In understanding the rule, it is important to remember that "overtime" is defined in terms of working beyond when a nurse is scheduled to work and not in terms of working beyond a certain number of hours. These rules largely track the mandatory overtime law. The following is an outline of this rule.

(A) Definitions
(B) Prohibited overtime
(C) Voluntary overtime not prohibited
(D) On-call time
(E) Exceptions
(F) Process when exception applies
(G) Retaliation prohibited

Note that "overtime" is defined in terms of working beyond when a nurse is scheduled to work and not in terms of working beyond a certain number of hours. Understanding how overtime is defined is necessary to understanding the rule. This definition tracks the definition in the mandatory overtime law.

Mandatory overtime is prohibited, that is, requiring a nurse to work beyond when she/he is scheduled.

A nurse working voluntary overtime is not prohibited.

On-call time cannot be used as a substitute for mandatory overtime. Because of the intricacies of how facilities utilize on-call time, DSHS requires that the nurse staffing plan address how on-call time will be used. Hospitals must ensure that their nurse staffing plan provides for contingency staffing that does not involve the use of on-call as a substitute for mandatory overtim. For example, scheduling nurses for on-call immediately following their scheduled shifts and then routinely requiring "on-call" nurses to work past their scheduled shift could be considered using on-call as a substitute for mandatory overtime.

There are exceptions to the prohibition on mandatory overtime, that is, the law recognizes there are situations in which patient care is promoted by permitting hospitals to require nurses work overtime.

1. A healthcare disaster.

2. A declared emergency.

3. An unforeseen emergency.

(III) could not prudently be anticipated by the hospital; or

(iv) the nurse is actively engaged in an ongoing medical or surgical procedure and the continued presence of the nurse through the completion of the procedure is necessary to ensure the health and safety of the patient. The nurse staffing committee shall ensure that scheduling a nurse for a procedure that could be anticipated to require the nurse to stay beyond the end of his or her scheduled shift does not constitute mandatory overtime.

(F) [Process when Exception] If a hospital determines that an exception exists under subparagraph (E) of this paragraph, the hospital shall, to the extent possible, make and document a good faith effort to meet the staffing need through voluntary overtime, including calling per diems and agency nurses, assigning floats, or requesting an additional day of work from off-duty employees.

(G) [Retaliation Prohibited] A hospital may not suspend, terminate, or otherwise discipline or discriminate against a nurse who refuses to work mandatory overtime.

SUBPART C.
HOSPITAL WORKPLACE ISSUES

1. WORKPLACE SAFETY AND PREVENTION OF VIOLENCE

HEALTH AND SAFETY CODE, CHAPTER 241, HOSPITALS

Sec. 241.029. Policies and Procedures Relating to Workplace Safety. (a) The governing body of a hospital shall adopt policies and procedures related to the work environment for nurses to:

(1) improve workplace safety and reduce the risk of injury, occupational illness, and violence; and

(2) increase the use of ergonomic principles and ergonomically designed devices to reduce injury and fatigue.

(b) The policies and procedures adopted under Subsection (a), at a minimum, must include:

(1) evaluating new products and technology that incorporate ergonomic principles;

(2) educating nurses in the application of ergonomic principles;

(3) conducting workplace audits to identify areas of risk of injury, occupational

4. The hours nurses work in surgical and procedural areas are largely driven by how cases are scheduled. While it is understood that a nurse who is actively engaged in a medical or surgical procedure cannot abandon the patient if the procedure extends beyond his/her scheduled shift, questions have been posed about whether requiring a nurse to begin a procedure that is expected to extend beyond his/her scheduled shift or requiring a nurse to stay beyond his/her scheduled shift for emergent or non-emergent add-on cases would constitute prohibited mandatory overtime. Recognizing the complexity of scheduling, staffing, and using on-call in surgical and procedural areas, DSHS determined that the hospital's nurse staffing committee is best equipped to evaluate the needs of the patient population and the practices of the hospital and develop policies and procedures that would ensure that practices would not constitute mandatory overtime. In response to TNA/THA comments submitted when this rule was adopted, DSHS stated:

> *Members of the nurse staffing committee are selected by their peers, and at least 60% of the committee is composed of registered nurses involved in direct patient care. This selection of committee members ensures that the nurses' scheduling needs are met and that nurses have an active voice in the scheduling process...[This approach] requires each hospital, through the nurses and other staff on the nurse staffing committee to address the issue of scheduling nurses for procedures and mandatory overtime.*

Even if an exception exists that permits the hospital to mandate overtime, it must first attempt to find other nurses to cover.

A nurse may not be retaliated against for refusing to work prohibited mandatory overtime.

The two laws set out in this Subpart C were the result of legislative initiatives by the Texas Nurses Association to create a practice environment more likely to attract and retain nurses. The Texas Department of State Health (DSHS) has adopted rules directing hospitals to "develop, implement and enforce" the policies required by these two laws.

Hospitals must have policies which address both safety and ergonomics in the work environment for nurses. The Safe Patient Handling Law set out below imposes specific requirements with respect to patient handling. Legislation (HB 705) was passed in 2013 enhancing the penalty for assaulting an ER nurse to a Class C felony.

illness, or violence and recommending ways to reduce those risks;

(4) controlling access to those areas identified as having a high risk of violence; and

(5) promptly reporting crimes committed against nurses to appropriate law enforcement agencies.

DEPARTMENT OF STATE HEALTH SERVICES, TITLE 25, CHAPTER 133, RULE 133.41, HOSPITAL FUNCTIONS AND SERVICES

(o) Nursing Services

(1)-(5) *[omitted]*

(6) Policies and procedures related to workplace safety.

(A) The hospital shall adopt, implement and enforce policies and procedures related to the work environment for nurses which:

(i) improve workplace safety and reduce the risk of injury, occupational illness, and violence; and

(ii) increase the use of ergonomic principles and ergonomically designed devices to reduce injury and fatigue.

(B) The policies and procedures adopted under subparagraph (A) of this paragraph, at a minimum, must include:

(i) evaluating new products and technology that incorporate ergonomic principles;

(ii) educating nurses in the application of ergonomic practices;

(iii) conducting workplace audits to identify areas of risk of injury, occupational illness, or violence and recommending ways to reduce those risks;

(iv) controlling access to those areas identified as having a high risk of violence; and

(v) promptly reporting crimes committed against nurses to appropriate law enforcement agencies.

(7) *[omitted]*

2. ABUSE AND HARASSMENT PROTECTIONS

§133.45(e). MISCELLANEOUS POLICIES AND PROTOCOLS.

(e) Harassment and Abuse. A hospital shall adopt, implement and enforce a written policy for identifying and addressing instances of alleged verbal or physical abuse or harassment of hospital employees or contracted personnel by other hospital employees or contracted personnel or by a health care provider who has clinical privileges at the hospital.

3. SAFE PATIENT HANDLING

A. HEALTH & SAFETY CODE, CHAPTER 256. SAFE PATIENT HANDLING AND MOVEMENT PRACTICES

Sec. 256.001. DEFINITIONS. In this chapter:

(1) "Hospital" means a general or special hospital, as defined by Section 241.003, a private mental hospital licensed under Chapter 577, or another hospital that is maintained or operated by the state.

(2) "Nursing home" means an institution licensed under Chapter 242.

Sec. 256.002. REQUIRED SAFE PATIENT HANDLING AND MOVEMENT POLICY

(a) The governing body of a hospital or the quality assurance committee of a nursing home shall adopt and ensure implementation of a policy to identify, assess, and develop strategies

An assault against an ER nurse carries an enhanced penalty of a Class C felony.

This Rule 133.41(o)(6) implements Sec. 241.029 above. Hospitals are required to "adopt, implement and enforce" the policies.

At the same time it adopted the hospital nurse staffing rules, the Department of State Health Services adopted this rule requiring hospitals to have written policies for preventing verbal and physical abuse and harassment.

When Texas enacted this law in 2005, it was the first state in the nation to pass safe patient handling legislation. The Texas Nurses Association initiated the legislation as part of a national "Handle with Care" initiative by the American Nurses Association.

This law applies to hospitals and nursing homes.

Hospitals and nursing homes are required to implement a policy governing patient handling. The policy must be adopted by the facility's governing board in the hospital setting and by the quality assurance committee in the nursing home facility. The intent of this requirement was to to control risk of injury to patients and nurses associated with the lifting, transferring, repositioning, or movement of a patient.

(b) The policy shall establish a process that, at a minimum, includes:

(1) analysis of the risk of injury to both patients and nurses posed by the patient handling needs of the patient populations served by the hospital or nursing home and the physical environment in which patient handling and movement occurs;

(2) education of nurses in the identification, assessment, and control of risks of injury to patients and nurses during patient handling;

(3) evaluation of alternative ways to reduce risks associated with patient handling, including evaluation of equipment and the environment;

(4) restriction, to the extent feasible with existing equipment and aids, of manual patient handling or movement of all or most of a patient's weight to emergency, life-threatening, or otherwise exceptional circumstances;

(5) collaboration with and annual report to the nurse staffing committee;

(6) procedures for nurses to refuse to perform or be involved in patient handling or movement that the nurse believes in good faith will expose a patient or a nurse to an unacceptable risk of injury;

(7) submission of an annual report to the governing body or the quality assurance committee on activities related to the identification, assessment, and development of strategies to control risk of injury to patients and nurses associated with the lifting, transferring, repositioning, or movement of a patient; and

(8) in developing architectural plans for constructing or remodeling a hospital or nursing home or a unit of a hospital or nursing home in which patient handling and movement occurs, consideration of the feasibility of incorporating patient handling equipment or the physical space and construction design needed to incorporate that equipment at a later date.

B. Department of State Health Services, Title 25, Chapter 133, Rule 133.41(o), Hospital Nursing Services

(o) Nursing Services

(1)-(6) *[omitted]*

(7) Safe patient handling and movement practices.

(A) The hospital shall adopt, implement and enforce policies and procedures to identify, assess, and develop strategies to control risk of injury to patients and nurses associated with the lifting, transferring, repositioning, or movement of a patient.

(B) The policies and procedures shall establish a process that, at a minimum, includes the following:

(i) analysis of the risk of injury to both patients and nurses posed by the patient handling needs of the patient populations served by the hospital and the physical environment in which patient handling and movement occurs;

(ii) education of nurses in the identification, assessment, and control of risks of injury to patients and nurses during patient handling;

(iii) evaluation of alternative ways to reduce risks associated with patient handling, including evaluation of equipment and the environment;

(iv) restriction, to the extent feasible with existing equipment and aids, of manual patient handling or movement of all or most of a patient's weight to emergency, life-threatening, or otherwise exceptional circumstances;

(v) collaboration with and annual report to the nurse staffing committee;

(vi) procedures for nurses to refuse to perform or be involved in patient handling *assure that the policy be set at a high level within the facility's administrative structure. The facility is not mandated to purchase new equipment but most do a risk analysis relating to patient handling and develop strategies to reduce the risk. Most studies have shown that the use of patient lifting aids, devices and equipment is cost effective.*

The policy must address the eight items listed.

Nurses must have the right to refuse if they believe the situation is unsafe.

The intent of this section is to ensure that the facility's administrative leadership was aware of patient handling issues.

This requirement is intended to ensure facilities plan for patient handling equipment at the time of new construction rather than later when installing may be considerably more difficult and expensive.

This Rule 133.41(o)(7) implements Sec. 256.001-.002 set out above. Hospitals are required to "adopt, implement and enforce" the policies.

or movement that the nurse believes in good faith will expose a patient or a nurse to an unacceptable risk of injury;

(vii) submission of an annual report to the governing body on activities related to the identification, assessment, and development of strategies to control risk of injury to patients and nurses associated with the lifting, transferring, repositioning, or movement of a patient; and

(viii) development of architectural plans for constructing or remodeling a hospital or a unit of a hospital in which patient handling and movement occurs, with consideration of the feasibility of incorporating patient handling equipment or the physical space and construction design needed to incorporate that equipment at a later date.

4. POLICIES ON MANDATORY VACCINATIONS OF PATIENT CARE PROVIDERS.

HEALTH & SAFETY CODE, SECS. 224.001 - .005; POLICY ON VACCINE PREVENTABLE DISEASES

Sec. 224.001. DEFINITIONS. In this chapter:

(1) "Covered individual" means:

(A) an employee of the health care facility;

(B) an individual providing direct patient care under a contract with a health care facility; or

(C) an individual to whom a health care facility has granted privileges to provide direct patient care.

(2) "Health care facility" means:

(A) a facility licensed under Subtitle B, including a hospital as defined by Section 241.003; or

(B) a hospital maintained or operated by this state.

(3) "Regulatory authority" means a state agency that regulates a health care facility under this code.

(4) "Vaccine preventable diseases" means the diseases included in the most current recommendations of the Advisory Committee on Immunization Practices of the Centers for Disease Control and Prevention.

Sec. 224.002. VACCINE PREVENTABLE DISEASES POLICY REQUIRED. (a) Each health care facility shall develop and implement a policy to protect its patients from vaccine preventable diseases.

(b) The policy must:

(1) require covered individuals to receive vaccines for the vaccine preventable diseases specified by the facility based on the level of risk the individual presents to patients by the individual's routine and direct exposure to patients;

(2) specify the vaccines a covered individual is required to receive based on the level of risk the individual presents to patients by the individual's routine and direct exposure to patients;

(3) include procedures for verifying whether a covered individual has complied with the policy;

(4) include procedures for a covered individual to be exempt from the required vaccines for the medical conditions identified as contraindications or precautions by the Centers for Disease Control and Prevention;

(5) for a covered individual who is exempt from the required vaccines, include procedures the individual must follow to protect facility patients from exposure to disease, such as the use of protective medical equipment, such as gloves and masks, based on the level of risk the individual presents to patients by the individual's routine and direct exposure to patients;

Ths law was passed in 2011 and requires hospitals adopt policies on mandatory vaccination of patient care providers.

This definition means hospital mandated vaccination policies will apply not only to traditional employees but anyone who provides direct patient care to patients in the hospital including practitioners such as APRNs who have privileges at the hospital.

The policies will apply to all "vaccine preventable diseases."

Each hospital must adopt a policy

The policy must address eight issues.

The facility will determine which vaccine preventable diseases will be covered.

Individuals must be exempted from the vaccinations if they have a medical condition identified as a contraindication or precaution by CDC.

Individuals exempted may be required to wear protective equipment such as a mask.

(6) prohibit discrimination or retaliatory action against a covered individual who is exempt from the required vaccines for the medical conditions identified as contraindications or precautions by the Centers for Disease Control and Prevention, except that required use of protective medical equipment, such as gloves and masks, may not be considered retaliatory action for purposes of this subdivision;

(7) require the health care facility to maintain a written or electronic record of each covered individual's compliance with or exemption from the policy; and

(8) include disciplinary actions the health care facility is authorized to take against a covered individual who fails to comply with the policy.

(c) The policy may include procedures for a covered individual to be exempt from the required vaccines based on reasons of conscience, including a religious belief.

Sec. 224.003. DISASTER EXEMPTION. (a) In this section, "public health disaster" has the meaning assigned by Section 81.003.

(b) During a public health disaster, a health care facility may prohibit a covered individual who is exempt from the vaccines required in the policy developed by the facility under Section 224.002 from having contact with facility patients.

Sec. 224.004. DISCIPLINARY ACTION. A health care facility that violates this chapter is subject to an administrative or civil penalty in the same manner, and subject to the same procedures, as if the facility had violated a provision of this code that specifically governs the facility.

Sec. 224.005. RULES. The appropriate rulemaking authority for each regulatory authority shall adopt rules necessary to implement this chapter.

[Continue on Next Page]

The policy may but is not required to exempt individuals for reasons of conscience. This provision was a source of controversy, but the decision was patient safety outweighed the individual's right to refuse to receive the vaccine. The concern was that requiring an exemption for "reasons of conscience" would negate the value of having a policy.

[Continue on Next Page]

ANNOTATOR'S NOTE

The remaining Subparts D - J will not include line-by-line annotations. Rather they are set out in newspaper column format with Annotator's Notes at beginning of the Subpart or individual provision.

SUBPART D. CIRCULATING RN

HEALTH & SAFETY CODE, CHAPTER 241

Sec. 241.0262. CIRCULATING DUTIES FOR SURGICAL SERVICES. Circulating duties in the operating room must be performed by qualified registered nurses. In accordance with approved medical staff policies and procedures, licensed vocational nurses and surgical technologists may assist in circulatory duties under the direct supervision of a qualified registered nurse circulator.

DEPARTMENT OF STATE HEALTH SERVICES, TITLE 25, CHAPTER 133, RULE 133.41(w), HOSPITAL SURGICAL SERVICES

(w) Surgical services. If a hospital provides surgical services, the services shall be well-organized and provided in accordance with acceptable standards of practice. If outpatient surgical services are offered, the services shall be consistent in quality with inpatient care in accordance with the complexity of services offered. A special hospital may not offer surgical services.

(1) Organization and staffing. The organization of the surgical services shall be appropriate for the scope of the services offered.

(A) The operating rooms shall be supervised by an experienced RN or physician.

(B) Licensed vocational nurses (LVNs) and surgical technologists (operating room technicians) may serve as scrub nurses or technologists under the supervision of an RN.

(C) Circulating duties in the operating room must be performed by qualified RNs. In accordance with approved medical staff polices and procedures, LVNs and surgical technologists may assist in circulatory duties under the direct supervision of a qualified RN circulator.

(D) Surgical privileges shall be delineated for all physicians, podiatrists, and dentists performing surgery in accordance with the competencies of each. The surgical services shall maintain a roster specifying the surgical privileges of each.

(E) If the facility employs surgical technologists, the facility shall adopt, implement, and enforce policies and procedures to comply with Health and Safety Code, Chapter 259 (relating to Surgical Technologists at Health Care Facilities).

(2) *[omitted]*

SUBPART E. RNS DETERMINING DEATH

ANNOTATOR'S NOTE: *This section permits RNs to pronounce and determine death if and only if the client is not on artificial life support. It does not authorize the signing of the death certificate, and RNs are not authorized to sign death certificates. See BON Position Statements 15.2 (The Role of the LVN in the Pronouncement of Death) and 15.20 (RNs in the Management of an Unwitnessed Arrest in a Resident in a Long-Term Care Facility).*

HEALTH & SAFETY CODE SECS. 671.001 -.002

§671.001 Standard Used in Determining Death.

(a) A person is dead when, according to ordinary standards of medical practice, there is irreversible cessation of the person's spontaneous respiratory and circulatory functions.

(b) If artificial means of support preclude a determination that a person's spontaneous respiratory and circulatory functions have ceased, the person is dead when, in the announced opinion of a physician, according to ordinary standards of medical practice, there is irreversible cessation of all spontaneous brain function. Death occurs when the relevant functions cease.

(c) Death must be pronounced before artificial means of supporting a person's respiratory and circulatory functions are terminated.

(d) A registered nurse or physician assistant may determine and pronounce a person dead in situations other than those described by Subsection (b) if permitted by written policies of a licensed health care facility, institution, or entity providing services to that person. Those policies must include physician assistants who are credentialed or otherwise permitted to practice at the facility, institution, or entity. If the facility, institution, or entity has an organized nursing staff and an organized medical staff or medical consultant, the nursing staff and medical staff or consultant shall jointly develop and approve those policies. The board shall adopt rules to govern policies for facilities, institutions, or entities that do not have organized nursing staffs and organized medical staffs or medical consultants.

Sec. 671.002. Limitation of Liability.

(a) A physician who determines death in accordance with Section 671.001(b) or a registered nurse or physician assistant who determines death in accordance with Section 671.001(d) is not liable for civil damages or subject to criminal prosecution for the physician's, registered nurse's, or physician assistant's actions or the actions of others based on the determination of death.

(b) A person who acts in good faith in reliance on a physician's, registered nurse's, or physician assistant's determination of death is not liable for civil damages or subject to criminal prosecution for the person's actions.

SUBPART F.
RNs PERFORMING RADIOLOGIC PROCEDURES

TEXAS DEPARTMENT OF STATE HEALTH SERVICES, TITLE 25, CHAPTER 140. MEDICAL RADIOLOGIC TECHNOLOGISTS

> ***ANNOTATOR'S NOTE.*** *The authority of RNs to perform radiologic procedures identified as dangerous or hazardous in this rule is limited to what is explicitly permitted under this rule. RNs performing dangerous and hazardous procedures need to complete required training. See DSHS Rule below. RNs performing radiologic procedures must comply with these rules and with BON Rule 217.14 (relating to RNs performing radiologic procedures).*

Rule 140.516. Dangerous Hazardous or Procedures

(a) General. This section identifies radiologic procedures which are dangerous or hazardous and may only be performed by a practitioner, medical radiologic technologist (MRT) or limited medical radiologic technologist (LMRT). There are specific procedures identified in §140.517 of this title (relating to Registered Nurses and Physician Assistants Performing Radiologic Procedures) which may be performed by a registered nurse (RN) or a physician assistant trained under §140.518 of this title (relating to Mandatory Training Programs for

Non-Certified Technicians) or §140.522 of this title (relating to Alternative Training Programs). A person trained under §140.518 or §140.522 of this title is not an MRT, LMRT or otherwise certified under the Act and shall not perform a dangerous or hazardous procedure identified in this section unless expressly permitted by this section or by §140.517 of this title.

(b) Dangerous procedures. Except as otherwise provided in this chapter, the list of dangerous procedures which may only be performed by a practitioner or MRT are:

(1) nuclear medicine studies to include positron emission tomography (PET);

(2) administration of radio-pharmaceuticals; administration does not include preparation or dispensing except as regulated under the authority of the Texas State Board of Pharmacy;

(3) radiation therapy, including simulation, brachytherapy and all external radiation therapy beams including Grenz rays:

(4) computed tomography (CT) or any variation thereof;

(5) interventional radiographic procedures, including angiography, unless performed by an LMRT with a certificate issued in the cardiovascular category;

(6) fluoroscopy unless performed by an LMRT with a certificate issued in the cardiovascular category; and

(7) cineradiography (including digital acquisition techniques), unless performed by an LMRT with a certificate issued in the cardiovascular category.

(c) Hazardous procedures. Unless otherwise noted, the list of hazardous procedures which may only be performed by a practitioner or MRT are:

(1) conventional tomography;

(2) skull radiography, excluding anterior-posterior/posterior-anterior (AP/PA), lateral, Townes, Caldwell, and Waters views;

(3) portable x-ray equipment;

(4) spine radiography, excluding AP/PA, lateral and lateral flexion/extension views;

(5) spine radiography;

(6) shoulder girdle radiographs, excluding AP and lateral shoulder views, AP clavicle and AP scapula;

(7) pelvic girdle radiographs, excluding AP or PA views;

(8) sternum radiographs; and

(9) radiographic procedures which utilize contrast media;

(10) pediatric radiography, excluding extremities, unless performed by an LMRT with the appropriate category. Pediatric studies must be performed with radioprotection so that proper collimation and shielding is utilized during all exposures sequences during pediatric studies. If an emergency condition exists which threatens serious bodily injury, protracted loss of use of a bodily function or death of a pediatric patient unless the procedure is performed without delay, or if other extenuating circumstances deemed by the practitioner exist, a pediatric radiographic procedure is also excluded. The emergency condition or extenuating circumstance must be documented by the ordering practitioner in the patient's clinical record and the record must document that a regularly scheduled MRT, LMRT, RN or physician assistant is not reasonably available to perform the procedure.

(d)-(f) *[omitted]*

(g) Mammography. In accordance with the Health and Safety Code, §401.421 et seq, mammography is a radiologic procedure which may only be performed by an MRT who meets the qualifications set out in 25 TAC Chapter 289 of the Radiation Control Program rules relating to mammography. Mammography shall not be performed by an LMRT, an NCT, or any other person.

(h) *[omitted]*

Rule 140.517. Registered Nurses and Physician Assistants Performing Radiologic Procedures

(a) An appropriately trained registered nurse (RN) or physician assistant (PA) may perform the following procedures:

(1) administration of radio-pharmaceuticals, performed by an RN or physician assistant who is appropriately trained as authorized by the department's Radiation Control Program for licensure of radioactive materials and who meets the training requirements identified in §140.518 of this title (relating to Mandatory Training Programs for Non-Certified Technicians) or §140.522 of this title (relating to Alternate Training Requirements); administration does not include preparation or dispensing as regulated under the authority of the Texas State Board of Pharmacy.

(2) fluoroscopy by an RN or physician assistant who assists in the performance of the procedure under the direct supervision of a practitioner.

(3) spine radiography lumbar oblique views performed by an RN or physician assistant who performs the procedure under the supervision of a practitioner.

(4) shoulder girdle radiographs--AP and lateral shoulder views, AP clavicle and AP scapula performed by an RN or physician assistant who performs the procedure under the direct supervision of a practitioner.

(5) sternum radiographs performed by an RN or physician assistant under the direct supervision of a practitioner; and

(6) radiographic procedures which utilize contrast media, performed by an RN or physician assistant who assists in the performance of the procedure under the supervision of a practitioner.

(7) pediatric radiography performed by an RN or physician assistant who is appropriately trained, as set out in §140.518 or §140.522 of this title.

(b) Appropriately trained in this section means an RN or physician assistant must be trained under §140.518 of this title or §140.522 of this title, or have been approved to perform radiologic procedures under a hardship exemption granted under §140.520 of this title (relating to Hardship Exemptions), in addition to performing the listed procedure under the direction and supervision of a practitioner. Subsections (a)(2), (a)(5), and (a)(6) of this section shall not be construed to authorize an RN or physician assistant to independently perform fluoroscopy or procedures utilizing contrast media.

SUBPART G
UNLICENSED ASSISTIVE PERSONNEL
PROVIDING CARE TO CERTAIN CLIENT POPULATIONS

ANNOTATOR'S NOTE: *The two laws set out in this Subpart permit unlicensed persons to perform tasks that normally fall within the practice of nursing. Because of the special circumstances of clients and a policy decision to promote their residing in a non-institutional setting, unlicensed persons are authorized to perform these tasks with less RN involvement. The first law was enacted in 2001 and the second in 2011.*

1. CONSUMER DIRECTED SERVICES PROGRAM

GOVERNMENT CODE, SEC. 531.051(e), (f). CONSUMER DIRECTION OF CERTAIN SERVICES FOR PERSONS WITH DISABILITIES AND ELDERLY PERSONS.

(e) Section 301.251(a), Occupations Code, does not apply to delivery of a service for which payment is provided under the consumer-directed service option developed under this section if:

(1) the person who delivers the service:

(A) has not been denied a license under Chapter 301, Occupations Code;

(B) has not been issued a license under Chapter 301, Occupations Code, that is revoked or suspended; and

(C) performs a service that is not expressly prohibited from delegation by the Texas Board of Nursing; and

(2) the consumer who receives the service:

(A) has a disability and the service would have been performed by the consumer or the consumer's legally authorized representative except for that disability; and

(B) if:

(i) the consumer is capable of training the person in the proper performance of the service, the consumer directs the person to deliver the service; or

(ii) the consumer is not capable of training the person in the proper performance of the service, the consumer's legally authorized representative is capable of training the person in the proper performance of the service and directs the person to deliver the service.

(f) If the person delivers the service under Subsection (e)(2)(B)(ii), the legally authorized representative must be present when the service is performed or be immediately accessible to the person who delivers the service. If the person will perform the service when the representative is not present, the representative must observe the person performing the service at least once to assure the representative that the person performing the service can competently perform that service.

DADS Rule 48.6040. Registered Nurse (RN) Delegation of Nursing Tasks

Delegation and supervision of selected nursing tasks is permitted in the Nursing Facility Waiver:

(1) by RNs employed by the home and community support services agencies to personal care attendants and adult foster care providers of Level I and II adult foster care homes. Delegation will occur in accordance with the Texas Department of Health Home and Community Support Services licensure rules for the provider agency's licensure category; or

(2) by independent RNs to adult foster care providers of Level I and II adult foster care homes. Delegation will occur in accordance with the rules from Texas Board of Nurse Examiners, 22 TAC Chapter 218; or

(3) by RNs who are adult foster care providers of a Level I and II adult foster care home who delegate to substitute providers. Delegation will occur in accordance with the rules from Texas Board of Nurse Examiners, 22 TAC Chapter 218.

2. SERVICES TO CERTAIN PERSONS WITH DEVELOPMENTAL AND INTELLECTUAL DISABILITIES

HUMAN RESOURCES CODE, SEC 161.091-.096. ADMINISTRATION OF MEDICATION FOR CLIENTS WITH INTELLECTUAL AND DEVELOPMENTAL DISABILITIES

Sec. 161.091. DEFINITIONS. In this subchapter:

(1) "Administration of medication" means:

(A) removing a unit or dose of medication from a previously dispensed, properly labeled container;

(B) verifying the medication with the medication order;

(C) giving the proper medication in the proper dosage to the proper client at the proper time by the proper administration route; and

(D) recording the time of administration and dosage administered.

(2) "Client" means a person with an intellectual and developmental disability who is receiving services from a facility or program listed in Section 161.092.

(3) "Unlicensed person" means an individual not licensed as a health care provider who provides services at or for a facility or program listed in Section 161.092, including:

(A) a nurse aide, orderly, assistant, attendant, technician, home health aide, medication aide with a permit issued by a state agency, or other individual who provides personal health care-related services;

(B) a person who is monetarily compensated to perform certain health-related tasks and functions in a complementary or assistive role to a licensed nurse who provides direct client care or performs common nursing functions;

(C) a person who performs those tasks and functions as a volunteer but does not qualify as a friend providing gratuitous nursing care of the sick under Section 301.004, Occupations Code; or

(D) a person who is a professional nursing student who provides care for monetary compensation and not as part of a formal educational program.

Sec. 161.092. APPLICABILITY. This subchapter applies only to administration of medication provided to certain persons with intellectual and developmental disabilities who are served:

(1) in a small facility with not less than one and not more than eight beds that is licensed or certified under Chapter 252, Health and Safety Code;

(2) in a medium facility with not less than nine and not more than 13 beds that is licensed or certified under Chapter 252, Health and Safety Code; or

(3) by one of the following Section 1915(c) waiver programs administered by the Department of Aging and Disability Services to serve persons with intellectual and developmental disabilities:

(A) the Home and Community-Based Services waiver program; or

(B) the Texas Home Living waiver program.

Sec. 161.093. ADMINISTRATION OF MEDICATION. (a) Notwithstanding other law, an unlicensed person may provide administration of medication to a client without the requirement that a registered nurse delegate or oversee each administration if:

(1) the medication is:

(A) an oral medication;

(B) a topical medication; or

(C) a metered dose inhaler;

(2) the medication is administered to the client for a stable or predictable condition;

(3) the client has been personally assessed by a registered nurse initially and in response to significant changes in the client's health status, and the registered nurse has determined that the client's health status permits the administration of medication by an unlicensed person; and

(4) the unlicensed person has been:

(A) trained by a registered nurse or licensed vocational nurse under the direction of a registered nurse regarding proper administration of medication; or

(B) determined to be competent by a registered nurse or licensed vocational nurse under the direction of a registered nurse regarding proper administration of medication, including through a demonstration of proper technique by the unlicensed person.

(b) The administration of medication other than the medications described by Subsection (a)(1) is subject to the rules of the Texas Board of Nursing regarding the delegation of nursing tasks to unlicensed persons in independent living environments such as the facilities and programs listed in Section 161.092.

Sec. 161.094. DEPARTMENT DUTIES. (a) The department shall ensure that:

(1) administration of medication by an unlicensed person under this subchapter is reviewed at least annually and after any significant change in a client's condition by a registered nurse or a licensed vocational nurse under the supervision of a registered nurse; and

(2) a facility or program listed in Section 161.092 has policies to ensure that the determination of whether an unlicensed person may provide administration of medication to a client under Section 161.093 may be made only by a registered nurse.

(b) The department shall verify that:

(1) each client is assessed to identify the client's needs and abilities regarding the client's medications;

(2) the administration of medication by an unlicensed person to a client is performed only by an unlicensed person who is authorized to perform that administration under Section 161.093; and

(3) the administration of medication to each client is performed in such a manner as to ensure the greatest degree of independence, including the use of an adaptive or assistive aid, device, or strategy as allowed under program rules.

(c) The department shall enforce this subchapter.

Sec. 161.095. LIABILITY. (a) A registered nurse performing a client assessment required under Section 161.093, or a registered nurse or licensed vocational nurse training an unlicensed person or determining whether an unlicensed person is competent to perform administration of medication under Section 161.093, may be held accountable or civilly liable only in relation to whether the nurse properly:

(1) performed the assessment;

(2) conducted the training; and

(3) determined whether the unlicensed person is competent to provide administration of medication to clients.

(b) The Texas Board of Nursing may take disciplinary action against a registered nurse or licensed vocational nurse under this subchapter only in relation to whether:

(1) the registered nurse properly performed the client assessment required by Section 161.093;

(2) the registered nurse or licensed vocational nurse properly trained the unlicensed person in the administration of medication; and

(3) the registered nurse or licensed vocational nurse properly determined whether an unlicensed person is competent to provide administration of medication to clients.

(c) A registered nurse or licensed vocational nurse may not be held accountable or civilly liable for the acts or omissions of an unlicensed person performing administration of medication.

Sec. 161.096. CONFLICT WITH OTHER LAW. This subchapter controls to the extent of a conflict with other law.

DADS RULE §90.43. Administration of Medication

(a) Administration of medication to a resident of a facility may be performed only by:

(1) a person who holds a license under state law that authorizes the person to administer medication;

(2) in a facility, as defined in §95.101 of this title (relating to Introduction):

(A) a person who holds a permit issued under Texas Health and Safety Code §242.610 and acts under the authority of a person described in paragraph (1) of this subsection; or

(B) a person who is exempt from licensure or permit requirements in accordance with Texas Health and Safety Code §242.607;

(3) a person to whom a registered nurse has delegated the administration of medication under 22 TAC Chapter 224 or 225 (relating to Delegation of Nursing Tasks by Registered Professional Nurses to Unlicensed Personnel for Clients with Acute Conditions or in Acute Care Environments and RN Delegation to Unlicensed Personnel and Tasks Not Requiring Delegation in Independent Living Environments for Clients with Stable and Predictable Conditions); or

(4) in a facility with a licensed or certified capacity of less than 14 residents, an unlicensed person who administers medication in accordance with Texas Human Resource Code, Chapter 161, Subchapter D-1.

(b) A person may perform administration of medication in accordance with subsection (a)(4) of this section without the requirement that a registered nurse delegate or oversee each administration if:

(1) the medication is:

(A) an oral medication;

(B) a topical medication; or

(C) a metered dose inhaler;

(2) the medication is administered to the resident for a stable or predictable condition;

(3) the resident has been personally assessed by a registered nurse initially and in response to significant changes in the resident's health status, and the registered nurse has determined that the resident's health status permits the administration of medication by an unlicensed person; and

(4) the unlicensed person has been:

(A) trained by a registered nurse or licensed vocational nurse under the direction of a registered nurse regarding proper administration of medication; or

(B) determined to be competent by a registered nurse or licensed vocational nurse under the direction of a registered nurse regarding proper administration of medication, including through a demonstration of proper technique by the unlicensed person.

(c) A registered nurse or a licensed vocational nurse under the supervision of a registered nurse must review the administration of medication to a resident by a person described in subsection (a)(4) of this section at least annually and after any significant change in the resident's condition.

SUBPART H.
VIOLENCE AGAINST ER NURSES

***ANNOTATOR'S NOTE**: Legislation (HB 581) passed in 2013 enhanced the penalty for assaulting ER nurses and other personnel to a Class C Felony. This was accomplished by amending the definition of "emergency services personnel to explicitly include "emergency room personnel."*

PENAL CODE SEC. 22.01. ASSAULT. Subsecs. (a), (b), (e)(1). (a) A person commits an offense if the person:

(1) intentionally, knowingly, or recklessly causes bodily injury to another, including the person's spouse;

(2) intentionally or knowingly threatens another with imminent bodily injury, including the person's spouse; or

(3) intentionally or knowingly causes physical contact with another when the person knows or should reasonably believe that the other will regard the contact as offensive or provocative.

(b) An offense under Subsection (a)(1) is a Class A misdemeanor, except that the offense is a felony of the third degree if the offense is committed against:

(1) a person the actor knows is a public servant while the public servant is lawfully discharging an official duty, or in retaliation or on account of an exercise of official power or performance of an official duty as a public servant;

(2) - (4) *[omitted]*

(5) a person the actor knows is emergency services personnel while the person is providing emergency services.

(b-1) - (d) *[omitted]*

(e) In this section:

(1) "Emergency services personnel" includes firefighters, emergency medical services personnel as defined by Section 773.003, Health and Safety Code, emergency room personnel, and other individuals who, in the course and scope of employment or as a volunteer, provide services

for the benefit of the general public during emergency situations.

SUBPART I.
PHARMACY

1. Designated Agents

__ANNOTATOR'S NOTE:__ Nurses can be designated agents to communicate prescriptions to pharmacies on behalf of a practitioner (physicians, dentists and podiatrists). The practitioner is to designate the agent in writing and to provide the pharmacy a copy of the designation upon request. The prescription can be communicated verbally or electronically. Pharmacy Board Rule 291.34(b)(4) provides that electronic orders shall be considered the same as verbal orders. Subsection (B) permits RNs and LVNs in facilities to act as designated agents without being individually designated as such.

Occupation Code, Sec. 551.003(14). Definitions.

(14) "Designated agent" means:

(A) an individual, including a licensed nurse, physician assistant, or pharmacist:

(i) who is designated by a practitioner and authorized to communicate a prescription drug order to a pharmacist; and

(ii) for whom the practitioner assumes legal responsibility;

(B) a licensed nurse, physician assistant, or pharmacist employed in a health care facility to whom a practitioner communicates a prescription drug order; or

(C) a registered nurse or physician assistant authorized by a practitioner to administer a prescription drug order for a dangerous drug under Subchapter B, Chapter 157.

2. Agents Calling In Prescriptions for APRNs

Occupation Code, Sec. 563.051(e). General Delegation of Administration and Provision of Dangerous Drugs

(e) A practitioner may designate a licensed vocational nurse or a person having education equivalent to or greater than that required for a licensed vocational nurse to communicate the prescriptions of an advanced practice nurse or physician assistant authorized by the practitioner to sign prescription drug orders under Subchapter B, Chapter 157.

SUBPART J.
MEDICINE

1. Medical Practice Act, Occupations Code (Excerpts)

a. Chapter 151. General Provisions
- Sec. 151.002. Definitions.
- Sec. 151.052. Exemptions.
- Sec. 151.053. Application to Certain Persons Providing Nutritional Advice.
- Sec. 151.054. Application to Self-Care.

b. Chapter 157, Secs. 157.001-.006. Physician Delegation
- Sec. 157.001. General Authority of Physician to Delegate.
- Sec. 157.002. General Delegation of Administration and Provision of Dangerous Drugs.

Sec. 157.005. Performance of Delegated Act Not Practicing Without Medical License.
Sec. 157.006. Limitation on Board Rules Regarding Delegation
Sec. 157.005. Performance of Delegated Act Not Practicing Without Medical License.
Sec. 157.006. Limitation on Board Rules Regarding Delegation
c. Chapter 157, Secs. 157.051-.060. Delegation of Prescriptive Authority to APNs and PAs
d. Chapter 157, Sec. 157.101. Delegation of Drug Therapy Management to Pharmacists

a. CHAPTER 151. GENERAL PROVISIONS

Sec. 151.002(a)(11), (13). Definitions.
(11) "Person" means an individual, unless the term is expressly made applicable to a partnership, association, or corporation.

> ***ANNOTATOR'S NOTE:*** *Unlike the practice of nursing, the practice of medicine is defined exclusively in terms of curing disease, illness, injury, etc. rather than prevention of illness or the maintenance of health. Because the practice of medicine is defined in this way, the Texas Attorney General, in Opinion H-1293, held that the practice of midwifery (assisting with normal childbirth) did not constitute the practice of medicine because normal pregnancy is not a disease or abnormality. The Attorney General in Opinion MW-318 suggested similar reasoning would apply to the administration of immunizations and that persons administering vaccines may not be engaged in the practice of medicine.*

(13) "Practicing medicine" means the diagnosis, treatment, or offer to treat a mental or physical disease or disorder or a physical deformity or injury by any system or method, or the attempt to effect cures of those conditions, by a person who:
(A) publicly professes to be a physician or surgeon; or
(B) directly or indirectly charges money or other compensation for those services.

Sec. 151.052. Exemptions. (a) This subtitle does not apply to:

> ***ANNOTATOR'S NOTE:*** *Nurses practicing within the scope of their nursing license are exempted from the medical practice act and no physician delegation is involved. However, if nurses perform acts outside the scope of professional nursing, they will have engaged in the unauthorized practice of medicine unless the act has been delegated by a physician. Under Sec. 157.053, the giving of nutritional advice does not constitute the practice of medicine. Under Sec. 157.054, the giving of advice about self-treatment or self-care does not constitute the practice of medicine.*

[(1) - (3) omitted]
(4) a registered nurse or licensed vocational nurse engaged strictly in the practice of nursing in accordance with the applicable licensing acts and other laws of this state;
[(5) - (10) omitted]

Sec. 151.053. Application to Certain Persons Providing Nutritional Advice. (a) This subtitle does not prohibit a person from giving advice regarding the use and role of food and food ingredients, including dietary supplements.
(b) Subsection (a) does not authorize a person to:
(1) practice medicine; or
(2) state, in violation of law, that a product might cure a disease, disorder, or condition.

Sec. 151.054. Application to Self-Care. (a) This subtitle does not prohibit:

(1) a person from providing or seeking advice or information relating to that person's self-care; or

(2) the dissemination of information relating to self-care.

(b) This section does not confer authority to practice medicine.

b. CHAPTER 157, SECS. 157.001-.006 PHYSICIAN DELEGATION

Sec. 157.001. General Authority of Physician to Delegate.

> ***ANNOTATOR'S NOTE.*** *This section authorizes physician delegation provided the criteria set out are met. Because "person" is defined in Sec. 151.002 to mean an individual, this subdivision does not authorize physicians to delegate to hospitals or other facilities.*

(a) A physician may delegate to a qualified and properly trained person acting under the physician's supervision any medical act that a reasonable and prudent physician would find within the scope of sound medical judgment to delegate if, in the opinion of the delegating physician:

(1) the act:

(A) can be properly and safely performed by the person to whom the medical act is delegated;

(B) is performed in its customary manner; and

(C) is not in violation of any other statute; and

(2) the person to whom the delegation is made does not represent to the public that the person is authorized to practice medicine.

(b) The delegating physician remains responsible for the medical acts of the person performing the delegated medical acts.

(c) The board may determine whether:

(1) an act constitutes the practice of medicine, not inconsistent with this chapter; and

(2) a medical act may be properly or safely delegated by physicians.

Sec. 157.002. General Delegation of Administration and Provision of Dangerous Drugs.

(a) In this section:

(1) "Administering" means the direct application of a drug to the body of a patient by injection, inhalation, ingestion, or any other means.

(2) "Provision" means the supply of one or more unit doses of a drug, medicine, or dangerous drug.

(b) A physician may delegate to any qualified and properly trained person acting under the physician's supervision the act of administering or providing dangerous drugs in the physician's office, as ordered by the physician, that are used or required to meet the immediate needs of the physician's patients. The administration or provision of the dangerous drugs must be performed in compliance with laws relating to the practice of medicine and state and federal laws relating to those dangerous drugs.

(c) A physician may also delegate to any qualified and properly trained person acting under the physician's supervision the act of administering or providing dangerous drugs through a facility licensed by the Texas State Board of Pharmacy, as ordered by the physician, that are used or required to meet the immediate needs of the physician's patients. The administration of those dangerous drugs must be in compliance with laws relating to the practice of medicine, professional nursing, and pharmacy and state and federal drug laws. The provision of those dangerous drugs must be in compliance with:

(1) laws relating to the practice of medicine, professional nursing, and pharmacy;

(2) state and federal drug laws; and

(3) rules adopted by the Texas State Board of Pharmacy.

(d) In the provision of services and the administration of therapy by public health departments, as officially prescribed by the Texas Department of Health for the prevention or treatment of specific communicable diseases or health conditions for which the Texas Department of Health is responsible for control under state law, a physician may delegate to any qualified and properly trained person acting under the physician's supervision the act of administering or providing dangerous drugs, as ordered by the physician, that are used or required to meet the needs of the patients. The provision of those dangerous drugs must be in compliance with laws relating to the practice of medicine, professional nursing, and pharmacy. An order for the prevention or treatment of a specific communicable disease or health condition for which the Texas Department of Health is responsible for control under state law may not be inconsistent with this chapter and may not be used to perform an act or duty that requires the exercise of independent medical judgment.

(e) The administration or provision of the drugs may be delegated through a physician's order, a standing medical order, a standing delegation order, or another order defined by the board.

(f) Subsections (b) and (c) do not authorize a physician or a person acting under the supervision of a physician to keep a pharmacy, advertised or otherwise, for the retail sale of dangerous drugs, other than as authorized under Section 158.003, without complying with the applicable laws relating to the dangerous drugs.

(g) A drug or medicine provided under Subsection (b) or (c) must be supplied in a suitable container labeled in compliance with applicable drug laws. A qualified and trained person, acting under the supervision of a physician, may specify at the time of the provision of the drug the inclusion on the container of the date of the provision and the patient's name and address.

[Sec. 151.003 - 151.004 omitted]

Sec. 157.005. Performance of Delegated Act Not Practicing Without Medical License. A person to whom a physician delegates the performance of a medical act is not considered to be practicing medicine without a license by performing the medical act unless the person acts with knowledge that the delegation and the action taken under the delegation is a violation of this subtitle.

Sec. 157.006. Limitation on Board Rules Regarding Delegation. The board shall promote a physician's exercise of professional judgment to decide which medical acts may be safely delegated by not adopting rules containing, except as absolutely necessary, global prohibitions or restrictions on the delegation of medical acts.

c. CHAPTER 157, SECS. 157.051 - .060. DELEGATION OF PRESCRIPTIVE AUTHORITY TO APNS AND PAS

ANNOTATOR'S NOTE. *Sections 157.051-.060 govern physician delegation of prescriptive authority to APRNs (and PAs). Those sections were extensively amended in 2013 (SB 406). The changes expanded prescriptive authority for APRNs and moved from a site-based model for delegation to a prescriptive authority agreement model.*

SUBCHAPTER B. DELEGATION TO ADVANCED PRACTICE REGISTERED NURSES AND PHYSICIAN ASSISTANTS

Sec. 157.051. Definitions.

ANNOTATOR's NOTE: *A key definition is "prescribe or order a drug or device" because this term is used throughout Subchapter to define what may be delegated. "Order" refers to a "medication order" which is an order for hospital inpatients.*

In this subchapter:

(1) "Advanced practice registered nurse" has the meaning assigned to that term by Section 301.152. The term includes an advanced nurse practitioner and advanced practice nurse.

(2) "Controlled substance" has the meaning assigned to that term by Section 481.002, Health and Safety Code.

(3) "Dangerous drug" has the meaning assigned to that term by Section 483.001, Health and Safety Code.

(4) "Device" has the meaning assigned by Section 551.003, and includes durable medical equipment.

(5) "Health professional shortage area" means:

(A) an urban or rural area of this state that:

(i) is not required to conform to the geographic boundaries of a political subdivision but is a rational area for the delivery of health services;

(ii) the secretary of health and human services determines has a health professional shortage; and

(iii) is not reasonably accessible to an adequately served area;

(B) a population group that the secretary of health and human services determines has a health professional shortage; or

(C) a public or nonprofit private medical facility or other facility that the secretary of health and human services determines has a health professional shortage, as described by 42 U.S.C. Section 254e(a)(1).

(6) "Hospital" means a facility that:

(A) is:

(i) a general hospital or a special hospital, as those terms are defined by Section 241.003, Health and Safety Code, including a hospital maintained or operated by the state; or

(ii) a mental hospital licensed under Chapter 577, Health and Safety Code; and

(B) has an organized medical staff.

(7) "Medication order" has the meanings assigned by Section 551.003 of this code and Section 481.002, Health and Safety Code.

(8) "Nonprescription drug" has the meaning assigned by Section 551.003.

(9) "Physician assistant" means a person who holds a license issued under Chapter 204.

(10) "Physician group practice" means an entity through which two or more physicians deliver health care to the public through the practice of medicine on a regular basis and that is:

(A) owned and operated by two or more physicians; or

(B) a freestanding clinic, center, or office of a nonprofit health organization certified by the board under Section 162.001(b) that complies with the requirements of Chapter 162.

(11) "Practice serving a medically underserved population" means:

(A) a practice in a health professional shortage area;

(B) a clinic designated as a rural health clinic under 42 U.S.C. Section 1395x(aa);

(C) a public health clinic or a family planning clinic under contract with the Health and Human Services Commission or the Department of State Health Services;

(D) a clinic designated as a federally qualified health center under 42 U.S.C. Section 1396d(l)(2)(B);

(E) a county, state, or federal correctional facility;

(F) a practice:

(i) that either:

(a) is located in an area in which the Department of State Health Services determines there is an insufficient number of physicians providing services to eligible clients of federally, state, or locally funded health care programs; or

(b) is a practice that the Department of State Health Services determines serves a disproportionate number of clients eligible to participate in federally, state, or locally funded health care programs; and

(ii) for which the Department of State Health Services publishes notice of the department's determination in the Texas Register and provides an opportunity for public comment in the manner provided for a proposed rule under Chapter 2001, Government Code; or

(G) a practice at which a physician was delegating prescriptive authority to an advanced practice registered nurse or physician assistant on or before March 1, 2013, based on the practice qualifying as a site serving a medically underserved population.

(12) "Prescribe or order a drug or device" means prescribing or ordering a drug or device, including the issuing of a prescription drug order or a medication order.

(13) "Prescription drug" has the meaning assigned by Section 551.003.

(14) "Prescriptive authority agreement" means an agreement entered into by a physician and an advanced practice registered nurse or physician assistant through which the physician delegates to the advanced practice registered nurse or physician assistant the act of prescribing or ordering a drug or device.

Sec. 157.0511. Delegation of Prescribing and Ordering Drugs and Devices.

ANNOTATOR'S NOTE*: The main change made by SB 406 to this Section was adding Subsection (b-1) authorizing delegation of prescribing of controlled substances Schedule II in 1) hospitals for inpatients and ER patients and 2) hospice.*

(a) Types of Drugs. A physician's authority to delegate the prescribing or ordering of a drug or device this subchapter is limited to:

(1) nonprescription drugs;

(2) dangerous drugs; and

(3) controlled substances to the extent provided by Subsections (b) and (b-1).

(b) Controlled Substances Schedules III-IV. Except as provided by Subsection (b-1), a physician may delegate the prescribing or ordering of a controlled substance only if:

(1) the prescription is for a controlled substance listed in Schedule III, IV, or V as established by the commissioner of the Department of State Health Services under Chapter 481, Health and Safety Code;

(2) the prescription, including a refill of the prescription, is for a period not to exceed 90 days;

(3) with regard to the refill of a prescription, the refill is authorized after consultation with the delegating physician and the consultation is noted in the patient's chart; and

(4) with regard to a prescription for a child less than two years of age, the prescription is made after consultation with the delegating physician and the consultation is noted in the patient's chart.

(b-1) Controlled Substances Schedule II. A physician may delegate the prescribing or ordering of a controlled substance listed in Schedule II as established by the commissioner of the Department of State Health Services under Chapter 481, Health and Safety Code, only:

(1) in a hospital facility-based practice under Section 157.054, in accordance with policies approved by the hospital's medical staff or a committee of the hospital's medical staff as provided by the hospital bylaws to ensure patient safety, and as part of the care provided to a patient who:

(A) has been admitted to the hospital for an intended length of stay of 24 hours or greater; or

(B) is receiving services in the emergency department of the hospital; or

(2) as part of the plan of care for the treatment of a person who has executed a written certification of a terminal illness, has elected to receive hospice care, and is receiving hospice treatment from a qualified hospice provider.

(b-2) Registration with Medical Board. The board shall adopt rules that require a physician who delegates the prescribing or ordering of a drug or device to register with the board the name and license number of the physician assistant or advanced practice registered nurse to whom a delegation is made. The board may develop and use an electronic online delegation registration process for registration under this subsection.

(c) Application of Other Laws. This subchapter does not modify the authority granted by law for a licensed registered nurse or physician assistant to administer or provide a medication, including a controlled substance listed in Schedule II as established by the commissioner of the Department of State Health Services under Chapter 481, Health and Safety Code, that is authorized by a physician under a physician's order, standing medical order, standing delegation order, or protocol.

Sec. 157.0512. Prescriptive Authority Agreement.

ANNOTATOR'S NOTE: *This is a new section governing delegation of prescriptive authority for all practices other than facility-based (hospitals and long-term care facilities). It authorizes delegation through a prescriptive authority agreement and sets out the required elements of the agreement. Delegation at facility-based practices (hospitals and long-term care facilities) will continue to be governed by Section 157.054. It consists of fifteen subsections:*

Subsec. (a) Authority to Delegate
Subsec. (b) Practitioners Ineligible to Sign Prescriptive Authority Agreement
Subsec. (c), (d) Limit of FTEs to Whom May Delegate
Subsec. (e) Content of Prescriptive Authority Agreement
Subsec. (f) Frequency of Face-to-Face Meetings
Subsec. (g) Additional Provisions In Prescriptive Authority Agreement
Subsec. (h) Physician Group Practice
Subsec. (i) Required Specificity in Prescriptive Authority Agreement
Subsec. (j) Retention of Agreement
Subsec. (k) Provisions Cannot Be Waived
Subsec. (l) Complaint Against Practitioner
Subsec. (m) Annual Review; Agreement Available to Boards
Subsec. (n) Promote Exercise of Professional Judgment
Subsec. (o) Liberal Construction
Subsec. (p) Limitation on Rulemaking
Subsec. (q) Joint FAQ Responses

(a) Authority To Delegate Via Prescriptive Authority Agreement. A physician may delegate to an advanced practice registered nurse or physician assistant, acting under adequate physician supervision, the act of prescribing or ordering a drug or device as authorized through a prescriptive authority agreement between the physician and the advanced practice registered nurse or physician assistant, as applicable.

(b) Practitioners Ineligible To Sign Agreement. A physician and an advanced practice registered nurse or physician assistant are eligible to enter into or be parties to a prescriptive authority agreement only if:

(1) if applicable, the Texas Board of Nursing has approved the advanced practice registered nurse's authority to prescribe or order a drug or device as authorized under this subchapter;

(2) the advanced practice registered nurse or physician assistant:

(A) holds an active license to practice in this state as an advanced practice registered nurse or physician assistant, as applicable, and is in good standing in this state; and

(B) is not currently prohibited by the Texas Board of Nursing or the Texas Physician Assistant Board, as applicable, from executing a prescriptive authority agreement; and

(3) before executing the prescriptive authority agreement, the physician and the advanced practice registered nurse or physician assistant disclose to the other prospective party to the agreement any prior disciplinary action by the board, the Texas Board of Nursing, or the Texas Physician Assistant Board, as applicable.

(c) Limit On FTEs To Whom Can Delegate. Except as provided by Subsection (d), the combined number of advanced practice registered nurses and physician assistants with whom a physician may enter into a prescriptive authority agreement may not exceed seven advanced practice registered nurses and physician assistants or the full-time equivalent of seven advanced practice registered nurses and physician assistants.

(d) Exceptions to Limit on FTEs To Whom Can Delegate. Subsection (c) does not apply to a prescriptive authority agreement if the prescriptive authority is being exercised in:

(1) a practice serving a medically underserved population; or

(2) a facility-based practice in a hospital under Section 157.054.

ANNOTATOR'S NOTE: See Section 157.054(a-1) which provides that the exclusion of hospitals from the FTE limit does not include a freestanding clinic, center or practice of a hospital, i.e., these practice settings would be subject to the seven FTE limit imposed by Subsection (c).

(e) Content of Prescriptive Authority Agreement. A prescriptive authority agreement must, at a minimum:

(1) *[in writing]* be in writing and signed and dated by the parties to the agreement;

(2) *[identification of parties]* state the name, address, and all professional license numbers of the parties to the agreement;

(3) *[nature of practice]* state the nature of the practice, practice locations, or practice settings;

(4) *[drugs to be prescribed]* identify the types or categories of drugs or devices that may be prescribed or the types or categories of drugs or devices that may not be prescribed;

(5) *[consultation and referral]* provide a general plan for addressing consultation and referral;

(6) *[patient emergencies]* provide a plan for addressing patient emergencies;

(7) *[communication and information sharing]* state the general process for communication and the sharing of information between the physician and the advanced practice registered nurse or physician assistant to whom the physician has delegated prescriptive authority related to the care and treatment of patients;

(8) *[alternate physician supervision]* if alternate physician supervision is to be utilized, designate one or more alternate physicians who may:

(A) provide appropriate supervision on a temporary basis in accordance with the requirements established by the prescriptive authority agreement and the requirements of this subchapter; and

(B) participate in the prescriptive authority quality assurance and improvement plan meetings required under this section; and

(9) *[quality assurance and improvement plan]* describe a prescriptive authority quality assurance and improvement plan and specify methods for documenting the implementation of the plan that includes the following:

(A) chart review, with the number of charts to be reviewed determined by the physician and advanced practice registered nurse or physician assistant; and

(B) periodic face-to-face meetings between the advanced practice registered nurse or physician assistant and the physician at a location determined by the physician and the advanced practice registered nurse or physician assistant.

(f) Face-To-Face Meetings. The periodic face-to-face meetings described by Subsection (e)(9)(B) must:

(1) include:

(A) the sharing of information relating to patient treatment and care, needed changes in patient care plans, and issues relating to referrals; and

(B) discussion of patient care improvement; and

(2) be documented and occur:

(A) except as provided by Paragraph (B):

(i) at least monthly until the third anniversary of the date the agreement is executed; and

(ii) at least quarterly after the third anniversary of the date the agreement is executed, with monthly meetings held between the quarterly meetings by means of a remote electronic communications system, including videoconferencing technology or the Internet; or

(B) if during the seven years preceding the date the agreement is executed the advanced practice registered nurse or physician assistant for at least five years was in a practice that included the exercise of prescriptive authority with required physician supervision:

(i) at least monthly until the first anniversary of the date the agreement is executed; and

(ii) at least quarterly after the first anniversary of the date the agreement is executed, with monthly meetings held between the quarterly meetings by means of a remote electronic communications system, including videoconferencing technology or the Internet.

ANNOTATOR'S NOTE*: SECTION 28 of SB 406 permits time an APRN practiced with the physician prior to the effective date of SB 406 [11/1/13] to be included when calculating how long the prescriptive authority agreement has been in effect:*

SECTION 28. The calculation under Chapter 157, Occupations Code, as amended by this Act, of the amount of time an advanced practice registered nurse or physician assistant has practiced under the delegated prescriptive authority of a physician under a prescriptive authority agreement shall include the amount of time the advanced practice registered nurse or physician assistant practiced under the delegated prescriptive authority of that physician before the effective date of this Act. It applies to calculating both the three-year period under Subsection (f)(2)(A)(i) and the one-year period under (f)(2)(B)(i).

(g) Additional Provisions. The prescriptive authority agreement may include other provisions agreed to by the physician and advanced practice registered nurse or physician assistant.

(h) Physician Group Practice. If the parties to the prescriptive authority agreement practice in a physician group practice, the physician may appoint one or more alternate supervising physicians designated under Subsection (e)(8), if any, to conduct and document the quality assurance meetings in accordance with the requirements of this subchapter.

ANNOTATOR'S NOTE: This is the first recognition that group practices may function as an entity rather than simply as a collection of individuals. It permits one or more physician(s) within the group to conduct the quality assurance meeting for all APRNs within the group. "Physician group practice" is defined in Section 157.001(10).

(i) Required Specificity in Prescriptive Authority Agreement. The prescriptive authority agreement need not describe the exact steps that an advanced practice registered nurse or physician assistant must take with respect to each specific condition, disease, or symptom.

(j) Retention of Agreement. A physician, advanced practice registered nurse, or physician assistant who is a party to a prescriptive authority agreement must retain a copy of the agreement until the second anniversary of the date the agreement is terminated.

(k) Provisions May Not Be Waived. A party to a prescriptive authority agreement may not by contract waive, void, or nullify any provision of this section or Section 157.0513.

(l) Notification of Complaint Against Practitioner. In the event that a party to a prescriptive authority agreement is notified that the individual has become the subject of an investigation by the board, the Texas Board of Nursing, or the Texas Physician Assistant Board, the individual shall immediately notify the other party to the prescriptive authority agreement.

(m) Annual Review; Agreement Available to Baords. The prescriptive authority agreement and any amendments must be reviewed at least annually, dated, and signed by the parties to the agreement. The prescriptive authority agreement and any amendments must be made available to the board, the Texas Board of Nursing, or the Texas Physician Assistant Board not later than the third business day after the date of receipt of request, if any.

(n) Promote Exercise of Professional Judgment. The prescriptive authority agreement should promote the exercise of professional judgment by the advanced practice registered nurse or physician assistant commensurate with the advanced practice registered nurse's or physician assistant's education and experience and the relationship between the advanced practice registered nurse or physician assistant and the physician.

(o) Liberal Construction. This section shall be liberally construed to allow the use of prescriptive authority agreements to safely and effectively utilize the skills and services of advanced practice registered nurses and physician assistants.

(p) Limitation on Rule-Making. The board may not adopt rules pertaining to the elements of a prescriptive authority agreement that would impose requirements in addition to the requirements under this section. The board may adopt other rules relating to physician delegation under this chapter.

(q) Joint FAQ Responses. The board, the Texas Board of Nursing, and the Texas Physician Assistant Board shall jointly develop responses to frequently asked questions relating to prescriptive authority agreements not later than January 1, 2014. This subsection expires January 1, 2015.

Sec. 157.0513. Prescriptive Authority Agreement: Information.

***ANNOTATOR'S NOTE**: This a new Section addressing 1) sharing of information by the medical board, nursing board and physician assistant board, 2) opening of investigations based on shared information, and 3) providing information to practitioners and public.*

(a) Sharing of Information by Licensing Boards. The board, the Texas Board of Nursing, and the Texas Physician Assistant Board shall jointly develop a process:

(1) to exchange information regarding the names, locations, and license numbers of each physician, advanced practice registered nurse, and physician assistant who has entered into a prescriptive authority agreement;

(2) by which each board shall immediately notify the other boards when a license holder of the board becomes the subject of an investigation involving the delegation and supervision of prescriptive authority, as well as the final disposition of any such investigation; and

(3) by which each board shall maintain and share a list of the board's license holders who have been subject to a final adverse disciplinary action for an act involving the delegation and supervision of prescriptive authority.

(b) Opening Investigation Against Parties To Prescriptive Authority Agreement. If the board, the Texas Board of Nursing, or the Texas Physician Assistant Board receives a notice under Subsection (a)(2), the board that received notice may open an investigation against a license holder of the board who is a party to a prescriptive authority agreement with the license holder who is under investigation by the board that provided notice under Subsection (a)(2).

(c) Searchable Database Prescribing Practitioners. The board shall maintain and make available to the public a searchable online list of physicians, advanced practice registered nurses, and physician assistants who have entered into a prescriptive authority agreement authorized under Section 157.0512 and identify the physician, advanced practice registered nurse, or physician assistant with whom each physician, advanced practice registered nurse, and physician assistant has entered into a prescriptive authority agreement.

(d) List of Practitioners Prohibited From Executing Prescriptive Authority Agreement. The board shall collaborate with the Texas Board of Nursing and the Texas Physician Assistant Board to maintain and make available to the public a list of physicians, advanced practice registered nurses, and physician assistants who are prohibited from entering into or practicing under a prescriptive authority agreement.

Sec. 157.0514. Prescriptive Authority Agreement: Inspections.

***ANNOTATOR'S NOTE**: Permits medical board to conduct an onsite audit at any* *site where a party (physician, APRN, or PA) to a prescriptive authority agreement practices. Reasonable notice is required unless giving notice would jeopardize the investigation.*

If the board receives a notice under Section 157.0513(a)(2), the board or an authorized board representative may enter, with reasonable notice and at a reasonable time, unless the notice would jeopardize an investigation, a site where a party to a prescriptive authority agreement practices to inspect and audit any records or activities relating to the implementation and operation of the agreement. To the extent reasonably possible, the board and the board's authorized representative shall conduct any inspection or audit under this section in a manner that minimizes disruption to the delivery of patient care.

Sec. 157.052 *[Repealed] Prescribing at Sites Serving Medically Underserved Populations*
Sec. 157.053 *[Repealed] Prescribing Physician Primary Practice Site*

Sec. 157.054. Prescribing at Facility-based Practice Sites.

ANNOTATOR'S NOTE: *This Section remains largely unchanged and will continue to govern delegation at facility-based practices (hospitals and long-term care facilities). It permits the delegation of prescriptive authority to continue to occur through protocols and the content of protocols will continue to be governed by Section 157.055. New language added to this Section is primarily designed to clarify and eliminate ambiguities in current law.*

(a) Authority to Delegate at Facility-Based Practice. One or more physicians licensed by the board may delegate, to one or more physician assistants or advanced practice registered nurses acting under adequate physician supervision whose practice is facility-based at a hospital or licensed long-term care facility, the administration or provision of a drug and the prescribing or ordering of a drug or device if each of the delegating physicians is:

(1) the medical director or chief of medical staff of the facility in which the physician assistant or advanced practice registered nurse practices;

(2) the chair of the facility's credentialing committee;

(3) a department chair of a facility department in which the physician assistant or advanced practice registered nurse practices; or

(4) a physician who consents to the request of the medical director or chief of medical staff to delegate the prescribing or ordering of a drug or device at the facility in which the physician assistant or advanced practice registered nurse practices.

(a-1) Exclusion From Limitation on FTEs To Whom May Delegate. The limits on the number of advanced practice registered nurses or physician assistants to whom a physician may delegate under Section 157.0512 do not apply to a physician under Subsection (a) whose practice is facility-based under this section, provided that the physician is not delegating in a freestanding clinic, center, or practice of the facility.

ANNOTATOR'S NOTE: *Section 157.0512 imposes a FTE limit of seven on all practices other than facility-based practices and practices serving a medically underserved population. The seven FTE limit will apply to "a freestanding clinic, center or practice of a hospital." Although this Subsection refers generically to "facility-based practices," Subdivision (b)(4) sets a seven FTE limit for long term care facilities.*

(b) Conditions for Delegating. A physician's authority to delegate under Subsection (a) is limited as follows:

(1) the delegation must be made under a physician's order, standing medical order, standing delegation order, or another order or protocol developed in accordance with policies approved by the facility's medical staff or a committee of the facility's medical staff as provided by the facility bylaws;

(2) the delegation must occur in the facility in which the physician is the medical director, the chief of medical staff, the chair of the credentialing committee, a department chair, or a physician who consents to delegate under Subsection (a)(4);

ANNOTATOR'S NOTE: *The language "or physician who consents to delegate under Subsection (a)(4)" at the end of this Subdivision (2) and the phrase "one or more physicians" at the beginning of Subsection (a) were added to clarify 1) that the medical director may designate more than one physician to delegate in a facility-based practice, and 2) that the physician designated may be someone other than the chair of the credentialing committee or a department chair.*

(3) the delegation may not permit the prescribing or ordering of a drug or device for the care or treatment of the patients of any other physician without the prior consent of that physician; and

(4) delegation in a long-term care facility must be by the medical director and is limited to the prescribing or ordering of a drug or device to not more than seven advanced practice registered nurses or physician assistants or their full-time equivalents.

(b-1) Limitation on Number of Facilities At Which May Delegate. A facility-based physician may not delegate at more than one hospital or more than two long-term care facilities under this section unless approved by the board. The facility-based physician may not be prohibited from delegating the prescribing or ordering of drugs or devices under Section 157.0512 at other practice locations, including hospitals or long-term care facilities, provided that the delegation at those locations complies with all the requirements of Section 157.0512.

ANNOTATOR'S NOTE: *This Subsection was added to clarify that being a delegating physician for a facility-based practice under this Section 157.054 doesn't prevent that physician from also delegating prescriptive authority in his or her private practice.*

(c) Required Supervision. Physician supervision of the prescribing or ordering of a drug or device must conform to what a reasonable, prudent physician would find consistent with sound medical judgment but may vary with the education and experience of the particular advanced practice registered nurse or physician assistant. A physician shall provide continuous supervision, but the constant physical presence of the physician is not required.

(d) Supervision By Alternate Physician. An alternate physician may provide appropriate supervision on a temporary basis as defined and established by board rule.

Sec. 157.0541 *[Repealed] Prescribing Physician Alternate Practice Site*
Sec. 157.0542 *[Repealed] Board (TMB) Waiver of Delegation Requirements*

Sec. 157.055. Orders and Protocols.

ANNOTATOR'S NOTE: *This Section will now primarily apply to delegation of prescriptive authority at facility-based practices under Section 157.054. Delegation of prescriptive authority at other practices will be through a prescriptive authority agreement under Section 157.0512 which sets out the requirements such agreements must meet.*

A protocol or other order shall be defined in a manner that promotes the exercise of professional judgment by the advanced practice registered nurse and physician assistant commensurate with the education and experience of that person. Under this section, an order or protocol used by a reasonable and prudent physician exercising sound medical judgment:

(1) is not required to describe the exact steps that an advanced practice registered nurse or a physician assistant must take with respect to each specific condition, disease, or symptom; and

(2) may state the types or categories of medications that may be prescribed or the types or categories of medications that may not be prescribed.

Sec. 157.056. Prescription Information. The following information must be provided on each prescription subject to this subchapter:

(1) the patient's name and address;

(2) the drug to be dispensed;

(3) directions to the patient regarding the taking of the drug and the dosage;

(4) the intended use of the drug, if appropriate;

(5) the name, address, and telephone number of the physician;

(6) the name, address, telephone number, and identification number of the registered nurse or physician assistant completing or signing the prescription drug order;

(7) the date; and

(8) the number of refills permitted.

Sec. 157.057. Additional Implementation Methods. The board may adopt additional methods to implement:

(1) a physician's prescription; or

(2) the delegation of prescriptive authority.

Sec. 157.058. Delegation to Certified Registered Nurse Anesthetist. (a) In a licensed hospital or ambulatory surgical center, a physician may delegate to a certified registered nurse anesthetist the ordering of drugs and devices necessary for the nurse anesthetist to administer an anesthetic or an anesthesia-related service ordered by the physician.

(b) The physician's order for anesthesia or anesthesia-related services is not required to specify a drug, dose, or administration technique.

(c) Pursuant to the physician's order and in accordance with facility policies or medical staff bylaws, the nurse anesthetist may select, obtain, and administer those drugs and apply the medical devices appropriate to accomplish the order and maintain the patient within a sound physiological status.

(d) This section shall be liberally construed to permit the full use of safe and effective medication orders to use the skills and services of certified registered nurse anesthetists.

Sec. 157.059. Delegation Regarding Certain Obstetrical Services. (a) In this section, "provide" means to supply, for a term not to exceed 48 hours, one or more unit doses of a controlled substance for the immediate needs of a patient.

(b) A physician may delegate to a physician assistant offering obstetrical services and certified by the board as specializing in obstetrics or an advanced practice registered nurse recognized by the Texas Board of Nursing as a nurse midwife the act of administering or providing controlled substances to the physician assistant's or nurse midwife's clients during intrapartum and immediate postpartum care.

(c) The physician may not delegate:

(1) the use of a prescription sticker or the use or issuance of an official prescription form; or

(2) the authority to issue an electronic prescription under Section 481.075, Health and Safety Code.

(d) The delegation of authority to administer or provide controlled substances under Subsection (b) must be under a physician's order, medical order, standing delegation order, prescriptive authority agreement, or protocol that requires adequate and documented availability for access to medical care.

(e) The physician's orders, medical orders, standing delegation orders, prescriptive authority agreements, or protocols must require the reporting of or monitoring of each client's progress, including complications of pregnancy and delivery and the administration and provision of controlled substances by the nurse midwife or physician assistant to the clients of the nurse midwife or physician assistant.

(f) The authority of a physician to delegate under this section is limited to:

(1) seven nurse midwives or physician assistants or their full-time equivalents; and

(2) the designated facility at which the nurse midwife or physician assistant provides care.

(g) The controlled substance must be supplied in a suitable container that is labeled in compliance with the applicable drug laws and must include:

(1) the patient's name and address;

(2) the drug to be provided;

(3) the name, address, and telephone number of the physician;

(4) the name, address, and telephone number of the nurse midwife or physician assistant; and

(5) the date.

(h) This section does not authorize a physician, physician assistant, or nurse midwife to operate a retail pharmacy as defined under Subtitle J

(i) This section authorizes a physician to delegate the act of administering or providing a controlled substance to a nurse midwife or physician assistant but does not require physician delegation of:

(1) further acts to a nurse midwife; or

(2) the administration of medications by a physician assistant or registered nurse other than as provided by this section.

(j) This section does not limit the authority of a physician to delegate the prescribing or ordering of a controlled substance under this subchapter.

Sec. 157.060. Physician Liability for Delegated Act. Unless the physician has reason to believe the physician assistant or advanced practice registered nurse lacked the competency to perform the act, a physician is not liable for an act of a physician assistant or advanced practice registered nurse solely because the physician signed a standing medical order, a standing delegation order, or another order or protocol, or entered into a prescriptive authority agreement, authorizing the physician assistant or advanced practice registered nurse to administer, provide, prescribe, or order a drug or device.

d. SUBCHAPTER C. DELEGATION TO PHARMACISTS

Sec. 157.101. Delegation of Drug Therapy Management to Pharmacist. (a) In this section, "pharmacist" has the meaning assigned by Section 551.003.

(b) A physician may delegate to a properly qualified and trained pharmacist acting under adequate physician supervision the performance of specific acts of drug therapy management authorized by the physician through the physician's order, standing medical order, standing delegation order, or other order or protocol as defined by board rule.

(b-1) A delegation under Subsection (b) may include the implementation or modification of a patient's drug therapy under a protocol, including the authority to sign a prescription drug order for dangerous drugs, if:

(1) the delegation follows a diagnosis, initial patient assessment, and drug therapy order by the physician;

(2) the pharmacist practices in a hospital, hospital-based clinic, or an academic health care institution;

(3) the hospital, hospital-based clinic, or academic health care institution in which the pharmacist practices has bylaws and a medical staff policy that permit a physician to delegate to a pharmacist the management of a patient's drug therapy;

(4) the pharmacist provides the name, address, and telephone number of the pharmacist and of the delegating physician on each prescription signed by the pharmacist; and

(5) the pharmacist provides a copy of the protocol to the Texas State Board of

Pharmacy.

(c) Physician supervision is considered to be adequate for the purposes of this section if a delegating physician:

(1) is responsible for the formulation or approval of the physician's order, standing medical order, standing delegation order, or other order or protocol and periodically reviews the order or protocol and the services provided to a patient under the order or protocol;

(2) has established a physician-patient relationship with each patient who is provided drug therapy management by a delegated pharmacist;

(3) is geographically located so as to be able to be physically present daily to provide medical care and supervision;

(4) receives, as appropriate, a periodic status report on each patient, including any problem or complication encountered; and

(5) is available through direct telecommunication for consultation, assistance, and direction.

(d) This section does not restrict the use of a preestablished health care program or restrict a physician from authorizing the provision of patient care by use of a preestablished health care program if the patient is institutionalized and the care is to be delivered in a licensed hospital with an organized medical staff that has authorized standing delegation orders, standing medical orders, or protocols.

(e) This section does not limit, expand, or change any provision of law relating to therapeutic drug substitution or administration of medication, including Section 554.004.

(f) The board by rule shall establish the minimum content of a written order or protocol. The order or protocol may not permit the delegation of medical diagnosis.

Drug Management

2. TEXAS MEDICAL BOARD RULES RELATING TO DELEGATION

§193.1. Purpose.
§193.2. Definitions.
§193.3. Exclusion from the Provisions of this Chapter.
§193.4. Scope of Standing Delegation Orders.
§193.5 Enforcement.
§193.6 Delegation of Prescriptive Authority to APNs and PAs

ANNOTATOR'S NOTE. *The Texas Medical Board (TMB) has adopted extensive rules governing physician delegation. The majority of the rules (§§193.1 and 193.3-193.5) were adopted before the delegation provisions of the Medical Practice Act were enacted in 1981. Because of the exceptions in §193.3(6) for licensed professionals and (8) for delegation of prescriptive authority to APRNs, the only rules that would appear to apply to nurses are §193.2 (Definitions), §193.5 (Enforcement), and Rule §193.6 relating to APRNs' prescribing. However, some of the other rules do provide useful guidance to nurses on issues such as the format and content of standing orders. The rules were originally adopted in response to the Texas Attorney General's holding in Opinion H-1295 (1978) that medications could be administered only under a prescription for a particular medication for a particular person and not under protocols or standing orders.*

Rule §193.6 is the primary rule governing physicians' delegating prescriptive authority to APRNs. Rule §193.2 (Definitions) is applicable to the extent it defines terms used in Rule §193.6, §§193.1 (Purpose), and 193.5 (Enforcement) are very general and provide little specific direction. If physician/APRN collaborative practices comply with Rules §§193.2 and 193.6, they will be in compliance with TMB regulations. Although Rules §193.3 and

193.4 relate to physician delegation, they include exemptions for physician delegation to APRNs and consequently have little direct applicability for APRNs. Trying to determine exactly how these other TMB rules apply or do not apply to APRNs and mesh with §193.6 is likely to be more confusing than helpful. Less confusion will occur if APRNs and physicians focus on Rules §193.6 (Delegation of Prescribing) and §193.2 (Definitions) and don't worry about the others.

§193.1. Purpose. (a) The purpose of this chapter is to encourage the more effective utilization of the skills of physicians by establishing guidelines for the delegation of health care tasks to qualified non-physicians providing services under reasonable physician control and supervision where such delegation is consistent with the patient's health and welfare; and to provide guidelines for physicians in order that existing legal constraints should not be an unnecessary hindrance to the more effective provision of health care services. Tx Occupations Code Annotated §§164.052 & 164.053, empower the Texas Medical Board to cancel, revoke or suspend the license of any practitioner of medicine upon proof that such practitioner is guilty of failing to supervise adequately the activities of persons acting under the physician's supervision, allowing another person to use his license for the purpose of practicing medicine, or of aiding or abetting, directly or indirectly, the practice of medicine by a person or entity not licensed to do so by the board. The board recognizes that the delivery of quality health care requires expertise and assistance of many dedicated individuals in the allied health profession. The provisions of this chapter are not intended to, and shall not be construed to, restrict the physician from delegating administrative and technical or clinical tasks not involving the exercise of medical judgment, to those specially trained individuals instructed and directed by a licensed physician who accepts responsibility for the acts of such allied health personnel. The board recognizes that statutory law shall prevail over any rules adopted and that the practice of medicine is, by statute, defined as follows: "A person shall be considered to be practicing medicine within the Medical Practice Act:

(1) who shall publicly profess to be a physician or surgeon and shall diagnose, treat, or offer to treat, any disease or disorder, mental or physical, or any physical deformity or injury, by any system or method, or to effect cures thereof; or

(2) who shall diagnose, treat, or offer to treat any disease or disorder, mental or physical or any physical deformity or injury by any system or method and to effect cures thereof and charge therefor, directly or indirectly, money or other compensation."

(b) Likewise, nothing in this chapter shall be construed as to prohibit a physician from instructing a technician, assistant, or nurse to perform delegated tasks so long as the physician retains supervision and control of the technician, assistant, or employee. Nothing in this chapter should be construed to relieve the supervising physician of the professional or legal responsibility for the care and treatment of those persons with whom the delegating physician has established a physician-patient relationship. Nothing in this chapter shall enlarge or extend the applicable statutory law relating to the practice of medicine, or other rules and regulations previously promulgated by the board.

§193.2. Definitions.

***ANNOTATOR'S NOTE**. Among the more important definitions are the three types of physician orders: 1) physician orders, 2) standing medical orders, and 3) standing delegation orders. The definition of "protocol" is another key definition, particularly for APRNs.*

The following words and terms, when used in this chapter, shall have the following meanings, unless the contents clearly indicate otherwise.

(1) Advanced practice nurse--A registered nurse approved by the Texas Board of Nursing to practice as an advanced practice nurse on the basis of completion of an advanced educational program. The term includes a nurse practitioner, a nurse midwife, nurse anesthetist, and clinical nurse specialist, as defined by Texas Occupations Code Annotated, §301.152.

(2) Authorizing physician--A physician or physicians licensed by the board who execute a standing delegation order.

(3) Carrying out or signing a prescription drug order– *[Definition omitted]*

(4) Controlled substance--A substance, including a drug, an adulterant, and a dilutant, listed in Schedules I through V or Penalty Groups 1, 1-A, or 2 through 4 as described under the Texas Health and Safety Code, Chapter 481 (Texas Controlled Substances Act). The term includes the aggregate weight of any mixture, solution, or other substance containing a controlled substance.

(5) Dangerous drug--A device or a drug that is unsafe for self medication and that is not included in the Texas Health and Safety Code, Schedules I-V or Penalty Groups I-IV of Chapter 481 (Texas Controlled Substances Act). The term includes a device or a drug that bears or is required to bear the legend: "Caution: federal law prohibits dispensing without prescription".

(6) Health professional shortage area (HPSA)-- *[Definition omitted]*

(7) Medically underserved area (MUA)– *[Definition omitted]*

(8) Physician Assistant– *[Definition omitted]*

(9) Physician's orders--The instructions of a physician for the care of an individual patient.

(10) Protocols--Delegated written authorization to initiate medical aspects of patient care including authorizing a physician assistant or advanced practice nurse to carry out or sign prescription drug orders pursuant to the Medical Practice Act, Texas Occupations Code Annotated, §§157.051 - 157.060 and §193.6 of this title (relating to the Delegation of the Carrying Out or Signing of Prescription Drug Orders to Physician Assistants and Advanced Practice Nurses). The protocols must be agreed upon and signed by the physician, the physician assistant and/or advanced practice nurse, reviewed and signed at least annually, maintained on site, and must contain a list of the types or categories of dangerous drugs and controlled substances available for prescription, limitations on the number of dosage units and refills permitted, and instructions to be given the patient for follow-up monitoring or contain a list of the types or categories of dangerous drugs and controlled substances that may not be prescribed. Protocols shall be defined to promote the exercise of professional judgment by the advanced practice nurse and physician assistant commensurate with their education and experience. The protocols used by a reasonable and prudent physician exercising sound medical judgment need not describe the exact steps that an advanced practice nurse or a physician assistant must take with respect to each specific condition, disease, or symptom.

(11) Site serving a medically underserved population--A site located in a medically underserved area; a site located in a health manpower shortage area; a rural health clinic designated under Public Law 95-210, the Rural Health Clinic Services Act of 1977; a public health clinic or a family planning clinic operating under contract with the Texas Department of Human Services or the Department of State Health Services; a site located in an area in which there exists an insufficient number of physicians providing services to eligible clients of federal, state, or locally funded health care programs, as determined by the Department of State Health Services; or a site that serves a disproportionate number of clients eligible to participate in federal, state, or locally funded health care programs, as determined by the Department of State Health Services.

(12) Standing delegation order--Written instructions, orders, rules, regulations, or procedures prepared by a physician and designed for a patient population with specific diseases, disorders, health problems, or sets of symptoms. Such written instructions, orders, rules, regulations or procedures shall delineate under what set of conditions and circumstances action should be instituted. These instructions, orders, rules, regulations or procedures are to provide authority for and a plan for use with patients presenting themselves prior to being examined or evaluated by a physician to assure that such acts are carried out correctly and are distinct from specific orders written for a particular patient, and shall be limited in scope of authority to be delegated as provided in §193.4 of this title (relating to Scope of Standing Delegation Orders). As used in this chapter, standing delegation orders do not refer to treatment programs ordered by a physician following examination or evaluation by a physician, nor to established procedures for providing of care by personnel under direct, personal supervision of a physician who is directly supervising or overseeing the delivery of medical or health care. Such standing delegation orders should be developed and approved by the physician who is responsible for the delivery of medical care covered by the orders. Such standing delegation orders, at a minimum, should:

(A) include a written description of the method used in developing and approving them and any revision thereof;

(B) be in writing, dated, and signed by the physician;

(C) specify which acts require a particular level of training or licensure and under what circumstances they are to be performed;

(D) state specific requirements which are to be followed by persons acting under same in performing particular functions;

(E) specify any experience, training, and/or education requirements for those persons who shall perform such orders;

(F) establish a method for initial and continuing evaluation of the competence of those authorized to perform same;

(G) provide for a method of maintaining a written record of those persons authorized to perform same;

(H) specify the scope of supervision required for performance of same, for example, immediate supervision of a physician;

(I) set forth any specialized circumstances under which a person performing same is to immediately communicate with the patient's physician concerning the patient's condition;

(J) state limitations on setting, if any, in which the plan is to be performed;

(K) specify patient record-keeping requirements which shall, at a minimum, provide for accurate and detailed information regarding each patient visit; personnel involved in treatment and evaluation on each visit; drugs, or medications administered, prescribed or provided; and such other information which is routinely noted on patient charts and files by physicians in their offices; and

(L) provide for a method of periodic review, which shall be at least annually, of such plan including the effective date of initiation and the date of termination of the plan after which date the physician shall issue a new plan.

(13) Standing medical orders--Orders, rules, regulations or procedures prepared by a physician or approved by a physician or the medical staff of an institution for patients which have been examined or evaluated by a physician and which are used as a guide in preparation for and carrying out medical or surgical procedures or both. These orders, rules, regulations or procedures are authority and direction for the performance for certain prescribed acts for patients by authorized persons as distinguished from specific orders written for a particular patient.

(14) Submit– *[Definition omitted]*

§193.3. Exclusion from the Provisions of this Chapter.

***ANNOTATOR'S NOTE**. The Texas Attorney General in Opinion MW-318 (1981) held that persons falling under an exception are neither bound by these rules nor benefit from the specific legal guidance they provide persons to which they apply. Subsections (6) and (8) would exempt nurses in most situations other than APRNs prescribing medications. This is because any of the activities listed in §193.4 as ones that can be done under standing delegation orders are also activities nurses can do under their professional nursing license when ordered by a physician, dentist or podiatrist. This would cover nurses. The activities listed in §193.4 as ones that can be done under standing delegation orders are ones that could most likely be performed by nurses (certainly RNs and probably LVNs) under their professional nursing license.*

The provisions of this chapter shall not be applicable, nor shall they restrict the use of pre-established programs of health care, nor shall they restrict physicians from authorizing the provision of patient care by use of pre-established programs under the following circumstances listed in paragraphs (1)-(8) of this section:

(1) where a patient is institutionalized and the care is to be delivered in a hospital, nursing home, or other institution which has an organized medical staff which has authorized or approved standing delegation orders or standing medical orders;

(2) where care is rendered in an emergency. Emergency care is that care provided to a person who is unconscious, ill, or injured, when the reasonable apparent circumstances require prompt decisions and actions in care and when the necessity of immediate care is so reasonably apparent that any delay in the rendering of care or treatment would seriously worsen the physical condition or endanger the life of the person;

(3) where care is rendered as a part of disaster relief and charges for the services are not made;

(4) where limitation from civil liability is provided under the Texas Civil Practice and Remedies Code, §74.001;

(5) where first aid care is provided at the site of an injury or as an interim measure prior to transfer of the patient to a medical facility where medical services are available;

(6) where care rendered is provided by licensed health professional acting within the scope of the licensed profession as defined by Texas Occupations Code Annotated;

(7) where care is to be delivered in any setting under standing medical orders as defined in this chapter;

(8) where care is to be delivered as authorized by the Medical Practice Act, Tx Occup Code Anno, §§157.051-157.060, except as provided in §193.6 of this title (relating to the Delegation of the Carrying Out or Signing of Prescription Drug Orders to Physician Assistants and Advanced Practice Nurses).

§193.4. Scope of Standing Delegation Orders.

> ***ANNOTATOR'S NOTE****. Most of the activities listed are ones a nurse can do without a physician's order. The others require a physician's order but still are activities that the actual performance of constitutes the practice of nursing. As such, nurses can perform them under the authority of their nurse's license and not under the delegated authority of physicians. No standing delegation order is required. Delegation to APRNs authorized by Subchapter C of Chapter 157 of the Medical Practice Act or Rule §193.6 is not covered by this rule.*

Providing the authorizing physician is satisfied as to the ability and competence of those for whom the physician is assuming responsibility, and with due regard for the safety of the patient and in keeping with sound medical practice, standing delegation orders may be authorized for the performance of acts and duties which do not require the exercise of independent medical judgment. Limitations on the physician's use of standing delegation orders which are stated in this section shall not apply to patient care delivered by physician assistants or advanced practice nurses, as authorized by the Medical Practice Act, Tx. Occup. Code Anno., §§157.051-157.060 or §193.6 of this title (relating to Delegation of the Carrying Out or Signing of Prescription Drug Orders to Physician Assistants and Advanced Practice Nurses). When care is delivered under other circumstances, standing delegation orders may include authority to undertake the following as listed in paragraphs (1)-(8) of this section:

(1) the taking of personal and medical history;

(2) the performance of appropriate physical examination and the recording of physical findings;

(3) the ordering of tests appropriate to the services provided under such orders, such as tuberculin tests, skin tests, VD tests, VDRL tests, gram stains, pap smears, and serological tests;

(4) the administration or providing of drugs ordered by direct personal or voice communication by the authorizing physician who shall assume responsibility for the patient's welfare, providing such administration or provision of drugs shall be in compliance with other state or federal laws and providing further that pre-signed prescriptions shall be utilized by the authorizing physician only under the following conditions shown in subparagraphs (A)-(D) of this paragraph.

(A) The prescription shall be prepared in full compliance with the Texas Health and Safety Code, §483.001(13) except for the inclusion of the name of the patient and the date of issuance.

(B) The prescription shall be for one of the following classes or types of drugs:

(i) oral contraceptives;

(ii) diaphragms and contraceptive creams and jellies;

(iii) topical anti-infectives for vaginal use;

(iv) oral anti-parasitic drugs for treatment of pinworms;

(v) topical anti-parasitic drugs; or

(vi) antibiotic drugs for treatment of venereal disease.

(C) The prescriptions may not be issued for any controlled substance.

(D) The providing of the drugs shall be in compliance with the Texas Pharmacy Act and rules adopted by the Texas State Board of Pharmacy.

(5) the administration of immunization vaccines providing the recipient is free of any condition for which the immunization is contraindicated;

(6) the providing of information regarding hygiene and the administration or providing of medications for health problems resulting from a lack of hygiene, including the institution of treatment for conditions such as scabies, ringworm, pinworm, head lice, diaper rash and other minor skin disorders, provided the administration or providing of drugs adheres to paragraph (4) of this section;

(7) the provision of services and the administration of therapy by public health departments as officially prescribed by the Department of State Health Services for the prevention or treatment of specific communicable diseases or health conditions for which the Department of State Health Services is responsible for control under state law;

(8) the issuance of medications which do not require a prescription (over the counter medications) for the symptomatic relief of minor illnesses provided that such medications are packaged and labeled in compliance with state and federal laws and regulations.

§193.5 Enforcement. Any physician authorizing standing delegation orders or standing medical orders which authorize the exercise of independent medical judgment or treatment shall be subject to having his or her license to practice medicine in the State of Texas revoked or suspended under Texas Occupations Code Annotated, §§164.052 and 164.053.

§193.6. Delegation of the Carrying Out or Signing of Prescription Drug Orders to Physician Assistants and Advanced Practice Nurses.

ANNOTATOR'S NOTE. *This rule implements Secs. 157.051-.060, Medical Practice Act, (relating to physician delegation of prescribing to APRNs) enacted as part of HB 18 in 1989 and amended by SB 673 (1995), SB 1166 (2001), HB 1095 (2003), SB 532 (2009), and SB 406 (2013). It will need to be extensively amended to reflect the changes made by SB 406 (2013). SB 406 requires the medical board to adopt rules by November 1, 2013.rules*

Since physicians can delegate prescribing only to APRNs and PAs, this rule is applicable only to APRNs and not to other RNs. Rule §193.2 (Definitions) defines a number of the key terms used in this rule including protocol and should be read in conjunction with this section.

As indicated above, other TMB rules (e.g., §§193.3 and .4) governing physician delegation are largely inapplicable to physician delegation to APRNs because of exclusions in those rules for delegation to APRNs. Trying to apply those rules to APRNs is likely to be more confusing than helpful. It is recommended that physicians and APRNs look only to Rule §193.6 (Delegated Prescriptive Authority) and, as applicable, Rule §193.2 (Definitions) in structuring a collaborative practice.

SUBPART K. ADDITIONAL LAWS OF POTENTIAL INTEREST TO NURSES

ANNOTATOR'S NOTE: *In addition to the laws set out above, a number of other laws are relevant to nursing practice. The significance of each for an individual nurse will vary with the nurse's practice setting. The following is a partial listing of laws that may be relevant across practice settings. These statutes can be found at http://www.statutes.legis.state.tx.us/. Select the code, then chapter and section or use the Quick Search Feature to find a specific section.*

1. Informed Consent (Generally). Civil Practice & Remedies Code, Secs. 74.001-.002
2. Good Samaritan Law. Civil Practice & Remedies Code, Sec. 74.151
3. Volunteer Immunity from Liability. Civil Practice & Remedies Code, Secs. 84.001.-.007
4. Illegal Remuneration for Referrals. Occupations Code, Secs. 102.001-102.011
5. Advertising and Billing By Health Professionals. Occupations Code, Sec. 101.201-.351
6. Right Not To Participate in Abortion Procedure. Occupations Code, Secs. 301.001-.004
7. Sexual Exploitation of Patient (Civil Liability). Civil Practice & Remedies Code, 81.001-81.006
8. Sexual Exploitation of Patient (Criminal Liability). Penal Code, Sec. 22.011
9. Rights of Elderly To Be Free of Restraints. Human Resources Code, Sec. 102.003
10. Reports of Abuse, Neglect, and Exploitation of Residents of Certain Facilities. Health & Safety Code, Secs. 260A.001-.018
11. Pharmacists Administering Medications and Immunizations, Occupations Code, Secs. 554.004, .052.
12. Uniform Emergency Volunteer Health Practitioners Act, Occupations Code, Secs. 115.001-.011.

PART X.

APPENDICES

SUBPART A.
BON WEBSITE: *WWW.BON.TEXAS.GOV*.

The BON website can be a valuable resource for RNs and LVNs for guidance on specific questions. The following is an outline of the website as of July 2013. The BON updates and adds new information on an ongoing basis.

A more detailed outline of practice-related materials on the BON website is set out in Part V of this Guide.

1. Main Sections of BON Site

Verification & Licensing
Advanced Practice
Nursing Practice
Nursing Education
Nursing Law and Rules
Disciplinary Action
Nursing Statistics
About the Board
Nurse Employers
Military News

Verification & Licensing Section

Verify a License Online
Check Status of Application for Initial Licensure (Endorsement, Examination or Advanced Practice Registered Nurse) OR Reinstatement of Licensure
Online Renewal Application
Online Endorsement Application
Online Examination Application
Online Nursing Jurisprudence Examination (for Endorsement and Exam Applicants only)
Online Nursing Jurisprudence Course
Online (Initial Recognition) APRN Application (with option for Prescriptive Authority)
Download Paper Renewal Form
Download other Paper Applications and Forms
FAQs - Licensing
Multistate Regulation of Nursing - Nurse Licensure Compact

Advanced Practice Section

Advanced Practice Credentials
Advanced Practice Nurse - Scope of Practice
Advanced Practice Applications
Prescriptive Authority
Renewals
Regulation of Advanced Practice Registered Nurses
Advanced Practice Nursing Education
National Certification
BON Rules Relating to Advanced Practice Nursing
Current BON Position Statements Relating to Advanced Practice Nursing Issues
Information on the Nurse Licensure Compact

Nursing Practice Section

A detailed outline of this section of the BON website is set out in Part V of this Guide.

Nursing Practice Information
Nurse Licensure Compact (NLC) Fact Sheet
Frequently Asked Questions
Nursing Peer Review/Incident-Based and Safe Harbor
Delegation Resource Packet
Scope of Practice
Guidelines & Interpretive Guidelines
Advanced Practice Information
Position Statements
APRN Scope of Practice
H1N1 Influenza, Seasonal Influenza, and Pneumococcal Vaccinations
TERCAP Pilot Project

NURSING EDUCATION SECTION

Approved Programs
BON CE Offerings
Continuing Competency Requirements For Nurses (CE)
Education Frequently Asked Questions
Faculty, Program & Student Information
Guidelines
Innovation in Nursing Education
Refresher Courses, Extensive Orientations and Nursing Programs of Study
Starting a Nursing Program
Students/Prospective Students Frequently Asked Questions

NURSING LAW AND RULES SECTION

Nursing Practice Act
Rules & Regulations
Proposed Rules

DISCIPLINARY ACTION SECTION

Recent Disciplinary Action
Disciplinary Action Pages
Nurse Licensure Compact Discipline
Imposter Alerts
Disciplinary Sanction Policies
Disciplinary Guidelines for Criminal Conduct
Guidelines for Physical and Psychological Evaluations
Disciplinary Matrix
Courses that Meet Board Stipulations
Frequently Asked Questions About Enforcement
Investigatory & Disciplinary Process
What To Do If You Are Under Investigation
How to File A Complaint
Unprofessional Conduct Statutes/Rules
Study on Criminal Background Checks

NURSING STATISTICS SECTION

National Nursing Statistics
Texas Nursing Statistics
- APRN by County
- APRN: Clinical Nurse Specialist - Breakdown by County

APRN: Nurse Practitioner - Breakdown by County
RNs & LVN's by Clinical Practice Area and County
RNs & LVN's by County and Employment Status
RNs & LVN's by Employment Field and County
RNs & LVN's by Highest Degree
RNs & LVN's by Position Type and County
RNs & LVN's by Race/Ethnic Group, Age and Sex
Health Professions Statistics
Past Statistical Data 2011-2000

ABOUT THE BOARD SECTION

Board Members
BON CE Offerings
BON Meetings
Complaint Process
News for Consumers
BON News
Policy - Use of Technology to Improve Board Functions
BON Expenditures
BON Resource Efficiency Plan
Statistical Information
Quarterly Newsletters
Publications
Jobs at BON

NURSE EMPLOYERS SECTION

Nursys E-notification Service
Bulletins
Compact
Contact Information
Discipline
Employment Issues
Frequently Asked Questions
Licensing Information
Nursing Peer Review
Nursing Practice and Advanced Practice Information
Nursing Statistics
Scope of Practice
TERCAP Pilot Project

MILITARY NEWS SECTION

Educational Opportunities
Military Medical Education and Training Comparison Report
BON Rules Related to Military Nurses and Families
Military Application Exception Process
Multistate Registration of Nursing – Nursing Licensure Compact
National Council of State Boards of Nursing
Nursing Associations
Resources for Transitioning to Civilian Life

SUBPART B.
NURSING DATA

Nurses may have questions about the number of nurses practicing in Texas or the number of RNs in a particular county. Such information is available online. This section identifies some of the main websites for data on nurses.

1. BON WEBSITE
2. TEXAS CENTER FOR NURSING WORKFORCE STUDIES (TCNWS)
3. HEALTH PROFESSIONS RESOURCE CENTER
4. NATIONAL CENTER FOR HEALTH WORKFORCE ANALYSIS

1. BON WEBSITE - NURSING STATISTICS SECTION

See Nursing Statistics Section under BON website outline set out under Subpart A above.

2. TEXAS CENTER FOR NURSING WORKFORCE STUDIES (TCNWS)

www.dshs.state.tx.us/chs/cnws/

The Texas Center for Nursing Workforce Studies has significant information about the nursing workforce in Texas. The following is a listing of areas of information available on its website.

NURSING WORKFORCE REPORTS
- Nursing Workforce in Texas - Demographics and Trends Reports
- Other Reports

NURSING EDUCATION REPORTS
- Maps of Nursing Programs in Texas
- Professional Nursing Program Reports
- Advanced Practice Nursing Program Reports
- Vocational Nursing Program Reports
- White Paper Briefs

HOSPITAL SURVEY REPORTS
- Hospital Nurse Staffing Survey Reports
- White Paper Briefs

HOME HEALTH AND HOSPICE CARE STUDY REPORTS

LONG TERM CARE STUDY REPORTS

SUPPLY AND DEMAND REPORTS

3. HEALTH PROFESSIONS RESOURCE CENTER

www.dshs.state.tx.us/chs/hprc/

The Health Professions Resource Center at the Department of State Health Service has statistical information about nursing and other health care professions.

4. NATIONAL CENTER FOR HEALTH WORKFORCE ANALYSIS

http://bhpr.hrsa.gov/healthworkforce/

National nursing statistics are available through the National Center for Health Workforce Analysis, a division of the US Department of Health and Human Services - Health Resources and Services Administration (HRSA).

SUBPART C.
NURSES' DUTY TO REPORT UNSAFE CARE BY FACILITIES AND OTHER PRACTITIONERS

Prepared by Texas Nurses Association

The NPA imposes a direct duty on nurses to report other nurses for unsafe practice. It also gives nurse a right to report unsafe care by facilities and other practitioners to regulatory and accrediting agencies and to report patient care concerns but does not impose a direct duty on them to do so.

Sec. 301.4025 (a), (b), (c)

(a) In a written, signed report to the appropriate licensing board or accrediting body, a nurse may report a licensed health care practitioner, agency, or facility that the nurse has reasonable cause to believe has exposed a patient to substantial risk of harm as a result of failing to provide patient care that conforms to:

(1) minimum standards of acceptable and prevailing professional practice, for a report made regarding a practitioner; or

(2) statutory, regulatory, or accreditation standards, for a report made regarding an agency or facility.

(b) A nurse may report to the nurse's employer or another entity at which the nurse is authorized to practice any situation that the nurse has reasonable cause to believe exposes a patient to substantial risk of harm as a result of a failure to provide patient care that conforms to minimum standards of acceptable and prevailing professional practice or to statutory, regulatory, or accreditation standards. For purposes of this subsection, an employer or entity includes an employee or agent of the employer or entity.

(c) A person may not suspend or terminate the employment of, or otherwise discipline, discriminate against, or retaliate against, a person who:

(1) reports in good faith under this section; or

(2) advises a nurse of the nurse's right to report under this section.

The question arises whether a nurse ever has a duty to report unsafe care by facilities and practitioners other than nurse. There won't be a definitive answer until a court rules or regulatory agency adopts rules on this specific question, but the answer appears to be yes. The right to report becomes a duty to report when the nurse believes her or his patients have been placed at risk of harm because of a facility's or practitioner's failure to provide care at an acceptable standard. The following sets out the rationale for believing nurses do have such a duty.

A review of Texas court cases, Board of Nursing (BON) rules and information on its website leads to the conclusion that the right to report facilities and non-nursing practitioners under Sec. 301.4025 <u>becomes a duty to report</u> when the nurse believes her or his patients have been placed at substantial risk of harm because of the facility's or practitioner's failure to provide care at an acceptable standard.

The starting point is the court case Lunsford v. Board of Nurse Examiners [648 S.W. 2d 391 (Tex. App.--Austin, 1983)] which was the first Texas court case to explicitly hold that a distinct nurse-patient relationship exists, that this nurse-patient relationship creates a duty directly to the patient, and that neither facility policies nor physician orders supersedes this duty.

> . . . we hold that her duty to [the patient] is not derivative from such a third party relationship. Her duty to [the patient] stems from the privilege granted to her by the State of Texas in licensing her as a nurse, and therefore, could not be relieved by a hospital policy or a physician's order. (Pg 395)

The Lunsford case is set out in Subpart L of these Appendices.

What is the nurse's duty to the patient? Sec. 303.005 of the Nursing Peer Review Law defines it as "conduct required by standards of practice or professional conduct adopted by the board [BON] for nurses." The BON's standards of practice [Rule 217.11] and professional conduct [Rule 217.12] impose a duty on nurses to intervene to protect patients from harm. This duty to intervene to protect patients from harm includes reporting unsafe care by facilities and practitioners. Standard of Nursing Practice Rule 217.11(1)(B) requires nurses to:

> "implement measures to promote a safe environment for clients and others."

Unprofessional Conduct Rule 217.12(6)(c) defines unprofessional conduct to include:

> Causing or permitting physical, emotional or verbal abuse or injury or neglect to the client or the public, or failing to report same to the employer, appropriate legal authority and/or licensing board;

And Rule 217.20(1) (Safe Harbor Nursing Peer Review and Whistleblower Protections) defines "duty to patient" as:

> A nurse's duty is to always advocate for patient safety, including any nursing action necessary to comply with the standards of nursing practice (§217.11 of this title) and to avoid engaging in unprofessional conduct (§217.12 of this title). This includes administrative decisions directly affecting a nurse's ability to comply with that duty.

A "frequently asked question" posted in the Practice Section of the Board's website is "When Does a Nurse's Duty to a Patient Begin? The BON's response reads, in part:

> . . . The standard that serves as the foundation for all other standards is Rule 217.11(1)(B)"...maintain a safe environment for clients and others." This standard supersedes any physician order, facility policy, or administrative directive. . . As the case of Lunsford points out, when a nurse knows, or should have known that a situation potentially places a patient at risk of harm, the nurse has a duty to intervene . . .

Summary

While the Nursing Practice Act does not explicitly mandate a nurse report a facility, practitioner, or unsafe care, it does recognize a nurse's right to do so. That right <u>becomes a duty</u> a nurse owes her or his patients when the nurse believes the failure to provide an acceptable standard of care places those patients at risk of harm. Furthermore, this duty cannot be superseded by facility policy and is not one the nurse can contract away.

[INTENTIONAL BLANK PAGE]

SUBPART D.
FLOW CHART FOR REPORTING MINOR INCIDENTS

Prepared by Texas Nurses Association

This flowchart reflects the BON Minor Incident Rule 217.16 as amended in Fall 2008.
On the next page are two flowcharts setting out the process for handling reporting of errors generally.

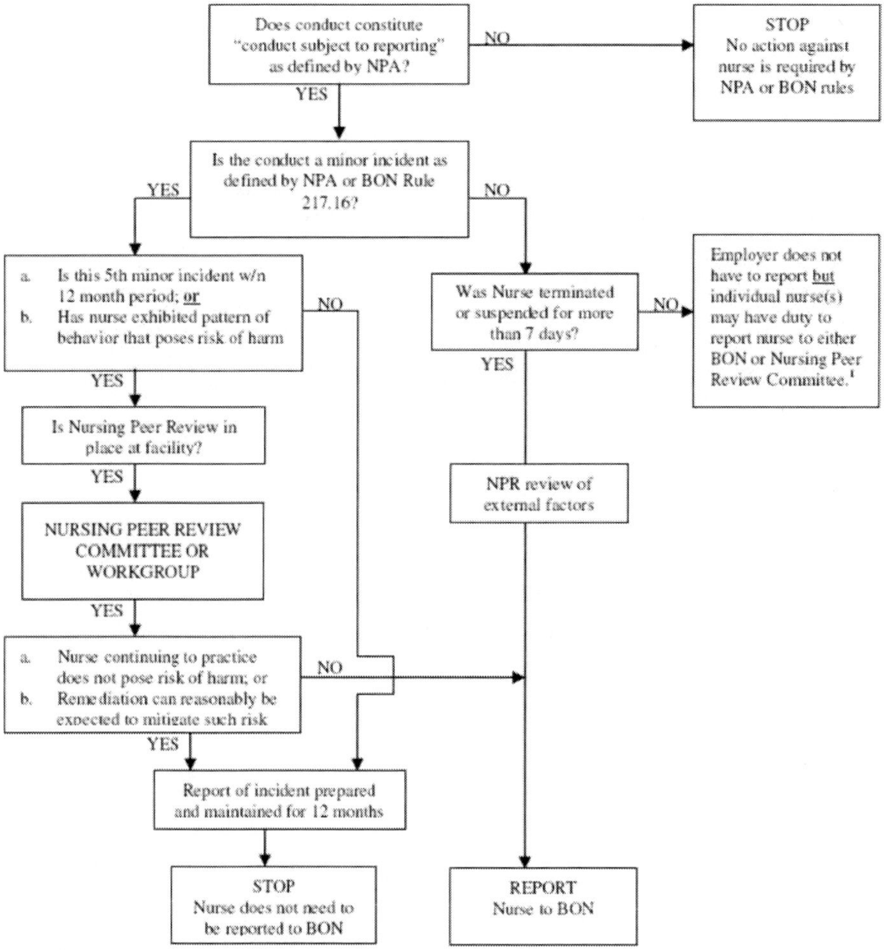

NOTE:
[1] Employers have duty to report only if terminate or suspend nurse for >7 days because of conduct subject to reporting. However, for individual nurses, conduct subject to reporting alone triggers the duty to report to either BON or nursing peer review committee. A nursing peer review committee does not have to report to BON if not reportable as a minor incident under BON Rule 217.16.

SUBPART E.
PROCESS FOR HANDLING NURSING ERRORS

Prepared by Texas Nurses Association

The flowchart on this page and the facing page were developed by the Texas Nurses Association (TNA) to depict graphically the process for reporting errors reflected in the NPA and BON peer review rules. See annotations to NPA Subchapter I (Secs. 301.401-.419) in Part I (NPA) of this Guide. The flowchart illustrates:

- *the exchange of information between nursing peer review (NPR) and other committees that address patient safety which is shown by the dashed lines*
- *how a nurse goes through NPR and the options available for remediation before a report must be made to the BON*

ABRIDGED VERSION

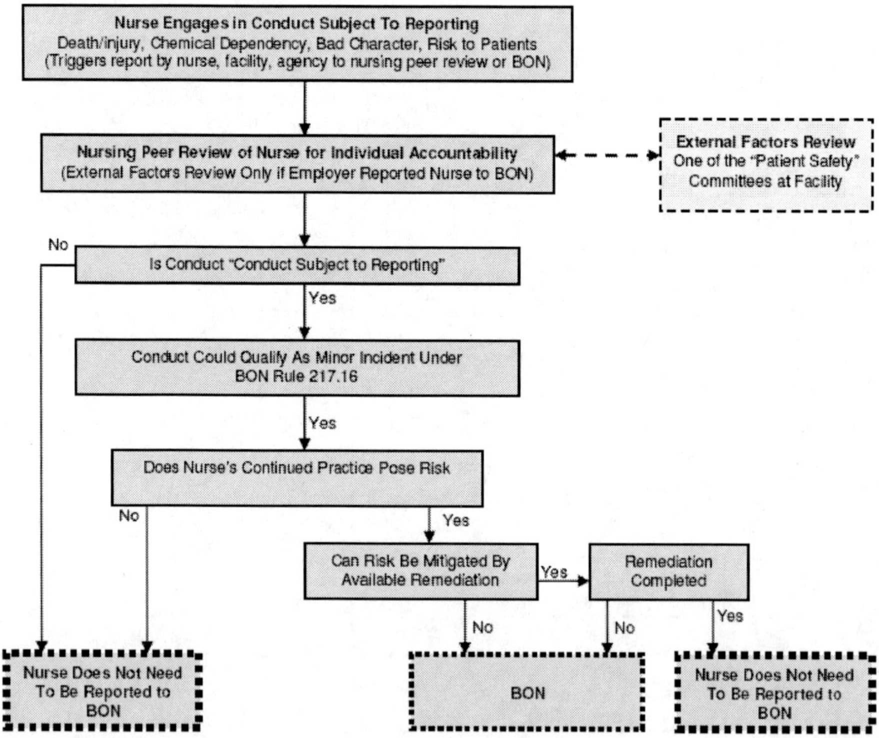

UNABRIDGED VERSION

This unabridged version shows more detail and includes employer reporting to the BON and reporting to peer assistance.

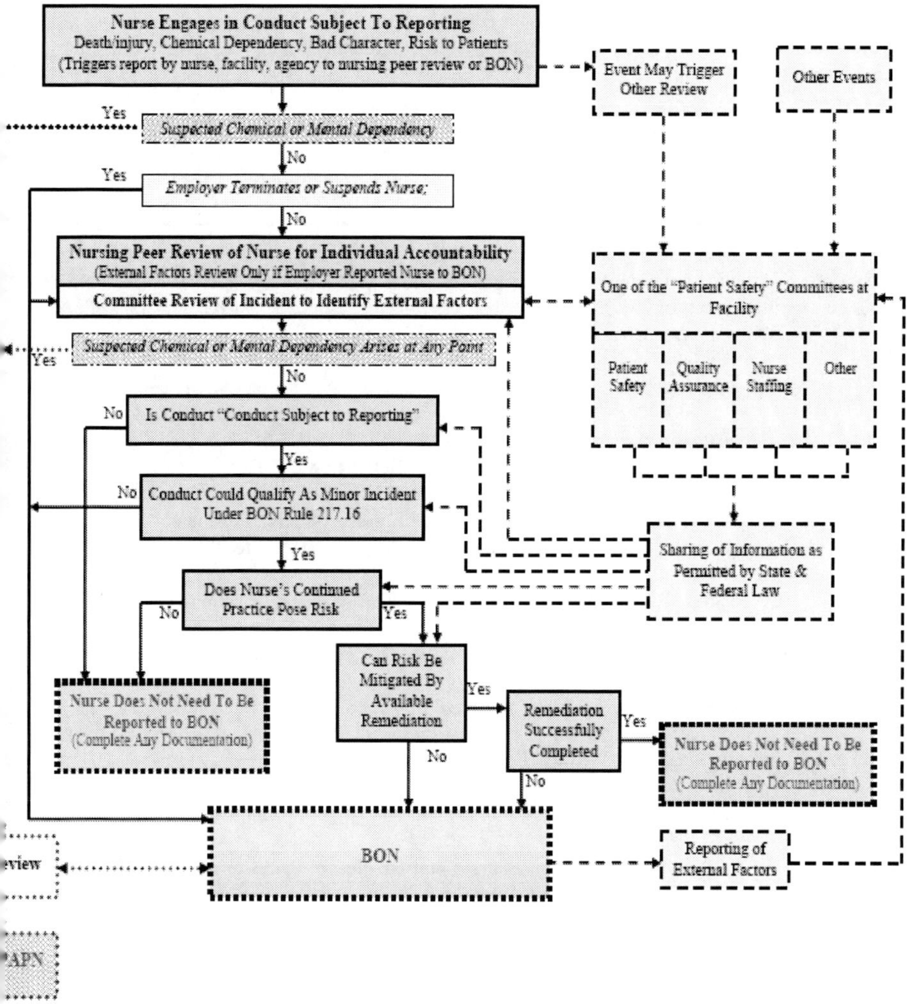

SUBPART F.
BON SIX-STEP DECISION-MAKING MODEL FOR DETERMINING NURSING SCOPE OF PRACTICE

This decision-making flowchart was developed by Board of Nursing (BON) staff to assist nurses in making good professional judgments about the nursing tasks or procedures they choose to undertake. It references parts of the NPA and Rules, and asks the nurse to apply other questions to his/her specific practice situation. These same sections of the nursing laws and targeted questions are tools board staff utilize when nurses call and ask "Is this task/procedure in my scope of practice?"

A nurse always has a duty to his/her clients/patients to assure that they are safe. One of the most important actions a nurse can take toward that goal is making sure that he/she only accepts those assignments for which the nurse has the education, training, and skill competency. Physical and emotional ability can also impact a nurse's ability to maintain client safety when accepting an assignment.

The BON does not maintain that this is the only model a nurse may use for assistance in determining his/her scope of practice in a given situation; however, all nurses practicing in Texas must comply with the Nursing Practice Act and Board Rules as they apply to LVNs, RNs, and\or RNs with advanced practice authorization in a given role and specialty.

Step One: Is the act consistent with the Texas Nursing Practice Act (NPA)? Do the Board's rules or positions statements address this specific act? *(This may be all the information you need to make your decision. If not, continue to the next step.)*

The following Information available on the BON's web page may be of assistance:

a. NPA, Ch. 301.002(2) Definition of Professional Nursing & Ch. 301.002(5), Definition of Vocational Nursing
b. Standards of Professional Nursing Practice (BON Rule 217.11)
c. Unprofessional Conduct Rule (BON Rule 217.12)
d. Delegation Rules for RN Delegation to Unlicensed Assistive Personnel (224 & 225)
e. Document listed under "Scope of Practice" in the Nursing Practice Section on the BON web site
f. BON Position Statements, Guidelines, & Frequently Asked Questions(FAQ's)

*If NO, the act is **NOT** within your scope of practice; If **YES**, continue to the next step.*

Step Two: Is the activity appropriately authorized by a valid order when necessary, and in accordance with current policies and procedures? Clarification of the orders(s) should be sought as needed [Rule 217.11(1)(N)].

*If NO, the act is **NOT** within your scope of practice; If **YES**, continue to the next step.*

Step Three: Is the act supported by positive and conclusive data from nursing literature, nursing research, and/or research from a health related field (such as evidenced-based practice standards)? Has a national nursing organization issued a position statement, guideline, or standard supporting LVNs, RNs, or both engaging in this practice?

*If NO, the act is NOT within your scope of practice; If **YES**, continue to the next step.*

Step Four Do you personally possess current clinical competence to perform the task safely from knowledge acquired in a basic nursing education program, post-basic program, or continuing education program? Documentation to validate competency should be maintained in accordance with agency/facility policy and procedure. Each nurse is also encouraged to maintain his/her own copies of competency forms.

*If NO, the act is **NOT** within your scope of practice; If **YES**, continue to the next step.*

Step Five: Is the performance of the act within the accepted "standard of care" which would be provided in similar circumstances by reasonable and prudent nurses who have similar training and experience? An additional related question to ask is: If an untoward event/reaction occurs as a result of your nursing actions, can the untoward consequences/reaction be resolved through nursing intervention alone?

RN Rule 217.11(1)(B) states that the nurse (LVN, RN, or RN with advanced practice authorization) shall: "Know and conform to the Texas Nursing Practice Act and the board's rules and regulations as well as all federal, state, or local laws, rules or regulations affecting the nurse's current area of nursing practice."

Review of the applicable rules in their entirety is recommended for the nurse in this step of the six-step model. In addition, human, material, and equipment resources can vary greatly across the spectrum of possible practice settings, and may contribute to the nurse's decision in a given circumstance.

*If NO, the act is **NOT** within your scope of practice; If **YES**, continue to the next step.*

Step Six: Are you prepared to accept the consequences of your actions?

*If NO, the act is **NOT** within your scope of practice; if **YES**, then:*

- Perform the act based upon valid order when necessary, and in accordance with appropriately established and current policies and procedures; and
- Assume accountability for provision of safe care.

ACKNOWLEDGMENTS:
Kentucky State Board of Nursing
North Carolina State Board of Nursing
Ohio Board of Nursing Newsletter, 11/94
ANA, Professional Standards of Practice
Paper prepared by Barbara Quick, BS, RN, Masters Student, UT Austin, Fall, 1994
Florida State Board of Nursing
National Council of State Boards of Nursing
Pennsylvania State Board of Nursing, March 18, 1992
Nevada State Board of Nursing "Determining Your Scope of Practice," 12/94

FLOW CHART - SIX-STEP DECISION-MAKING MODEL FOR DETERMINING NURSING SCOPE OF PRACTICE

A BON-prepared Poster of this six-step process set out below can be found in Part V (Practice Materials) of this Guide.

1. Is the activity consistent with the Nursing Practice Act (NPA), Board Rules, and Board Position Statements and/or Guidelines?

Yes ⟶ **Continue** **No** ⟶ **STOP**

2. Is the activity appropriately authorized by valid order/protocol and in accordance with established policies and procedures?

Yes ⟶ **Continue** **No** ⟶ **STOP**

3. Is the act supported by either research reported in nursing and health-related literature or in scope of practice statements by national nursing organizations?

Yes ⟶ **Continue** **No** ⟶ **STOP**

4. Do you possess the required knowledge and have you demonstrated the competency required to carry out this activity safely?

Yes ⟶ **Continue** **No** ⟶ **STOP**

5. Would a reasonable and prudent nurse perform this activity in this setting?

Yes ⟶ **Continue** **No** ⟶ **STOP**

6. Are you prepared to assume accountability for the provision of safe care and the outcome of the care rendered?

Yes ⟶ **Perform the Activity** **No** ⟶ **STOP**

SUBPART G.
BON PRACTICE-RELATED MATERIALS

See Part V of this Guide for a detailed outline of practice-related materials on BON website.

SUBPART H.
BON FAQs

The BON has a number of practice-related "frequently asked questions" (FAQs) on its website. The following two addressing question of when does a nurse's duty start and overtime are examples of FAQs. A complete list of the BON FAQs can be found in Part V of this Guide.

1. FAQ - When Does a Nurse's Duty to a Patient Begin and End?

Employment versus Licensure

A nurse's duty to his or her patient(s) is a frequent topic of e-mails and phone calls to Board of Nursing (BON) staff. A nurse's duty is not defined by any single event such as clocking in, or taking report. From a BON standpoint, the focus is on the relationship and responsibility of the nurse to the patient(s), not to the nurse's employer or employment.

One example is a nurse who notifies his or her employer that he or she is quitting a job at the end of an assigned shift. Some nurses in this position have relayed to BON staff that the employer "said they would report me to the Board for patient abandonment." Board Position Statement 15.6 Board Rules Associated with Alleged Patient Abandonment explains that typically this is an employment, not a licensure issue when a nurse decides to quit his or her job, with or without notice, provided the nurse does not have responsibility for patients at the time. If the employer has a policy that "requires a two-week notice", this is an employment issue, but not a violation of the Nursing Practice Act (NPA) or Board Rules. In other words, the BON would not take action on a nurse's license just because the nurse quit his or her job without notice at the end of a shift. It should also be noted that Rule 217.12(12) regarding leaving a nursing assignment does not apply to the situation where the nurse completes his or her scheduled shift, and then turns in notification of job resignation.

Frequently Asked Questions (FAQs) on the BON web page that also address the nurse's duty to the patient with respect to employment issues include:

Floating to Unfamiliar Practice Settings
Mandatory Overtime and Consecutive Shifts
Staffing Ratios

A Nurse's Duty: Not Limited to Assignment

All nurses, regardless of practice setting, position, title or role, are required to adhere to the NPA and other statutes, as well as the Board Rules. Two of the main rules that relate to nursing practice are Rules 217.11 Standards of Nursing Practice, and 217.12 Unprofessional Conduct. The standard that serves as the foundation for all other standards is rule 217.11(1)(B)"...maintain a safe environment for clients and others." This standard supersedes any physician order, facility policy, or administrative directive. The concept of the nurse's duty to maintain client safety also serves as the basis for behavior that could be considered unprofessional conduct by a nurse.

Position Statement 15.14, Duty of a Nurse in Any Setting, explains the nurse's duty that was established by a landmark case, Lunsford v. Board of Nurse Examiners, 648 S.W. 2d 391 (Tex. App. -- Austin 1983). As the case of Lunsford points out, when a nurse knows, or should have known that a situation potentially places a patient at risk of harm, the nurse has a duty to intervene. The nurse's knowledge based on educational preparation, experience, and licensure as a nurse establishes that the nurse understands the minimum standards of care and has the ability and duty to recognize potentially harmful situations for the patient.

This is why the nurse's duty does not incur solely based on a nurse being "assigned" to provide nursing care to a patient. A nurse who has knowledge that a situation places a patient at risk of harm has a duty to the patient or potential patient, as in Lunsford.

Rule 217.11(1)(S) relates to nurses who supervise other staff. This standard requires nurses in supervisory positions to "make assignments to others that take into consideration client safety and which are commensurate with the educational preparation, experience, knowledge, and physical and emotional ability of the persons to whom the assignments are made." Likewise, staff nurses are required to accept assignments within the nurse's educational preparation, experience, knowledge, and physical and emotional ability Rule 217.11(1) (T). The standards do not exist or apply in isolation, but complement each other; thus, all applicable standards should be considered by a nurse in determining the most appropriate course of action.

Safe Harbor Peer Review

Request for Peer Review Committee Determination or Safe Harbor applies to all nurses when the nurse believes an assignment may place patients at risk of harm, thus violating the nurse's duty to the patient. Safe Harbor provides a means by which a nurse protects his or her nursing license from board action as well as has nursing peers in the same practice setting review the requested assignment. The Nursing Peer Review section of the Board's website contains safe harbor forms, a Frequently Asked Question (FAQ), and the peer review rules. Nursing associations that represent LVNs, RNs and APRNs (advanced practice registered nurses) may also have information about Safe Harbor Peer Review for their members and other nurses.

The BON has no authority over employment issues, but a nurse does have civil recourse in matters where the nurse's decision to invoke Safe Harbor was made in good faith, but negative employment action occurred as a result of the nurse's request. A nurse also has whistleblower protections when the nurse reports a facility, physician, or other entity for violations of laws relating to patient care and or illegal acts, such as fraud, NPA Section 301.4025, NPR 303.005 and Rule 217.20(i). You may wish to also seek your own legal counsel for advice. The BON cannot provide legal advice, and has no authority in civil matters.

In summary, BON staff have heard a number of nurses disciplined by the board proclaim "if I had only known and understood about my "duty to the patient" under the NPA and Board Rules, I would not have gotten into trouble with the Board of Nursing." Please do not wait to become familiar with the laws that govern your nursing practice. A sound knowledge base regarding the laws and rules will help you protect your patients as well as your nursing license.

Revised October 2009

2. FAQ - Mandatory Overtime/Consecutive Shifts

Can an employer require a nurse to work longer than scheduled, or to work overtime? How many consecutive hours or shifts can a nurse work?

The Texas Board of Nursing (BON) does not have authority over work-place issues, such as schedules or number of hours worked, either consecutively, in a given time period or "on-call". In 2009, during the 81st Legislative Session, SB 476 made changes to the Nursing Practice Act (NPA) and the Health & Safety Code. SB 476 applies to hospitals and nurses working in hospital settings only.

The NPA changed with the addition of Section 301.356, Retaliation Prohibited. This new language states that "the refusal by a nurse to work mandatory overtime as authorized by Chapter 258, Health and Safety Code, does not constitute patient abandonment or neglect."

The NPA and Board Rules have always emphasized the nurse's responsibility and duty to the patient is to provide safe and effective nursing care. While the BON has not defined the term abandonment, SB 476, permits nurses to refuse to work overtime. However, this does not diminish the duty of each individual nurse to always act in the best interest of the patient and provide for their safety. If a nurse knows, or should have known, that a patient was potentially in danger by being left unattended the nurse's duty is always to act in the best interest of the patient.

In relation to overtime and or consecutive hours worked, the nurse has a duty to recognize when he or she is unfit to practice secondary *[sic]* to physical, mental, and or emotional fatigue. Nursing judgment and provision of nursing care may be impaired if a nurse is physically, mentally or emotionally exhausted, which could lead to nursing errors.

Nurses must "know and conform" with the NPA and Board Rules as well as all the laws, rules and regulations for their particular practice setting. The NPA and Board Rules have the force of law for nurses; any nurse who violates some part(s) of the NPA or Board Rules is subject to possible reporting to the Board and possible disciplinary action on his or her license.

Rule 217.11, Standards of Nursing Practice is the primary rule applied to nursing practice issues. The following standards are applicable to most practice questions, regardless of the practice setting:

- Standard 217.11(1) (B) requires each nurse to promote a safe environment for clients and others. This standard establishes each nurse's duty to his or her patient.
- Standard 217.11(1) (T) holds each nurse accountable to accept only assignments that are within the nurse's ability. If a nurse accepts an assignment, he or she is responsible for adhering to the NPA and Board Rules in delivering safe patient care.
- Standard 217.11(1) (S) applies to charge nurses or nurses who are in management positions. This standard is the "companion" standard to (1) (T), as it requires the nurse who is supervising other nurses to "make assignments" that take into account the educational preparation, knowledge, skills, and physical, mental and emotional abilities of the nurses for whom the supervisor is administratively responsible. This does not mean other nurses are working under the supervisor's license, or that the supervisor is responsible for every aspect of care delivered by other staff nurses. Assignments made to other licensed nurses do require forethought and adequate supervision.
- Standard 217.11(1) (U) holds supervisors responsible to oversee the nursing care provided by others for whom the supervisor is professionally responsible, from a licensure standpoint, the responsibility for overall patient care is the responsibility of the staff nurse accepting the assignment.

While the BON does not have authority in employment situations, there are protections in both the NPA and the Safe Harbor Rule 217.20 for a nurse who declares safe harbor in good faith. If adverse employment action was taken against a nurse, then the nurse may choose to seek private legal counsel. Rule 217.20 (e) outlines the requirements the nurse must meet in order to secure the protections, what the protections are, and where they are listed in the Texas Occupations Code, Section 303.005.

Additional resources and contact information to guide nurses as they implement the new laws are:

- Board Position Statement 15.14, Duty of a Nurse in Any Practice Setting.
- Board Position Statement 15.6, Board Rules Associated with Alleged Patient "Abandonment".
- Frequently Asked Question (FAQ), Staffing Ratios.
- Frequently Asked Question (FAQ), When Does a Nurse's Duty to a Patient Begin.
- Nurses, who practice in hospital settings, may wish to contact the Department of State Health Services (DSHS) – Health Facility
- Program at http://www.dshs.state.tx.us/hfp/default.shtm or 1-888-973-0022 for specific guidance related to the regulations for the official nurse staffing policies and plans that took effect on September 1, 2009.
- Nursing specialty organizations, such as the Texas Nurses Association at www.texasnurses.org or 512-452-0645.
- A Nurse Staffing Law Toolkit developed by The Texas Hospital Association at www.tha.org or 512-465-1000.

Revised October 2009

SUBPART I.
DELEGATION RESOURCE PACKET

Because of the complexity surrounding delegation, the Board has developed a Delegation Resource Packet for RNs which can be found on its website under the Practice Section tab. The packet was created to afford RNs clearer direction for delegation in a variety of settings thereby improving the delegation process. It includes the following documents.

Conflict Resolution Model
Delegation and the Advanced Practice Nurse
Delegation of CPAP and BiPAP Procedures
Links to Delegation Resources
Rule 224 Flow Chart
Rule 225 Flow Chart
The Five Rights of Delegation
Delegation Don'ts
Rule 225 Professional Nursing Assessment Grid with examples
Rule 225 Quick Reference Guide

SUBPART J.
DISCIPLINARY SANCTION POLICIES

The BON has adopted disciplinary sanction policies on four types of misconduct:

Lying and Falsification
Fraud, Theft, and Deception
Sexual Misconduct
Nurses with Chemical Dependency

All four are set out on the BON website inder the "Disciplinary Action" tab.

SUBPART K.
CONTINUING COMPETENCY REQUIREMENTS FOR NURSES

On its website, the BON publishes information about Continuing Competency under the "Nursing Education" tab.

SUBPART L.
COURT CASES

***ANNOTATOR'S NOTE**: This section sets out several significant Texas court opinions and cases relating to the practice of nursing.*

LUNSFORD CASE -- NURSE'S DUTY TO PATIENT

LUNSFORD, Appellant
vs.
BOARD OF NURSE EXAMINERS, Appellee
648 S.W.2d 391, Tex. App. -- Austin 1983

***ANNOTATOR'S NOTE:** This case, Lunsford vs. BON, [then named Board of Nurse Examiners] is perhaps the most significant Texas case relating to professional nursing. It specifically recognizes a nurse-patient relationship. Because of this relationship, nurses owe a duty directly to their patients that cannot be superseded by facility policies. This opinion was issued before the NPA was codified so statutory references are to precodified NPA. Also the Rule 217.13(1) referred to what is now BON Rule 212.12 (Unprofessional Conduct).*

Appellant appeals the judgment of the district court affirming an order of the Board of Nurse Examiners, which had suspended appellant's license to practice as a nurse in the State of Texas for one year.

On March 9, 1980, appellant was employed as a registered nurse at the Willacy County Hospital in Raymondville, Texas. On this date, Donald Wayne Floyd, suffering from chest pains, sought medical assistance at the Willacy County Hospital. Floyd's companion, Frances Farrell, entered the hospital with Floyd, and after leaving Floyd in the waiting room, sought medical assistance from further within the hospital structure. Floyd, traveling through Raymondville with Farrell on their way to Houston, complained of great pain and pressure in his chest accompanied by a pain and numbness radiating down his left arm. Farrell also testified that Floyd was extremely anxious and quite gray in color. Farrell, in her search for medical help, found a physician sitting at the nursing station outside one of the treatment rooms. She requested his assistance, but was instructed to seek help from a nurse because he was quite busy. Farrell insisted that the physician help Floyd, who she explained was suffering from chest pains, but was again instructed to seek the assistance of the nurse on duty.

Appellant Nurse Lunsford then approached the nurse's station and was instructed by the physician to send Floyd onto Valley Baptist Hospital in Harlingen, twenty-four miles away. In instructing appellant, the physician pointed to the hospital's only cardiac care equipment then in use on another patient. Appellant then went into the waiting room and found Floyd lying on a table complaining of his chest pains, which were also radiating into and under his arms. After questioning Floyd, appellant learned that he had not eaten anything unusual that day, nor had he engaged in any heavy physical exercise. Although she admittedly suspected "cardiac involvement," she failed to take Floyd's vital signs. She instead instructed Farrell to drive Floyd the twenty-four miles to Valley Baptist Hospital in Harlingen. She instructed Farrell to "speed" there and to drive with the auto's emergency flashers on. Appellant also instructed Farrell to use the auto's c.b. radio to summon aid on the way into Harlingen. The last thing appellant did was ask Farrell if she knew C.P.R. since there was a chance that she might have to use it while in route to Harlingen. Appellant then sent them on their way.

Floyd died shortly thereafter, less than five miles from the Willacy County Hospital in Raymondville.

The Board of Nurse Examiners . . . suspended appellant's license to practice as a nurse in the State of Texas for one year,[2] after a hearing on appellant's actions with respect to Floyd's death. The Board found that appellant's conduct had been "unprofessional and dishonorable conduct likely to injure the public."

Appellant challenges the district court's judgment affirming the administrative order to suspension because (1) the order is not supported by substantial evidence, (2) appellant had no legal duty to care for Floyd, (3) the order is based upon an unconstitutionally vague agency rule which fails to state when a nurse becomes responsible to care for a patient, . . .

We overrule all points of error and affirm the judgment below.

I.

The primary question is whether the evidence as a whole is such that reasonable minds could have reached the conclusion the board must have reached in justifying its order suspending appellant's license.

[section deleted]

The testimony adduced at the hearing before the Board shows that Floyd presented himself, complaining of chest pains, to appellant at the hospital where appellant was employed as a registered nurse, that appellant turned him away to another hospital twenty-four miles away, and that Floyd died minutes thereafter.

Appellant contends that she had no choice but to send Floyd onto the other hospital. Appellant claims that the hospital policy precluded Floyd's treatment. It appears that the hospital had a policy to send all patients to Valley Baptist Hospital unless they had a physician on the hospital's staff or unless it was a "life-death situation."[3] Clearly Floyd was in such a "life-death situation," and was not precluded treatment by the hospital's policy. Appellant also claims that it would have been futile to take Floyd's vital signs and inform the on-duty physician since the physician had already ordered appellant to send Floyd onto Valley Baptist Hospital. At the hearing, the physician admitted telling the appellant to send Floyd to Harlingen, but stated that he had no idea of Floyd's fatal instability since the only information he had was that Floyd was having chest pains. The physician also testified that the cardiac E.K.G. equipment was available to use on Floyd, along with various medications.

Appellant, in violation of Board Rule 22 T.A.C. § 217.13--which requires a registered nurse to evaluate the status of a patient and to institute appropriate nursing care to stabilize a patient's condition and prevent complications--failed to (1) assess Floyd's condition, (2) inform the attending physician of the "life-death" nature of Floyd's instability, and (3) take appropriate measures to stabilize Floyd's condition and prevent his demise. This clearly appears to be "unprofessional and dishonorable conduct likely to injure the public." Accordingly, we find reasonable minds could agree on the Board's order revoking appellant's license, and therefore, such order was based upon substantial evidence.

II.

Appellant next claims she had no "legal duty" to care for Floyd since he was not her "patient" or "client." Appellant contends that Texas law does not recognize a "nurse-patient" relationship. Initially, we hold that appellant's contentions that she owed Floyd no duty because Floyd was neither a patient of the hospital nor of the on-duty physician are without merit, since we hold that her duty to Floyd is not derivative from such a third party relationship. Her duty to Floyd stems from the privilege granted to her by the State of Texas in licensing her as a nurse, and therefore, could not be relieved by a hospital policy or a physician's order.

This appeal deals with the suspension of a privilege, granted by the State, for appellant's "unprofessional and dishonorable conduct," which resulted in the death of an individual. When appellant received the privilege of being licensed as a nurse in this State, she entered into a covenant to serve the people of this State with all her professional skills and powers. This suit is not brought in contract or in tort by one individual who feels he or she has been wronged by appellant's action or inaction, but this suit is brought by the people of this State for appellant's violation of her contractual duties to them to always act in a professional and honorable manner.

[*section deleted*]

[4]We hold that a nurse situated such as appellant in this cause, has a duty to evaluate the medical status of the ailing person seeking his or her professional care, and to institute appropriate nursing care to stabilize a patient's condition and prevent further complications of physical and mental harm.

[*section deleted*]

III.

Appellant next contends that "Board Rule [217.13] is unconstitutionally vague because it fails to state, when and under what circumstances one becomes a 'patient' or 'client,' which status triggers a nurse's duty to evaluate or intervene in that person's behalf."

This rule, . . . 22 T.A.C. § 217.13 states:

> The term "unprofessional conduct that is likely to injure the public" means any act, practice, or omission that fails to conform to the accepted standards of the nursing profession and which results from conscious disregard for the health and welfare of the public and of the patient/client under the nurse's care and includes but is not limited to the conduct listed as follows:
>
> (1) Failing to assess and evaluate a patient's/client's status or failing to institute nursing intervention which might be required to stabilize a patient's /client's condition or prevent complications.

[*section deleted*]

Appellant's argument that the rule fails to state when the duty to act arises pales in the light of the clear language of the rule, the facts advanced in this case, and our previous holding in this case that such a duty exists when an ailing person seeks medical assistance from a person situated such as appellant in this cause, and after assessment, the person whose help is sought determines that he or she must institute appropriate nursing care to stabilize the ailing person's condition and to prevent complications of further physical or mental harm.

Appellant has failed to rebut the presumption that the agency rule is constitutional, and in our review of the rule we hold that it sufficiently apprises reasonable minds of what actions are prescribed by the mandate of the rule; accordingly, we overrule appellant's point of error.

[*section deleted*]

Footnotes

2. Appellant's license was revoked for a period of one year. This sentence was probated on the unique condition that she remain professionally employed as a nurse, and that her future employer make quarterly reports on her job performance in assessing patient's medical conditions.

3. Although various protocols were supposedly promulgated at the time of Floyd's death, it is not necessary to determine if they were or were not provided to the employees of the hospital at this time, since, as will be explained within the opinion, the appellant owed the duty to Floyd through the receipt of her license from the State. This privilege was conditioned on her practicing her professional skills in a "professional and honorable" manner. Any policy, real or imagined, of her employer had no effect upon appellant's obligation to perform her job professionally and honorably. Her obligation to the public of this State far overrides any contractual agreement with her employer to act in a certain and prescribed manner.

4. This State is not alone in holding that a "nurse-patient" relationship exists. See Daniel v. St. Francis Cabrini Hospital of Alexandria, Inc., 415 So.2d 586 (La. 1982); Plutshack v. University of Minnesota Hospital, 316 N.W. 2d 1 (Minn. 1982); Vassey v. Burch, 262 S.E.2d 865 (N.C. 1980); Hunsaker v. Boyeman Deaconness Foundation, 588 P.2d 493 (Mont. 1978); Woods v. Rowland, 592 P.2d 1332 (Colo. 1978); Stone v. Sisters of Charity of House of Providence, 469 P.2d 229 (Wash. 1970); Larrimore v. Homeopathic Hospital Assoc., 176 A.2d 362 (Del. 1962); Baur v. Westa Wash Co., 176 A.2d 684 (Pa. 1962); Ybarra v. Spangard, 154 P.2d 687 (Ca. 1944).

CLARK CASE -- WHISTLEBLOWER PROTECTIONS

KAREN CLARK, LAVERN WORRELL, AND JAN WOODARD, PETITIONERS
v.
TEXAS HOME HEALTH, INC., RESPONDENT
971 S.W.2d 435 (Tex 1998)

ANNOTATOR'S NOTE: *This case involves the proper interpretation of the whistleblower protections in NPA for nurses reporting unsafe care. The Texas Supreme Court interpreted as providing broad protections to nurses against retaliation for reporting. The court refused to give a narrow, technical approach to the law that would negate the Texas Legislature's intent in passing the law. This opinion was issued before the NPA was codified, so statutory references are to precodified NPA.*

* * * * *

We must decide two issues in this case: (1) whether an employer can avoid liability for retaliating against nurses who expressed an intent to make a report under Texas Revised Civil Statutes article 4525a, section 11(a), simply by acting before the report was made; and (2) whether the 1992 version of Texas Revised Civil Statutes article 4525b, section 6 protected nurses serving on "peer review" committees for their review of a licensed vocational nurse.

Three nurses brought claims against their employer under both of these sections. The trial court granted summary judgment for the employer, and the court of appeals affirmed. 940 S.W.2d 835. We affirm in part and reverse in part the judgment of the court of appeals, and we remand this cause for trial.

Facts

. . . in April 1992, Ursula Shaw, a licensed vocational nurse employed by Texas Home Health, caused a medication error that eventually resulted in a patient's death. Home Health terminated Shaw on May 1. At the time of the incident, Karen Clark, Lavern Worrell, and Jan Woodard ("the Nurses"), all registered nurses, were serving on the peer review committee ("the Committee") for Home Health. The Nurses met on June 18 to discuss the incident, and on June 23, Clark wrote to Shaw on behalf of the Committee to inform her that the Committee had a responsibility to report the matter to the Texas Board of Vocational Nurse Examiners. Shaw was given ten days to provide a rebuttal. Home Health's attorney advised Home Health not to report until Shaw had time to provide her rebuttal. Although Shaw did not comply within the ten-day period, the Committee had another meeting on July 17, with Shaw and her attorney present, at which Stephen Abshier[1] told Shaw that the Committee would take no action until it received Shaw's rebuttal. Sidney Dauphin, Home Health's chief executive officer, expressed concern over the potentially negative consequences for Home Health if it reported Shaw. Dauphin told the Nurses that he would personally guarantee their salaries for ten years if they lost their licenses for failing to report Shaw.

On July 29, the Committee met a third time. During this meeting, the Nurses told Home Health that they had decided to report the incident without any further delay. Without adjourning the meeting, Dauphin immediately removed the Nurses from the Committee and relieved them of their administrative duties. The Nurses then resigned.

The Nurses presented summary judgment evidence showing that they mailed a report to the Board on or about July 31, 1992, two days after they were demoted and resigned, although Home Health presented evidence that as late as March 13, 1993, the Board had not received the report. In any event, it is undisputed that Home Health's retaliation, if any, occurred before the Nurses sent in the report, but after the Nurses expressed their intent to make a report.

The Nurses sued Home Health, Abshier, Dauphin, and Charlene Dauphin[2] under the Nurse Practice Act. TEX. REV. CIV. STAT. art. 4525a, § 11(a) ("Section 11"). Section 11 allows a cause of action for a retaliatory employment decision taken because of an employee's report of a licensed health care practitioner under article 4525a. After Home Health filed a separate lawsuit against the Nurses alleging libel and slander based upon the Nurses' report of Shaw, the Nurses amended their complaint in this case to include a cause of action for damages and costs incurred as a result of participating in "peer review." TEX. REV. CIV. STAT. art. 4525b, §6 ("Section 6").

The trial court granted summary judgment for all defendants on both the Section 6 and the Section 11 claims.[3] The court of appeals affirmed, concluding that the Nurses could not recover under Section 6 because the 1992 version of Section 6 did not include within its definition of "peer review" the evaluation of a licensed vocational nurse. 940 S.W.2d at 843. Thus, the court reasoned, the statute's protection from unwarranted civil actions did not apply to the Nurses' review of Shaw, a licensed vocational nurse. *Id.* The court of appeals further concluded that the Nurses could not recover under Section 11 because, as a matter of law, the Nurses could not "establish [that] they had filed with the Board a written report *prior to their demotion.*" 940 S.W.2d at 841 (emphasis added).

We agree with the court of appeals' analysis and holding that Section 6 provides no protection for the Nurses because Shaw, as a licensed vocational nurse, was not a proper subject of peer review. But we disagree with the court of appeals' conclusion that the Nurses are not protected by Section 11 solely because their signed, written report was not filed before the alleged retaliation by their employer. Consequently, we affirm in part and reverse in part the court of appeals' judgment.

Retaliation Claim Under Section 11

Section 11 is clear and unambiguous; it provides a cause of action for retaliatory acts taken against a person reporting under article 4525a:

> No person shall suspend, terminate, or otherwise discipline or discriminate against a person reporting, without malice, under this article. A person has a cause of action against an individual, organization, agency, facility, or other person that suspends or terminates the employment of the person or otherwise disciplines or discriminates against the person for reporting under this article.
> TEX. REV. CIV. STAT. art. 4525a, §11(a).

Home Health argues that the Nurses have no cause of action under Section 11 because it is undisputed that no report was filed with the Board before the Nurses' demotion and, therefore, they could not show that Home Health demoted them in retaliation for "reporting under the article." Home Health bases its argument on the definition of "report" found in article 4525a, section 7, the provision that applies to the permissive reporting of a licensed vocational nurse. TEX. REV. CIV. STAT. art. 4525a, § 7 ("A registered nurse may file a signed, written report [with] the appropriate licensing board to report a licensed health care practitioner . . . ."). Section 11 does not require the result urged by Home Health.

Home Health correctly states that the proper way to initiate disciplinary proceedings against a person who violates the Nurse Practice Act is to file a signed, written report with the appropriate licensing board. *See id.* But Section 11 does not deal with initiating proceedings; it provides protection for someone who is the victim of retaliation in response to "reporting." Home Health's reading of Section 11 impermissibly limits protection only to those who have already actually reported under the article. Section 11 is not so narrowly written. The statute prohibits retaliation, not just against those persons who "had reported" under the article, but also against those "reporting" under the article.

The conduct alleged against Home Health is precisely the type of behavior prohibited by Section 11. Home Health knew that the Nurses intended to make a report under the article and immediately demoted them because of that intent. Sidney Dauphin and Charlene Dauphin both admit that Home Health initially directed the Nurses to delay reporting Shaw and that Home Health then demoted the Nurses after the Nurses insisted on reporting. Home Health cannot escape liability for its retaliatory act simply because it was able to demote the Nurses before they made their report. Section 11 protects reporters; this protection would be significantly diluted if employers were permitted to retaliate with impunity simply by acting before the employee files a report, thus interdicting the protection afforded to the employee by a report to the nursing board.

We emphasize that our ruling is governed by the narrow circumstances under which this case arose. The employee must demonstrate a causal relationship between the retaliatory action and the reporting. *See* TEX. REV. CIV. STAT. art. 4525a, § 11(c). In this case, the summary judgment evidence shows that Home Health knew the Nurses intended to make an imminent report to the nursing board, that it demoted the Nurses because of their intended report, and that the Nurses filed their report shortly thereafter.

Home Health misplaces reliance on *City of Beaumont v. Bouillion*. 896 S.W.2d 143 (Tex. 1995). In *Bouillion*, we considered what constitutes a report to an appropriate law enforcement authority under the Texas Whistleblower Act. *Id.* at 144. We held that neither holding a press conference nor making a complaint to an employer was a "report" that implicated the protection afforded by the Whistleblower Act. *Id.* at 144-46. Here, the Nurses made a report to the proper authority: the Board of Vocational Nurse Examiners.

We do not suggest that informing an employer of a reportable incident is a "report." It is not. *See Bouillion*, 896 S.W.2d at 144-46. And in this case, the Nurses do not contend that their "report" was to Home Health; they assert only that they informed Home Health of their intent to make a report to the proper authority and that Home Health demoted them because of that intent. In essence, Home Health argues that a bright line should be drawn requiring an employee to go directly to the proper authority before the employee receives protection. But we should not discourage an employee from informing an employer that a nurse poses a potential threat to patients. Certainly, informing one's employer of a potential threat furthers the legislative intent behind the reporting requirements and the protection afforded by Section 11: ensuring a safe and monitored system of nursing care. Consequently, we cannot fault the Nurses for attempting to work with their employer before making the formal report. Their demotion was a retaliatory act that gives rise to a cause of action under Section 11.

In an effort to explain its actions, Home Health claims that it demoted the Nurses because they insisted upon reporting in their official capacities as administrators for Home Health instead of filing a report in their individual capacities. On the other hand, the Nurses claim that they told Home Health that they felt it was critical that a report be made soon and that they intended to report despite Home Health's disapproval, even if it meant reporting as individuals. Regardless, Home Health's explanation for the demotion is irrelevant. Section 11 specifically prohibits any adverse employment decision in response to "reporting." TEX. REV. CIV. STAT. art. 4525a, § 11(a) ("No person shall suspend, terminate, or otherwise *discipline or discriminate* against a person reporting, without malice, under this article.") (emphasis added).

Underlying Home Health's explanation is an apparent fear that it would not have been protected from retaliation by Shaw for a false report. The Statute provides protection against civil liability and other retaliatory action for any "organization [or] agency . . . that, without malice, makes a report required or permitted or reasonably believed to be required or permitted under this *article* or *chapter* . . . ." TEX. REV. CIV. STAT. art. 4525a, § 10(a) (emphasis added). The Nurses, all registered nurses, were permitted to make a report under section 7 of article 4525a, and Home Health, an agency or organization, was protected for this permitted report under section 10(a) of article 4525a. TEX. REV. CIV. STAT. art. 4525a, § 7; *Id.* § 10(a).

We agree that the court of appeals correctly affirmed the trial court's summary judgment for Home Health on the Nurses' Section 6 claim. We conclude that the court of appeals erred in affirming the trial court's summary judgment for Home Health on the Nurses' Section 11 claim. An employer cannot avoid liability under Section 11 by demoting an employee knowing she intends to, but before she makes a report; the protection provided for those who make a report to the Board does not turn on which party can act faster. In order to obtain summary judgment, Home Health had to conclusively demonstrate that there was no causal relationship between the Nurses' expressed intent to report and their retaliatory action; Home Health did not make this showing. Therefore, we affirm in part and reverse in part and remand for trial on the Section 11 claim.

* * * * *

Footnotes

1. In addition to Clark, Worrell, and Woodard, the Committee initially included Rae Horton, Phyllis Galatas, and Janice Moulder, all registered nurses. Home Health appointed Abshier, a

Home Health vice president, to the Committee following the incident involving Shaw.

2. Charlene Dauphin was also a Home Health vice president.

3. The lawsuit against the individual defendants is not before this Court.

WINKLER COUNTY NURSES CASE - WHISTLEBLOWER

ANNOTATOR'S NOTE: *This is not a court opinion but rather simply a description of a Texas case that involved the termination and criminal indictment of two nurses for reporting a physician to the Texas Medical Board. They reported the physician because of concern his practice was below an acceptable standard of care. The Texas Nursing Association established a legal defense fund to assist the nurses. Ultimately, the charges against one of the nurses was dropped, and the other nurse was found not guilty by a jury. Based on lessons learned from the case, legislation was passed in 2011 enhancing patient advocacy protections for nurses in Texas.*

In April 2009, two RNs employed by Winkler County Memorial Hospital, a county hospital, reported a physician to the Medical Board for practicing below an acceptable standard of care. When the physician was notified by the Medical Board that a report had been made against him, he filed a complaint with the Winkler County sheriff saying someone was harassing him. In June 2009, based on the fact the report used information they acquired as county employees, the nurses were indicted for misuse of official information, a third degree felony. The Medical Board wrote the Winkler County Attorney and District Attorney expressing concern the indictments would have a chilling effect on nurses' willingness to report unsafe care. The County Attorney refused to dismiss the case alleging the nurses were motivated by vindictiveness toward the physician.

In June 2009, the nurses also were terminated by the Winkler County Memorial Hospital. In July 2009, the Texas Nurses Association filed a complaint with the Department of State Health Services against the hospital for illegally terminating the nurses for reporting the physician to the Medical Board.

In August 2009, the two nurses filed a civil suit in federal court against Winkler County, the hospital, the sheriff, County Attorney, District Attorney, hospital administrator and physician. The suit alleged violation of the nurses' civil rights under federal law, violation of the Texas Public Employee Whistleblower Law and the whistleblower provisions of the Nursing Practice Act, and malicious prosecution. The defendants asserted a number of defenses including sovereign immunity and official immunity. One of the defenses the physician asserted was that the state whistleblower laws only prohibited retaliation by employers, and he was not the nurses' employer.

In February 2010, the charges against one of the nurses were dismissed and after a four day trial, the other nurse was found not guilty by the jury after deliberating for less than an hour.

In April 2010, the Texas Department of State Health Services issued a letter of violation against the hospital finding several violations including wrongful termination of the nurses. Final action was taken on August 9, 2010. Because the Hospital Licensing Law (Health & Safety Code §241.059) sets the maximum administrative fine per violation at $1000 and Department fining guidelines set $650 as maximum when no direct patient injury is involved, the hospital was fined $1300 or $650 per nurse for the wrongful terminations.

In July 2010, the Medical Board filed a formal complaint against the physician alleging nine practice violations and one charge of intimidating witnesses. In August 2010, the case was sent to mediation.

In August 2010, the federal civil suit settled for a lump settlement of $750,000 ($375,000 for each nurse) which included attorney fees and litigation costs. One of the nurses testified that after taxes the amount she recovered was approximately a one and one-half years salary but now had income of about one-half what she had been receiving and had lost some of her retirement benefits.

In December 2010, the Texas Medical Board and the physician engaged in a SOAH mediation that resulted in a Proposed Agreed Order that the Medical Board approved at its February 2011 meeting. The Order included findings of several practice violations and one of unprofessional conduct of intimidating witnesses. He was fined $5,000, required to engage in supervised practice for a period of time, and ordered to enroll in a designated physician evaluation program. As discussed in the next paragraph The physician was subsequently criminally charged because of his actions against the two nurses and ultimately entered into an agreed order to surrender his license in November 2011.

In December 2010 and January 2011, the physician, sheriff, county attorney and hospital administrator were arrested and indicted for misuse of official information (same offense the nurses were charged with) and retaliation. The hospital administrator entered into a plea bargain. The sheriff was found guilty on all counts in June 2011 and the county attorney Fall 2011. The physician ultimately entered into a plea bargain that resulted in surrender of his medical license.

SUBPART M.
ATTORNEY GENERAL OPINIONS

One of the roles of the the Texas Attorney General is to respond to requests from state officials and agencies as to his office's opinion as to how courts would interpret certain Texas laws. This responses are referred to as Attorney General Opinions or simply as AG Opinions. They are identified by the initials of the AG who issued the opinion and a number, e.g., GA-236 (2004) which identifies it the 236th opinion issued by Attorney General Greg Abbott and that it was issued in 2004. Below is a listing of AG opinions that have address specific nursing issues. The opinions can be found on the Attorney General's website at www.oag.state.tx.us under the "Opinions" tab and then selecting "Index to Opinions."

H-395 (1974). Held that hospital employment alone does not qualify a person as meeting the Nursing Practice Act exemption for persons acting at the instruction of a physician.

H-1293 (1978). Held that assisting with the delivery of a normal childbirth was not the practice of medicine and that CNMs assisting with normal childbirth were not engaged in the unauthorized practicing of medicine.

H-1295 (1978). Held that a physician prescription had to be a specific order for a specific patient and that physicians could not prescribe using standing orders. The opinion led to passage of legislation in 1981 permitting use of standing delegation orders and the first recognition of advanced nursing practice.

MW-318 (1981). Addressed a variety of issues relating to the physician delegation and medical board rules governing delegation to nurses.

JM-173 (1984). Extensive discussion of the exemption in the Nursing Practice Act for acts done under physician supervision. Recognized the significant overlap between medicine and nursing.

JC-117 (1991). Held that practice of anesthesia was the practice of medicine but that CRNAs could administer anesthesia without physician supervision.

GA-236 (2004). Held that definition of professional nursing does not include RNs administering medications prescribed by therapeutic optometrist. Also confirmed that nurses could administer medications prescribed by APRNs.

SUBPART N.
HISTORY OF AMENDMENTS TO NURSING PRACTICE ACT AND OTHER NURSING-RELATED LEGISLATION

The following are the more significant amendments to the Nursing Practice Act since it was first passed in 1909. Also included is other significant legislation that affected nurses' scope of practice even if NPA was not amended.

1909. Original act passed. Its passage was the result of work of the Texas Nurses Association (then called Graduate Nurses Association) which was formed in 1907 for the purpose of passing a licensing act. The act created the Board of Nurse Examiners and provided for the examining and licensing of registered nurses. The act had some notable deficiencies including 1) being a "title-control" act that applied only to individuals using the title registered nurse, 2) not containing a definition of professional nursing, 3) imposing no educational requirements for licensure, and 4) giving the BON no authority over nursing education.

1923. BON given authority over nursing education and requirement added that applicants for licensure must be graduates of an accredited school approved by the BON. The appointment of a paid educational secretary was provided for and board members were required to have at least three years educational experience.

1925. All Texas statutes were re-codified. Laws relating to professional nursing were codified as Articles 4513 through 4528. This was the first and last systemic rewrite of the NPA.

1929. BON increased from 5 to 6 members and 6-year staggered terms established.

1935. Because of concern that the BON was discriminating against small general hospitals, a provision was added declaring all general hospitals of 25 beds with average daily occupancy of 15 patients that taught the BON-prescribed course of study to be "accredited schools." The minimum educational requirements were changed from "two years of continuous study" to "three full years of work and study." Nursing opposed these amendments as lowering the educational standards and permitting hospitals to add a third year of service at little or no wages. Twenty-two states refused Texas reciprocity because of the lower standards.

1941. Provision added authorizing the organizing of non-profit Nursing Registration Bureaus. The apparent purpose was to remove nursing bureaus from regulation by the Department of Labor and relieve them from having to pay occupational taxes and licensing fees.

1959. BON given explicit authority to prescribe the course of study for nursing schools but mandated that include both theory and clinical. It was also given greater accrediting authority over education but was prohibited from setting length of programs at less than 2 or more than four years. These changes undid the 1935 amendment.

1961. Licensure by endorsement extended to nurses licensed by foreign countries and U.S. territories and possessions.

1967. Added a definition of professional nursing. This was first time since originally enacted in 1909 that NPA contained a definition of professional nursing. The definition was based on the model definition then being recommended by the American Nurses Association. Adding a definition of professional nursing and getting the NPA amended to be a practice-control act in 1969 was the result of a 10 year legislative effort by the Texas Nurses Association.

1969. NPA changed from a "title-control" to a "practice-control" act regulating not only persons using the title "RN" but anyone engaged in the practice of professional nursing. Unlicensed persons were prohibited from practicing professional nursing unless explicitly exempted from the NPA. Because of this change, the exemptions to the NPA were expanded to exempt other licensed practitioners, LVNs, etc. The exemption that proved to be particularly troublesome was one for "acts done under the control or supervision or at the instruction of one licensed by the Texas Medical Board." Some hospitals argued this exemption applied to all care in a hospital since care in a hospital was done "at the instruction of a physician." The exemption was relied on by hospitals to employ large numbers of foreign educated nurses who did not hold a Texas license. Ultimately, the Texas Attorney General ruled (but not until 1983) that the exemption applied only to persons to whom a physician delegated care in accordance with the Medical Practice Act.

The NPA was also amended to require that only 3 BON members have teaching experience instead of all six and to provide for the board to employ an Executive Secretary (now Executive Director) rather than appoint one of its members to serve in that capacity.

1973. Established a system of variable expiration dates for licenses.

1977. Although the only amendment passed was one changing the minimum education program from two years to two academic years, this was a significant session for nursing because the Texas Nurses Association initiated legislation to enact a Model Practice Act. The legislation would have made substantial changes to the NPA that nursing wanted. Although the legislation failed, it marked the beginning of a commitment by the Texas Nurses Association to maintain a continuous nursing presence at the Texas Legislature. It was also at this time that TNA established the first political action committee for RNs -- called at various times Tex-N-Cap, RN-PAC and most recently Texas RN/APN PAC.

1977 was also the year Texas passed its Sunset Act providing for periodic review of state agencies. The first sunset review for the BON was set for 1981.

1979. A number of significant amendments made including: 1) increasing BON's rule-making authority to "regulate the practice of professional nursing," 2) changing definition of professional nursing to include the "observation, assessment, intervention, evaluation, rehabilitation, care and counsel and health teachings of persons who are ill, injured or infirm or experiencing changes in normal health processes," 3) giving BON injunctive power and authority to probate disciplinary penalties, and 4) requiring all fees collected by BON be placed in the State Treasury and expended only as appropriated by the Legislature. Legislation recognizing APN practice was defeated.

1981. BON underwent its first sunset review. Significant amendments to NPA that resulted included 1) adding three public members to the BON, 2) requiring BON to recognize the three types of educational programs (diploma, ADN, BSN), 3) requiring the three educator members be representative of the three types of educational programs, and 4) expanding the BON's rule-making authority to include defining which acts constitute the practice of professional nursing. An attempt to strip BON of its regulatory authority over nursing education was defeated. Legislation recognizing APN practice was again defeated as was legislation addressing 3rd party reimbursement for APNs.

BON successfully defended suit by the Texas Hospital Association and Texas Medical Association challenging BON's authority to adopt rules regulating APNs.

1983. Legislation to prohibit insurers from discriminating against APNs by denying reimbursement simply because they were licensed as RNs was again defeated.

1985. RNs secured exemption from respiratory therapists licensing act. Recognition that medication aides in LTC facilities must function under the delegated authority of RN or physician.

1987. Legislation popularly known as "Professional Nursing Quality Assurance Act" passed adding mandatory reporting and nursing peer review provisions to the NPA. Texas was among the first, if not the first state, to pass peer review legislation for RNs. Peer assistance statute covering RNs and other health professionals experiencing problems with chemical dependency or mental illness was passed as a separate statute. RNs secured exemption from the radiologic technologists licensing act.

1989. APNs were given limited prescriptive authority at sites serving medically underserved populations. (Most of this legislation involved amendments to Medical Practice Act but some conforming amendments were made to the NPA.) BON given authority to require continuing nursing education for license renewal. A financial aid program for nurses was established and initially funded with a license surcharge, and a special study of an existing nursing shortage authorized. Definition of professional nursing amended to include carrying out orders of podiatrists. Third party reimbursement for RNs defeated for a third time as was legislation authorizing RNs to determine death.

1991. RNs given authority to determine death. Exemptions to NPA clarified and expanded to address nursing students, care provided in disaster situations, and RNs temporarily in state. BON given more authority to issue temporary permits and to do criminal background checks, and a process was established for students to obtain declaratory order of eligibility for licensure. Legislation to combine all health professionals licensing boards into a super agency was defeated.

1993. BON underwent sunset review for second time. There was some attempt to combine the former Board of Nurse Examiners (RNs) with the Board of Vocational Nurse Examiners, but that failed. A Health Professions Council was created to co-ordinate activities of the various health professions licensing boards but it isn't the super agency attempted in 1991. Nursing peer review was amended to require that: 1) three-fourths of the committee's members be RNs, 2) the nurse being reviewed be afforded minimum due process and 3) at least one member of the committee have a working familiarity with area of practice of the nurse being reviewed. Mandatory reporting was amended: 1) to give BON authority to adopt rules to minimize reporting of minor incidents and duplicative reporting and 2) to require mandatory reporting by peer review committees to the BON. The sunset legislation also made substantial changes to the BON's disciplinary process. Legislation expanding prescriptive authority for APNs was defeated. 1993 also saw pharmacists obtain limited authority to administer medications.

1995. Peer review expanded to include LVNs. RNs given protection from retaliation for refusing to engage in reportable conduct. The qualification relating to practice experience of practice members of BON clarified. Proof of good professional character added as requirement for licensure and mandatory reporting expanded to include students experiencing problems with chemical dependency. Limited prescriptive authority for APNs expanded to include a physician's primary practice site and facility based practice.

1997. Enhanced protections for RNs who refuse to engage in reportable conduct by giving them a right to request a determination by peer review as to the RN's duty and providing the RN a safe harbor pending that determination. BON authorized, and appropriated funds, to conduct pilot test mechanisms to help assure: 1) RNs maintain their competency after initial licensure and 2) RNs are knowledgeable of the laws and regulations governing their practice. The Diploma educator slot on BON changed to an APN educator slot. BON given authority to collect information needed to identify students who may be disqualified for licensure upon graduation. In addition, the Medical Practice Act and Insurance Code were amended to: 1) expand slightly prescriptive authority for Advanced Practice Nurses (APNs) and 2) address reimbursement problems APNs had encountered with managed care.

1999. The Nursing Practice Act underwent a complete, nonsubstantive rewrite as part of being codified into the Occupations Code. The Nurse Licensure Compact was adopted making Texas one of the first states to begin the implementing of a system of multistate licensure for nurses. Nurses were given additional protections against getting a "bad job reference" for refusing to engage in conduct believed to violate a nurse's duty to the patient. School nurses were added to the teacher minimum salary scale. Legislation was enacted for advanced practice addressing nondiscrimination in reimbursement, due process in hospital clinical privileging, against calling in prescriptions, documentation of services provided, and performing physicals for cosmetologists licensure. RNs were added to those professionals whose services, when contracting with the State, are covered by the Professional Services Procurement Act. Legislation regulating CRNAs administering anesthesia in outpatient settings was also passed.

2001. There were relatively few amendments to the NPA in 2001. Sections 301.525 (relating to RN First Assistants) and 301.304 (relating to HEP C CNE) were added. Chapter 304 establishing a Nursing Workforce Data Center (not implemented because not funded by Legislature) was added as part of nursing shortage legislation. That shortage legislation also amended the Education Code by adding 61.921-.926 to create a professional nursing shortage reduction program. Legislation expanding limited prescriptive authority for APNs to a physician's alternate practice site and creating a process for practices to receive a wavier of certain requirements for prescriptive authority. Legislation mandating reimbursement for RN First Assistants was passed. Since the 1999 NPA codification did not include any legislation passed in 1999, that legislation was incorporated into the codified NPA in 2001. The most significant change of this type was adding 301.601-.607 relating to outpatient anesthesia. The Nurse Licensure Compact passed in 1999 was codified as Chapter 304 (numbering duplicates that of Nursing Workforce Data Center and will have to be corrected by a future Legislature). Sec. 531.051 of the Government Code relating to a voucher program for persons with disabilities was amended to exempt from professional nursing certain activities of daily living and health maintenance acts performed by attendants for clients who could not perform those tasks for themselves because of a functional disability. Legislation was introduced, but not passed, that would have given the BON general authority to conduct pilot projects, conduct criminal background checks and develop alternates to CNE for how RNs demonstrate competency as part of the licensure renewal process.

2003. A single board of nursing and licensing act for RNs and LVNs was passed. RNs and LVNs will be licensed and regulated under the Nursing Practice Act that will be a practice act (Chapter 301, Occupations Code) for both RNs and LVNs. Safe Harbor Nursing Peer Review and all the other patient advocacy protections afforded RNs were extended to LVNs. Use of the generic title "nurse" was restricted to use by RNs and LVNs and titles such as "nurse aide" and "nurse assistant" limited to unlicensed personnel functioning under the delegated authority of an RN. Prescriptive authority for APNs was expanded to include controlled substances, Schedules III-V. APNs were added to the standardized credentialing statute passed for physicians in 2001. The Nursing Workforce Data Center enacted but not funded in 2001 was moved from the BON to the Statewide Health Coordinating Council and funded through a surcharge on nurses' license renewal fee ($2 for RNs and $1 for LVNs). The BON was given authority to conduct FBI criminal background checks as part of the licensing and licensing renewal process. To address certain RN-substitution issues, the 2001 legislation addressing RN first assisting was amended to permit certain RNs to "directly assist at surgery" which is a more limited function than first assisting. The BON was given extensive authority to conduct pilot programs and a mandate to conduct a pilot to evaluate systems designed to encourage identification of system errors. Legislation passed requiring RNs and LVNs to take two hours of CNE in bioterrorism.

2005. The nursing shortage was again addressed by the Texas Legislature. It appropriated $6 million to fund the Nursing Shortage Reduction Program originally created in 2001. Senate Bill

(SB) 132 directed the Higher Education Coordinating Board to conduct study of retention rates in the Texas nursing education programs and created financial incentives for nursing faculty including tuition reduction for faculty children and preceptors and a home loan program. The practice environment of nursing was addressed through several bills. A Safe Patient Handling Law (SB1525) was passed making Texas the first state in the nation to pass such legislation. House Bill (HB) 1718 addressed assisting at surgery, first assisting and the role of the circulating RN. The regulatory environment for nursing was addressed by HB 1000, HB 1366 and HB 2680. HB 1000 made several amendments to the NPA including adding a definition of "vocational nursing," clarifying that conduct exposing a patient to risk of harm requires reporting only when conduct creates an unnecessary risk, clarifying facilities' mandatory reporting requirements with respect to temporary agency nurses, and making the Nurse Licensure Compact permanent. HB 1366 expanded the BON's disciplinary authority and added a list of offenses to NPA that requires the BON to deny/suspend/revoke a nursing license. HB 2680 reduced the licensure requirements for retired health professionals whose practice is limited to volunteer charity work.

2007. The BON underwent Sunset review. The legislation ("BON Sunset Bill") implementing the Sunset Commission's recommendations was HB 2426. The bill 1) continued the Board for 10 years, 2) changed its name from the Board of Nurse Examiners (BON) to the Texas Board of Nursing (BON), 3) reduced, but did not eliminate, the role that the BON has historically played in the regulation of nursing education, 4) changed the way impaired nurses involved in a practice violation are reported, 5) addressed BON's use of arrest and convictions in disciplining nurses, 6) set a jurisprudence exam requirement for new licensees, 7) adopted the APRN Multistate Licensure Compact for persons applying for a nursing license, and 8) gave the BON more flexibility in implementing targeted CNE. Legislation (SB 993) initiated by the Texas Nurses Association made substantial changes to mandatory reporting and nursing peer review including 1) simplifying definition of conduct subject to reporting, 2) limiting peer review committees to identifying the extent to which external factors affected an incident when an employer reports a nurse, 3) authorizing greater sharing of information between nursing peer review and patient safety committees, 4) extending safe harbor nursing peer review to persons that advise nurses on their right to request safe harbor, and 5) clarifying the protections and remedies nurses have when advocating for patients. The nursing shortage was addressed for the fourth consecutive session with over $20 million being appropriated to nursing education. The dedication to nursing of certain tobacco lawsuit settlement funds was extended until 2011. A number of other bills passed relating to nursing education (SB 138, 139, 141, 201, 289) that were recommended by an interim report of the Senate Committee on Health and Human Services. None made major changes. The BON was given authority to require that all 20 hours of CNE for licensure renewal be Type 1 (SB 993). The Legislature also passed and funded legislation (SB 156) implementation of the Nurse-Family Partnership Program in Texas on a pilot program basis.

2009. The Hospital Safe Staffing Law (SB 476) was the most important nursing legislation passed in 2009. The legislation built on the existing staffing rules DSHS adopted in 2002. The most significant changes made by the legislation were to require the hospital board be involved in staffing issues and to make the nurse staffing committee a standing committee, whose responsibilities include evaluating the adequacy of the staffing plan and reporting to the hospital board on the results of its evaluation. SB 476 also included a provision prohibiting mandatory overtime in hospitals. The shortage of RNs was addressed with the appropriation of $45 million, which was three times the amount appropriated in 2007. SB 1415 provided the BON another option in addressing minor violations by being given the authority to take nondisciplinary, corrective action against the nurse, and also authorized it pilot test a deferred disciplinary model for minor violations under which it could dismiss a complaint once the nurse fulfilled certain conditions imposed by the board. There were a number of amendments made to the Nursing Practice Act by HB 3961 including clarifying that personal contact information and personal health information collected by the BON was confidential and clarifying the BON's authority to request physical and psychological evaluations as part of the licensing and disciplinary process. The

Center for Nursing Workforce Studies was directed to conduct a study of the clinical component of nursing education, particularly at clinical competency assessments and prior work experience. Some changes were made to APRN delegated prescriptive authority to address needs of pharmacy-based minute/convenience clinics. Other legislation making more significant improvements to APRNs' prescribing did not pass. Legislation assuring publicly employed nurses the same patient advocacy protections as privately-employed nurses also did not pass.

2011. The most significant practice-related legislation passed was SB 192 enhancing patient advocacy protections for nurses based on lessons learned from case of the Winkler County nurses who were terminated and indicted for reporting a physician to medical board. The enhancements included: 1) immunity from criminal liability; 2) authorizing regulatory agencies to impose fine up to $25,000 for illegal retaliation; and 3) extending protections to nurses who advise other nurses about protections for engaging in patient advocacy activities. The Appropriations Bill included $30 million special funding for the Nursing Shortage Reduction Program to increase the number of RN graduates. The dedication of certain tobacco lawsuit settlement funds to nursing education was extended to 2015. These funds are used by the Texas Higher Education Coordinating Board to fund the Nursing Education Innovation Grant Program. Legislation (SB 193) was passed making several amendments to the NPA. The main substantive changes were: 1) enhanced protection for personal information provided as part of licensure process, and 2) establishing a confidential depository to which facilities may report error classification data to facilitate identification of recurring errors so action can be taken to reduce the occurrence of such errors. The bill also made technical and cleanup changes to the NPA. Though not nursing-initiated, SB 1360 passed to give unlicensed persons expanded authority to administer medication in certain Medicaid waiver programs for persons with developmental and intellectual disabilities. Legislation requiring hospitals to have policies on mandatory vaccinations of individuals providing direct care passed (as part of SB 7 in Special Session). There were several bills filed to expand the prescriptive authority of APRNs but none passed. Legislation supported by nursing and hospitals to address violence against nurses and other health care workers did not pass. The BON also unsuccessfully sought to have the Legislature give it what is referred to as "self-directed, semi-autonomous status."

2013. Several significant pieces of legislation affecting nursing practice passed. SB 406 expanded the scope of prescriptive authority for APRNs, replaced the current site-based model with a prescriptive authority agreement model, and authorized APRNs to prescribe CS II for hospital inpatients, hospital ER patients and hospice patients. This was the first significant expansion of APRN prescriptive authority since 2003. HB 581 expanded the patient advocacy protections for public hospital employed nurses by giving them the right to file a lawsuit for damages suffered from retaliation because engaged in protected patient advocacy activities. HB 705 enhanced the penalty for assaulting ER nurses from a misdemeanor to a felony. SB 1058 made several amendments to the Nursing Practice Act. The most significant changes were 1) making permanent the Board of Nursing's (BON) current pilot authority to take deferred action against a nurses license for certain minor violations, 2) making BON orders sending nurses to the Texas Peer Assistance Program confidential, and 3) mandating criminal background checks for nursing students. Nursing education was appropriated $33.75 million in special funding and a loan repayment program was established for nursing faculty. A study was mandated of "self-directed, semi-independent status" for health professions licensing agencies.

SUBPART O.
INTERNET RESOURCES

The following are internet resources not only for obtaining the most current changes to the laws and regulations covered in this Guide, but also other information relating to the regulation of health professions and health care.

Texas Nurses Association: www.texasnurses.org
TNA's site includes a governmental affairs section that provides information about nursing legislation at the state level.

Texas Board of Nursing: www.bon.texas.gov
The BON's site contains BON rules, position statements, FAQ's and other information related to professional nursing practice including announcements of proposed rule changes.

National Council of State Boards of Nursing: www.ncsbn.org
The National Council of State Boards of Nursing (NCSBN) is the association of state BONs. NCSBN's site contains information about variety of topics relating to the regulation of nursing and includes links to all state BONs.

Texas Center for Nursing Workforce Studies: www.dshs.state.tx.us/chs/cnws
The Center for Nursing Workforce Studies collects and analyzes nursing workforce data. It is funded by a surcharge on nurses' license renewal fees and is overseen by a Nursing Advisory Committee.

Texas Legislature Online: www.legis.state.tx.us
The official site of the Texas Legislature. It contains information about all laws considered by the Texas Legislature as well as a large amount of other information related to the Legislature. It has extensive search capabilities that include locating proposed and adopted amendments to specific laws. During legislative sessions, information about legislation is updated daily . The site also has links to many other state sites including those listed below.

Texas Statutes: http://www.statutes.legis.state.tx.us
This site contains all the laws of Texas. One has to be sure to check through what Legislative Session the laws are current. To find nursing related laws on this site, select "Occupations Code" and then particular profession.

Texas Administrative Code: www.sos.state.tx.us/tac
This site contains the rules and regulations promulgated by state agencies. One has to be sure to check through what date the rules are current. To find nursing related rules on this site use the following steps: Select TAC Viewer, then Title 22, Examining Boards (or other appropriate Title), and finally, the desired board or agency, e.g., BON

Texas Register: www.sos.state.tx.us/texreg
All rules proposed and adopted by state agencies are published in the Texas Register. It also publishes notice of all open meetings. The Register is published once a week. This site includes copies of current and previous Texas Registers. The site has search capabilities to find specific rules that have been amended or proposed for amendment.

Texas Attorney General Opinions: www.oag.state.tx.us
This site is maintained by the Office of the Texas Attorney General. Copies of opinions issued by the Texas Attorney General can be downloaded from this site.

Legislative Reference Library: www.lrl.state.tx.us
This site provides legislative information such as tables that cross-reference chapters of session laws to bill number and vice versa; an index to the sections of statutes affected by bills; the number of bills introduced, passed, and vetoed; and interim committee charges and reports. It also includes directions on how to compile legislative history.

Legislative Budget Board: www.lbb.state.tx.us
This site provides information relating to the Texas budget, including the Texas Fact Book and the General Appropriations Act.

Texas Legislative Council: www.tlc.state.tx.us
This site provides legislative-related information including explanation of legislative process, how to read legislation, internet resources and redistricting.

House Research Organization: www.hro.house.state.tx.us
This site provides includes bill analysis of bills considered by the full House of Representatives and other background information on legislation and legislative issues.

SUBPART P.
RESOURCES AND FORMS FOR SAFE HARBOR NURSING PEER REVIEW

1. Introduction

Nurses may be given an assignment that the nurse supervisor believes is safe but which the nurse believes is unsafe. In such situations, the nurse may be faced with the undesirable choice of:

- refusing the assignment and risking possible disciplinary action by the facility.
- accepting the assignment despite her or his concern that it is not safe and risking possible disciplinary action against her or his license by the Board of Nursing (BON) - particularly if there is a bad patient outcome.

Safe Harbor Nursing Peer Review gives nurses a more desirable third option:

- requesting a nursing peer review committee review the assignment to determine whether it violates a nurse's duty to the patient;
- protection from being disciplined by the facility for making the request; and
- protection from being disciplined by the BON for engaging in the assignment awaiting the peer review committee's deliberations.

Since nurses can honestly disagree about a nurse's duty to a patient in a particular situation, the ability to seek guidance as to what is a nurse's duty without negative consequences is an important protection. Safe harbor nursing peer review is an option for nurses that is in addition to the more traditional whistleblower protections in which the nurse is provided a right to seek a remedy (normally retain an attorney and file a lawsuit) after the nurse has been retaliated against. Safe harbor is designed to provide the nurse a "before-harm-occurs" remedy.

See Part VI (Advocacy) for laws and BON rules governing nursing safe harbor peer review.

A flowchart of the safe harbor nursing peer review process, a practical guide to nurses' right under safe harbor, and forms for requesting safe harbor are set out below.

2. Safe Harbor Nursing Peer Review Flowchart

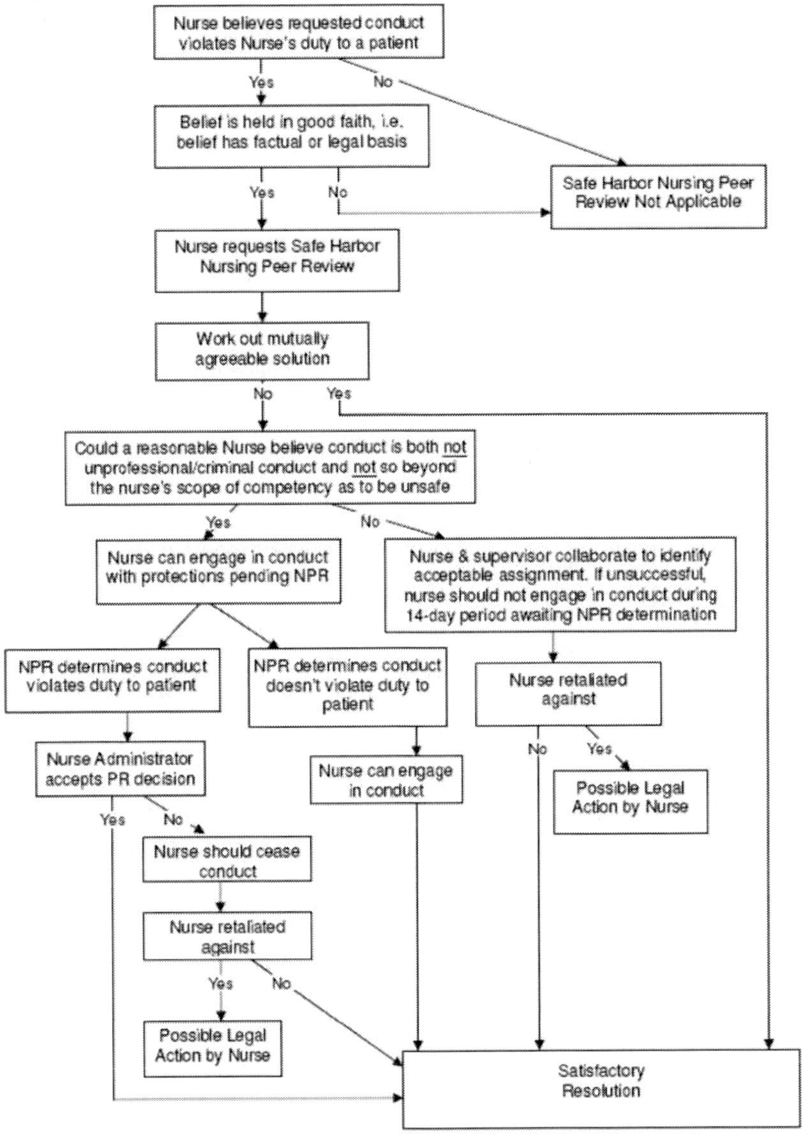

3. Forms for Requesting Safe Harbor Nursing Peer Review

BON Rule 217.20(d)(3) and (4) require a request for safe harbor nursing peer review be in writing and include either:

- the information required for the Quick Request Form under 217.20(d)(3); or
- the information required for the Comprehensive Written Request Form under 217.20(d)(4)

If a nurse uses the Quick Request Form to make the initial request, **the nurse must submit in writing the information required by the Comprehensive Written Request Form before she/he leaves the work setting at the end of the work period.** If the Comprehensive Written Request Form is used to make the initial request, no additional information need be submitted.

The Quick Request Form can be in any written format as long as it contains the following information:

1. the nurse(s) name making the safe harbor request and her/his signature(s);
2. the date and time of the request;
3. the location of where the conduct or assignment is to be completed;
4. the name of the person requesting the conduct or making the assignment; and
5. a brief explanation of why safe harbor is being requested.

As indicated above, the Texas Nurses Association believes the following request meets these requirements.

> *2/12/08 1800. I request safe harbor nursing peer review. Near the end of my 3-11 shift my supervisor, Sue Super RN, told me I would have to work the 11-7 shift because two nurses called in sick. My 3-11 shift was very hectic and I feel exhausted and too fatigued to do a double shift. Also double shifts seem to be becoming routine on this unit.*
>
> *Mary Smith RN*
> Mary Smith RN

The Comprehensive Request Form in any written format as long as it contains the following information:

1. the conduct assigned or requested, including the name and title of the person making the assignment or request;
2. a description of the practice setting, e.g., the nurse's responsibilities, resources available, extenuating or contributing circumstances impacting the situation;
3. a detailed description of how the requested conduct or assignment would have violated the nurse's duty to a patient or any other provision of the NPA and Board Rules. If possible, reference the specific standard (217.11 of this title) or other section of the NPA and/or Board rules the nurse believes would have been violated. If a nurse refuses to engage in the requested conduct or assignment, the nurse must document the existence of a rationale listed under subsection (g) of this section.
4. if applicable, the rationale for the nurse's not engaging in the requested conduct or assignment awaiting the nursing peer review committee's determination as to the nurse's duty. The rationale should refer to one of the justifications described in subsection (g)(2) of this section for not engaging in the conduct or assignment

awaiting a peer review determination.

5. any other copies of pertinent documentation available at the time. Additional documents may be submitted to the committee when available at a later time; and
6. the nurse's name, title, and relationship to the supervisor making the assignment or request.

4. BON Official Forms and Other Resources

The BON promulgates three official Safe Harbor Nursing Peer Review Request Forms. They are:

1. Quick Request Form
2. Comprehensive Request Form
3. Request Form When the Medical Reasonableness of a Physician's Order is Involved

These can be found on the BON website along with other information about nursing peer review including a FAQ section.

Even if a nurse does not use the BON official forms, **the nurse should follow the process outlined in the forms.** Doing so will ensure compliance with the steps in the safe harbor nursing peer review process.

[Continue on Next Page]

5. Practical Guide To Nurses' Rights Under Safe Harbor Nursing Peer Review

Prepared by Texas Nurses Association

The following is from a pamphlet that the Texas Nurses Association makes available to facilities on a license to reprint basis.

IMPORTANT PRACTICAL TIP
READ BEFORE YOU NEED!

Nurses should not wait until a situation arises to familiarize themselves with their right to request Safe Harbor Nursing Peer Review. That is best done without the pressures of having to make an immediate decision on whether and how to make the request.

A. Who Is Protected by Safe Harbor Nursing Peer Review
B. When Do Safe Harbor Protections Apply
C. Who Can Request Safe Harbor Nursing Peer Review
D. Requesting Safe Harbor Nursing Peer Review
    Condition 1: Facility is required to provide
    Condition 2: Request made in good faith
    Condition 3: Request contains required information
    Condition 4: Request is timely
E. Process Once Request Made
F. Nurse's Engaging in Requested Conduct Awaiting Nursing Peer Review Determination
G. Remedies if Nurse Retaliated Against
H. Record Keeping
I. Engaging In Reportable Conduct Pending Peer Review
J. What If Patient Harm Occurs
K. Practical Tips
L. Other Patient Advocacy Protections for Texas Nurses

Near the end of 3-11 shift on a post-op unit, Mary Smith, RN, is told by her supervisor that two of the nurses on the 11-7 shift have called in sick and that no replacements have been located. The supervisor says she regrets the situation, but that Mary and one other RN will have to stay and work the 11-7 shift. Mary expresses concern that her 3-11 shift was busy, she felt exhausted and that her fatigue will increase the chance of her making patient care errors. Mary also expresses concern that double shifts are becoming a pattern on the unit and points out that recent research shows increased patient care errors when nurses work extended shifts. The supervisor acknowledges Mary's concern, but indicates no one else is available to staff the unit. Mary is faced with the undesirable choice of:

- refusing the assignment and risking possible disciplinary action by the facility.[1]
- accepting the assignment despite her concern that it is not safe and risking possible disciplinary action against her license by the Board of Nursing (BON) - particularly if there if there is a bad patient outcome.[2]

---

[1]1. "Facility" is being used broadly to refer to a hospital., clinic, long-term care facility, home health agency, and any other entity that utilizes RNs or LVNs

[2]2. If the facility disciplines a nurse for refusing the assignment, the nurse may have a right to sue the facility under Nursing Practice Act which prohibits retaliation against a nurse for refusing to engage in conduct that violates the NPA or a BON rule.

Safe Harbor Nursing Peer Review gives nurses a more desirable third option:

- requesting a nursing peer review committee review the assignment to determine whether it violates a nurse's duty to the patient;
- protection from being disciplined by the facility for making the request; and
- protection from being disciplined by the BON for engaging in the assignment awaiting the peer review committee's deliberations.

Since nurses can honestly disagree about a nurse's duty to a patient in a particular situation, the ability to seek guidance as to what is a nurse's duty without negative consequences is an important protection. Laws designed to provide individuals with protections against having to put themselves at risk in situations where the correct action is unclear are commonly referred to as "safe harbor" laws - therefore the name "safe harbor nursing peer review."

A. WHO IS ENTITLED TO THE PROTECTIONS OF SAFE HARBOR NURSING PEER REVIEW

The protections provided by safe harbor nursing peer review are available to both:

- nurses and nurse supervisors who request safe harbor nursing peer review in good faith; and
- nurses and other individuals who advise a nurse on the nurse's right to safe harbor nursing peer review and how to request.

B. WHEN DO THE SAFE HARBOR PROTECTIONS APPLY

It is the "making of the request" that triggers the protections of safe harbor nursing peer review, and its protections apply only after the request is made. An option for a nurse requesting safe harbor is to indicate when making the request that she/he will withdraw the request if a mutually satisfactory solution is reached. Any mutually satisfactory solution must be consistent with the nurse's duty to the patient.

C. WHO CAN REQUEST SAFE HARBOR NURSING PEER REVIEW

Nurses who can request safe harbor nursing peer review are:

- nurses providing patient care.
- nurse supervisors making or carrying out administrative decisions directly affecting patient care.

Nurse supervisors can request because the Safe Harbor Nursing Peer Review Law defines "duty to patient" as including administrative decisions that directly affect a nurse's ability to comply with a nurse's duty to a patient. An example of when a nurse supervisor might invoke safe harbor nursing peer review is a facility's adopting a policy that would require nurses to work such long hours that fatigue is very likely to put patients at risk of unsafe care. The supervisor could request safe harbor nursing peer review to determine if the policy would require her/him to make administrative decisions that would cause nurses to violate their duty to their patients by providing care when overly fatigued.

D. REQUESTING SAFE HARBOR NURSING PEER REVIEW

The protections of safe harbor nursing peer review are available only when the following conditions are met.

Condition 1: Facility is required to provide safe harbor
Condition 2: Nurse in good faith believes requested conduct violates the nurse's duty

to the patient

Condition 3: Request is in writing and includes certain BON-required information

Condition 4: Request is timely

Condition 1. Facility is required to provide safe harbor or elects to do so voluntarily.

A facility is required to establish safe harbor nursing peer review:

- for LVNs if the facility utilizes 10 or more nurses; and
- for RNs if the facility utilizes 10 or more nurses and at least 5 of those 10 or more nurses are RNs

If a facility is not required to provide safe harbor nursing peer review, it can do so voluntarily.

Condition 2. Nurses providing patient care must believe in good faith the requested conduct violates a nurse's duty to a patient.

Nurse supervisors must believe in good faith the administrative decision will require them to request a nurse violate a nurse's duty to the patient.

The request for safe harbor nursing peer review must be based on the nurse's good faith belief that she/he is being requested to engage in conduct that violates the nurse's duty to the patient. The Safe Harbor Nursing Peer Review Law and BON Rule 217.20 define:

- **"duty to patient"** as advocating for patient safety including any nursing action necessary to comply with the standards of practice (BON Rule 217.11) and to avoid engaging in unprofessional conduct rules (BON Rule 217.12); and
- **"good faith"** as taking action supported by a reasonable factual or legal basis.

Since safe harbor provides the nurse protection from both retaliation by the facility and action against her/his license by the BON, the request must be made in good faith both with respect to the facility and with respect to the BON (i.e., the public).

The nurse **acts in good faith with respect to the facility** when the nurse believes that the requested conduct or assignment violates a nurse's duty to a patient and there is a reasonable factual or legal basis for the belief -- that is, a belief a reasonable nurse could hold. For example, a belief that any request to float is a request to engage in conduct that violates a nurse's duty to a patient is not a good faith belief, because standards of practice rules do not prohibit all floating -- only floating to units or assignments for which the nurse is not qualified. Another example of lack of good faith would be subsequent requests for review of the same conduct after the nursing peer review committee had found the conduct did not violate a nurse's duty to a patient.

The nurse **acts in good faith with respect to the BON** (i.e., the public) by acting in the best interest of the patient. Normally, this means engaging in the conduct while nursing peer review determines what is the nurse's duty. BON Rule 217.20(g)(2) explicitly states that a nurse may engage in the conduct or assignment **unless** the requested conduct/assignment:

1. would constitute unprofessional conduct and/or criminal conduct such as fraud, theft, patient abuse, exploitation, or falsification; or
2. would be beyond the nurse's scope of competency because the nurse lacks the basic knowledge, skills, and abilities that would be necessary to render the care or engage in the conduct requested or assigned at a minimally competent level such that engaging in the requested conduct or assignment would expose one or more patients to an unjustifiable risk of harm.

A request to falsify a patient record is an example of conduct that should not be engaged in. It is unreasonable to expect a nursing peer review committee would ever find the requested conduct does not violate a nurse's duty to the patient or be in the patient's best interest. Consequently, providing the nurse protection from disciplinary action by the BON is not in the public interest.

The nurse's decision whether to engage in the requested conduct or assignment is perhaps the most difficult aspect of requesting safe harbor and is discussed in more detail below in Section F. A nurse who is considering not engaging in the conduct or assignment awaiting the nursing peer review committee's determination should be sure she or he has read Section F below.

Condition 3. Request must be in writing and include certain information.

Safe harbor nursing peer review gives nurses protection against the BON's taking action against a nurse's license pending the nursing peer review committee's deliberations. To protect the public, it is important that it be clear when safe harbor nursing peer review has been requested. BON Rule 217.20 permits the request for safe harbor nursing peer review to be made using either a:

- Quick Request Form; or
- Comprehensive Request Form.

The Quick Request Form can be made in any format (the back of a progress note would work) as long as it is in writing and contains the following information:

1. the nurse(s) name(s) making the safe harbor request and her/his signature(s);
2. the date and time of the request;
3. the location of where the conduct or assignment is to be completed;
4. the name of the person requesting the conduct or making the assignment; and
5. a brief explanation of why safe harbor is being requested.

Below is an example of a request for safe harbor nursing peer review that should meet the requirements for a Quick Request Form.

> *2/12/08 1800. I request safe harbor nursing peer review. Near the end of my 3-11 shift my supervisor, Sue Super RN, told me I would have to work the 11-7 shift because two nurses called in sick. My 3-11 shift was very hectic and I feel exhausted and too fatigued to do a double shift. Also double shifts seem to be becoming routine on unit.*
>
> Mary Smith RN
> *Mary Smith RN*

If the Quick Request Form is used, the nurse must submit a Comprehensive Request Form before she/he leaves the work setting at the end of the work period.

The Comprehensive Request Form can also be in any format as long as it is in writing and contains the following information:

1. the conduct assigned or requested, including the name and title of the person making the assignment or request;
2. a description of the practice setting, e.g., the nurse's responsibilities, resources available, extenuating or contributing circumstances impacting the situation;
3. a detailed description of how the requested conduct or assignment would have violated the nurse's duty to a patient or any other provision of the NPA and Board Rules. If possible, reference the specific standard (BON Rule '217.11) or other section of the NPA and/or Board rules the nurse believes would have been violated;
4. if applicable, the rationale for the nurse's not engaging in the requested conduct or

assignment awaiting the nursing peer review committee's determination as to the nurse's duty. The rationale should refer to one of the justifications described in Rule 217.20(g)(2) [See Section F below] for not engaging in the conduct or assignment awaiting a peer review determination;

5. any other copies of pertinent documentation available at the time. Additional documents may be submitted to the committee when available at a later time; and
6. the nurse's name, title, and relationship to the supervisor making the assignment or request.

Nurses should familiarize themselves with the information required when requesting safe harbor and have readily available copies of the Quick Request Form and Comprehensive Request Form -- either by keeping copies themselves or knowing they have ready access through the facility. If the Quick Request Form is used, the nurse must submit a Comprehensive Request Form before she/he leaves the work setting at the end of the work period. If the Comprehensive Request Form is used to make the initial request, no additional form is required.

The BON's website includes samples of both the Quick Request Form and Comprehensive Request forms as well as other information about requesting safe harbor nursing peer review. The site has a special form that can be used when the reasonableness of a physician's order is involved. The BON website is www.bon.texas.gov. From Main Menu, select "Nursing Practice" and then "Nursing Peer Review."

Condition 4. Request Must be Timely.

BON Rule 217.20(d) requires the request be made before the nurse engages in the conduct and at one of the following three times:

1. when the conduct is requested or assignment made;
2. when changes occur in the request/assignment that so modify the level of nursing care or supervision required compared to what was originally requested or assigned that a nurse believes in good faith that patient harm may result; or
3. when the nurse refuses to engage in the requested conduct or assignment.

It is important to note that Rule 217.20 recognizes an assignment can so change during the course of the work period that in fact a new assignment occurs and a request for safe harbor can be made when this occurs.

E. PROCESS ONCE REQUEST MADE

1. Process to be followed. BON Rule 217.20 outlines the process to be followed once a request for safe harbor nursing peer review has been made. Both the nurse and supervisor must follow this process. The process is designed to produce a mutually satisfactory resolution. Possible resolutions include:

- the nurse's learning additional facts about the situation that cause the nurse to change her/his belief that the requested conduct or assignment violates a nurse's duty to the patient;
- the nurse's being provided additional resources or support that permit the nurse to engage in the requested conduct or assignment without violating her/his duty to the patient; and
- changing the conduct or assignment requested.

In the example set out at the beginning of this document, a mutually satisfactory resolution may be the supervisor agreeing to stay and help cover the shift, and Mary feeling this would provide adequate coverage for the unit.

If the nurse and her/his supervisor are unable to reach a mutually satisfactory resolution, the issue goes to a nursing peer review committee. The nursing peer review committee must make its determination within no more than 14 days of the nurse's request for safe harbor nursing peer review. Even if there is a mutually satisfactory resolution, the nurse still has the right to have the committee review the request.

2. Nurse's right to participate. BON Rule 217.20(h) gives the nurse the right:
(1) to appear before the committee;
(2) to ask questions and respond to questions of the committee; and
(3) to make a verbal and/or written statement to explain why she or he believes the requested conduct would have violated a nurse's duty to a patient.

3. Determination by committee. Once the nursing peer review committee makes its determination, it submits its report to the CNO or nurse administrator. The CNO or nurse administrator has 48 hours to review the nursing peer review committee's determination and deliver it to the nurse with the administrator's decision about whether the nurse will continue to be requested to engage in the conduct.

a. Committee finds requested conduct or assignment does not violate the nurse's duty. Since the nursing peer review committee has found the conduct or assignment does not violate the nurse's duty to the patient, the nurse can engage in the conduct.

b. Committee finds requested conduct or assignment violates the nurse's duty. The protection that the facility is prohibited from retaliating against the nurse for making the request continues indefinitely. The protection that the BON cannot discipline the nurse for engaging in the conduct ends 48 hours after the nurse administrator notifies the nurse of the nursing peer review committee's determination.

F. DECIDING TO ENGAGE IN THE REQUESTED CONDUCT OR ASSIGNMENT AWAITING NURSING PEER REVIEW'S DETERMINATION

1. Making the Decision. A nurse requesting safe harbor will have to decide if it is in the patient's best interest to engage in the conduct while awaiting nursing peer review's determination. This is perhaps the most difficult decision for the nurse who is requesting safe harbor. However, assuming the facility and nurse are both acting in good faith, it will normally be in the patients' best interest for the nurse to engage in the conduct or assignment. BON Rule 217.20(g)(2) states that a nurse may engage in the conduct or assignment unless the requested conduct/assignment:

1. would constitute unprofessional conduct and/or criminal conduct such as fraud, theft, patient abuse, exploitation, or falsification; or
2. would be beyond the nurse's scope of competency because the nurse lacks the basic knowledge, skills, and abilities that would be necessary to render the care or engage in the conduct requested or assigned at a minimally competent level such that engaging in the requested conduct or assignment would expose one or more patients to an unjustifiable risk of harm.

Conversely, the nurse's reason for not engaging in the conduct or assignment should be that the conduct or assignment either:

1. constitutes unprofessional conduct and/or criminal conduct; or
2. is so beyond the nurse's scope of competency (because the nurse lacks the basic knowledge, skills, and abilities necessary to render the care at a minimally competent level) that patients would be exposed to an unjustifiable risk of harm.

A nurse should be very cautious about not engaging in the conduct/assignment awaiting the nursing peer review committee's determination. First, the nurse's not engaging in the conduct/assignment may result in even less staffing which is normally not in the patients' best interest. Second, the facility may believe patients were put at risk and decide to take personnel action against the nurse for not engaging in the conduct/assignment while awaiting nursing peer review. While the Nursing Peer Review Law specifically prohibits retaliation against the nurse for requesting safe harbor, it does not prohibit personnel action against the nurse for not engaging in the conduct/assignment while awaiting the nursing peer review determination.

If the reason the nurse decides not to engage in the conduct/assignment is because she/he believes it is so beyond her/his scope of competency that patients would be put at an unjustifiable risk, BON Rule 217.20(g) requires that:

1. the nurse and supervisor collaborate in an attempt to identify an acceptable assignment that is within the nurse's scope and enhances the delivery of safe patient care; and
2. the results of this collaborative effort be documented in writing and maintained in peer review records.

However, if 1) a nurse is convinced the requested conduct/assignment is conduct that is either unprofessional and/or criminal conduct or beyond the nurse's scope of competency and 2) the collaborative attempt with the supervisor to identify an acceptable assignment was unsuccessful, the nurse should not engage in the conduct or assignment while awaiting nursing peer review and complete the documentation required by BON Rule 217.20(g)(2).

In summary, it is normally to the patient's and nurse's benefit for the nurse to engage in the conduct during the 14-day period while nursing peer review makes its determination - unless she/he is confident the conduct/assignment 1) involves unprofessional and/or criminal conduct or 2) is conduct any reasonable nurse would consider to be so beyond the nurse's scope of competency that patients are put at unjustifiable risk. Safe harbor nursing peer review is designed to provide a mechanism for resolving situations in which reasonable nurses can differ about what is the nurse's duty to a patient in that particular case. In such situations, it is normally in the patients' interest for the nurse to engage in the conduct while awaiting nursing peer review's determination. Before deciding not to engage in the conduct/assignment while awaiting nursing peer review, the nurse should discuss that decision with another nurse whose judgment the nurse respects.

2. Personnel Action by Facility against Nurse for Not Engaging in Conduct or Assignment Awaiting Nursing Peer Review. While the Nursing Peer Review Law specifically prohibits retaliation against the nurse for requesting safe harbor, it does not prohibit personnel action against the nurse for not engaging in the conduct/assignment while awaiting the nursing peer review determination. The Nursing Peer Review Law and BON Rule 217.20 require that:

a. the nursing peer review's determination be considered in making that personnel decision; and
b. if nursing peer review determines the requested conduct violates the nurse's duty, the CNO or nurse administrator must both:
   (1) believe in good faith that nursing peer review is wrong; and
   (2) document the reasons for that belief in the nursing peer review record.

Only the CNO or nurse administrator can make the decision to take personnel action against the nurse for not engaging in the conduct awaiting nursing peer review's determination.

If personnel action is taken against the nurse, then the nurse still would have protection of NPA §301.352 if the nurse is correct in her/his belief that conduct violates NPA or BON rule. Section 303.352 prohibits a facility from retaliating against a nurse for refusing to engage in conduct that violates the NPA or BON rules - that is, violates the nurse's duty to a patient. However, if the nursing peer review committee finds the requested conduct or assignment did not violate the nurse's duty to her/his patient, then the personnel action cannot be described as "retaliation for refusing to violate the nurse's duty to a patient."

G. REMEDIES IF A NURSE IS RETALIATED AGAINST BECAUSE REQUESTED SAFE HARBOR OR BECAUSE ADVISED ANOTHER NURSE ABOUT SAFE HARBOR

The Safe Harbor Nursing Peer Review Law prohibits a facility from discriminating against a nurse because she/he requested safe harbor nursing peer review and also against any individual advising a nurse on her/his rights under safe harbor nursing peer review. This protection from retaliation by the facility does not expire. If a nurse is retaliated against, she/he has several remedies. The nurse can:

1. report the facility to the state agency that licenses it (Department of State Health Services for hospitals and long-term care facilities; Department of Aging and Disability Services for home health agencies).
2. report any nurse involved in the retaliation to BON.
3. file a lawsuit seeking damages.

Nurses may also fear being labeled "trouble-makers" and receiving unfavorable job references should they seek new employment. If so, this would be a type of retaliation that the Safe Harbor Nursing Peer Review Law prohibits. In addition, Section 103.003(b) of the Texas Labor Code explicitly prohibits an employer from giving a nurse an unfavorable job reference for refusing to engage in conduct reportable to the BON or for requesting Safe Harbor Nursing Peer Review.

H. RECORD KEEPING

BON Rule 217.20 (d)(3) makes the nurse requesting safe harbor nursing peer review responsible for keeping a copy of the request. The rule also requires the facility provide the nurse a copy of the committee's determination and the nurse administrator's review. The nurse should keep these documents as her/his permanent records. In the event the BON would ever investigate the conduct, the nurse will need to be able to show that she/he engaged in the conduct only after requesting safe harbor nursing peer review.

I. NURSE'S ENGAGING IN CONDUCT SUBJECT TO REPORTING DURING 14-DAY PERIOD AWAITING PEER REVIEW'S DETERMINATION

Though not likely, it is possible that a nurse may engage in conduct subject to being reported during the 14-day period nursing peer review is making its determination. That conduct will either be related to or unrelated to the reason the nurse requested safe harbor. If that conduct relates to the reason for which safe harbor was requested, then the nurse is not reportable to the BON. If this were not the case, the protections of safe harbor nursing peer review would be practically meaningless. An example of such a situation might be that the nurse requested safe harbor because she or he was requested to work on a pediatric unit and did not feel she/he was qualified, and the subsequent conduct was giving an adult dose to a child. The nurse should not be held accountable for that error, because it relates directly to the reason for the request for safe harbor. On the other hand, safe harbor is not a license for the nurse to engage in bad practice. If the subsequent conduct does not relate to the safe harbor request, then the nurse should be held accountable for that conduct. In the above example, such conduct might be giving the medication by a route that would not be correct for adult patients either. BON Rule 217.20(e)(2) addresses the process that should occur when a nurse engages in conduct subject to reporting pending the nursing peer review committee's evaluation of a request for safe harbor. That process includes the nursing peer review committee's determination whether the conduct relates to the nurse's request for safe harbor nursing peer review.

J. WHAT IF THE NURSE MAKES A PATIENT CARE ERROR THAT RESULTS IN PATIENT INJURY

The patient is an innocent third-party with respect to safe harbor nursing peer review. The Nursing Peer Review Law does not prohibit the patient from suing the facility and nurse for any injury caused by a nursing error committed by the nurse during the period awaiting nursing peer review's determination. The patient would have to prove negligence by the nurse. As a practical matter, the facility is probably more at risk of a lawsuit than is the nurse but there can be no guarantee the nurse would not be sued. On the other hand, if the nurse does not engage in the conduct or assignment and a patient is injured, the nurse may be subject to disciplinary action by the BON if it determines the nurse did not act in the best interests of patients. She/he may also be subject to possible personnel action by the facility. Because of the possibility of an injury to the patient, it is in the facility's and nurse's interest that nursing peer review makes its determination as quickly as possible.

K. PRACTICAL TIPS

***Practical Tip** 1: Nurses should not wait until a situation arises to familiarize themselves with their right to request safe harbor nursing peer review. That is best done without the pressures of having to make an immediate decision on whether and how to make the request. The nurse should also check to see if the facility keeps forms readily available for nurses. If not, nurses should know how they will obtain the form if needed, have a form that meets the requirements of the BON, or at the very least have a list of the information that must be in the Quick Request Form.*

***Practical Tip 2:** Not only is the nurse requesting safe harbor nursing peer review protected from retaliation, but also nurses (and other individuals) advising a nurse of her/his rights to request safe harbor nursing peer review.*

***Practical Tip 3:** Because safe harbor protections do not apply until a proper request is made, a nurse should request safe harbor nursing peer review when she/he first believes her/his engaging in the requested conduct or assignment would violate her/his duty to a patient.*

***Practical Tip 4:** A nurse can request safe harbor nursing peer review if during the course of the work period, the original assignment so changes that a new assignment in fact occurs.*

***Practical Tip 5:** A nurse supervisor may request safe harbor nursing peer review on an administrative decision the supervisor believes will directly affect the ability of nurses to comply with their duty to patients.*

***Practical Tip** 6: Nurses requesting safe harbor nursing peer review must remember that "a nurse's duty to a patient" is defined by the BON standards of practice and unprofessional conduct rules. Nurses should be familiar with those rules and able to identify the specific standards of practice or unprofessional conduct rules that the requested conduct or assignment violates. Nurses should not wait until a situation occurs to review the BON standards of practice and unprofessional conduct rules. That is best done without the pressures of having to make an immediate decision on how they apply to the situation at hand.*

***Practical Tip** 7: A nurse refusing to engage in requested conduct/assignment (because violates* *duty) should be prepared to collaborate with her/his nurse supervisor regarding how the requested conduct/assignment could be modified so would not violate duty to a patient. If a nurse is convinced that any reasonable nurse would believe the requested conduct involves unprofessional/criminal conduct or is so beyond the nurse's scope of competency that patients are put at unjustifiable risk, she/he should both request safe harbor nursing peer review and not engage in the requested conduct during the 14-day period awaiting nursing peer review's determination. The nurse should be sure she/he complies with the requirements of BON Rule 217.20(g). If disciplined for not engaging in the conduct, the nurse may have legal recourse under NPA Sec. 301.352. A nurse, who is considering refusing to engage in the conduct or assignment while awaiting peer review's determination, should be familiar with Section F.*

Practical Tip 8: *Protections that a nurse cannot be disciplined by the BON for engaging in the requested conduct end 48 hours after the nurse receives the nursing peer review committee's decision from the nurse administrator. The protection that the facility is prohibited from retaliating against the nurse for making the request continues indefinitely.*

Practical Tip 9: *Nurses who are retaliated against for requesting safe harbor nursing peer review or for advising a nurse on the nurse's right to request safe harbor have several remedies available to them and should use these as appropriate.*

L. WHAT OTHER PROTECTIONS DO TEXAS NURSES HAVE WHEN ADVOCATING FOR THEIR PATIENTS

Texas nurses have a number of patient advocacy protections in addition to safe harbor nursing peer review. These protections are described in Section 7 of the Reference Materials. These protections should be available even if the nurse does not request Safe Harbor.

M. BON AND TNA WEBSITES

The BON's website has useful information about safe harbor nursing peer review including sample forms. The BON website is www.bon.texas.gov. From Main Menu, select "Nursing Practice" and then "Nursing Peer Review."

Nurses may wish to periodically check the TNA website at www.texasnurses.org for any changes and updates to Safe Harbor Nursing Peer Review or other patient advocacy protections for nurses.

PART XI.

INDEXES

BON RULES CROSS-INDEX
LISTING BON RULES AND LOCATION IN THIS GUIDE

The following table lists the BON Rules in numerical order and indicates where they can be found in this Guide. It is designed to assist the reader who knows the number of the BON rule and wants to know where it appears in this Guide. Copies of BON rules can be found on the BON website at www.bon.texas.gov or at Texas Legislature Online at www.legis.state.tx.us.

"n/i" denotes not included in Annotated NPA

BON Rule
In Numerical Order — **Location In Guide**

LICENSURE, PEER ASSISTANCE AND PRACTICE - §§217.1 - 217.20

RULE 218 - *VACANT*

ADVANCED PRACTICE NURSE PROGRAM - §§219.1 - 219.13

ANNOTATOR'S NOTE. This Rule 221 is being completely revised by the BON to implement legislation passed in 2013. The BON issued proposed rules in July2013 and is expected to adopt final rules at its October meeting.

RN DELEGATION IN INDEPENDENT LIVING ENVIRONMENTS - §§225.1-225.14

PATIENT SAFETY PILOT PROGRAMS ON NURSE REPORTING SYSTEMS- §§226.1-226.7

PILOT PROGRAMS FOR INNOVATIVE APPLICATIONS TO PROFESSIONAL NURSING EDUCATION §§227.1-227.7

BON POSITION STATEMENTS AND GUIDELINES CROSS-INDEX LISTING AND LOCATION IN THIS GUIDE

The following table lists the BON Rules in numerical order and indicates where they can be found in this Guide. It is designed to assist the reader who knows the number of the BON rule and wants to know where it appears in this Guide. Copies of BON rules can be found on the BON website at www.bon.texas.gov or at Texas Legislature Online at www.legis.state.tx.us.

"n/i" denotes not included in Annotated NPA

BON POSITION STATEMENTS

BON GUIDELINES

SUBJECT-MATTER INDEX